Chemistry

A FIRST COURSE

G. RAYNER-CANHAM   A. LAST

R. PERKINS   M. VAN ROODE

CONSULTANT: ROY HARRISON

Addison-Wesley Publishers

Don Mills, Ontario • Reading, Massachusetts • Menlo Park, California
Wokingham, England • Amsterdam • Sydney
Tokyo • Madrid • Bogota • Santiago • San Juan

DESIGN: Brant Cowie/Artplus Limited
TECHNICAL ILLUSTRATION: Alan Gaunt, Cathy Campion, Jack McMaster
SPONSORING EDITOR: Ron Doleman
DEVELOPMENTAL EDITOR: Jean Reavley
COPY EDITOR: Tom Shields
INDEXER: Cecilia Chan

COVER PHOTO: A photomicrograph of crystallized tartaric
acid. The vivid colours are caused by the unequal
refraction of columnated, polarized light. Photo by
Mark Moldaver.

Canadian Cataloguing in Publication Data

Rayner-Canham, Geoffrey.
  Chemistry, a first course

Includes index.
ISBN 0-201-17880-X

1. Chemistry.   I. Last, A. (Arthur).   II. Title.

QD33.R39   1986   540   C86-094126-4

ISBN 0-201-17880-X

Printed and bound in Canada

A B C D E –BP– 91 90 89 88 87

Table of Contents

Preface

The preparation of this introductory high school chemistry text has proven to be a greater challenge than we originally anticipated. For a first formal course in the subject we have attempted to provide a balance between the historical development and accomplishments of the science, and its importance to our lives. In so doing we have examined some of the major social issues and the responsibilities of the Canadian chemical industry.

Within the scope of these larger goals our aim has been to present the basic concepts of the subject in a clear and understandable manner, supported and illustrated with practical examples. To accomplish this we have built in the pedagogical elements described below.

We hope that this text will provide a solid base of knowledge and problem-solving skills for further study, while creating an awareness of the impact of chemistry on our society.

PROBLEM SOLVING · This key skill receives constant attention throughout the text. We have used the conversion-factor (dimensional analysis) method of problem solving. Many of the solved examples offer strategies designed to assist in the recognition of problem types and the development of more effective problem-solving skills.

FEATURE ARTICLES · Each chapter contains two or three short articles. Some of these features describe a practical application of the concepts presented in the text; others provide biographies of important chemists. These biographies are not simply a catalogue of discoveries; they show the individuality of chemists and relate the difficulties they have encountered in convincing their peers of the validity of their results. They also show that modern chemistry is the result of centuries of development.

DESCRIPTIVE CHEMISTRY · In our view, many recent high school texts have underplayed the fundamental fact that chemistry involves the direct study of chemicals. To avoid a preoccupation with the quantitative aspects of the subject, we have integrated descriptive chemistry throughout the text whenever possible. In addition, one complete chapter is devoted to a discussion of the chemistry of the common elements.

INDUSTRIAL CHEMISTRY	No introductory text would be complete without an examination of the role and responsibilities of industry. In Chapter 16 we present an overview of the most important Canadian chemical industries and their role in our economy. As this chapter points out, decisions regarding industrial chemical processes are often governed by factors other than the chemistry involved.
THE INTERNATIONAL OUTLOOK	In keeping with the international nature of chemistry, readers will discover a number of chemistry-related topics from around the world: from the Chernobyl nuclear disaster to the problems facing the phosphate-mining island of Nauru.
EVERYDAY CHEMISTRY	Whenever possible, we have tried to relate chemicals and chemical reactions to observable phenomena: from the formation of stalagmites to the mechanisms used by insects to communicate with one another. Two separate features explore the vital role played by different elements in human nutrition.
SOCIAL ISSUES	Many controversial issues that arise today either involve chemicals or are chemistry-related: issues such as lead and mercury pollution, acid rain, and the disposal of nuclear waste. Each of the industrial case studies reviews the environmental hazards related to that particular industry and discusses the methods used to minimize pollution.
THE NATURE OF SCIENCE	In keeping with the recommendations of the Science Council of Canada, we have tried to represent the discovery process in a realistic light. In Chapter 1 we point out that there is no rigid scientific method. Certain biographical features also describe the unusual way in which some of the more important scientific discoveries have been made.

Chapter Elements

Each chapter contains a wide range of testing and review material. Within each chapter we have included solved examples, many of which include suggested strategies, and end-of-section questions that verify understanding of the fundamental principles.

Each chapter closes with a summary, a list of key terms, answers to end-of-section questions, a set of comprehension questions, problems, and suggested projects.

Acknowledgements

We are greatly indebted to Robert Perkins and Mark van Roode, our co-authors in the previously-published *Foundations of Chemistry*. Many of their original ideas will be found in this new text.

No project of this dimension could have been successfully completed without the assistance of reviewers, who countless times steered us in the right direction. It is fitting, therefore, that we acknowledge the contribution made by the following:

Brian Bennett, *R.S. McLaughlin Collegiate, Ontario*
Ted Farion, *Jasper Place Composite High School, Alberta*
Art Frankel, *Saunders Secondary School, Ontario*
Fred Gainer, *Bonnie Doon Composite, Alberta*
Bob Graham, *Champlain High School, Ontario*
Len Jones, *Eastdale Collegiate & Vocational Institute, Ontario*
Krishan Joshee, *Holy Trinity Catholic High School, Alberta*
John Li, *The Woodlands School, Ontario*
E.J. Marks, *Lord Beaverbrook Secondary School, Alberta*
Desmond Pearce, *De La Salle College, Ontario*
Fred Ritchie, *Father Lacombe Collegiate, Alberta*
Wayne Rowley, *Sentinel Secondary School, British Columbia*
Mike Webb, *formerly at St. George's College, Ontario*

We are grateful for the enthusiastic support of Addison-Wesley Publishers, particularly the tireless efforts of Ron Doleman, who initiated the project and encouraged us throughout its long gestation, and the advice and counsel of Andy Yull, who helped shepherd the manuscript through the production phase. Many thanks, as well, go to Marion Garner, who tracked down many hard-to-get photos.

Finally, we would like to express our gratitude to Marelene Rayner-Canham and Sheelagh Last. Without their constant support and encouragement, this task would not have been possible.

The Study of Matter

Mendeleev

When you begin to study a new language one of the first steps is to learn some of the basic words of that language. Likewise, as you start your study of chemistry, you will need to acquire a new vocabulary. This chapter will introduce you to some of the key words in the chemist's language.

What Is Chemistry?

1.1 Chemistry is the study of the composition and properties of matter. One focus of this study is to understand how substances change under different conditions. We can generalize by saying that chemists are concerned with:

1. The composition and structure of substances.
2. The properties of these substances.
3. The conditions under which these substances change to form new ones.

Many new materials that have made substantial differences to our lives have been produced by chemists — for example, new building materials and new types of fibres for clothing.

1

Figure 1.1
Fitting ceramic tiles to the surface of a U.S. space shuttle. These tiles are made from a super-insulating ceramic material that was specially developed by chemists to prevent the shuttles from burning up during re-entry.

In this text we are mainly concerned with *pure* chemistry, which is the study of the principles of chemistry. When these principles are used in a practical application, then we are dealing with *applied* chemistry.

TABLE 1.1 *Some Fields of Applied Chemistry*

Agricultural chemistry	The chemistry of soils, fertilizers, pesticides, and herbicides
Environmental chemistry	The effect of the activity of humans on the chemistry of the land, the waters, and the air
Food chemistry	The chemical composition of foods and food additives
Marine chemistry	The study of chemical compounds present in marine life, as well as the study of sea water
Nuclear chemistry	The study of the atomic nucleus

The Origins of Chemistry 1.2

Figure 1.2
The alchemists of the Middle Ages learned a great deal about chemistry as they searched for ways to change common metals into gold.

There have been numerous occasions in the history of civilization where chemistry has contributed to human progress. One example was the development of a smelting process to obtain metals from ores. The replacement of stone and bone implements by metal tools and weapons was an important advance in the development of civilization.

The earliest records that mention the names of chemists are cuneiform tablets which were found in Mesopotamia in the Middle East. These tablets, which have been dated from around 1000 B.C., describe the activities of women chemists who extracted perfumes from plant and animal sources. To do this the chemists developed sophisticated scientific procedures and designed special equipment.

The ancient Greeks and Romans (800 B.C. to 400 A.D.) began studies into the nature of matter. One of the most interesting documents of the period was by the Roman poet, Lucretius. In his work titled, *On the Nature of Matter*, Lucretius developed ideas that relate very closely to many of our modern concepts of chemistry and physics.

After the decline of the Roman Empire, the study of science continued in the Arab world. There, the scientists who studied matter were called alchemists. Alchemy was a mixture of chemistry and philosophy, and alchemists often explained their observations in terms of the movement of the heavenly bodies. Alchemy spread throughout Europe and the Middle Eastern countries. In Western Europe, alchemists of the Middle Ages were obsessed with the idea of changing common metals into gold. Because of this obsession, alchemists and their profession acquired a bad reputation. Nevertheless, the techniques and investigations of the alchemists led to the development of modern chemistry. As we develop each topic in this text, we will show how the early discoveries in chemistry relate to our current understanding of the subject.

The Methods of Scientists

1.3

Figure 1.3
A modern chemical laboratory. Most chemical experimentation is performed in such a facility.

In their search for explanations, scientists often follow a series of logical steps. However, there is no set method for studying scientific phenomena, and scientists take different approaches in their investigations. Some are very methodical and carefully plan the course of their experiments. Although most textbooks lead us to believe that all scientists operate in this way, this is not the case. Many of this century's most noted discoveries resulted from flashes of intuition or from unanticipated findings. These, however, have to be followed up by experimentation to see if they are valid.

Experimentation is, in fact, the prime work of a chemist. Chemists can make observations, or have brilliant ideas, but these are of little value unless they have been validated by careful experimentation. When publishing reports about their work, chemists must be able to explain the methods they used to obtain their results.

Keen powers of observation and an enquiring mind are important attributes of a scientist. An essential part of scientific training is learning how to become more observant and how to ask pertinent questions. The scientist not only asks why something happens, but also devises experiments to discover why it happens. After new insights have been applied to a problem, the scientific community undertakes to test the validity of the new approach. New experiments are carried out to see if what worked for one scientist will work for another. It is this additional follow-up work that reinforces the validity of the earlier work.

As we refine our knowledge through experimentation, we often construct models that allow us to check our understanding of a process. The recent breakthroughs in computer technology have allowed chemists to use computer models to help predict what might happen in various situations.

If a pattern of behaviour has been established from experiments, a general statement about the behaviour can be made. This statement, which is based on fact, is referred to as a law. A **law** is a rule that nature seems to follow. For example, the Law of Gravity was based on observations that anything released from a height always drops towards the earth.

A **hypothesis** is a tentative explanation for the observations we have made. **Theories** are usually constructed from hypotheses, laws, or observations to explain phenomena encountered in a variety of situations. After hypotheses and theories have been formulated, we can then design experiments to see if our reasoning is correct.

The Discovery of Teflon

The keen powers of observation and the enquiring mind of Dr. Roy Plunkett, a scientist who worked for the du Pont company, resulted in the discovery of a new material that had many practical applications in both industry and the home.

In 1938, Dr. Plunkett was conducting research on a gas called tetrafluoroethylene (TFE). His supply of TFE was stored under pressure in steel cylinders. One morning he discovered that he could obtain no TFE from one cylinder. This surprised him, because after the last time he had used the cylinder, there had appeared to be plenty of the gas left in it. At this stage, most people would assume that the gas had leaked from the cylinder, and would replace the cylinder with a new one.

Dr. Plunkett, however, did not see how the gas could have leaked out. He compared the weight of the cylinder with its weight when it had last been used. As the weight had not changed he concluded that no TFE had leaked from the cylinder. When he shook the cylinder, he heard something rattling inside it. This aroused his curiosity, and he cut open the cylinder. Inside, he found a white, slippery solid.

He devised a number of experiments to try to find out what the solid was. In conducting these experiments he found that the solid had a number of very unusual properties. It was, in fact, a new type of plastic. Dr. Plunkett also wanted to know why the solid had formed in only one cylinder, as he had used many cylinders of TFE in his work. After many more experiments, he found that the white solid only formed in the presence of certain chemicals which had been present in very small amounts as impurities in the cylinder.

Because of its unusual properties, it was realized that the new plastic would be very useful. After a method of manufacturing it in large quantities had been devised, practical applications were found in situations as varied as aircraft motor bearings and nonstick frying pans. The plastic is known as Teflon. Had it not been for Dr. Plunkett's observations and curiosity, it may have taken years for this very useful substance to be discovered.

Figure 1.4
New discoveries are published in scientific journals. Two prominent Canadian chemical journals are The Canadian Journal of Chemistry and Canadian Chemical News.

Hypotheses, laws, and theories are all based on observations and experimentation. Many hypotheses and theories are modified or discarded over time as new discoveries are made. Scientists spend many hours arguing, in private or in public, about the relative merits of various theories. A great deal of this argument takes place in scientific literature, as most scientists publish the results of their work. By doing so, they help to expand scientific knowledge. Other scientists can then try to duplicate these experiments or make use of the published theories in their own work.

QUESTIONS

1. Explain briefly the difference between a law and a theory.
2. Why is it important for the experiments of one scientist to be tested by another?

The Properties of Matter

1.4

As we said earlier, chemistry is the study of the composition and properties of matter. Matter has two general properties: it occupies space and has mass.

Figure 1.5
An astronaut floating in space. Although the astronaut is weightless, he or she possesses the same mass as on Earth.

The **mass** of an object is the quantity of matter in that object. Mass should not be confused with weight, which is the gravitational force acting upon an object. The mass of an object is the same anywhere in the universe, and therefore we call mass a constant property. If you were to visit the moon you would find that your mass does not change. However, your weight would be one sixth that of your weight on the earth. This is because the gravitational force exerted by the moon is one sixth that exerted by the earth. Weight, therefore, is *not* a constant property of matter.

The space that matter occupies is called its **volume**. As we shall see in the next section, volume is not a constant property of matter.

A property of matter that combines volume and mass is **density**. Density is the mass of a substance contained in a specific volume. If we take the same mass of two substances, the substance with the higher density will occupy less space, that is, have a smaller volume, than the substance with the lower density.

The Phases of Matter

1.5

Matter is usually found in one of three phases (or states): solid, liquid, or gas.

The Solid Phase

A **solid** has a definite shape and volume and cannot be compressed to any significant extent. Solids tend to have higher densities than liquids and gases. Normally when a solid object, such as a piece of metal, is placed in a liquid, the solid will sink to the bottom. There are, however, some exceptions. For example, wood, which is a solid, has a lower density than water, and therefore floats on water.

Some solids form crystals. The tiny particles of matter that make up crystals are arranged in an ordered geometrical structure. Crystals of single substances have the same basic arrangement. This property is often used for identifying substances. Sugar and table salt are examples of crystals. Snowflakes are crystals of water. If you examine crystals of a number of substances under a microscope you can see their different shapes.

Figure 1.6
Snowflakes — these beautiful ice crystals are the most perfect form of solid water.

The Liquid Phase

A **liquid** has a definite volume, but its shape is determined by the shape of its container. For example, if you take a bottle of cola and pour the cola into a glass, the volume of cola will remain the same, but the shape will change from that of the bottle to that of the glass. Like solids, liquids are difficult to compress.

The liquid form of a substance is usually less dense than its solid form. You may have noticed that, as hot cooking oil cools, a solid starts to form at the bottom of the container. This happens because solid cooking oil is denser than liquid cooking oil. Water is one of the few substances with a

Figure 1.7
Icebergs — solid water floating in liquid water. Although for most substances the solid form is denser than the liquid form, in the case of water it is just the opposite — the liquid form is the denser.

solid form (ice) that is less dense than the liquid form. In cold climates, as the water in rivers and lakes cools, ice forms on the surface. This ice layer acts as a blanket and keeps the water below it relatively warm. Fish and other aquatic life can then survive the very severe winters.

An important property of a liquid is its viscosity, which is a measure of the ease with which a liquid flows. Liquids with low viscosities, such as alcohol and water, flow very easily. Liquids such as syrup have a higher viscosity, and some liquids hardly flow at all. One of the reasons why it is very difficult to extract oil from the tar sands in Western Canada is that the oil has a very high viscosity.

The Gas Phase

A **gas** has neither a definite volume nor a definite shape. A sample of gas will fill an entire container, regardless of the shape of that container. Gases have much lower densities than either liquids or solids, and can be easily compressed.

Other Phases

There are two other phases of matter which we shall mention here but which we will not discuss further in this text. These are the plasma phase and the liquid crystal phase. **Plasma** is a phase in which a gas has been broken down into electrically charged components. This phase is achieved either by heating the gas to an extremely high temperature or by subjecting it to a high-voltage electric current. The sun is an example of a plasma. **Liquid crystals** are liquids with ordered structures similar to those found in crystalline solids. Liquid crystals are used in the digital displays of calculators, watches, and other electronic equipment.

Figure 1.8

Swirling plasma on the surface of the sun. Plasma is one of the less common phases of matter.

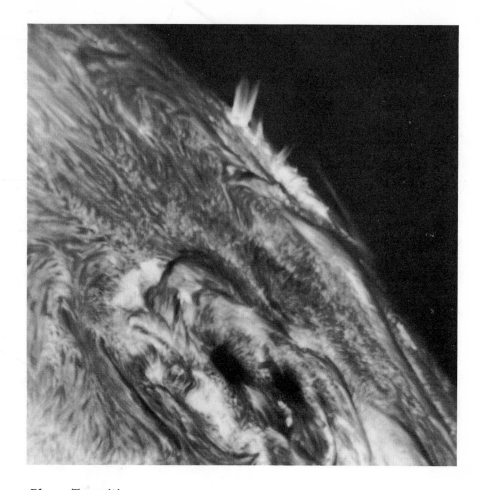

Phase Transitions

Many substances can exist in either the solid, liquid, or gas phase. Water, for example, can exist as ice, water, or water vapour. The process of changing from one phase to another is known as a phase transition (or phase change). When a solid changes to a liquid, the transition is called **melting**. The reverse process, the change from a liquid to a solid, is known as **solidification**. The term freezing is also sometimes used if the solidification process takes place at a low temperature.

The phase transition from liquid to gas is called either boiling or **evaporation**, and the reverse, from gas to liquid, is known as **condensation**.

Most substances change from solids to liquids and then to gases, or, in the reverse process, from gas to liquid to solid. However, some substances can change from solids to gases without going through the liquid phase. The process of transition from solid to gas, or from gas to solid, is known as **sublimation**.

Figure 1.9

Two commonly used compounds that sublime: naphthalene, a moth repellent; and dichlorobenzene, an air freshener.

Figure 1.10

Pouring molten steel. Although we usually think of steel as a solid, at a high enough temperature it changes to a liquid.

Figure 1.11

The terms used for different phase changes.

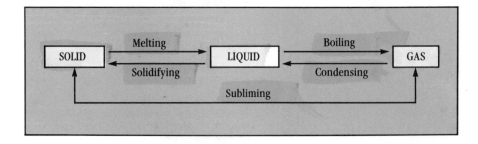

The Kinetic-Molecular Theory of Matter

1.6 Phase transitions can be explained using the kinetic-molecular theory. In this theory it is assumed that matter consists of tiny particles that are in constant motion and therefore possess kinetic energy. It is also assumed that these particles are attracted to each other. The kinetic-molecular theory relates each phase of a substance to its temperature and to the strength of attraction of its particles.

Figure 1.12
Particles packed closely together in a solid.

The Solid Phase.   In this phase, the particles are neatly packed together, vibrating slightly about fixed positions. The kinetic energy of the particles is very small in comparison to the energy of attraction between the particles.

Figure 1.13
Particle behaviour in a liquid.

The Liquid Phase.   As we heat a solid, the heat energy is absorbed by the solid and converted to kinetic energy. The vibration of the particles therefore increases. If the heating is continued long enough, the vibration becomes so strong that the particles escape from their fixed positions and the substance is converted to the liquid phase. The temperature at which the particles are no longer in their fixed positions is called the melting point.

Figure 1.14
Particles escaping from the surface of a liquid during boiling.

The Gaseous Phase.   If we continue to heat the liquid substance, it eventually reaches a temperature at which the particles have enough kinetic energy to overcome the attractive forces. The particles break away from each other and move independently in the available surrounding space. This explains why a gas always occupies the total volume of a container. The temperature at which the attractive forces in a liquid are overcome is called the boiling point.

The kinetic-molecular theory can also be used to explain why different substances melt and boil at different temperatures. The attractive forces between particles are stronger in some substances than in others. Substances with strong attractive forces require more heat energy to break down these forces, and therefore have higher melting and boiling points.

EXAMPLE   **1.1**   Use the kinetic-molecular theory to explain why solids and liquids are almost impossible to compress, whereas gases are easily compressed.

SOLUTION   In the liquid and solid phases the particles are very close together with practically no space between them. In the gas phase the particles are moving about freely with plenty of empty space between them. Compressing the gas will just reduce this space.

Identification of a Substance

1.7

Phase transitions do not change the chemical identity of a substance. For example, ice, water, and water vapour are different phases of the same chemical substance. Processes in which the chemical identity of a substance remains the same are called **physical changes**. The reversal of a physical change will usually restore the matter to its original form. For example, if an ice cube is allowed to melt, it will change back to the original water from which it formed.

A **chemical change** involves the formation of new, chemically different substances. For example, if we heat white sugar crystals, they melt and form an almost colourless liquid. However, if we continue heating the colourless liquid, it will gradually turn brown and thicken. If this brown liquid is cooled it does not change back into a white solid. We can therefore say that the continued heating caused a chemical change to occur in the sugar.

Substances can be identified from their physical and chemical properties. If we compare sugar and table salt we see that both are white crystalline solids. However, we know they have very different tastes. Differences in properties are used to distinguish one substance from another.

Physical Properties. Examples of physical properties are colour, odour, density, melting point, and boiling point. Physical properties can be observed without the chemical identity of the substance being changed.

Chemical Properties. Chemical properties can only be observed when a chemical change takes place. The ability of a substance to burn is a chemical property. For example, after we burn a piece of paper, we are left with a small pile of ashes. The paper has undergone a chemical change.

How do we identify a substance from its chemical and physical properties? Suppose we are presented with a sample of liquid that we suspect is either water or alcohol. First we examine the liquid and note its colour and

TABLE 1.2 *Some Properties of Water and Alcohol*

Property	Water	Alcohol
Phase at room temperature	Liquid	Liquid
Colour	Colourless	Colourless
Odour	None	Slight "sharp" odour
Boiling point	100 °C	78 °C
Viscosity	Low	Low
Does it burn?	No	Yes

whether it has any odour. (We *never* taste any substances we work with in the laboratory as many of them are poisonous.) We then consult a reference book to determine some of the properties of water and alcohol.

From the table we can see that water and alcohol have three properties that are the same and three that are different. As the odour, boiling point, and ability to burn are different, we can conduct experiments to determine these properties for the unknown liquid. If the liquid has properties identical in every respect to either water or alcohol it can be positively identified as one or the other. If, however, the properties do not match those of either water or alcohol we will have to compare the observed properties with the known properties of other substances. We will only be certain of the identity of our sample when we find a substance with identical properties.

QUESTIONS

3. Identify which of the following processes involves a chemical change:
   a) boiling water
   b) frying an egg
   c) burning wood

4. Are the following properties of sulfur physical or chemical?
   a) It is a yellow solid.
   b) Its melting point is 119 °C.
   c) It burns when heated in air.

The Classification of Matter

1.8

We can only identify a substance from its physical and chemical properties if we are dealing with a pure sample. If the sample discussed above had been a mixture of water and alcohol, its boiling point would have been different from the boiling point of either water or alcohol. Therefore when we have to identify a substance we need to know if we are dealing with a pure substance or a mixture of substances.

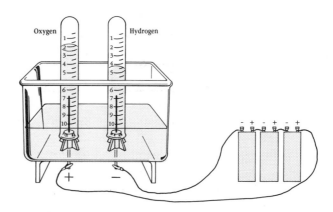

Figure 1.15
We can break down the compound water into its constituent elements of hydrogen and oxygen by using an electric current.

Pure Substances. A pure substance is defined as matter that is uniform throughout and has a definite set of physical and chemical properties. Pure substances can be classed as either elements or compounds: an **element** is a substance that cannot be broken down into simpler substances by chemical methods; a **compound** is a substance that can be broken down into two or more simpler substances by means of chemical changes. Sulfur is an element, whereas water is a compound. (Water can be broken down into the elements hydrogen and oxygen.)

Mixtures. Mixtures are composed of two or more elements or compounds that can be separated by physical methods. Mixtures can be either homogeneous or heterogeneous.

A **homogeneous** mixture, or **solution** as it is more often called, resembles a pure substance in that it has a uniform composition. For example, if we put some table salt in water, the salt disappears. We say the salt has *dissolved* in the water to form a solution. If we examine several small portions of the solution we will find that the proportion of salt in the water is always the same. We can separate the salt from the water by heating the solution. The water will evaporate (a physical change) leaving the salt in the container. This technique has been used for centuries to separate salt from seawater.

A homogeneous mixture of two liquids can usually be separated by distillation. In this procedure the mixture is placed in a distillation flask (Figure 1.16) and the flask is gently heated. The component of the mixture with the lower boiling point will change to the gas phase. The gas then passes through a cooled condenser where it condenses to the liquid phase and is then collected in another flask. Distillation is used in many industries to separate liquids.

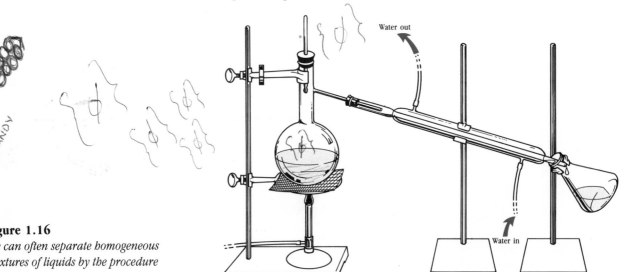

Figure 1.16
We can often separate homogeneous mixtures of liquids by the procedure called distillation.

Figure 1.17

We can separate heterogeneous mixtures of liquids and solids by the procedure called filtration.

A **heterogeneous** mixture does not have a uniform composition throughout. Heterogeneous mixtures can be composed of solids, or of liquids and solids. The individual components of heterogeneous mixtures retain their physical properties. These components can sometimes be separated by making use of the differences in their physical properties. For example, salt dissolves in water but sand does not. We can therefore separate a mixture of salt and sand by adding water to the mixture. The salt will dissolve in the water, leaving the sand on the bottom of the container. We can then separate the salt solution from the sand by filtration (Figure 1.17), a process in which we pour the mixture through fine, porous paper. The salt solution will pass through the paper and the sand will remain on the paper. The salt can be separated from the water by evaporation, as described above.

Most rocks are heterogeneous mixtures of substances. If, for example, you examine a piece of granite you will see that it is composed of a number of different types of crystals. In the mineral processing industry, knowledge of the differences in the physical properties of the components of rocks is used to develop ways to separate the components from crushed samples of the rock.

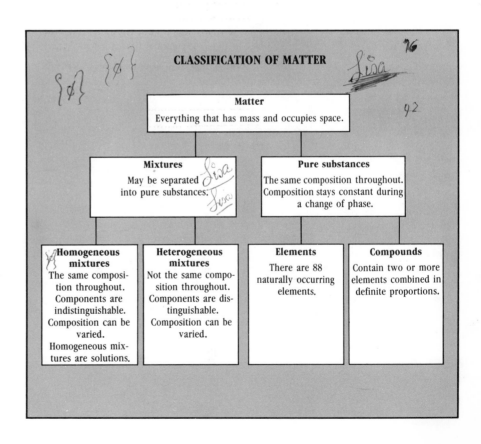

Figure 1.18

A summary of the classification of matter.

The Paper Industry

Figure 1.19

a) *In a paper mill, wood fibres are separated from other wood components.*

b) *Wood-fibres.*

c) *Layers of wood fibres make up the paper produced by a machine such as this.*

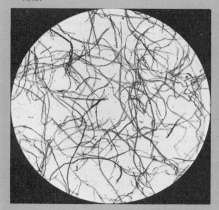

The paper industry, like the mineral processing industry, depends on processes that separate heterogeneous mixtures into their component parts.

Wood is a heterogeneous mixture of a number of substances. As most paper is made from wood fibres, the major task in paper manufacturing is to separate the wood fibres from the other components of the tree trunk.

Two basic methods are used for this separation process. One uses physical separation techniques and the other chemical. In the physical separation method, the logs are first ground to very fine particles by means of giant grinding stones. Filtration methods are then used to separate the wood fibres from the other components of the logs.

In the chemical separation method, log chips are mixed with chemicals that dissolve all the components of the wood except for the wood fibres. The wood fibres can then be extracted from the solutions by physical methods.

The different methods of extraction produce wood fibres that make different qualities of paper. The fibres extracted by physical methods produce an off-white paper that tears easily but is easy to print on, whereas the fibres obtained by chemical methods give fine, white paper that is strong but difficult to print on. In practice, a combination of physical and chemical methods is used by most paper mills to produce fibres that, when mixed, will give a paper combining the best features of the paper produced by each process.

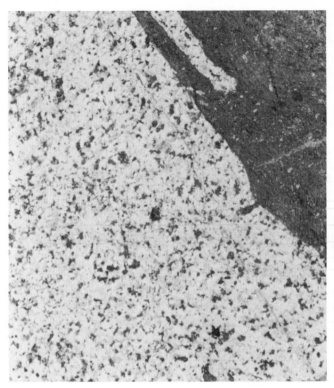

Peter Butt

Figure 1.20

a) *Granite is an example of a heterogeneous mixture: its individual components can be seen as light and dark patches.*

b) *We can confirm the heterogeneous nature of granite by examining a thin slice of it under a microscope. The crystals of the different minerals that comprise granite can be seen clearly.*

QUESTIONS

5. Classify each of the following as being an element, compound, solution, or heterogeneous mixture:
a) salt   d) lead
b) a cup of black coffee   e) nylon
c) potting soil

6. How would you separate a mixture of salt and iron filings?

The Classification of Pure Substances

1.9

As we have seen, substances can be classed as either elements or compounds. Each of these classes can be subdivided further in a number of ways. We will discuss some of the simpler classifications here.

Elements

On the basis of their physical properties, most of the elements can be classed as either metals or nonmetals. **Metals** are shiny and conduct heat and

borderline can have properties of either/or

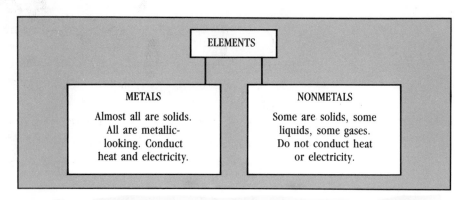

electricity. At room temperature, most metals are solids. **Nonmetals** have few properties in common, but they are all poor conductors of heat and, with one exception, do not conduct electricity. Nonmetals can be either solids, liquids, or gases.

Compounds

Compounds can be subdivided in a number of ways. One is by classifying them as being acidic, basic, or neutral. **Acids** are sharp-tasting, corrosive substances. Many substances, including many metals, dissolve in acid solutions. **Bases** are bitter tasting, usually have a slippery feel to them, and can also be corrosive.

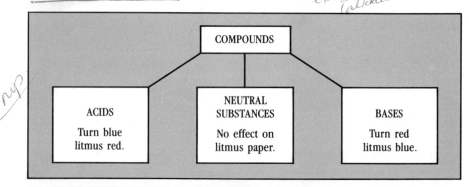

Figure 1.22

A method of classifying compounds.

TABLE 1.3 *Some Acids and Their Uses*	
Acid	**Common Use**
Hydrochloric acid	In your stomach, this acid helps in the digestion process. It can also be used to clean metal surfaces.
Sulfuric acid	This acid is used in car batteries.
Nitric acid	This acid has industrial uses.
Acetic acid	Acetic acid is a component of vinegar.

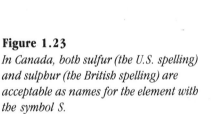

NOTE.

Ex. HYDROCHLORIC ACID –
occurs naturally in stomach
as part of digestion

Ex. Sulfuric Acid –
in car batteries

TABLE 1.4 *Some Bases and Their Uses*

Base	Common use
Sodium hydroxide *caustic Soda.*	Used in oven cleaners, this compound is often referred to as ''lye''.
Ammonia	This strong-smelling substance is used in many window cleaning liquids. *; fertilizers.*
Lime	Used as a soil conditioner in agriculture.

As we mentioned before, you should never taste any substances in the laboratory. It is also unwise to touch unknown substances because many chemicals react with the skin. We therefore have to find other methods of identifying acids and bases. One method involves using an indicator, which is a type of dye that is one colour in a base and another colour in an acid. An indicator often used in the laboratory is litmus. This is available in a convenient paper form in either red or blue. Acids turn blue litmus paper red, and bases turn red litmus paper blue. **Neutral compounds** have no effect on either red or blue litmus paper.

Names and Symbols of Elements

1.10

As there are 109 known elements it is difficult to memorize the names of all of them. It is also very cumbersome to write out the name of an element every time we want to refer to it. To overcome this problem, in the early 19th century Jöns Jacob Berzelius devised a system of symbols to represent the elements. This system is still used today.

The symbols consist of one or two letters derived from the names of the elements. Where possible, the initial letter of the name of the element is used as the symbol.

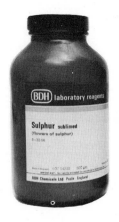

Figure 1.23
In Canada, both sulfur (the U.S. spelling) and sulphur (the British spelling) are acceptable as names for the element with the symbol S.

Berzelius — Originator of Chemical Symbols

Jöns Jacob Berzelius was born in Sweden in 1779. He originally intended to become a clergyman, but his strong interest in understanding nature led him into the sciences. He was a self-taught chemist and spent much of his life determining the proportions of various elements in minerals. In the course of this work, he and his students discovered many new elements, including selenium, thorium, lithium, and vanadium. The problems in dealing with a large number of elements and their compounds made him realize that there was a need for a simpler system of representing them.

Berzelius suggested that, where possible, the first letter of the Latin name of the element should be used as the symbol for the element. If more than one element had the same initial letter, then the first two letters of the name should be used. From this base, a complete symbolic system for the chemical elements was compiled.

Berzelius was always keenly aware of the importance of reading the current scientific journals to find out about the most recent discoveries. One of his great achievements was discerning patterns in the facts reported by other chemists. From these patterns, he deduced principles and proposed theories for the behaviour of chemical compounds.

As he grew older, Berzelius became more set in his ideas and refused to accept new developments in chemistry that contradicted some of his own theories. He withdrew more and more from the laboratory and spent a great deal of his time trying to discredit the ideas that the growth of the new field of organic chemistry was forcing on younger chemists. At the time of his death in 1848, Berzelius was a respected figure, but one whose opinions were generally disregarded by his younger colleagues.

Figure 1.24
J.J. Berzelius (1779–1848).

TABLE 1.5 *Examples of Elements Symbolized by the First Letter of Their Names*

Element	Symbol	Derivation
Carbon	C	Carbo — charcoal (Latin)
Fluorine	F	Fluor — a flow, a flux (Latin)
Hydrogen	H	Hydro genes — water producer (Greek)
Iodine	I	Iodes — violet-coloured (Greek)
Nitrogen	N	Nitron — nitre (Greek)
Oxygen	O	Oxys genes — acid producer (Greek)
Phosphorus	P	Phosphoros — bearing light (Greek)
Sulfur	S	Sulfur (Latin)
Uranium	U	Uranus — named after the planet

Because there are over 100 elements and only 26 letters of the alphabet, combinations of letters are used to represent most elements. As far as possible, these combinations are the first two letters of the names of the elements.

TABLE 1.6 *Examples of Elements Symbolized by the First Two Letters of Their Names*

Element	Symbol	Derivation
Aluminum	Al	Alumen — bitter salt (Latin)
Barium	Ba	Barys — heavy (Greek)
Bromine	Br	Bromos — stink (Greek)
Calcium	Ca	Calx — lime (Latin)
Helium	He	Helios — sun (Greek)
Lithium	Li	Lithos — stone (Greek)
Neon	Ne	Neos — new (Greek)
Silicon	Si	Silex — flint (Latin)

Again there would be duplication if only the first two letters were used because several elements have the same first two letters in their names. Therefore some elements are symbolized by the first and third letters of their names. Table 1.7 shows two pairs of examples.

TABLE 1.7 *Examples of Elements Symbolized by the First and Third Letters of Their Names*

Element	Symbol	Derivation
Chlorine	Cl	Chloros — pale green (Greek)
Chromium	Cr	Chroma — colour (Greek)
Magnesium	Mg	Magnesia — district in Western Turkey
Manganese	Mn	Manganese (Italian)

Some elements, or compounds formed by them, have been known for hundreds of years. The symbols for many elements in this category are derived from their Latin names.

Note that the symbols for the elements are used internationally, although in some languages the names for the elements do not contain the letters used to represent them. You will find it helpful to memorize the names and symbols of the elements in Tables 1.5 to 1.8 as we will be referring to many of them throughout the text.

were 1st named by first; conflicts resulted; 2nd was first two again conflicts; 3rd was first and Third letters. Others are a little different due to their origins. from different languages.

TABLE 1.8 *Examples of Elements Whose Symbols are Derived from Their Latin Names*

Element	Symbol	Latin Name
Copper	Cu	Cuprum (*cyprium*, from Cyprus)
Gold	Au	Aurum
Iron	Fe	Ferrum
Lead	Pb	Plumbum
Mercury	Hg	Hyrargyrum (Greek: *hydrargyros*)
Potassium	K	Kalium (Arabic: *al qaliy*)
Silver	Ag	Argentum
Sodium	Na	Natrium (Arabic: *natrun*; Greek: *nitron*)
Tin	Sn	Stannum

Summary

- Chemistry is the study of the composition and structure of substances, the properties of these substances, and the conditions under which they change.

- Pure chemistry is the study of the principles of chemistry: applied chemistry is the application of these principles for practical uses.

- A hypothesis is a tentative explanation for observations made. A theory is a more general explanation of related phenomena. A law is a general statement about a pattern of behaviour. All three are based on observation and experimentation.

- Matter has mass and occupies space. The mass of an object is the amount of matter in that object. The space that matter occupies is its volume. Density is the mass of a substance contained in a specific volume.

- Matter is usually found in one of three phases: solid, liquid, or gas. The process of changing from one phase to another is known as a phase transition (phase change). A different term is used for each phase change.

- The kinetic-molecular theory of matter assumes that matter consists of tiny particles that are in constant motion and therefore possess kinetic energy. The phase of a substance is related to the temperature of its particles and to the strength of the attraction between them. Differences in the melting and boiling points of various substances can be explained by the strength of attraction of their individual particles.

- When a physical change occurs, the chemical identity of a substance remains the same. If a chemical change occurs, chemically different substances are formed.

- A pure substance is uniform throughout. An element is a pure substance that cannot be broken down into simpler substances by chemical methods. Elements can be divided into metals and nonmetals.

- A compound is a pure substance that can be broken down into two or more simpler substances by chemical methods. Compounds can be acidic, basic, or neutral.

- There are 109 known elements, each with a unique name and symbol. The symbols consist of one or two letters derived from the English or Latin names of the elements.

KEY WORDS

acid	homogeneous	physical change
base	hypothesis	physical property
chemical change	law	plasma
chemical property	liquid	pure substance
compound	liquid crystal	solid
condensation	mass	solidification
density	melting	solution
element	metal	sublimation
evaporation	mixture	theory
gas	neutral compound	volume
heterogeneous	nonmetal	

ANSWERS TO SECTION QUESTIONS

1. A law is a general statement, established by experiment, that allows us to predict a particular outcome. A theory is also predictive in nature; however it attempts to explain *why* a particular set of events occurs.

2. It is important to check that the work can be repeated to ensure that the first scientist had not overlooked some important aspect of the problem.

3. b) frying an egg   c) burning wood

4. a) physical   b) physical   c) chemical

5. a) compound   c) heterogeneous mixture   e) compound
   b) solution   d) element

6. Dissolve the salt in water and filter off the solution, or use a magnet to attract the iron.

COMPREHENSION QUESTIONS

1. Explain the difference between the following terms:
   a) weight; mass
   b) physical change; physical property
   c) melting; sublimation
   d) homogeneous mixture; heterogeneous mixture
   e) element; compound

2. Distinguish between the following terms:
   a) pure chemistry; applied chemistry
   b) physical change; chemical change
   c) theory; law
   d) weight; density
   e) observation; experimentation

3. What is the correct term to describe each of the following:
   a) a solid changing directly to a gas
   b) a liquid changing to a gas
   c) the measure of the ease with which a liquid flows

4. Give the name for each of the items listed below:
   a) a solid in which the particles are arranged in an ordered geometrical structure
   b) the result of dissolving salt in water
   c) a substance that cannot be broken down into simpler substances by chemical means.

5. Give a brief description of each of the three phases of matter.

6. Copy the following diagram into your book and label the phase changes.

SOLID ⇌ LIQUID ⇌ GAS

7. Why do two pure substances have different melting and boiling points?

8. Is a phase transition a physical or chemical change? Why?

9. List the properties that allow you to distinguish between metals and nonmetals.

10. What properties are used to classify compounds as acidic, basic, or neutral?

PROBLEMS   11. Identify the following as elements, compounds, solutions, or heterogeneous mixtures:
   a) milk   c) sugar   e) human body
   b) gold   d) buttered toast

12. Describe a way to separate the components of each of the following mixtures:
   a) powdered milk dissolved in water
   b) sugar and powdered glass
   c) pieces of iron and wood

13. Classify the following as chemical or physical changes:
   a) growing a flower   c) boiling water
   b) stretching a rubber band d) baking bread

14. Which of the following are chemical changes and which are physical changes:
  a) digesting a meal d) wood rotting
  b) butter melting in a pan
  c) burning gasoline

15. Are the following properties of iron physical or chemical?
  a) It melts at a high temperature.
  b) It rusts when exposed to moist air.
  c) It becomes warm when hit repeatedly with a hammer.
  d) It sinks when placed in water.

16. Indicate which of the following properties of sodium are physical properties and which are chemical properties.
  a) It burns in air when heated.
  b) It melts at 98 °C.
  c) It reacts violently with water.
  d) It can be cut with a knife.
  e) It conducts heat and electricity.

17. Classify each of the following elements as metals or nonmetals:
  a) oxygen b) aluminum c) iron d) carbon e) silver

18. Mercury has a higher boiling point (357 °C) than water (100 °C). Use the kinetic-molecular theory to explain why.

19. Why is it sometimes difficult to distinguish between a pure liquid substance and a solution? How would you try to distinguish them? Give an example to illustrate your answer.

20. An airtight cylinder with a piston contains a litre of water and a certain mass of air. What will happen to the mass, volume, and density of each of these two substances if we double the volume of the cylinder by moving the piston?

21. Would the density of a rock be the same on the earth as on the moon? Explain your reasoning.

22. A test tube containing a few crystals of moth flakes (a white solid) is carefully heated over a small flame. The crystals disappear from the bottom of the tube and a white ring appears near the top. No liquid can be observed during the process. Which phase transition is involved in the process? Is this a physical or chemical change?

23. Water is one of the few substances with a solid form that is less dense than its liquid form. Describe what would happen to a small lake if ice were more dense than water and the lake started to freeze.

24. Because of their obsession with trying to change common metals into gold, alchemists would not discuss their experiments with others. The scientific revolution, on the other hand, came about largely as the result of the publication and discussion of scientific information. Give at least three reasons why publication of information would help scientists in their work.

26. Test your ingenuity! Choose an element for which the chemical symbol has two letters. List its symbol and name. Now choose another element with a chemical symbol starting with the second letter of the previous symbol. Continue this process until no more new elements can be found. Do not use any elements more than once. One-symbol elements are a dead end. Ten elements is an average score; twenty is good; thirty is excellent.

EXAMPLE: Mn   (manganese)

       Ni   (nickel)

         I   (iodine)   (dead end)

SUGGESTED PROJECTS

1. Many of the artificially produced elements (above atomic number 92) have been named after famous scientists or after the place where they were produced (e.g., californium—produced at University of California). Try to find out where the names of these elements came from. If an element was named after a scientist, find out what the scientist is known for.

2. When scientific discoveries are used for purposes that may be harmful to life (e.g., the atomic bomb, or genetic engineering) questions arise about the moral obligation of the scientists to see that their discoveries are not misused. The scientists may reply that their interests are in pure research (the increase in human knowledge) and not in the application of that knowledge. Prepare a paper or organize a debate on this topic.

3. Obtain university or college calendars from your counsellor. Make a list of those fields of study that require some background in chemistry.

Measurement

When we study chemistry we are interested in examining the composition and properties of matter. These are the *qualitative* aspects of chemistry. We are also interested in the *quantitative* side of chemistry, or in other words, the numerical values of the properties of matter. For example, we are not just interested in the fact that water boils, but also in knowing the exact temperature at which it boils. In this chapter we will discuss the units of measurement used in chemistry and the ways in which they are used.

When we conduct experiments or solve problems we usually measure, or are given, the values of some properties of a substance. From these values, and from our knowledge about the relationships among the various properties of matter, we can then calculate the values of other properties. These calculations can be performed in a number of ways, one of the simplest of which is the *conversion-factor method*. As we will be using the conversion-factor method throughout this text, we will show you how it can be applied in the problem-solving process.

The Origins of the International System of Units (SI) 2.1

Many units of measurement were originally derived from dimensions of the human body: for example, an inch was defined as the length from the tip of the thumb to the first joint; a foot was the width of 16 fingers; a yard was the distance from the tip of the nose to the tip of the middle finger of

Figure 2.1
The origin of the units, inch, yard, and fathom.

the outstretched arm; a mile was 1000 double paces (from the Latin *mille passum*); and the fathom was "the spread of a Viking's embrace."

As you can imagine, these units proved to be inconvenient because the lengths of arms, thumbs, and paces varied. Different values could therefore be obtained for the same measurement. To try to overcome this problem, each city in Europe eventually developed its own standard measures. This also caused problems, because each city used different definitions for standard units. For example, an object that weighed 100 Amsterdam pounds weighed 105 Brussels pounds, and 81 Stockholm pounds!

Over the years, most of the units of measurement were standardized and were incorporated into a system of measurement that became known as the British, or *Imperial system* of units. During the 19th century, a parallel system of units, known as the metric system, was established in continental Europe. The **metric system** differed from the Imperial system in two main ways: first, the metric system used decimal units for all the measurement scales; and second, the units of the different scales were logically related to each other.

The metric system became the recognized system of measurement in most European countries, including France (where it originated), Germany, and Spain, and also in the colonies established by these countries. The Imperial system was used in Britain, Canada, the United States, and the Commonwealth countries. Scientists in these countries, however, tended to use the metric system of measurement in their laboratories.

The International System of Units

In 1960, an extensive revision and simplification of the metric system was adopted by the General Conference on Weights and Measures. The name **Le Système international d'unités** (The International System of Units), generally abbreviated to SI, was given to this modernized metric system. The SI is a strict metric system which relates measurements of all kinds to four common **base units** of length, mass, time, and temperature. In addition, it has three specialized base units for electric current, light intensity, and amount of substance.

Figure 2.2
This 1975 French stamp shows the base-unit symbols of the SI.

TABLE 2.1	*The Seven Base Units of the SI*	
Quantity	Name of Unit	Symbol
Length	metre	m
Mass	kilogram	kg
Time	second	s
Temperature	kelvin	K
Electric current	ampere	A
Luminous intensity	candela	cd
Amount of substance	mole	mol

Accuracy and Precision

2.2

Most people use the words accuracy and precision as if they had the same meaning. To a scientist, however, there is a distinct difference between an experimental result that is accurate and one that is precise. **Accuracy** is a measure of how closely a result (or the arithmetic mean of a set of results) approaches the true (or accepted) value. **Precision** is a measure of how closely the results within a set of results agree with one another.

We can illustrate the difference in meaning by using a dart board as an analogy. In Figure 2.3a, the dart player has achieved reasonable accuracy — the darts (test results) have a mean position (average value) that is quite close to the centre of the target (close to the desired result); the precision, however, is poor, as there is a considerable distance between each dart. In other words, the test results do not agree very well.

In Figure 2.3b, the mean position of the darts (test results) is not near the centre of the target (true value). The accuracy is therefore said to be poor. However, the precision is good as all the darts are very close together.

Figure 2.3c shows all the darts grouped close to the centre of the target. This is analogous to having several results that agree very well with the true

Figure 2.3
The difference between accuracy and precision —
a) Good accuracy, poor precision
b) Poor accuracy, good precision
c) Good accuracy, good precision

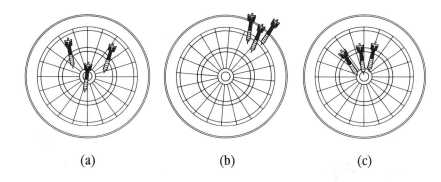

(a)   (b)   (c)

(or accepted) value; that is, they are both accurate and precise. As potential scientists, we should be striving in our experiments for a similar high degree of accuracy and precision.

The types of "errors" illustrated in Figures 2.3a and 2.3b are significantly different. Poor precision, such as that shown in Figure 2.3a is usually an indication of random error. A **random error** is often caused by limitations of either the equipment or of the method used. In this example, the quality of the darts may have been inconsistent or the dart thrower may have held each dart differently.

poor precision good accuracy

The poor accuracy but good precision illustrated in Figure 2.3b suggests a systematic error. A **systematic error** is a consistent factor that affects all the results equally. When conducting experiments in the laboratory, we have to first check (calibrate) our equipment to make sure that the readings obtained are both accurate and precise. Calibrating equipment minimizes the chances of systematic errors.

good precision. poor accuracy

Mass Measurement in the Laboratory

In the laboratory, balances are used to determine mass. Most laboratories have two types of balances. The type you will use in your work will depend on the precision you require. When only an approximate mass (for example, to the nearest 0.1 g) is required, a general-purpose balance is usually used. Figures 2.4a and 2.4b show two kinds of general-purpose balance.

If a more precise mass is required (perhaps to the nearest 0.0001 g), an analytical balance is used. Two types of analytical balance are shown in Figures 2.5a and 2.5b.

Figure 2.4

a) *A mechanical general-purpose balance (sometimes called a triple-beam balance) can measure mass to ±0.1 g.*

b) *An electronic general-purpose balance. Depending on the model, it can measure mass to ±0.1 g or ±0.01 g.*

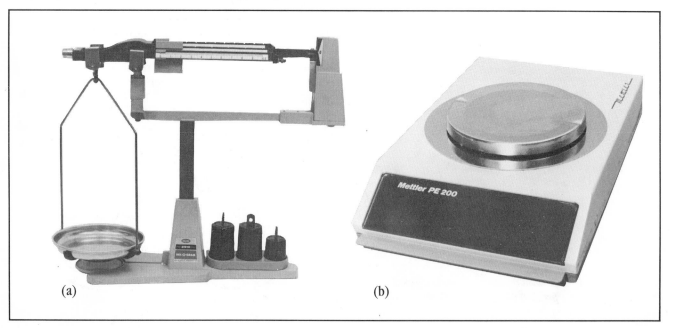

(a)   (b)

Figure 2.5

a) *A mechanical analytical balance. Most types can measure mass to ±0.0001 g.*

b) *An electronic analytical balance. Most models can measure mass to ±0.0001 g.*

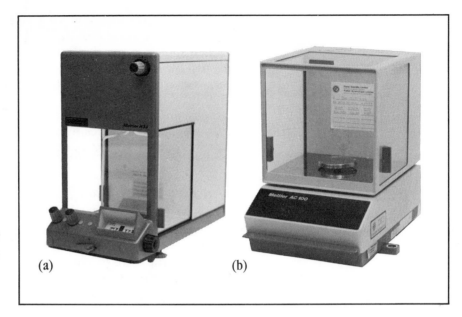

(a)   (b)

EXAMPLE   **2.1**   A piece of metal is known to have a mass of 18.01 g. When a student made three attempts to determine the mass of the metal, the following results were obtained:

   a) 18.00 g   b) 18.03 g   c) 18.02 g

Are these results accurate, precise, or both?

SOLUTION   The results are both accurate (because the mean value is very close to the true value) and precise (because the measurements are consistent, varying by only 3 parts in 1800, or 0.2%).

QUESTIONS

1. Two students determine the mass of a piece of copper metal. Joan's results are 15.64 g, 15.69 g, and 15.67 g. Rick's results are 15.77 g, 15.78 g, and 15.78 g. If the actual mass of the piece of copper was 15.67 g, who had the more accurate results and who had the more precise results? Did either set of results contain a systematic or a random error?

Significant Figures

2.3   If a person is 16 years old, you assume that they have passed their sixteenth birthday but have not yet reached their seventeenth birthday. If that person will be 17 in one month's time, it would be more precise to give the age as $16^{11}/_{12}$ years, but we do not usually talk about age in terms of twelfths of years. In science, however, precision is very important and we should give the precision of every measurement that we make. We can do this by using significant figures.

When someone says that a substance has a mass of 4 kg, we can assume only that the mass is closer to 4 kg than it is to 3 kg or 5 kg; that is, the mass is between 3.5 and 4.5 kg. Similarly, if we say that a substance has a mass of 4.000 kg, this means that the mass is between 3.9995 and 4.0005 kg. A mass written as 4 kg has only one significant figure, whereas one of 4.000 kg has four significant figures. The precision with which a scientific measurement was made is always indicated by the number of **significant figures** quoted.

When Zero is Significant

Zeros pose a problem when determining the number of significant figures in a measured quantity. For example, the number 2.000 has four significant figures. If this number is given as the value of a measurement, we assume that the zeros following the figure 2 were really measured and are equal to zero. On the other hand, 0.002 is considered to have only one significant figure as the zeros only tell us that the number is two-thousandths, and is not two-hundredths or two-tenths.

EXAMPLE *2.2*

Determine the number of significant figures in each of the following measured values:

a) 21.04   b) 0.0010

SOLUTION

a) 21.04 has four significant figures. The zero is part of the number.
b) 0.0010 has two significant figures. The first three zeros are required because of the position of the decimal point. They are not part of the measurement and are not significant. The last zero shows that the person making the measurement thought the value was closer to 0.0010 than to 0.0011. Therefore, the last zero is significant.

Numbers such as 2000 are difficult to assess in terms of significant figures. We don't really know whether the number is between 1995 and 2005 or between 1500 and 2500. Some scientists place a period after the number, e.g. "2000.", if the number is known precisely to the fourth significant figure. However, the best solution is to express the number in scientific notation.

QUESTIONS

2. How many significant figures are there in the following:
   a) 5.6 g   b) 846.2 mL

3. Determine the number of significant figures used for the values given in each of the following statements:
   a) The downtown temperature is 25.0 °C and the atmospheric pressure is 104.1 kPa.

b) Yesterday, the Canadian dollar gained 0.10 points on the U.S. dollar.

c) Our best sprinter is 1.9 m tall and has a mass of only 45 kg.

Scientific Notation

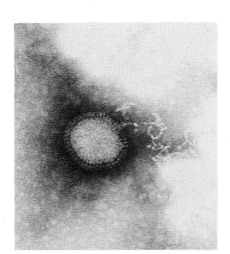

Figure 2.6
Scientists have to deal with very large and very small numbers. For example, this influenza virus has a diameter of 0.000 000 1 m (1 × 10⁻⁷ m).

Chemists are often concerned with very large and very small numbers. For example, one gram of iron contains about 10 000 000 000 000 000 000 000 atoms of iron. Each atom has a mass of about 0.000 000 000 000 000 000 000 1 g. Rather than writing out all these zeros, we can express the numbers in powers of ten by using **scientific**, or exponential, **notation**.

In addition to reducing the number of zeros, expressing a value in scientific notation removes any ambiguity about the number of significant figures.

Consider the number 700. This number can be obtained by multiplying 7 by 100. In turn, 100 can be obtained by multiplying 10 by 10. Thus, the number 700 can be represented as

$$700 = 7 \times 100 = 7 \times 10 \times 10 = 7 \times 10^2$$

When we use 7×10^2 to represent 700, we are using scientific notation. To convert 700 to scientific notation, we moved the decimal point *two* places to the left and raised 10 to the power *two*. The general rule for expressing numbers greater than unity in scientific notation is as follows:

> **Move the decimal point to the left until there is just one digit in front of it, count the number of places that the decimal has been moved and use this number as the *exponent* (i.e., the power of 10) in the exponential form of the number.**

Thus, to write 1256 in scientific notation, we move the decimal three places to the left and raise 10 to the power of three, to give an answer of 1.256×10^3. In our example above, we can use scientific notation to express the number of atoms in a gram of iron as 1×10^{22}.

This method of writing numbers can also be applied to numbers that are less than one. For these, we move the decimal point to the right until we have just one digit (other than zero) following the decimal point. Again the power of 10 is given by the number of places we move the decimal point, but this time we must give the exponent a *negative* sign. Thus, to convert the number 0.0068 into scientific notation we must move the decimal point three places to the right, which gives us 6.8×10^{-3}. Again, using this method, we would write the mass of each atom of iron as 1×10^{-22}.

Although there are no fixed rules about when to use scientific notation, it is preferable to use it for numbers greater than 100 or less than 0.1.

[handwritten: mol = 6.02 × 10²³]

[handwritten: Right - negative Left - positive]

| EXAMPLE | 2.3 | Convert the following numbers to scientific notation and identify the number of significant figures in each: |

EXAMPLE   **2.3**   Convert the following numbers to scientific notation and identify the number of significant figures in each:

     a) 0.004   b) 400.0   c) 0.040

SOLUTION

a) Moving the decimal point three places to the right gives a value of 4×10^{-3}. The number has only one significant figure.

b) Moving the decimal point two places to the left gives a value of 4.000×10^2. In this case, all the zeros are significant because the value was precise to the nearest tenth (that is, 400.0, not 399.9 or 400.1). There are four significant figures.

c) Moving the decimal point two places to the right gives a value of 4.0×10^{-2}. Only the zero after the four is significant (indicating the value is 0.040, not 0.039 or 0.041). There are two significant figures.

If we want to reverse the process and convert from scientific notation back to decimal notation, the operations are carried out in the reverse order.

EXAMPLE   **2.4**   Convert a) 8×10^{-4} and b) 8.0×10^{-4} to decimal notation.

SOLUTION

a) 0.0008   b) 0.000 80

(Spaces are left between each group of three digits when there are five or more places on either side of the decimal point.)

As we mentioned, use of scientific notation removes any ambiguity about the precision of a measurement. For example, if the distance from the earth to the sun is written as 150 000 000 km, we do not know the number of significant figures intended. Expressing the distance as 1.5×10^8 km suggests that the measurement has been made to the nearest ten million kilometres, whereas expressing it as 1.50×10^8 km implies that the measurement has been made to the nearest ten million kilometres.

Metric Prefixes

To minimize the use of exponents, large and small quantities can be expressed by attaching a **metric prefix** to the unit in which the measurement is made.

Instead of referring to a mass of 0.001 g (or 1×10^{-3} g) as "zero-point-zero-zero-one grams" (or "one-times-ten-to-the-power-minus-three grams"), it may simply be called one milligram, milli- being the prefix for 10^{-3}. With very large or very small numbers, the convenience of the system is even more apparent.

Timela (handwritten signature)

TABLE 2.2 *Common Metric Prefixes*

Prefix	Symbol	Value	Scientific Notation
mega-	M	1 000 000	10^6
kilo-	k	1 000	10^3
		1	10^0
deci-	d	0.1	10^{-1}
centi-	c	0.01	10^{-2}
milli-	m	0.001	10^{-3}
micro-	μ	0.000 001	10^{-6}
nano-	n	0.000 000 001	10^{-9}
pico-	p	0.000 000 000 001	10^{-12}

Scientific Notation and Calculators

As most of you will be using scientific calculators to solve the problems given in this text, it is important to know how to enter a number in scientific notation. First, locate on your calculator the function keys "EXP" and "+/−" (not the normal minus key). These keys are standard on most scientific calculators.

If you want to enter the number 1.2×10^{-3}, you first enter the number "1.2" and then press "EXP". At this point, the number "1.2" should shift to the left and two zeros should appear to the right. These two zeros represent the exponent. Next, enter "3". The display should now show "1.2 03". This represents the number 1.2×10^3. All we need now is a negative exponent. To change the exponent sign, press "+/−". The display should show "1.2 −03", representing 1.2×10^{-3}. Calculators do not show the base "10" in an exponential number.

Multiplication and Division in Scientific Notation

When multiplying or dividing numbers given in scientific notation, the coefficients and the exponents are treated separately; the coefficients are multiplied or divided normally, but the exponents are either added (for multiplication) or subtracted (for division). Thus, if we wish to multiply 3.4×10^2 by 2.0×10^3 we multiply the coefficients in the normal manner

$$3.4 \times 2.0 = 6.8$$

and add the exponents

$$10^2 \times 10^3 = 10^{2+3} = 10^5$$

to obtain the answer

$$6.8 \times 10^5$$

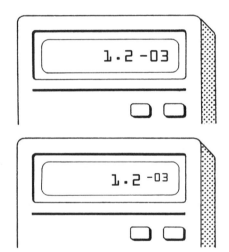

Figure 2.7
Two ways in which the number 1.2×10^{-3} can be displayed on a calculator.

3.4 EXP 2 x
2.0 EXP 3 =

NOTE: On some calculators,

EE = EXP

We can check to see if this is the correct answer by solving the problem using regular mathematical procedures:

$$3.4 \times 10^2 = 340$$
$$2.0 \times 10^3 = 2000$$

Thus, the problem could be solved as follows:

$$340 \times 2000 = 680\ 000$$

Since

$$680\ 000 = 6.8 \times 10^5$$

our answer is correct.

Division in scientific notation is done similarly. For example, to divide 3.4×10^2 by 2.0×10^3, we first divide the coefficients:

$$3.4 \div 2.0 = 1.7$$

We then subtract the exponents

$$10^2 \div 10^3 = 10^{2-3} = 10^{-1}$$

to arrive at the answer

$$1.7 \times 10^{-1}$$

EXAMPLE   *2.5*

Evaluate $\dfrac{(8.8 \times 10^9) \times (2.1 \times 10^8)}{3.3 \times 10^{-16}}$

SOLUTION   As multiplication and division can be done in any order, we can solve the problem as follows:

$$\frac{(8.8 \times 2.1)}{3.3} \times \frac{(10^9 \times 10^8)}{10^{-16}} = 5.6 \times \frac{10^{(9+8)}}{10^{-16}}$$

$$= 5.6 \times \frac{10^{17}}{10^{-16}}$$

$$= 5.6 \times 10^{(17-(-16))}$$

$$= 5.6 \times 10^{(17+16)}$$

$$= 5.6 \times 10^{33}$$

Addition and Subtraction in Scientific Notation

Numbers that are expressed in scientific notation can only be added or subtracted if the exponents of the numbers are the same.

Let us add 2.07×10^3 to 3.0×10^2. The first thing we notice is that the exponents are different. Therefore, the two numbers cannot be added as they stand. We must first modify one of the numbers so that both have the same exponent. In this case it is more convenient to convert 3.0×10^2 to 0.30×10^3, so that both terms have the same exponent. To add 2.07×10^3

to 0.30 × 10³, we just add 2.07 to 0.30; the answer has the same exponent as the numbers being added:

$$
\begin{array}{r}
2.07 \times 10^3 \\
+\ 0.30 \times 10^3 \\
\hline
2.37 \times 10^3
\end{array}
$$

KATHY   *Sandy*

Thus, the answer is 2.37×10^3. We can check this answer by conventional methods:

$$2.07 \times 10^3 = 2070$$
$$3.0 \ \ \times 10^2 = 300$$

$$2070 + 300 = 2370 = 2.37 \times 10^3$$

Exponents of Units

.600

Just as numbers can have exponents, so can units. In any problem, powers of units may be manipulated in the same way as powers of ten. Thus, the volume of a container whose sides are measured in metres would be given in units of m^3 (m × m × m), stated as "metres cubed" or the more usual term, "cubic metres".

Kathleen

EXAMPLE   **2.6**   The dimensions of an internationally approved table-tennis table are 2.74 m by 1.525 m. Calculate the surface area of the table.

SOLUTION   Area of table = 2.74 m × 1.525 m = 4.18 m²

If you multiply 2.74 by 1.525 or check the calculation with your calculator, the answer you get is 4.1785. You may wonder why we expressed the answer as 4.18. It was not an arbitrary decision on our part. We only used three digits in the answer because of the precision of the original measurements. Scientists are always concerned with the accuracy and precision of both the measurements they make and any values calculated using those measurements.

QUESTIONS

4. Convert the following numbers to scientific notation and identify the number of significant figures in each:
   a) 0.0087   b) 0.0870   c) 870.00
5. Convert the following to decimal notation:
   a) 9.60×10^2 c) 1.00×10^{-3}
   b) 8.402×10^3 d) 4.250×10^2
6. Express each of the following measurements using the correct metric prefix:
   a) 1.0×10^3 g   c) 3.4×10^{-6} m
   b) 2.0×10^{-2} m   d) 4.2×10^6 g

1000

7. Perform the following mathematical operations:
   a) $(4.34 \times 10^4) \times (2.00 \times 10^2)$
   b) $(4.34 \times 10^4) \div (2.00 \times 10^2)$
8. Perform the following mathematical operations:
   a) $(4.34 \times 10^3) + (2.0 \times 10^2)$
   b) $(4.34 \times 10^3) - (2.0 \times 10^2)$
9. What is the volume of a box having the following dimensions: length, 4.0 cm; width, 2.0 cm; and height, 1.5 cm?

Significant Figures in Calculations

2.5

When we add, subtract, multiply, or divide measured values, we must be careful when expressing the precision of the answer. It is important to be able to determine quickly the number of significant figures that an answer should have. The rules for determining the number of significant figures depend on the type of calculation: the rules for multiplication and division are different from those for addition and subtraction.

Multiplication and Division

In Example 2.6, we determined the area of the surface of a table-tennis table measuring 2.74 m by 1.525 m. We also noted that if we check the answer by multiplication, or by using a calculator, the answer would be 4.1785 m^2.

This answer is not very realistic as it is expressed to five significant figures, whereas one of the measurements was given to three significant figures and the other to four.

A calculated or derived value cannot be more precise than the measurements that were actually made.

We must therefore *round off* the answer so that it is given to the same precision as the *least* precise measurement. In the example, the least precise measurement for the table, 2.74 m, has three significant figures. Our answer must therefore contain the same number of significant figures.

When multiplying or dividing measured values, the answer must have the same number of significant figures as the measurement with the fewest significant figures.

Thus, the surface area of the table-tennis table is correctly expressed as 4.18 m^2.

You will also notice that we wrote 4.18 m^2 instead of using the first three digits and writing 4.17 m^2. We did this because when we round off numbers we must always take into consideration the digits we are discarding. The rules for rounding off are as follows:

1. If the first nonsignificant digit is less than 5, it is dropped and the last significant digit remains the same.

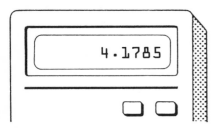

Figure 2.8
When an answer is obtained on a calculator, you cannot assume that all the numbers are meaningful.

2. **If the first nonsignificant digit is 5 or greater, it is dropped and the last significant digit is increased by one.**

In Example 2.6, rule 2 was applied. The first nonsignificant figure in 4.1786 is the 8. Thus the last significant figure (7) is increased by one when we round off to three significant figures.

EXAMPLE **2.7** Round off each of the following numbers to three significant figures:
a) 53.31 b) 9.426 c) 15.751

SOLUTION a) Following rule 1, the 1 is dropped to give an answer of 53.3.
b) As the first nonsignificant figure is a 6, we round up the third significant figure from 2 to 3 to give an answer of 9.43 (see rule 2).
c) Here the first nonsignificant figure is a 5. According to rule 2, we must round up the last significant figure to give an answer of 15.8.

EXAMPLE **2.8** If a plot of land is said to measure 11 m by 14 m, what is its area?

SOLUTION The measurements 11 m × 14 m mean that it is between 10.5 m and 11.5 m wide and between 13.5 m and 14.5 m long. Thus the area of the plot must lie between 141.75 m² (= 13.5 m × 10.5 m) and 166.75 m² (= 14.5 m × 11.5 m). The value of 1.5×10^2 (that is, 14 m × 11 m = 154 m² rounded off to two significant figures) represents the average of the maximum and minimum values (308.50 m² / 2) and is probably the most realistic value to report.

Calculators and Significant Zeros

As we have noted, calculators can give us too many digits in an answer. They can also give us too few digits. If we use a calculator to multiply 2.0 by 4.0, from the significant figure rules, we would expect to obtain an answer with two significant figures. The calculator, however, gives an answer of 8. If the calculator shows fewer digits than are required in an answer, we must assume the missing digits are zero. Thus our answer should be 8.0.

Addition and Subtraction

In chemistry it is often necessary to add or subtract measurements that have been taken during an experiment. For addition or subtraction, the rule is as follows:

The answer must be given to the same number of places after the decimal point as the measurement that has the least number of places after the decimal point.

Numbers that do not involve decimals should first be converted to scientific notation before applying this rule.

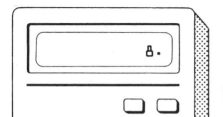

Figure 2.9
Until we have checked on the significant figures required, we cannot tell if the answer should be 8, 8.0, or 8.00, etc.

| EXAMPLE | 2.9 | An empty beaker has a mass of 32.41 g. When some water is placed in the beaker, the total mass is 33.7822 g. Find the mass of the water. |

SOLUTION Note that the first measurement was precise to a hundredth of a gram but the second measurement was precise to a ten-thousandth of a gram. Thus, when the figures are subtracted the answer can only be precise to a hundredth of a gram:

$$
\begin{array}{r}
33.7822 \text{ g} \\
-32.41 \text{ g} \\
\hline
1.37 \text{ g}
\end{array}
$$

As you can see, the rules for addition and subtraction are different from the rules for multiplication and division. Of the two measurements involved in this calculation, one (33.7822) has six significant figures and the other (32.41) has four. However, our answer can only be given to three significant figures. If the mass of the beaker is not known to a thousandth of a gram, then it is impossible to find the mass of the water to a thousandth of a gram.

The technique described in Example 2.9; that is, finding the mass of a substance by subtracting the mass of the empty container from the mass of the container plus the substance, is known as *weighing by difference*. The technique is used in both the laboratory and in everyday life (Figure 2.10).

Figure 2.10

The mass of sand delivered by the truck can be determined by weighing the truck when it is full and when it is empty. This is known as weighing by difference.

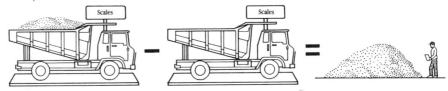

Exact Numbers

The difference between an exact number and a measurement must be emphasized. A measurement always has a finite number of significant figures that are determined by the precision of the instrument used. An **exact number** is one in which there is no uncertainty, and consequently an exact number can be regarded as having an infinite number of significant figures. If we have three books, each with a mass of 225 g, we know that three is an exact number as we could not possibly have 3.1 books or 2.9 books. However, 225 g is a measured quantity with three significant figures and some uncertainty in the last figure. We can calculate the total mass of the three books as follows:

Total mass = Number of books × Mass of each book
= 3 × 225 g = 675 g

The number of significant figures in the answer (3) is determined by the measured quantity and not by the exact number.

QUESTIONS

10. Round off each of the following numbers to four significant figures:
  a) 127.32   b) 127.35   c) 127.38

11. Find the volume of a brick with dimensions of 13.6 cm, 14.2 cm, and 8.4 cm.

12. Write the answers to the following problems to the correct number of significant figures:
  a) 4.20×5.00 b) 1.50×0.200

13. If 2.125 g of sugar is dissolved in 100.0 g of water in a beaker of mass 64.78 g, what is the total mass of the beaker and its contents?

The Conversion-Factor Method

2.6

Many of the numerical problems in this text will involve conversion from one set of units to another. We will first introduce you to the principles involved in handling units and then develop a problem-solving method that will be used throughout the rest of this book.

The Algebra of Units

In every calculation, the units must undergo the same mathematical operations as the numbers. As the following examples show, we can add two volumes, multiply a length by an area, and move a unit from the denominator of an expression to the numerator:

Adding two volumes:
$$5 \text{ cm}^3 + 3 \text{ cm}^3 = 8 \text{ cm}^3 \quad (\text{cm}^3 + \text{cm}^3 = \text{cm}^3)$$
Multiplying length by area:
$$3 \text{ cm} \times 2 \text{ cm}^2 = 6 \text{ cm}^3 \quad (\text{cm} \times \text{cm}^2 = \text{cm}^3)$$
Moving a unit to the numerator:
$$8 \text{ g} \div 4 \text{ cm}^3 = 2 \text{ g} \cdot \text{cm}^{-3} \quad (\text{g} \div \text{cm}^3 = \text{g} \cdot \text{cm}^{-3})$$

Conversion Factors

Before any conversion is possible we have to know the relationship between the units involved. In the case of centimetres and metres, the relationship is as follows:

$$100 \text{ cm} = 1 \text{ m}$$

If we divide both sides of this equation by 1 m we obtain

$$\frac{100 \text{ cm}}{1 \text{ m}} = \frac{1 \text{ m}}{1 \text{ m}} = 1$$

Metric Standards

Since the metric system was first introduced late in the eighteenth century, our ability to make precise measurements has increased dramatically.

A metre was originally defined as one ten-millionth (10^{-7}) of the distance from the north pole to the equator, measured along the meridian of the earth running near Dunkirk (France) and Barcelona (Spain); a kilogram was defined as the mass of one litre of water at its temperature of maximum density; and a second was defined as 1/86 400 of a mean solar day. However, there were difficulties in reproducing and comparing metric standards in different countries. By 1875, an international treaty on standards had been signed, and the International Bureau of Weights and Measures had been established to act as a custodian of these standards. Signatories to the treaty also agreed that a General Conference on Weights and Measures would be held periodically to update old standards and define new ones as the need arose.

To enable metric standards to be reproduced, definitions were rewritten based on physical objects. The original definitions were used as the basis for the new definitions of the metre and the kilogram. In 1889, the metre was redefined as the distance between two lines engraved on a bar of platinum-iridium alloy kept at 0 °C in a vault at Sèvres, France. The standard kilogram was defined as the mass of a platinum-iridium cylinder stored at the same location. Copies of the standard metre and standard kilogram were supplied to countries that were signatories to the international agreement.

Although the definition of the kilogram has not changed over the years, the definition of the metre is no longer based on the earth's circumference. In 1960 the metre was redefined as 1 650 763.73 times the wavelength of the light from a lamp containing krypton gas. In October 1983 the metre was again redefined. A metre is now the distance that light travels in a vacuum in 1/299 792 458 of a second.

Why has it been necessary to redefine the metre twice since 1889? First, chemical changes caused the platinum-iridium bars to increase in length by one part in ten million (1 part in 10^7) every year. The 1960 definition was more reliable because it was precise to one part in a billion (1 part in 10^9). The second redefinition resulted from technological advances since 1960 that have allowed even greater precision to be achieved in measuring length. It is hoped that the current definition, which gives a precision of one part in ten billion (1 part in 10^{10}), will suffice for several more years.

Figure 2.11
The standard kilogram under two protective bell jars. This platinum-iridium cylinder, brought to the U.S. from France in 1889, is the standard of mass measurement in the United States.

Any ratio which relates two quantities expressed in different units is called a **conversion factor.** Since these factors equal one, we can multiply any measurement by a conversion factor without changing the value of the measurement. Only the units will change. To illustrate, we will convert 0.015 m to centimetres.

$$0.015 \, \text{m} \times \frac{100 \, \text{cm}}{1 \, \text{m}} = 15 \, \text{cm}$$

If we wish to convert from centimetres to metres, we simply *invert* the conversion factor and then multiply. Therefore, to express 425 cm in metres, we write 425 cm and multiply it by the inverted or reciprocal form of the conversion factor. By so doing, the like units on either side of the multiplication sign cancel and we are left with an answer in metres:

$$425 \, \text{cm} \times \frac{1 \, \text{m}}{100 \, \text{cm}} = 0.425 \, \text{m}$$

EXAMPLE   **2.10**   Convert 275 ml to litres.

SOLUTION   To obtain the conversion factor we first need to know the relationship between the two units:

$$1 \, \text{L} = 1000 \, \text{mL}$$

If we divide both sides of this equation by 1 L, we obtain the following conversion factor:

$$\frac{1000 \, \text{mL}}{1 \, \text{L}}$$

As we need an answer in litres, we use the inverted form of the conversion factor in order to *cancel* millilitres (mL):

$$275 \, \text{mL} \times \frac{1 \, \text{L}}{1000 \, \text{mL}} = 0.275 \, \text{L}$$

Up to now we have dealt with the same type of measurement, such as length, within a calculation. However, we often have to relate one type of measurement, such as length, to a completely different type, such as time.

To illustrate, we will find how long it would take to drive 96 km at a constant speed of $48 \, \text{km} \cdot \text{h}^{-1}$. In this case the speed becomes our conversion factor (48 km/1 h). To obtain an answer in units of time, we invert the factor and multiply. The units of length thus cancel each other out:

$$96 \, \text{km} \times \frac{1 \, \text{h}}{48 \, \text{km}} = 2.0 \, \text{h}$$

NOTE: In a conversion problem such as this, we are *not* saying that 96 km is the same as 2.0 h, but rather that the two measurements are related.

2.11 If a baseball player pitcher throws a ball with a velocity of $44\,\text{m}\cdot\text{s}^{-1}$, how long does it take for the ball to reach home plate? The distance between the mound and home plate is $18\,\text{m}$.

SOLUTION The conversion factor is the velocity written in the form of a fraction:

$$\frac{44\,\text{m}}{1\,\text{s}}$$

We write the number that we wish to change and multiply it by the inverted conversion factor. The conversion factor must be inverted to cancel out the units of length and obtain an answer in seconds:

$$18\,\text{m} \times \frac{1\,\text{s}}{44\,\text{m}} = 0.41\,\text{s}$$

When performing calculations, we should always check to see that our answer seems reasonable. In this case, since the ball travels $44\,\text{m}$ each second, we would expect it to take less than half a second to travel $18\,\text{m}$.

Always remember to check the significant figures used in the calculation. In Example 2.11, both numbers had two significant figures; thus, the answer could only be expressed to two significant figures.

We can apply the conversion-factor method to any type of conversion, providing we can find a relationship between the units involved. In the next example, we use price to relate mass and money.

EXAMPLE **2.12** If the price of chicken is $\$2.28\cdot\text{kg}^{-1}$, how much will a $3.72\,\text{kg}$ chicken cost?

SOLUTION In this case, the relation is between dollars and kilograms. The conversion factor is simply the price of chicken per kilogram:

$$\frac{\$2.28}{1\,\text{kg}}$$

This time we need not invert the factor to cancel the unwanted units. Thus, our answer can be worked as follows:

$$3.72\,\text{kg} \times \frac{\$2.28}{1\,\text{kg}} = \$8.48$$

QUESTIONS

14. Perform the following calculations:
    a) $2\,\text{mL} + 6\,\text{mL}$ c) $15\,\text{m} \div 3\,\text{s}$
    b) $8\,\text{cm}^3 \div 2\,\text{cm}$ d) $2\,\text{m}\cdot\text{s}^{-1} \times 4\,\text{s}$
15. Convert the following using the appropriate conversion factor:
    a) $1.76\,\text{km}$ to metres   c) $2000\,\text{m}$ to kilometres
    b) $0.132\,\text{m}$ to centimetres   d) $1.09 \times 10^{-9}\,\text{m}$ to nanometres

$25 m \times \dfrac{1 s}{2.5 m} = 10 s$

16. Use the conversion-factor method to answer the questions below.

   a) How long will it take to swim the length of a 25 m pool if you can swim at a speed of $2.5 \ \text{m} \cdot \text{s}^{-1}$?

   b) If cabbage costs $1.19 \cdot \text{kg}^{-1}$, how much cabbage can you buy for $8.00?

   c) A cyclist plans to exercise for 3.5 h and to maintain a speed of $12 \ \text{km} \cdot \text{h}^{-1}$. How far will the cyclist travel?

Volume

2.7

Figure 2.12
Comparison of 1 cm and 1 dm.

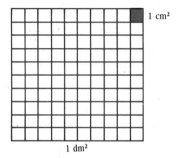

Figure 2.13
Comparison of 1 cm and 1 dm².

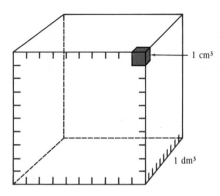

Figure 2.14
Comparison of 1 cm³ and 1 dm³.

In the previous sections we have emphasized the base units of the SI. A **derived unit** is formed by combining one or more base units. The cubic metre (m^3) and the cubic centimetre (cm^3) are examples. In chemistry, the most common derived units are those used for measuring volume. Since the cubic metre (m^3) is far too large a unit for the volumes measured in the laboratory, we use the prefixed units cubic centimetre (cm^3) and cubic decimetre (dm^3) instead.

The relationship between cubic centimetres and cubic decimetres can be readily understood if we use a stepwise approach: As 10 dm = 1 m and 100 cm = 1 m, we can use as our starting point the relationship 1 dm = 10 cm (Figure 2.12).

What is the relation between $1 \ dm^2$ and $1 \ cm^2$? We can solve this as follows:

$$1 \ dm^2 = 1 \ dm \times 1 \ dm = 10 \ cm \times 10 \ cm = 100 \ cm^2$$

This result (Figure 2.13) means that one hundred $1 \ cm^2$ squares will fit in a $1 \ dm^2$ square.

We can establish the cubic (volume) relationship in a similar way:

$$1 \ dm^3 = 1 \ dm \times 1 \ dm \times 1 \ dm$$
$$= 10 \ cm \times 10 \ cm \times 10 \ cm$$
$$= 1000 \ cm^3$$

The result (Figure 2.14) means that one thousand $1 \ cm^3$ cubes will fit in a $1 \ dm^3$ cube.

Although the cubic metre, cubic decimetre, and the cubic centimetre are true SI units of volume, the *litre* (L) is used more often both in everyday life and in science. The two simple equations below should help you to understand the relationship between the litre and the true SI units of volume:

$$1 \ L = 1 \ dm^3 \qquad 1 \ mL = 1 \ cm^3$$

| EXAMPLE | 2.13 | Convert 452 cm³ to litres. |

SOLUTION

We need two conversion factors to solve this problem. We can first convert from cubic centimetres to millilitres, and then from millilitres to litres using the relationships

$$1 \text{ mL} = 1 \text{ cm}^3 \qquad 1 \text{ L} = 1000 \text{ mL}$$

This gives us the following conversion factors:

$$\frac{1 \text{ mL}}{1 \text{ cm}^3} \quad \text{and} \quad \frac{1 \text{ L}}{1000 \text{ mL}}$$

Our calculation thus becomes

$$452 \text{ cm}^3 \times \frac{1 \text{ mL}}{1 \text{ cm}^3} = 452 \text{ mL}$$

$$452 \text{ mL} \times \frac{1 \text{ L}}{1000 \text{ mL}} = 0.452 \text{ L}$$

Figure 2.15
Graduated cylinders are available in sizes ranging from 5 mL to 2 L.

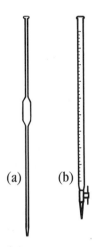

(a) (b)

Figure 2.16
Volumes of liquids can be precisely measured using: a) a pipette b) a burette

Volume Measurement in the Laboratory

Several different pieces of glassware can be used to measure the volume of a liquid. The type selected depends on the precision required. Most volume measurements require comparatively low precision, and for these a graduated cylinder can be used.

The precision obtained using a graduated cylinder depends on the size of the cylinder. A 10 mL graduated cylinder is precise to ±0.1 mL whereas a 100 mL cylinder is only precise to ±1 mL.

When you measure a volume of liquid, you can usually *estimate* a value beyond the precision of the equipment. For example, although a 10 mL graduated cylinder has markings every 0.1 mL, it is possible to estimate a volume to the nearest 0.02 mL. However, the second place after the decimal is not reliable.

Two pieces of equipment can give us greater precision in volume measurement. A **pipette** is used for measuring precise, predetermined volumes such as 5 mL (precise to ±0.01 mL) or 50 mL (precise to ±0.1 mL). A **burette** is used for measuring precise volumes that have not been predetermined.

QUESTIONS

17. A "two cubic feet" mover's carton measures 45.7 cm by 38.7 cm by 31.8 cm. Calculate the volume of the carton in

a) cm³   b) m³   c) L

Density   2.8

handwritten: Lisa DeLancey

handwritten: for a given temp & pressure

Density is defined as mass per unit volume. This is expressed mathematically as follows:

$$\text{Density} = \frac{\text{Mass}}{\text{Volume}}$$

The unit for mass is the gram. However, the unit for volume depends on the phase of the substance that we are measuring. We use millilitres and litres for liquids but cubic centimetres and cubic metres for solids as we often calculate the volume of a solid from its linear dimensions. Because gases have very low densities, we use litres to measure their volumes. Since 1 mL represents the same volume as 1 cm^3, any density expressed in g·mL^{-1} will have the same numerical value when written in g·cm^{-3}.

TABLE 2.3 *The Densities of Some Substances*

Substance	Phase	Density
Lead	Solid	11.35 g·cm^{-3}
Aluminum	Solid	2.70 g·cm^{-3}
Water	Liquid	1.00 g·mL^{-1}
Ethyl alcohol	Liquid	0.79 g·mL^{-1}
Air (at 20 °C)	Gas	1.20 g·L^{-1} (1.20^{-3} g·mL^{-1})
Helium	Gas	0.17 g·L^{-1} (1.7 × 10^{-4} g·mL^{-1})

If we know the density of a substance and want to find the volume of a specific mass, or the mass of a specific volume, we can approach the problem in two ways. The two ways are the formula method and the conversion-factor method. Example 2.14 shows how these methods are used to determine the mass when the volume and density are known.

EXAMPLE   2.14

Ethyl alcohol has a density of 0.789 g·mL^{-1}. Calculate the mass of 25.0 mL of this liquid.

SOLUTION

The Formula Method

You are probably most familiar with the formula method; that is, rearranging the formula for density to give:

$$\text{Density} = \frac{\text{Mass}}{\text{Volume}}$$

$$\text{Mass} = \text{Density} \times \text{Volume}$$

By substituting the known values for density and volume and then cancelling the volume units, we obtain the solution

$$\text{Mass} = \frac{0.789 \text{ g}}{\text{mL}} \times 25.0 \text{ mL}$$

$$= 19.7 \text{ g}$$

The Conversion-Factor Method

We can also regard the formula for density as a conversion factor:

$$\frac{0.789\,\text{g}}{1\,\text{mL}}$$

Using this method, we check first to see which units have to cancel. When solving for mass, it is not necessary to invert the conversion factor:

$$\text{Mass} = 25.0\,\cancel{\text{mL}} \times \frac{0.789\,\text{g}}{1\,\cancel{\text{mL}}}$$

$$= 19.7\,\text{g}$$

Many calculations can be solved by a number of methods. In this case, the two methods work equally well. For the more complex problems that occur later in the text, the conversion-factor method should prove to be easier to use.

Measuring Density in the Laboratory

Liquids. The approximate density of a liquid can be determined by first measuring the mass of an empty graduated cylinder. The cylinder is then filled to a specific level with the liquid and the mass of the cylinder plus its contents is determined. By subtraction, we obtain the mass of a known volume of liquid. The density of the liquid can then be calculated as shown in Example 2.15.

EXAMPLE   *2.15*   In an experiment to determine the density of corn oil, an empty 25 mL graduated cylinder was found to have a mass of 35.5 g. When 24.4 mL of corn oil was poured into the cylinder the mass of the cylinder plus its contents was found to be 57.5 g. Calculate the density of corn oil.

SOLUTION   Mass of cylinder + 24.4 mL of corn oil   = 57.5 g
Mass of empty cylinder   = 35.5 g

Therefore

Mass of 24.4 mL of corn oil   = 22.0 g

$$\text{Density of corn oil} = \frac{\text{Mass}}{\text{Volume}} = \frac{22.0\,\text{g}}{24.4\,\text{mL}} = 0.902\,\text{g}\cdot\text{mL}^{-1}$$

Solids. It is possible to measure the density of an irregularly shaped solid, such as a piece of metal, by using only a balance and a graduated cylinder. The mass of the piece of metal is first determined. The metal is then placed in a graduated cylinder containing a known volume of liquid. The level of the liquid in the cylinder rises and the new level is recorded. The difference between the new level and the original level gives us the volume of the metal. The density can then be calculated from the mass and the volume.

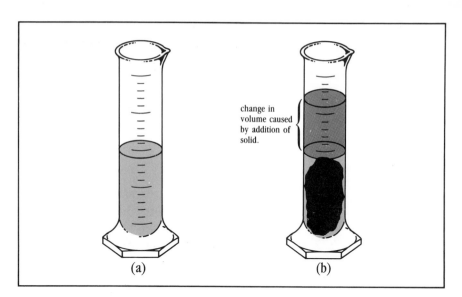

Figure 2.17

Determining the volume of a solid object:

a) *A volume of liquid is placed in a graduated cylinder*

b) *The solid object is inserted. The original liquid level is then subtracted from the new level to obtain the volume of the solid.*

EXAMPLE **2.16** When a piece of silver with a mass of 147 g is placed in a graduated cylinder containing 10.0 mL of water, the level of the water rises to 24.0 mL. Calculate the density of silver.

SOLUTION $\text{Density} = \dfrac{\text{Mass}}{\text{Volume}}$

$$\text{Mass of metal} = 147\,\text{g}$$

$$\text{Volume of metal} = 24.0\,\text{mL} - 10.0\,\text{mL} = 14.0\,\text{mL}$$

$$= 14.0\,\cancel{\text{mL}} \times \frac{1\,\text{cm}^3}{1\,\cancel{\text{mL}}} = 14.0\,\text{cm}^3$$

Therefore

$$\text{Density of metal} = \frac{147\,\text{g}}{14.0\,\text{cm}^3} = 10.5\,\text{g} \cdot \text{cm}^{-3}$$

If we have to determine the density of a solid object from its mass and linear dimensions rather than its volume, then we must calculate the volume from the data given, as shown in the following example.

EXAMPLE **2.17** A metal ingot has a mass of 681 g and measures 8.00 cm by 4.00 cm by 4.00 cm. Calculate the density of the metal.

SOLUTION The volume of the ingot is

$$8.00\,\text{cm} \times 4.00\,\text{cm} \times 4.00\,\text{cm} = 128\,\text{cm}^3$$

Therefore

$$\text{Density} = \frac{\text{Mass}}{\text{Volume}} = \frac{681\,\text{g}}{128\,\text{cm}^3} = 5.32\,\text{g}\cdot\text{cm}^{-3}$$

QUESTIONS

18. The density of chloroform is $1.49\,\text{g}\cdot\text{mL}^{-1}$. What volume of chloroform must be measured to give $50.0\,\text{g}$ of the liquid?

19. Calculate the mass of 25 mL of ether. The density of ether is $0.71\,\text{g}\cdot\text{mL}^{-1}$.

20. The experiment described in Example 2.15 was repeated using gas-line antifreeze and the same graduated cylinder. The mass of the cylinder plus 18.5 mL of gas-line antifreeze was 49.8 g. Calculate the density of the gas-line antifreeze.

21. When a piece of copper of mass 84.6 g is placed in a graduated cylinder containing 14.6 mL of water, the level of the water rises to 24.1 mL. Calculate the density of copper.

22. A cube of iron with an edge of 2.54 cm has a mass of 128.8 g. Calculate the density of iron in $\text{g}\cdot\text{cm}^{-3}$.

23. The density of zinc is $7.13\,\text{g}\cdot\text{cm}^{-3}$. Calculate the mass of a sheet of zinc measuring 60.5 cm by 28.6 cm by 2.1 mm.

Graphs and Their Uses

2.9

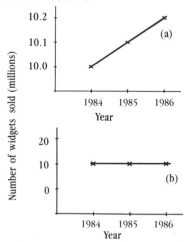

Figure 2.18

Two ways of plotting the same data:
a) Starting from near the first data point
b) Starting from zero value

In many experiments and also in real-life situations, we have to interpret numerical data. These data may be unemployment statistics, weather information, company sales figures, or as here, physical properties of substances. As we are often more interested in general trends rather than in actual values, an effective way of presenting numerical data is by means of a graph.

Plotting Graphs

When plotting graphs, the convention is to place the independent variable (that is, the controlled factor) along the horizontal axis and the dependent variable (the varying factor) along the vertical axis.

The next important point is the choice of scale. You must inspect your data and decide what size of unit each division on the graph paper should represent. In making your choice you should decide whether you want the scale to start with a zero value or from near the first data point. This decision can have an important effect on the appearance of the graph. For example, if you want to plot the sales of widgets (10.0 million in 1984, 10.1 million in 1985, and 10.2 million in 1986), you could plot these data as in Figure 2.18a or Figure 2.18b. Observe how the change of scale alters the appearance of the graph. Figure 2.18a, which shows the trend, is the correct way of displaying scientific data. Figure 2.18b is, however, a more honest way of looking at widget sales!

TABLE 2.4	Glycerol Volume and Mass Data
Volume (V)	Mass (m)
5.0 mL	6.4 g
10.0 mL	12.6 g
15.0 mL	19.0 g
20.0 mL	24.9 g
25.0 mL	31.5 g

As experimental data is likely to contain errors because of problems in taking precise measurements or in determining when a reaction is complete, it is incorrect to simply join all the points on the graph. Instead, you should look to see if a straight line or smooth curve can be drawn through as many of the points as possible.

We can illustrate the usefulness of plotting graphs by studying how the mass of a liquid is related to its volume. First, we collect the data by measuring out different volumes of a liquid (say glycerol) into a container and measuring the mass of the liquid. (Table 2.4).

When these data are plotted (Figure 2.19), we see that, within experimental error, the results lie on a straight line. This shows us that the mass and the volume of glycerol are related properties. As the graph shows us that it is a straight-line (linear) relationship which passes through the origin, we can write the result mathematically as follows:

$$\frac{m}{V} = \text{Constant (for glycerol)}$$

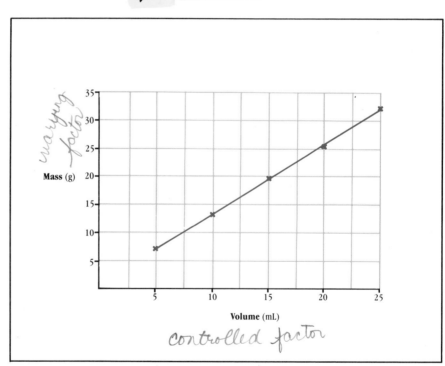

Figure 2.19
Plot of mass against volume for liquid glycerol

The constant is found from the slope of the line. In this case, it has a value of $1.26\,\text{g}\cdot\text{mL}^{-1}$. You may be tempted to assume that for all liquids mass and volume are related by the constant $1.26\,\text{g}\cdot\text{mL}^{-1}$. *Such assumptions should never be made.* It is unscientific and dangerous to assume that, if a relationship holds for one substance, it will hold for others. Experiments should be conducted on a number of different substances before a theory is formulated. The next task, therefore, should be to measure the mass–volume relationships for other liquids. When we do this, we do indeed obtain linear relationships, but the line for each liquid has a different slope. Thus, the constant relating mass and volume depends on the liquid. The constant is, in fact, the property called density.

Many properties are related in more complex ways that do not give linear plots on graphs. However, it is often possible to find mathematical functions of these properties (squares, reciprocals, etc.) that will give linear plots.

Summary

- The system of measurement used in science is based on Le Système international d'unités (SI), a metric system that relates measurements to four common base units of length, mass, time, and temperature. Three specialized base units are used for electric current, light intensity, and amount of substance.

- Accuracy is a measure of how closely a result approaches the true (or accepted) value. Precision is a measure of how closely the results within a set of results agree with each other.

- Poor precision is usually an indication of random error. Poor accuracy but good precision suggests a systematic error.

- It is important to know the precision of measurements. The precision is indicated by the number of significant figures.

- Use of scientific notation removes any ambiguity about the number of significant figures.

- A conversion factor is a fraction that relates two quantities that are expressed in different units.

- A derived unit is obtained by some combination of base units. Volume and density are measured in derived units.

- Density is mass per unit volume. Densities of liquids are usually expressed in grams per millilitre.

- An effective way of presenting numerical data is by a graph. The horizontal axis indicates the independent variable (the controlled factor) and the vertical axis indicates the dependent variable (the varying factor).

- Because of experimental error, a straight line or a smooth curve should be drawn through as many of the points as possible when plotting a graph of experimental results.

KEY WORDS	accuracy	metric system
	base unit	pipette

burette

conversion factor

derived unit

exact number

Le Système international d'unités (SI)

metric prefix

precision

random error

scientific notation

significant figures

systematic error

ANSWERS TO
SECTION QUESTIONS

1. Joan's results are more accurate; Rick's results are more precise. Joan's results contained random error; Rick's results contained systematic error.

2. a) 2   b) 4

3. a) 3, 4   b) 2   c) 2, 2

4. a) 8.7×10^{-3}, 2   b) 8.70×10^{-2}, 3   c) 8.7000×10^{2}, 5

5. a) 960   b) 8 420   c) 0.001 00   d) 425.0

6. a) 1.0 kg   b) 2.0 cm   c) 3.4 μm   d) 4.2 Mg

7. a) 8.68×10^{6} b) 2.17×10^{2}

8. a) 4.54×10^{3} b) 4.14×10^{3}

9. 12 cm^3

10. a) 127.3   b) 127.4   c) 127.4

11. 1.6×10^{3} cm^3

12. a) 21.0   b) 0.300

13. 166.9 g

14. a) 8 mL   b) 4 cm^2 c) 5 m·s^{-1} d) 8 m

15. a) 1.76×10^{3} m   b) 13.2 cm   c) 2.000 km   d) 1.08 nm   1.09 nm

16. a) 10 s   b) 6.72 kg   c) 42 km

17. a) 5.62×10^{4} cm^3 b) 5.62×10^{-2} m^3 c) 56.2 L

18. 33.6 mL

19. 18 g

20. 0.773 g·mL^{-1}

21. 8.9 g·cm^{-3}

22. 7.86 g·cm^{-3}

23. 2.6×10^{3} g

COMPREHENSION QUESTIONS

1. Name the SI unit for each of the following:
   a) length m b) time s c) light intensity

2. Name the SI unit for the following measurements:
   a) mass g b) temperature K (W?) c) amount of substance

3. What is the difference between accuracy and precision?

4. What is the difference between random error and systematic error?

5. How is the degree of precision of a measurement indicated?

6. What is meant by the term "exact number"?

7. Which metric prefixes have the following values:
   a) 10^6 b) 10^{-1} c) 10^{-9}

8. What are the values of the following metric prefixes:
   a) kilo   b) micro   c) pico

9. When using scientific notation, what must you do to the exponents when
   a) multiplying or dividing
   b) adding or subtracting

10. In general, how many significant figures will an answer have when two measurements are
    a) multiplied or divided
    b) added or subtracted

11. What is a conversion factor?

12. What is the difference between a base unit and a derived unit?

PROBLEMS   13. An object is known to have a mass of 3.145 g. A student makes three measurements of the mass and obtains values of 3.102 g, 3.105 g, and 3.101 g. Are the student's measurements accurate or precise?

14. A rock is known to have a mass of 12.650 g. A student makes three measurements of the mass and obtains the values of 12.650 g, 13.650 g, and 11.650 g. Are the student's measurements accurate or precise?

15. How many significant figures are there in each of the following numbers?
    a) 25.0   c) 0.2050   e) 0.0270
    b) 0.04   d) 600

16. How many significant figures are there in each of the following numbers:
    a) 5.0320   c) 150   e) 5.235×10^7
    b) 0.000 20   d) 70.70

17. Write the following numbers in scientific notation with the correct number of significant figures:
    a) 0.000 810   c) 58.36   e) 1.780
    b) 58 300   d) 10.00

18. Write the following numbers in scientific notation with the correct number of significant figures:
    a) 186 000   c) 0.000 042 0   e) 200.0
    b) 2.0003   d) 0.40

19. In scientific notation, will the exponent be positive, negative, or zero when the number is
    a) less than 1   b) greater than 1 but less than 10
    c) 10 or greater

20. When converting to decimal notation, which way is the decimal moved if the exponent is
    a) positive   b) negative   c) zero

21. Convert the following to decimal notation with the correct number of significant figures:
    a) 4.030×10^{-2} c) 4.02×10^4 e) 6.0×10^2
    b) 5.102×10^2 d) 3.98×10^{-6}

22. Convert the numbers below from scientific notation to decimal notation with the correct number of significant figures:
    a) 3.6×10^3 c) 4.265×10^{-2} e) 6.82×10^6
    b) 4×10^{-4} d) 1.00×10^{-1}

23. Perform the following calculations. Give your answers in scientific notation and follow the significant-figure rules:
    a) $9.25 + 4.10 - 2.05$ d) $(101.34) + (6.2 \times 10^{-2}) - (2.1 \times 10^{-2})$
    b) $4.49 + 0.597 + 10.0$ e) $(5.002 \times 10^{-3}) + (4.1 \times 10^{-4})$
    c) $12.25 - 6.184 - 5.47$

24. Perform the following calculations. Give your answers in scientific notation with the correct number of significant figures:
    a) $0.21 + 4.33 + 0.008$ d) $(3.45 \times 10^{-1}) - (4.789 \times 10^{-3})$
    b) $134.8 + 2.05 - 13$ e) $(7.95 \times 10^{-2}) + (2.05 \times 10^{-1})$
    c) $14.896 - 2.42 + 4.60$

25. A solution of sodium chloride (table salt) is prepared by dissolving 2.596 g of the compound in 100.7 g of water in a beaker of mass 42.10 g. Give the total mass of the beaker plus the solution to the correct number of significant figures.

26. A beaker containing 20 marbles was found to have a mass of 125.879 g. The mass of the empty beaker determined on a different balance was 87.8 g. Determine, to the correct number of significant figures
    a) the mass of the 20 marbles
    b) the average mass of each marble

27. Carry out the following calculations. Give your answers in scientific notation with the correct number of significant figures:
    a) $4.18 \times 0.051\,960$
    b) $0.50 \div 4.12$
    c) $(3.30 \times 10^{-2}) \times (4.162 \times 10^1)$
    d) $(1.981 \times 10^1) \div (2.5 \times 10^{-2})$
    e) $(4.68 \times 10^{-4}) \times (8.743 \times 10^5) \div (1.04 \times 10^{-2})$

28. Carry out the following calculations. Give your answers in scientific notation with the correct number of significant figures:
    a) $(5.4 \times 10^2) \times (3.09 \times 10^{-1})$
    b) $0.61 \div 7.582$
    c) $(4.4 \times 10^{-8}) \times (7.32 \times 10^9)$
    d) $(4.7258 \times 10^5) \div (8.92 \times 10^{-6})$
    e) $(3.69 \times 10^4) \div (8.2 \times 10^{-8}) \times (4.321 \times 10^{-2})$

29. Round off the following numbers to two significant digits:
    a) 18.3   c) 0.276   e) 1.549
    b) 2.851   d) 3.45

30. Round off the following numbers to three significant figures:
    a) 15 360   c) 0.025 38   e) 015.65
    b) 6.845   d) 1.6349

31. Re-express the following measurements by attaching the most suitable prefix to each metric unit (for example, 1×10^3 g = 1 kg):
    a) 4.2×10^{-5} g   c) 12 500 m   e) 0.014 L
    b) 3.8×10^{-3} g   d) 4.86×10^{-7} m   f) 2.5×10^{-6} L

32. Re-express the following measurements by attaching the most suitable prefix to each metric unit:
    a) 9.57×10^{-9} g   c) 1.53×10^{-2} m   e) 4.87×10^7 g
    b) 8.69×10^{-5} L   d) 0.0158 L   f) 8.64×10^{-6} m

33. Carry out the following conversions and give your answer in scientific notation:
    a) 0.54 km to m   c) 280.0 mm to m
    b) 15 mL to L   d) 0.80 g to kg

34. Convert the following measurements to the indicated units using scientific notation:
    a) 18 300 mm to km   c) 8.79×10^{-6} L to mL
    b) 9.40×10^{-4} kg to mg   d) 6.89×10^{-4} mg to g

35. a) Find the volume occupied by 1.0 g of air at 20 °C and 101 kPa. The density of air under these conditions is 1.20×10^{-3} g·cm^{-3}.
    b) What would be the radius of a balloon holding this volume of air? (Volume of a sphere is $4/3 \pi r^3$.)

36. A king-size water bed is 1.83 m long, 1.83 m wide, and 0.305 m deep. As water has a density of 1.00 g·cm^{-3}, what will be the mass of water in the bed, in kilograms, when it is filled to capacity?

37. The density of lead is 11.35 g·cm^{-3}. Determine the mass of a cube of lead with sides 2.5 cm long.

38. The density of gold is 19.3 g·cm^{-3}. Find the dimensions of a 125 g cube of gold.

39. A block of unknown metal, with a mass of 80.0 g, is placed at the bottom of a 50.0 mL cylinder. It is found that it takes 33.48 g of benzene (density = 0.786 g·mL^{-1}) to fill the cylinder. Determine the density of the unknown metal.

40. A block of unknown metal with a mass of 125 g, is placed at the bottom of a 100 mL graduated cylinder. It is found that 28.7 g of chloroform (density = 1.49 g·mL^{-1}) is required to fill the cylinder. Determine the density of the metal.

41. A student successively determined the mass of a 100.0 g object to be 100.25 g, 100.22 g, and 100.23 g. Do these results indicate a random or systematic error?

42. A metre stick, used to measure a length of wire that was known to be exactly 1.00 m long, gave measurements of 0.94 m, 0.95 m, and 0.94 m. Are the measurements accurate or precise?

43. Statistical tables give the population of Canada for every year since Confederation. In plotting a graph of the data, should population or time be plotted on the horizontal axis?

44. The density of a liquid was determined by measuring the mass of 5, 10, 15, 20, and 25 mL samples. The results were then plotted on the graph shown. What is wrong with the graph? Is the density of the liquid less than one or greater than one?

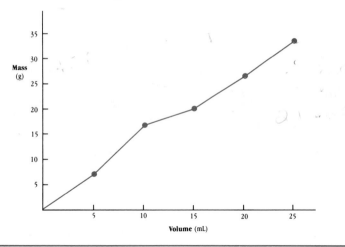

SUGGESTED PROJECTS

1. Design experiments to test the accuracy of measuring instruments used in the laboratory. Equipment to be tested could include a balance, graduated cylinder, pipette, burette, and thermometer.

2. Most measuring instruments are mass-produced. This results in a degree of systematic error in the instruments. Write to a company that produces instruments (thermometers, balances, metre sticks, etc.) or to the federal government, Department of Consumer and Corporate Affairs, Legal Metrology Branch, to see how standards are maintained to minimize systematic error.

3. Archimedes is said to have discovered the principle of determining the volume of an irregular object by displacement of a liquid. Find out more about this early scientist and prepare a report.

Atomic Theory

As we discussed in Chapter 1, chemists are concerned with the study of matter. All matter consists of tiny particles called atoms, and atoms themselves consist of even tinier, subatomic particles. Although it is impossible to see the structure of the atom, scientists have developed models of possible structures from experimental observations. In this chapter we will describe some of these models. We will also introduce you to the mole, an SI unit that is used as a means of counting very large numbers of atoms.

The History of the Concept of the Atom

3.1   Although modern atomic theory is only about 200 years old, its origin can be traced back to ancient Greece. Around 450 B.C., the philosophers Leucippus and Democritus proposed that if a substance could be divided into smaller and smaller portions, eventually a stage should be reached where the particles could not be divided any further. The Greeks named these extremely small particles **atoms** (from the Greek word for indivisible). The Greeks believed that atoms had various shapes and that objects were formed from atoms which combined by means of interlocking patterns and little hooks. It is interesting that Hindu philosophers independently developed the concept of minute, indivisible particles of matter.

Early atomic theory was almost forgotten until 1808 when John Dalton, an English schoolteacher, formulated his atomic theory. Dalton's theory provided explanations for several of the laws of chemistry known at the time. These laws were generalizations derived from observations made during experiments. Dalton's approach to understanding the structure of matter was different from that of the ancient Greek philosophers in that he based his theories on experimental evidence. Dalton's atomic theory can be summarized in the following statements:

1. All matter is composed of extremely small particles called atoms.
2. Atoms cannot be subdivided.
3. Atoms cannot be created or destroyed. *(law of conservation of matter)*
4. All atoms of the same element are identical in mass, size, and chemical and physical properties.
5. The properties of the atoms of one element differ from those of all other elements.
6. Atoms combine in small, whole-number ratios to form compounds. *(Balanced equations)*

Figure 3.1
John Dalton (1766–1844), the founder of modern atomic theory.

atomos
– uncuttable
– undevidable

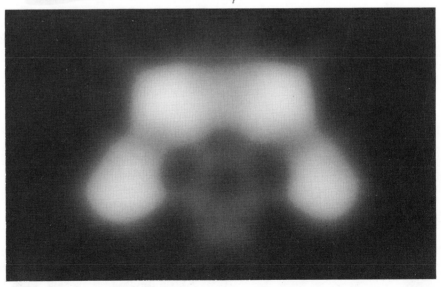

Figure 3.2
It is now possible to obtain images of individual atoms. The white spots represent sulfur atoms magnified 22 000 000 times.

Chemists still regard atoms as the basic building-blocks of matter. Modern advances in technology have enabled us to obtain very strong evidence of their existence.

The Internal Structure of the Atom

3.2

a given element has a fixed # of protons, whereas electrons & neutrons can vary.

Dalton's atomic theory is still useful for explaining many of the observations made in chemistry. Around the beginning of this century, however, new discoveries made it necessary to revise the picture of the atom as the smallest indivisible unit of matter. It was discovered that the atom itself consists of a number of smaller particles. (The study of these subatomic particles is the basis of nuclear physics.) The growing understanding of the nature and properties of subatomic particles has led to many important technological innovations, including nuclear reactors and the atom bomb. In addition, new ways of treating diseases and of dating objects of archeological or geological interest have been developed.

The three most important subatomic particles are the **proton**, the **neutron**, and the **electron**. Two of these particles carry electrical charges. The proton has a positive charge and the electron has an equal, but opposite, negative charge. The neutron has no electrical charge. The proton was discovered in 1886 and the electron in 1897. Although its existence had been postulated for many years, the neutron was not discovered until 1932, mainly because of its lack of charge. The mass of the proton is about the same as the mass of the neutron. The mass of the electron, on the other hand, is much smaller than the mass of either of these particles.

TABLE 3.1   *Three of the Particles That Make Up the Atom*

Particle	Relative Mass	Relative Charge
Proton	1	+1
Neutron	1	0
Electron	0.0005	−1

The Atomic Nucleus

How are protons, neutrons and electrons distributed throughout the atom? At the beginning of this century, scientists did not have a clear understanding of the answer. However, in 1911 in Manchester, England, Ernest Rutherford and his students carried out a simple experiment that revealed some of the inner secrets of the atom.

A thin sheet of gold foil was bombarded with a stream of alpha-particles from a radioactive source. (An alpha-particle has a positive charge and is much smaller than an atom.) Most of the alpha-particles passed through the gold foil in an almost straight line, indicating that the gold atom was virtually all empty space. An unexpected finding was that one in every 10 000 alpha-particles bounced back at an acute angle. This could only be explained by assuming that these particles had encountered very highly

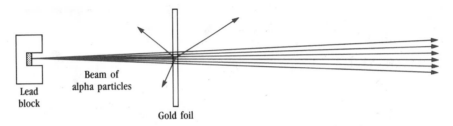

Figure 3.3
Rutherford's experiment. Most of the alpha-particles go straight through the gold foil, but a few bounce back at acute angles.

Beam of
alpha particles

Lead
block

Gold foil

concentrated regions of positive charge. The region of positive charge in an atom was named the **nucleus**.

We now know that the nucleus has a diameter of about 10^{-14} m, which is about 1/10 000 of the diameter of the atom itself. If we were to magnify an atom to the size of a backyard swimming pool, the nucleus would be the size of a grain of sand!

We also know that the protons and neutrons are located in the nucleus, and that the electrons are in the outer regions of the atom. (Because of their location in the nucleus, protons and neutrons are sometimes called **nucleons**.) The positive charge of the nucleus is determined by the number of protons it contains. In an electrically neutral atom the number of protons must be the same as the number of electrons.

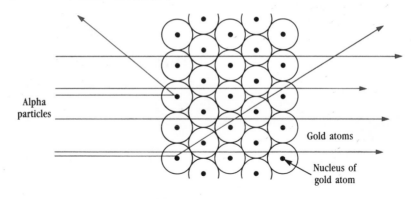

Figure 3.4
A representation of Rutherford's experiment showing the fate of six alpha-particles.

Alpha
particles

Gold atoms

Nucleus of
gold atom

Atomic Number and Mass Number

3.3 The identity of an element is determined by the number of protons in the nucleus. For example, the nucleus of every hydrogen atom contains one proton, and the nucleus of every carbon atom contains six protons. The number of protons in the nucleus of an atom is known as that atom's **atomic number**. We can therefore write

Atomic number = Number of protons

The atomic number of the element hydrogen is therefore 1, and that of the element carbon is 6. As we said earlier, an electrically neutral atom will always contain an equal number of protons and electrons. Thus, in a neutral atom the atomic number is also equal to the number of electrons.

Rutherford and the Atom

Ernest Rutherford was born near Nelson, New Zealand in 1871. In 1895 he left for Cambridge University, England to conduct research on new ways of detecting radio signals. He was hoping to obtain a patent on the results of this work and to use the money obtained from patent royalties to bring his fiancée to England from New Zealand. However, Lord Kelvin, a famous physicist, persuaded Rutherford that there would be little use for radio, except by lighthouse operators (one of many examples where the direction that science and technology would take was predicted wrongly). Instead, Kelvin recommended that Rutherford study the phenomenon of radioactivity. The opportunity to conduct basic research into the nature of matter interested Rutherford and he began his studies on radioactivity by investigating X-rays. As there were not the same opportunities to make money in basic physics research as there were in the applied sciences, Rutherford's marriage was delayed for a few years.

Rutherford successfully applied for a professorship in physics at McGill University. This was a very prestigious appointment, as the university had one of the best physics laboratories in the western hemisphere (financed by the tobacco millionaire, Sir William MacDonald). At McGill, Rutherford spent much of his time studying alpha-particles and became convinced that they were, in fact, the nuclei of helium atoms.

Rutherford's most important work at McGill was the development of the theory that rays were emitted by an element when it changed into a new, different element. This proposal, which some scientists dubbed "the new alchemy", was surprisingly well received when one remembers that, at that time, chemistry was based on the belief that one chemical element could not be changed into another. Rutherford's new discoveries and ideas brought him fame, including the Nobel prize for chemistry, and a steady stream of research students and collaborators.

In 1907 Rutherford was lured to the University of Manchester, where, in its new, well-equipped laboratories, he and his co-workers conducted the experiments that led to the modern model of the atom.

Rutherford died in England in 1937. If it had not been for Kelvin's influence on Rutherford's choice of research topic, we might have had television decades earlier and the atom bomb decades later.

Figure 3.5
Ernest Rutherford (1871–1937).

EXAMPLE	**3.1**	What is the atomic number of the element uranium, which has 92 electrons in each neutral atom?
SOLUTION		In a neutral atom, the number of protons must equal the number of electrons. Therefore, the nucleus of a uranium atom contains 92 protons, and the atomic number of uranium is 92.

The number of neutrons in the nucleus of an atom is always an integer. The sum of the numbers of protons and neutrons in an atom is known as the **mass number** of that atom. We can state this mathematically as follows:

Mass number = Number of protons + Number of neutrons

EXAMPLE	**3.2**	The nucleus of an atom of fluorine contains 9 protons and 10 neutrons. What is the atomic number and mass number of fluorine?

SOLUTION

$$\text{Atomic number} = \text{Number of protons} = 9$$

$$\text{Mass number} = \text{Number of protons} + \text{Number of neutrons}$$

$$= 9 + 10 = 19$$

In the atoms of most elements, the number of neutrons in the nucleus is greater than the number of protons. Some atoms have both types of nucleons present in equal numbers while some have fewer neutrons than protons. Hydrogen is an example of the latter.

Although neutrons are electrically neutral particles, it has been suggested that they are instrumental in keeping the positively charged protons together in the nucleus, and that proportionally more neutrons are required for a nucleus with a larger number of protons. This general trend is illustrated in Table 3.2.

TABLE 3.2 *Composition of the Most Common Atoms of Selected Elements*

Element	Number of Protons	Number of Electrons	Number of Neutrons	Neutron : proton Ratio
Hydrogen	1	1	0	1.0 : 1.0
Helium	2	2	2	1.0 : 1.0
Carbon	6	6	6	1.0 : 1.0
Iron	26	26	30	1.2 : 1.0
Iodine	53	53	74	1.4 : 1.0
Lead	82	82	126	1.5 : 1.0
Uranium	92	92	146	1.6 : 1.0

QUESTIONS

1. An atom of sodium has 11 electrons and a mass number of 23. How many neutrons and protons does it have?
2. An atom of aluminum has 14 neutrons and a mass number of 27. How many protons and electrons does it have?

Isotopes

3.4

note

Dalton's atomic theory states that all atoms of an element are identical in all respects. As with most theories, Dalton's concept of the atom had to be modified to accommodate later discoveries. Although all atoms of the same element contain the same number of electrons and therefore the same number of protons, the number of neutrons in atoms of the same element can be different.

Atoms that have nuclei with the same number of protons but a different number of neutrons are called **isotopes**. Thus, isotopes have the same atomic number but a different mass number. To distinguish between the isotopes of an element, the following symbolic representation is often used:

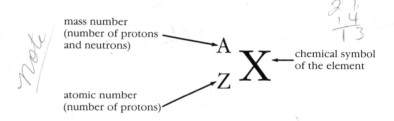

The most common isotope of the element hydrogen has 1 proton and no neutrons. The atomic number of this isotope is therefore 1 and its mass number is 1. We can represent this isotope as ^1_1H. The great majority of naturally occurring hydrogen atoms are this isotope.

In 1931, Harold Urey, an American chemist, discovered that about one in every 5000 hydrogen atoms contains a neutron in its nucleus. We can represent this isotope as ^2_1H. It is called heavy hydrogen or deuterium (from the Greek word meaning second).

In 1935, a very rare third isotope of hydrogen containing 2 neutrons was discovered. This isotope, called super-heavy hydrogen or tritium, can be represented as ^3_1H. Only about one hydrogen atom in every 10^{17} found in nature contains 2 neutrons. Tritium is an unstable isotope that gradually releases radiation and changes to an isotope of helium.

The **abundance** of an isotope is expressed as a percentage. It is calculated by dividing the number of atoms of the isotope by the total number of atoms of that element and multiplying the result by one hundred percent (100%).

Figure 3.6
Harold Urey (1893–1981), the discoverer of the rare isotope of hydrogen that has a neutron in its nucleus. Urey was also famous for his work on cosmochemistry (chemistry beyond the earth). He won the Nobel Prize for chemistry in 1934.

TABLE 3.3 *Abundance of Hydrogen Isotopes*

Isotope	Protons	Neutrons	Abundance
^1_1H	1	0	99.985 %
^2_1H	1	1	0.015 %
^3_1H	1	2	Negligible

Most elements have more than one isotope. Fluorine is one of the few elements with a single isotope. All naturally occurring fluorine atoms have nuclei with 9 protons and 10 neutrons. The fluorine atom can be represented by $^{19}_9F$. Tin, on the other hand, has no less than ten naturally occurring isotopes. Most elements have between one and ten isotopes.

A second system of representing isotopes is simply to write the mass number after the name of the element. For example, the isotope $^{19}_9F$ can also be represented as fluorine-19. No information is lost by omitting the atomic number, as it is the same for all isotopes of a given element.

C – 12 SCALE

Absolute zero – When all atoms are completely at rest.

EXAMPLE 3.3

Write the symbols for the three isotopes of oxygen (atomic number 8) in which there are 8, 9, and 10 neutrons, respectively.

SOLUTION

The symbol of the element is O. The atomic number is 8 for all three isotopes, because they all have 8 protons in the nucleus. The mass numbers are

$$8 + 8 = 16 \qquad 8 + 9 = 17 \qquad 8 + 10 = 18$$

Thus we have

$$^{16}_8O, \ ^{17}_8O, \text{ and } ^{18}_8O$$

EXAMPLE 3.4

The most common isotope of the element uranium can be represented by the symbol $^{238}_{92}U$. Find the number of protons, neutrons, and electrons in one atom of this isotope.

SOLUTION

As the atomic number of this uranium isotope is 92, the nucleus contains 92 protons. The number of electrons will also be 92. The mass number, 238, includes the protons and neutrons.

Therefore

$$
\begin{aligned}
\text{Number of neutrons} &= 238 - \text{Number of protons} \\
&= 238 - 92 \\
&= 146
\end{aligned}
$$

Radioactive Isotopes

Although most isotopes of an element retain their composition indefinitely, many elements have one or more unstable isotopes. In these, the composition of the nucleus (number of protons and number of neutrons) spontaneously changes over time. As unstable isotopes emit radiation, they are said to be **radioactive**. The type of radiation emitted varies. One component is always a vast quantity of energy, but the decay of an unstable isotope can also be accompanied by the release of subatomic particles or large fragments of nuclei.

We have already encountered several examples of radioactivity in this chapter, including the decomposition of tritium and the alpha-particles in Rutherford's gold-foil experiment. Alpha-particles are the nuclei of $_2^4He$ atoms, and are emitted in the radioactive decay of some isotopes of the elements uranium and thorium.

QUESTIONS

3. The two common isotopes of chlorine are $_{17}^{35}Cl$ and $_{17}^{37}Cl$. How many protons, neutrons, and electrons does each of these isotopes have?
4. Write the symbols for the two isotopes of bromine (atomic number 35) that contain 44 and 46 neutrons, respectively.

Atomic Mass

3.5

Atoms are extremely small particles with very low masses. An atom of the most common isotope of hydrogen has a mass of 1.67×10^{-24} g, and even an atom of one of the heavier elements, uranium, has a mass of only 3.96×10^{-22} g.

Ever since Dalton formulated his atomic theory, chemists and physicists have been interested in comparing the masses of the atoms of the elements. Instead of expressing the mass of an atom as a very small fraction of a gram or kilogram, attempts were made to define a standard mass that was closer to the mass of an individual atom. Tables of atomic mass could then be based on the standard mass. Several standards have been used over the past 200 years. In 1961, an international conference of chemists and physicists selected the most common isotope of carbon, carbon-12, as the new standard for the atomic mass scale.

Atomic mass can be regarded as a relative number compared to the standard. Alternatively, a new unit for measuring atomic mass can be used. The **unified atomic mass unit** (symbol u), is defined as $1/12$ of the mass of a carbon-12 atom. In other words, one atom of carbon-12 has a mass of 12 u.

On this scale, the proton and the neutron both have a mass close to 1 u. Compared to these, the mass of an electron is negligible. Thus, the mass of an isotope is very close in value to the mass number of that isotope. Table 3.4 illustrates this fact with the isotopes of hydrogen.

TABLE 3.4	*Atomic Masses of Hydrogen Isotopes*	
Isotope	**Mass Number**	**Atomic Mass**
^1_1H	1	1.008 u
^2_1H	2	2.014 u
^3_1H	3	3.016 u

Figure 3.7
A mass spectrometer. This instrument can be used to compare the mass of different atoms.

We can obtain precise values of atomic mass using an instrument called a **mass spectrometer.** A sample of the element is placed in a chamber in the mass spectrometer. Here it is bombarded by a stream (or beam) of electrons capable of knocking an electron out of each atom. Electric fields are then used to accelerate the remaining positively charged particles (ions) down a tube, at the end of which is a magnet. The magnetic field deflects the stream of ions and the degree of deflection is measured. The lower the mass of an ion, the more it is deflected. If the instrument has been calibrated (for example, with a sample of carbon-12) we can determine the atomic mass of each isotope present in the sample.

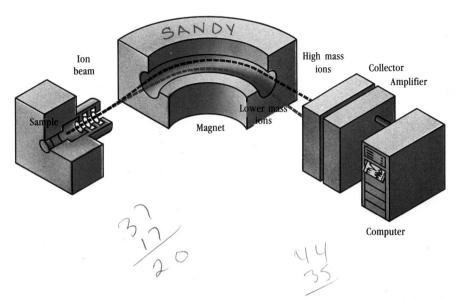

Figure 3.8
In the mass spectrometer, the ion beam passes through a magnetic field. Here, high-mass ions are not deflected as much as the low-mass ions.

Average Atomic Mass

3.6 Although we defined an atom of carbon-12 as having a mass of exactly 12 u, the measured atomic mass of natural carbon is 12.01 u. The discrepancy occurs because naturally occurring carbon is a mixture of two isotopes, carbon-12 and carbon-13. The measured value is therefore the average atomic mass of the isotopic mixture. In chemistry this is a very important value as we work with naturally occurring mixtures of isotopes.

We can calculate the average atomic mass of an element if we know the atomic mass and the abundance of each isotope. These can both be obtained from measurements made with the mass spectrometer (Figure 3.9). As we saw, we can find the mass from the degree of deflection of a beam of ions. To find the abundance, we measure the relative quantities of each isotope in a naturally occurring sample of the element.

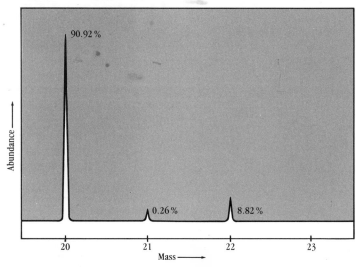

Figure 3.9

The mass spectrum of naturally occurring neon. We can see that neon consists of three isotopes. The height of the peaks gives us the relative abundance of each isotope.

If we have an element in which half of the atoms have an atomic mass of 8 u and the other half an atomic mass of 6 u, the average atomic mass is obviously 7 u. We can write the calculation as follows:

$$\text{Average atomic mass} = (8\,u)(0.5) + (6\,u)(0.5)$$
$$= 7\,u$$

where 0.5 is the fraction of atoms with atomic masses of 8 u and 7 u.

NOTE: Although the fractions in this example are equal, this rarely occurs in nature.

For an element with two isotopes, A and B, we can generalize the calculation above as follows:

$$\text{Average atomic mass} = (\text{Atomic mass of A}) \cdot (\text{Fraction of A})$$
$$+ (\text{Atomic mass of B}) \cdot (\text{Fraction of B})$$

EXAMPLE   *3.5* Calculate the average atomic mass of natural carbon, given that the relative atomic mass and abundance of each of its isotopes are as follows:

Isotope	Atomic mass (u)	Abundance (%)
$^{12}_{6}C$	12	98.89
$^{13}_{6}C$	13.004	1.11

NOTE: The atomic mass of carbon-12, 12 u, is an exact number. In multiplication and division, exact numbers are treated as if they had an infinite number of significant figures.

SOLUTION   Fraction of an isotope $= \dfrac{\text{Abundance (\%)}}{100\%}$

The isotope $^{12}_{6}C$, with an atomic mass of 12 u, has an abundance of 98.89%; the fraction of this isotope is therefore

$$\frac{98.89\%}{100\%} = 0.9889$$

The isotope $^{13}_{6}C$, with an atomic mass of 13.004 u, has an abundance of 1.11%; the fraction of this isotope is therefore

$$\frac{1.11\%}{100\%} = 0.0111$$

The average atomic mass of carbon can therefore be calculated as follows:

$$(12\,u)(0.9889) + (13.004\,u)(0.0111) = 11.87\,u + 0.144\,u$$
$$= 12.01\,u$$

Where can we find information on the atomic number and the average atomic mass of an element? We could use a data table, such as the one in the Appendix, that lists the elements in alphabetical order. Alternatively, we can obtain the information from the Periodic Table.

The **Periodic Table** (Figure 3.10) lists the symbols of the elements in order of increasing atomic number as we go from left to right across a row. If we take the element fluorine (near the upper right-hand corner) as an example, we see that its chemical symbol (F) is written in the centre of the rectangle that separates it from the neighbouring symbols for oxygen (O), neon (Ne), and chlorine (Cl). The atomic number (9 in this case) is written above the symbol and the atomic mass (19.0 u) is placed immediately below it. You should note that Periodic Tables in other texts may have the atomic number below the symbol and atomic mass above it. The different arrangement should cause no concern as the atomic number is always an integer,

Atomic Number — **H** — Symbol
1.01 — Atomic Mass

	Group IA	Group IIA	Group IIIB	Group IVB	Group VB	Group VIB	Group VIIB	Group VIIIB			Group IB	Group IIB	Group IIIA	Group IVA	Group VA	Group VIA	Group VIIA	Group 0
Period 1	1 **H** 1.01																	2 **He** 4.0
Period 2	3 **Li** 6.9	4 **Be** 9.0											5 **B** 10.8	6 **C** 12.0	7 **N** 14.0	8 **O** 16.0	9 **F** 19.0	10 **Ne** 20.2
Period 3	11 **Na** 23.0	12 **Mg** 24.3											13 **Al** 27.0	14 **Si** 28.1	15 **P** 31.0	16 **S** 32.1	17 **Cl** 35.5	18 **Ar** 40.0
Period 4	19 **K** 39.1	20 **Ca** 40.1	21 **Sc** 45.0	22 **Ti** 47.9	23 **V** 50.9	24 **Cr** 52.0	25 **Mn** 54.9	26 **Fe** 55.8	27 **Co** 58.9	28 **Ni** 58.7	29 **Cu** 63.5	30 **Zn** 65.4	31 **Ga** 69.7	32 **Ge** 72.6	33 **As** 74.9	34 **Se** 79.0	35 **Br** 79.9	36 **Kr** 83.8
Period 5	37 **Rb** 85.5	38 **Sr** 87.6	39 **Y** 88.9	40 **Zr** 91.2	41 **Nb** 92.9	42 **Mo** 95.9	43 **Tc** (98)	44 **Ru** 101.1	45 **Rh** 102.9	46 **Pd** 106.4	47 **Ag** 107.9	48 **Cd** 112.4	49 **In** 114.8	50 **Sn** 118.7	51 **Sb** 121.8	52 **Te** 127.6	53 **I** 126.9	54 **Xe** 131.3
Period 6	55 **Cs** 132.9	56 **Ba** 137.3	57 **La** 138.9	72 **Hf** 178.5	73 **Ta** 180.9	74 **W** 183.8	75 **Re** 186.2	76 **Os** 190.2	77 **Ir** 192.2	78 **Pt** 195.1	79 **Au** 197.0	80 **Hg** 200.6	81 **Tl** 204.4	82 **Pb** 207.2	83 **Bi** 209.0	84 **Po** (210)	85 **At** (210)	86 **Rn** (222)
Period 7	87 **Fr** (223)	88 **Ra** 226.0	89 **Ac** 227.0	104 **Unq** (257)	105 **Unp** (260)	106 **Unh** (263)	107 **Uns** (262)	108 **Uno** (265)	109 **Une** (266)									

58 **Ce** 140.1	59 **Pr** 140.9	60 **Nd** 144.2	61 **Pm** (147)	62 **Sm** 150.4	63 **Eu** 152.0	64 **Gd** 157.2	65 **Tb** 158.9	66 **Dy** 162.5	67 **Ho** 164.9	68 **Er** 167.3	69 **Tm** 168.9	70 **Yb** 173.0	71 **Lu** 175.0
90 **Th** 232.0	91 **Pa** 231.0	92 **U** 238.0	93 **Np** 237.0	94 **Pu** 242	95 **Am** (243)	96 **Cm** (247)	97 **Bk** (247)	98 **Cf** (249)	99 **Es** (254)	100 **Fm** (253)	101 **Md** (256)	102 **No** (254)	103 **Lr** (257)

Figure 3.10
The Periodic Table.

whereas the atomic mass, which may be an average of several isotopic masses, involves a decimal.

QUESTIONS

5. Boron (atomic number 5) has two naturally occurring isotopes. One, of mass 10.0 u, has an abundance of 19.6% and the other, of mass 11.0 u, has an abundance of 80.4%. How many protons and neutrons does each isotope have? What is the average atomic mass of boron?

6. Iron has four naturally occurring isotopes of masses 53.940 u, 55.935 u, 56.935 u, and 57.933 u with abundances of 5.84%, 91.68%, 2.17%, and 0.31% respectively. Calculate the average atomic mass of iron.

The Mole

3.7

As we discussed earlier, atoms are so small that one gram of an element contains about 10^{22} atoms. To make the numbers easier to handle, we work with moles. The **mole** (symbol mol) is the SI unit for the amount of substance and is defined as a group of 6.02×10^{23} units or particles.

We can regard a mole as a quantity similar to a pair or a dozen. When we say that we bought a new pair of shoes or a dozen eggs, the listener immediately knows that we bought two shoes or twelve eggs. Likewise, if chemists say that they have a mole of carbon, they mean that they have 6.02×10^{23} carbon atoms. In honour of the Italian scientist Amadeo Avogadro, the number 6.02×10^{23} is called **Avogadro's number** (symbol N).

To perform calculations involving moles, we will use the conversion-factor method introduced in Section 2.6. The following example provides an opportunity to review this concept.

(a) Pair (2) of shoes

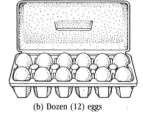
(b) Dozen (12) eggs

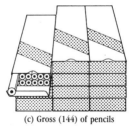
(c) Gross (144) of pencils

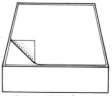
(d) Ream (500) of paper

(e) Mole (6.02×10^{23}) of sulfur atoms

Figure 3.11
Listed here are some terms used to denote groups of the following quantities: 2, 12, 144, 500 and 6.02×10^{23}.

3.6   Calculate the number of dozen eggs in a box containing 432 eggs.

SOLUTION   There are 12 eggs in a dozen (doz), or 12 egg·doz^{-1}. From this relationship we get our conversion factor:

$$\frac{12 \text{ eggs}}{1 \text{ doz}}$$

To obtain an answer in dozens of eggs, we invert the conversion factor and multiply:

$$\text{Number of dozen} = 432 \text{ eggs} \times \frac{1 \text{ doz}}{12 \text{ eggs}}$$

$$= 36 \text{ doz}$$

When we calculate moles of atoms, the conversion factor is Avogadro's number, 6.02×10^{23} atom·mol^{-1}. Other than using a very large number, the problem-solving method is no different from the one used in Example 3.6. For example, suppose we want to find the number of moles in 3.01×10^{24} atoms of an element. The conversion factor is Avogadro's number:

$$\frac{6.02 \times 10^{23} \text{ atoms}}{1 \text{ mol}}$$

Hence, by inverting the conversion factor

$$\text{Number of moles} = 3.01 \times 10^{24} \text{ atoms} \times \frac{1 \text{ mol}}{6.02 \times 10^{23} \text{ atoms}}$$

$$= 5.00 \text{ mol}$$

EXAMPLE   **3.7**   Calculate the number of atoms in 5.5 mol of an element.

SOLUTION   The conversion factor is $\dfrac{6.02 \times 10^{23} \text{ atoms}}{1 \text{ mol}}$

$$\text{Number of atoms} = 5.5 \text{ mol} \times \frac{6.02 \times 10^{23} \text{ atoms}}{1 \text{ mol}}$$

$$= 3.3 \times 10^{24} \text{ atoms}$$

QUESTIONS

7. How many gross of pencils are in a case of 864 pencils?
8. What is the total number of eggs in 150 cartons each containing a dozen eggs?
9. Calculate the number of moles in 1.0×10^{22} atoms.
10. Calculate the number of atoms in 4.15 mol of an element.

Molar Mass   3.8

We have not yet discussed a method of measuring the mass of a mole of atoms. Suppose we have a mole (Avogadro's number) of carbon-12 atoms. Each carbon-12 atom is known to have a mass of 1.99×10^{-23} g. What is the total mass of the carbon atoms?

$$\text{Total mass} = 1.99 \times 10^{-23}\,\text{g} \times 6.02 \times 10^{23}$$
$$= 12.0\,\text{g}$$

Numerically this is the same as the atomic mass of carbon! In other words

$$\text{Mass of one carbon atom} = 12\,\text{u}$$

$$\text{Mass of one mole of carbon atoms} = 12\,\text{g}$$

In general, therefore, we can say the following:

The mass of one mole of an element, expressed in grams, is numerically the same as the atomic mass of that element expressed in unified atomic mass units.

The mass of one mole of an element is called its **molar mass**. The units of molar mass are $\text{g} \cdot \text{mol}^{-1}$. Molar mass can be used as a conversion factor for converting moles to mass. Note, however, that the conversion factor has a different value for each element.

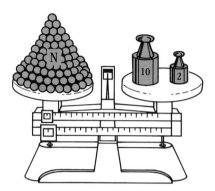

Figure 3.12
One mole of carbon-12 atoms (6.02×10^{23} atoms) has a mass of exactly 12 g.

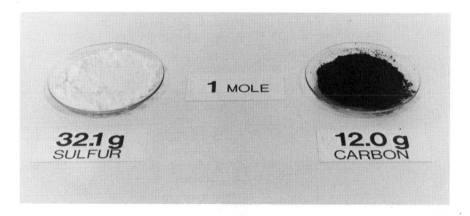

1 MOLE

32.1 g
SULFUR

12.0 g
CARBON

Figure 3.13
Each element has a different molar mass.

EXAMPLE   3.8   Calculate the mass of 0.50 mol of sulfur.

SOLUTION   From the Periodic Table (Figure 3.10), we see that the atomic mass of sulfur is 32.1 u. Thus the molar mass of sulfur is $32.1\,\text{g} \cdot \text{mol}^{-1}$, or as a conversion factor

$$\frac{32.1\,\text{g S}}{1\,\text{mol S}}$$

Therefore

$$\text{Mass of sulfur} = 0.50 \cancel{\text{mol S}} \times \frac{32.1 \text{ g S}}{1 \cancel{\text{mol S}}}$$

$$= 16 \text{ g}$$

EXAMPLE **3.9** How many moles are there in a mass of 10.0 g of iron?

SOLUTION From the Periodic Table, we see that the molar mass of iron is $55.8 \text{ g} \cdot \text{mol}^{-1}$ (corresponding to an atomic mass of 55.8 u). The conversion factor is inverted

$$\frac{1 \text{ mol Fe}}{55.8 \text{ g Fe}}$$

and the problem is solved as follows:

$$\text{Moles of iron} = 10.0 \cancel{\text{g}} \text{ Fe} \times \frac{1 \text{ mol Fe}}{55.8 \cancel{\text{g}} \text{ Fe}}$$

$$= 0.179 \text{ mol Fe}$$

We have just shown how moles and mass are related. In the previous section, we saw that moles and atoms were related by the factor 6.02×10^{23} atom $\cdot$ mol^{-1}. We now have a way of relating numbers of atoms to a measurable quantity, mass, using the mole as a link. The first step in this two-step process is always to calculate the number of moles of the substance in question (Figure 3.14).

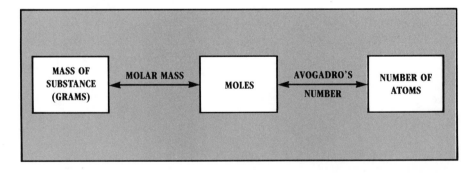

Figure 3.14
The relationship between mass and number of atoms.

EXAMPLE **3.10** Calculate the mass of 1.2×10^{23} atoms of aluminum.

SOLUTION

STRATEGY

1. Atoms $\longrightarrow$ Moles
2. Moles $\longrightarrow$ Mass

STEP 1:   First we must convert from number of atoms to moles, using Avogadro's number (6.02×10^{23} atoms·mol^{-1}) as the conversion factor. To obtain an answer in moles we invert the factor and multiply:

$$\text{Moles of aluminum} = 1.2 \times 10^{23} \text{ atoms Al} \times \frac{1 \text{ mol Al}}{6.02 \times 10^{23} \text{ atoms Al}}$$

$$= 0.20 \text{ mol Al}$$

STEP 2:   To convert from moles to mass, we need to know the molar mass of aluminum. From the Periodic Table (or an atomic mass table) we obtain the value 27.0 g·mol^{-1}.

$$\text{Mass of aluminum} = 0.20 \text{ mol Al} \times \frac{27.0 \text{ g Al}}{1 \text{ mol Al}}$$

$$= 5.4 \text{ g Al}$$

EXAMPLE   **3.11**   How many atoms are in 2.30 g of sodium?

SOLUTION

> **STRATEGY**
> 1. Mass ⟶ Moles
> 2. Moles ⟶ Atoms

STEP 1:   We convert from mass to moles using the molar mass as the conversion factor. From the Periodic Table, we find a value of 23.0 g·mol^{-1} for the molar mass of sodium. The conversion factor is inverted so our answer will be in moles:

$$\text{Moles of sodium} = 2.30 \text{ g Na} \times \frac{1 \text{ mol Na}}{23.0 \text{ g Na}}$$

$$= 0.100 \text{ mol Na}$$

STEP 2:   We then use Avogadro's number as the conversion factor to convert number of moles to number of atoms:

$$\text{Number of atoms} = 0.100 \text{ mol Na} \times \frac{6.02 \times 10^{23} \text{ atoms Na}}{1 \text{ mol Na}}$$

$$= 6.02 \times 10^{22} \text{ atoms Na}$$

QUESTIONS

11. What is the mass of 4.2 mol of helium?
12. What is the mass of 8.11×10^{-2} mol of lead?
13. How many moles are there in 63 g of carbon?
14. How many moles are there in 0.115 g of sodium?

15. What is the mass of 3.01×10^{22} atoms of helium? = 0.200 g

16. How many atoms are present in $6.20\,g$ of phosphorus?

The Visible Spectrum

3.9

In our discussion of the structure of the atom we have emphasized the importance of the nucleus. However, the electrons play the most important role in determining the chemistry of the element.

Although Rutherford's experiment provided a good model of the atom, the model had a number of deficiencies. It did not explain where the electrons were located nor why negatively charged electrons are not pulled into the positively charged nucleus. In 1913, Niels Bohr, a young Danish physicist, devised a model that accounted for these problems. To understand Bohr's model, we first need to understand the nature of light.

Visible light is a form of energy that makes up a very small portion of the electromagnetic spectrum (Figure 3.16). If we take a source of white light, such as an electric light bulb, and shine a narrow beam of light through a glass prism we see a pattern of colours. The blended pattern of colours leaving the prism is called a **continuous spectrum** (Figure 3.17). In the spectrum, the colours always appear in the same sequence. Violet is at one end of the spectrum, followed by blue, green, yellow, orange, and finally, red. These are the same colours that we see in a rainbow.

Classifying visible light according to its colour is imprecise because light of one colour still represents a range of energies. A more precise classification is based on the mathematical description of light as a wave. We describe a wave by its wavelength, which is represented by the Greek symbol λ (lambda). The units used for measuring wavelengths are nanometres (nm). The shorter the wavelength, the higher the energy of the wave. For instance, the wave in Figure 3.18a has a much shorter wavelength than that in Figure 3.18b. Thus, the light wave in Figure 3.18a has a higher energy than that in Figure 3.18b.

Figure 3.15
Niels Bohr (1885–1962). Bohr developed the quantum model of the atom that revolutionized theoretical chemistry. He won the Nobel Prize for Physics in 1922.

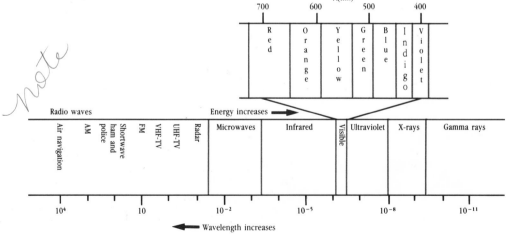

Figure 3.16
The electromagnetic spectrum.

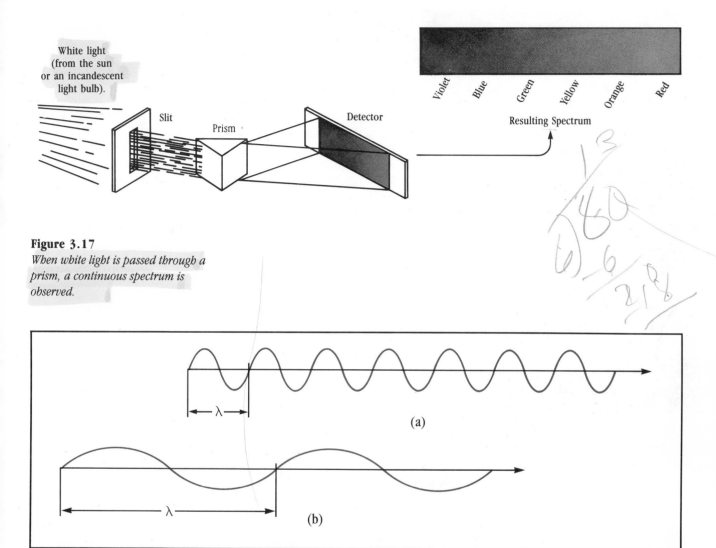

Figure 3.17
When white light is passed through a prism, a continuous spectrum is observed.

Figure 3.18
Two waves with correspondingly different energies:
a) The wave with the shorter wavelength has the higher energy level.
b) The wave with the longer wavelength has the lower energy.

In the visible spectrum, violet light has the shortest wavelength (about 400 nm) and, consequently, the highest energy. Red light, at the other end of the spectrum, has the longest wavelength (about 700 nm) and the lowest energy. There are no sharp dividing lines between the colours. Instead, there is a smooth transition from one colour to the next. For example, from green to blue, the colours change from green through bluish green and greenish blue to blue.

Radiation outside the 400 nm to 700 nm range cannot be detected by our eyes. The lower energy radiation beyond the red end of the visible spectrum is called infrared; the higher energy radiation beyond the violet end is called ultraviolet.

Infrared Radiation

All objects release infrared radiation. The amount of radiation emitted increases with increasing temperature.

Of the 14 families of snakes, two have infrared detectors (also called heat receptors or, sometimes, a 'third eye'). The snakes use the detectors to seek out and capture warm-bodied prey in the dark. One of the families with infrared detectors is the Crotalidae, or pit vipers. Species such as the rattlesnake, the water moccasin, and the copperhead belong to this family. The other family, the Boidae, includes the boa constrictor, the python, and the anaconda. Although all members of both families have heat receptors, the differences in the anatomy of the receptors in the families suggest that they evolved independently.

The ability to detect objects from the infrared radiation they emit is used for military purposes. At night, infrared ''snooperscopes'' are used to look for signs of enemy troops or vehicles. These are warmer than the surrounding trees and fields and emit more infrared radiation. Some types of air-to-air and air-to-ground missiles have infrared sensors that ''home in'' on the hot exhaust of enemy aircraft or vehicles.

We can make use of infrared radiation in energy conservation measures to reduce heat loss from buildings. Infrared film is used to take photographs of buildings at night. The parts of the buildings from which high levels of infrared radiation are being emitted, and therefore from which heat is being lost, will show up as bright spots on the photographs. An energy conservation expert can then suggest ways of reducing the heat loss from these areas.

Infrared photographs are also used in the medical field to identify regions of abnormally high or low skin temperature. This information can be used in the diagnosis of some medical problems, including the location of tumours.

Another use of infrared radiation is in home security systems. One type of alarm can detect the infrared radiation given off by a warm-bodied intruder. Another type aims an invisible beam of infrared light across a room to a detector. When an intruder interrupts the beam by walking through it, an alarm will sound.

Figure 3.19

a) The side of a factory photographed with film sensitive to visible light.

b) The same factory photographed with film sensitive to infrared light. Notice how this photograph pinpoints locations where heat is being lost by showing them as bright areas.

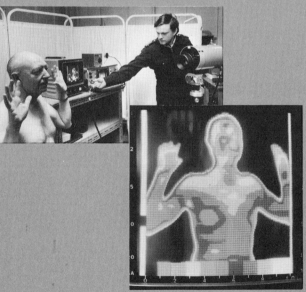

Figure 3.20

a) Recording an infrared image for medical use.

b) The infrared image shows locations of high and low skin temperatures.

The Emission of Light by Atoms

3.10

In the last section, we saw that a continuous spectrum is observed when white light is passed through a prism. If a sample of hydrogen gas is heated, only a few precise wavelengths of light are emitted (Figure 3.21). The spectrum produced when this light is passed through a prism is called a **line spectrum** or emission spectrum. Each element gives a characteristic line spectrum when it is heated. If a few crystals of table salt (sodium chloride) are placed in a flame, the flame turns bright yellow. This colour results from radiation of wavelength 589 nm being emitted by the sodium atoms.

Figure 3.21
When light from heated hydrogen is passed through a prism, a line spectrum is observed.

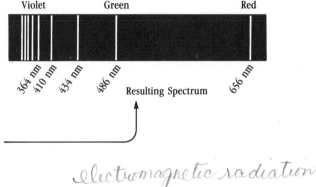

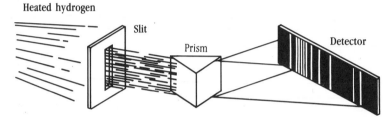

electromagnetic radiation

The Uses of Line Spectra in Chemistry

As each element has a unique line spectrum, we can use this property to identify elements in an unknown substance. The procedure is called a flame test. In this test, a small quantity of the unknown sample is heated in a flame. The flame is carefully observed to see if it changes colour. The colours that some common elements give to a flame are shown in Table 3.5.

Figure 3.22
This sodium flame emission spectrometer measures the intensity of light emitted at 589 nm. From this value, the quantity of sodium in a sample can be calculated.

TABLE 3.5 **Elements and Their Characteristic Colours in a Hot Flame**

Element	Colour
Lithium	Crimson red
Sodium	Orange yellow
Potassium	Lavender
Cesium	Blue
Calcium	Reddish orange
Strontium	Brilliant red
Barium	Yellowish green

We can find the quantity of an element in a sample by measuring the intensity of the light emitted. This technique, called flame emission spectroscopy, can be used to measure the sodium content of blood or food. A related technique, atomic absorption spectroscopy, is a method of chemical analysis frequently used in environmental studies.

The Bohr Model of the Atom

3.11

Bohr developed his model of the atom from a study of the line spectrum of the hydrogen atom. He proposed that electrons could only possess specific quantities of energy, and that each **energy level** corresponded to a specific distance from the nucleus. *AKA / Wave particles) theory*

Bohr used an integer, which he called the **principal quantum number** (symbol n) to identify each of the energy levels. The value of n could be any integer between one and infinity. The electron of the hydrogen atom would normally be in the lowest energy level (closest to the nucleus). This energy level, the **ground state**, corresponds to the principal quantum number, n, which is equal to one.

If heat or electrical energy is supplied to a hydrogen atom, its electron will be forced to a higher than normal energy level. When this happens, the electron is in an **excited state**. When the electron drops back to a lower energy level, it emits energy in the form of electromagnetic radiation.

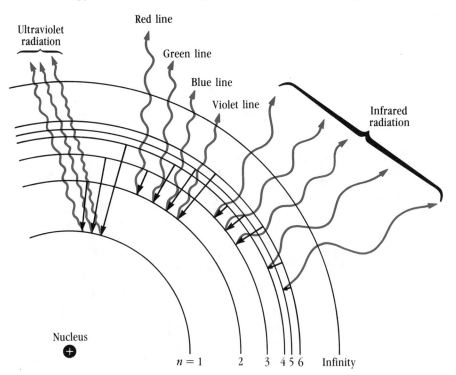

Figure 3.23

A schematic representation of the energy changes that give rise to the emission spectrum of hydrogen.

The energy of this radiation corresponds to the difference in energy between the two energy levels. For example, the emission spectrum of hydrogen shows a red line of wavelength 656 nm. This corresponds to electrons moving from the third energy level to the second energy level (Figure 3.23).

Bohr also showed that, as the quantum numbers increase, the energy levels become closer together. Thus the energy of the fiftieth level is almost the same as that of the five-hundredth level. In chemistry, however, we are usually only concerned with the first seven energy levels.

An Analogy of the Bohr Model

We can picture the energy levels of an atom as a series of steps in a sunken circular auditorium. We will consider gravity as being analogous to the electrostatic attraction of an electron to a nucleus.

The lowest step at the bottom of the centre well is equivalent to the first energy level in an atom. By using up some energy, we can climb up to the second step. This is equivalent to an electron absorbing energy and moving from the first energy level to the second energy level. By using more energy, we can climb higher and higher, gaining potential energy as we go. Similarly an electron can move to higher energy levels as it absorbs increasing amounts of energy. It is important to note that we cannot stay between steps. Our movement must be in whole numbers of steps, just as the electron can only absorb specific amounts of energy.

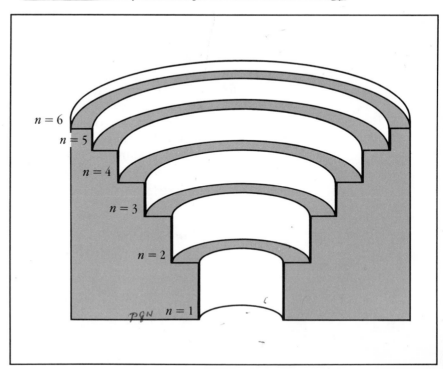

Figure 3.24

An analogy of electron transitions. A circular sunken auditorium with steps of different heights represents the lowest six energy levels of an electron in an atom.

When we move back down towards the centre of the auditorium, we can either jump from one step to the next lower one, or leap down several steps at a time. The further we jump down, the greater is our loss of potential energy. As electrons move to lower energy levels they also emit energy. More energy is emitted if they move down through a number of energy levels at a time than if they only move from one level to the next lower.

Note that in our sketch of the auditorium, the height of each step decreases as we go out from the centre. This is similar to the situation in the atom, where the biggest energy difference is between the first and second energy levels, and the difference decreases between successive levels.

Atoms Containing Many Electrons

3.12

In constructing a model of an atom with several electrons, two rules have to be followed:

1. Electrons always occupy the lowest possible energy level.
2. There is a maximum number of electrons for each energy level. This number is given by $2n^2$, where n is the principal quantum number.

Thus, the first energy level can hold a maximum of 2 electrons, the second a maximum of 8, and the third a maximum of 18. However, an energy level of principal quantum number 3 or above may not accommodate more than 8 electrons *when it is the outermost-occupied energy level*.

We can now determine the number of electrons present in each energy level for the first nineteen elements in the Periodic Table. Remember that for each successive element, the atomic number, and hence the number of electrons, increases by one.

Hydrogen has only one electron. In the ground state, this electron is found in the first energy level. Bohr established that the first energy level could hold a maximum of two electrons. Thus the second element, helium, has both its electrons in the first level.

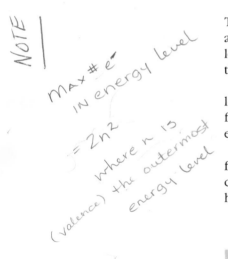

NOTE

Max # e⁻ in energy level = 2n² where n is (valence) the outermost energy level

2(5)²
2 × 25
50 e⁻

TABLE 3.6 *The Energy-Level Populations of Elements with Atomic Numbers 1 and 2*

Element	Atomic Number	Population of Energy Levels First ($n = 1$)
Hydrogen	1	1
Helium	2	2

As the first level is now full, one of the electrons of the next element, lithium, must occupy the second level. This level can hold a maximum of eight electrons, as shown by neon in Table 3.7.

TABLE 3.7 *The Energy-Level Populations of Elements with Atomic Numbers 3 to 10*

		Population of Energy Levels	
Element	Atomic Number	First ($n = 1$)	Second ($n = 2$)
Lithium	3	2	1
Beryllium	4	2	2
Boron	5	2	3
Carbon	6	2	4
Nitrogen	7	2	5
Oxygen	8	2	6
Fluorine	9	2	7
Neon	10	2	8

The third energy level starts to fill beginning with the element sodium (11 electrons). As this level is the outermost-occupied energy level, it is restricted to a maximum of 8 electrons. This maximum is reached with the element argon, as shown in Table 3.8. Potassium, with 19 electrons, has one more electron than argon. This additional electron is located in the fourth energy level.

TABLE 3.8 *The Energy-Level Populations of Elements with Atomic Numbers 11 to 19*

		Population of Energy Levels			
Element	Atomic Number	First ($n = 1$)	Second ($n = 2$)	Third ($n = 3$)	Fourth ($n = 4$)
Sodium	11	2	8	1	
Magnesium	12	2	8	2	
Aluminum	13	2	8	3	
Silicon	14	2	8	4	
Phosphorus	15	2	8	5	
Sulfur	16	2	8	6	
Chlorine	17	2	8	7	
Argon	18	2	8	8	
Potassium	19	2	8	8	1

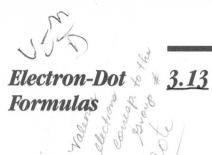

Electron-Dot Formulas

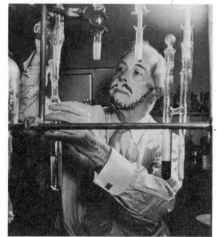

Figure 3.25
Gilbert N. Lewis (1875–1946). Lewis developed the electron-dot formula method for indicating the number of electrons in the valence level of an atom.

It would be very time consuming if we always had to write out the full energy-level populations of each atom. Fortunately, the chemical properties of an element depend to a large extent on the number of electrons in the highest occupied energy level. This level is called the valence level. The electrons in the valence level are referred to as **valence electrons**.

Chemists have devised a shorthand system for indicating the number of electrons in the valence level. The system is usually known as the electron-dot formula method, but is also called the **Lewis Formula** method, after G.N. Lewis who developed the system. The principles of this method are as follows:

1. The core is represented by the symbol for the element; valence electrons are represented by dots.

2. The symbol is assumed to have four sides and the valence electrons are distributed around the sides.

3. When we distribute valence electrons, we first place one dot on each of the four sides before we locate pairs of electrons on any one side.

4. No more than 2 electrons can be placed on any one side.

When writing the electron-dot formula of an element, it is obviously important to know the number of valence electrons possessed by that element. We can use the Periodic Table to obtain this information. The number of valence electrons in an element is the same as the group number appearing at the top of the column in which the element is found in the Periodic Table. For example, potassium (Group IA) has 1 valence electron, and oxygen (Group VIA) has 6 valence electrons.

EXAMPLE   *3.12*   Write electron-dot formulas for the following:
a) fluorine
b) chlorine
c) sodium

SOLUTION   a) Fluorine has a total of 9 electrons, 2 of which are in the first level. Thus the element has 7 valence electrons. As a shortcut, we see that fluorine is in Group VIIA, which indicates it has 7 valence electrons. The electron-dot formula will therefore be

$$\cdot \ddot{\underset{\cdot\cdot}{F}} \colon$$

b) Chlorine has 17 electrons, 2 in the first level, 8 in the second level, and 7 in the third level. Thus it has 7 valence electrons. Chlorine is also in Group VIIA. The electron-dot formula will be

$$\cdot \ddot{\underset{\cdot\cdot}{C}} l \colon$$

c) Sodium has 11 electrons, 2 in the first level, 8 in the second level, and 1 in the valence or third level (it is in Group IA). The electron-dot formula will therefore be

$$\mathbf{Na} \cdot$$

QUESTIONS

17. Write electron-dot formulas for the following elements:

a) potassium
b) nitrogen
c) phosphorus

d) argon
e) aluminum
f) carbon

M. M.

A Modified Model of the Atom

3.14 The simple Bohr model of the atom is still very useful, but for some purposes a more sophisticated model is required. However, the electron-dot formulas generated by the Bohr model will be used throughout this text because they provide one of the easiest ways of understanding how and why atoms combine to form compounds.

When the spectra of atoms other than hydrogen were examined, it was observed that there were more emission lines than the Bohr model had predicted. These spectral lines were classified by their appearance as sharp, principal, diffuse, and fundamental. The Bohr model had to be modified to account for these extra lines.

It was proposed that the energy levels of the Bohr model be split into sublevels. The letters *s*, *p*, *d*, and *f* (from the descriptions of the spectral lines) were used to identify these sublevels. Within any given level each sublevel had a slightly different energy. The *s* sublevel always had the lowest energy. This was followed by the *p* level, then the *d*, and finally the *f*. An *s* sublevel could hold a maximum of 2 electrons, a *p* sublevel could hold a maximum of 6 electrons, a *d* sublevel could hold a maximum of 10 electrons, and an *f* sublevel could hold a maximum of 14 electrons.

Some of the energy levels do not have all of the sublevels. The first level has only an *s* sublevel (designated 1*s*); the second level has only *s* and *p* sublevels (designated 2*s* and 2*p*); the third level has *s*, *p*, and *d* sublevels (designated 3*s*, 3*p*, and 3*d*); and the fourth level has *s*, *p*, *d*, and *f* sublevels (designated 4*s*, 4*p*, 4*d*, and 4*f*).

Sublevels and the Periodic Table

In Section 3.6, we saw how the chemical elements are organized in the Periodic Table. This arrangement arises from the way the sublevels are filled with electrons.

We can start our study of the modified Bohr model by looking again at the electron arrangements of the first nineteen elements of the Periodic Table. These arrangements are called **electron configurations**. The first element, hydrogen, has one electron. This electron occupies the $1s$ sublevel. The number of electrons in a sublevel is indicated by a superscript to the right of the sublevel symbol. Thus, the electron configuration of hydrogen is written as $1s^1$. Table 3.9 shows the electron configurations of the first ten elements. Notice that the maximum number of electrons in the $2s$ and $2p$ sublevels totals eight. This agrees with the simple Bohr model in which the maximum number of electrons permitted in the second energy level was also eight.

TABLE 3.9 *The Electron Configuration of Elements with Atomic Numbers 1 to 10*

Element	Atomic Number	Electron Configuration
Hydrogen	1	$1s^1$
Helium	2	$1s^2$
Lithium	3	$1s^2 2s^1$
Beryllium	4	$1s^2 2s^2$
Boron	5	$1s^2 2s^2 2p^1$
Carbon	6	$1s^2 2s^2 2p^2$
Nitrogen	7	$1s^2 2s^2 2p^3$
Oxygen	8	$1s^2 2s^2 2p^4$
Fluorine	9	$1s^2 2s^2 2p^5$
Neon	10	$1s^2 2s^2 2p^6$

You would expect the third row in the Periodic Table to have 18 elements corresponding to the filling of the $3s$, $3p$, and $3d$ sublevels. In fact it has only eight elements. This is because the third energy level can only hold a maximum of eight electrons when it is the valence level.

In order to explain this behaviour we must consider the relative energies of the $3d$ and $4s$ sublevels. As mentioned, within the same energy level the d sublevel has a higher energy than either the p or s sublevels. In fact, the $3d$ sublevel has a higher energy than the lowest sublevel of the fourth level, the $4s$, and as a consequence the $4s$ sublevel fills up before the $3d$. The complete filling order for the sublevels is shown in Figure 3.26.

left reactivity ↓ right reactivity ↑ increase

Only valence shells which aren't filled act because once a valence shell is completed it becomes inert thus very stable

left side of table forms cations right side of table forms anions

any imbalance causes ions (+ / -)

#P = #e

The shell describes the area occupied by an electron

The electron configurations of the elements with atomic numbers 11 to 19 are shown in Table 3.10. The elements sodium to argon correspond to the filling of the 3*s* and 3*p* sublevels. The filling of the 4*s* sublevel starts with potassium.

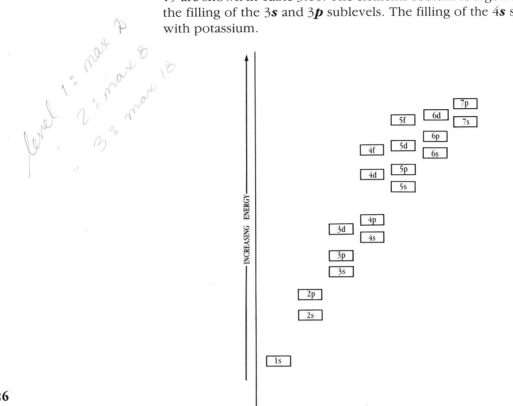

Figure 3.26
The order for filling electron sublevels.

TABLE 3.10	*The Electron Configuration of Elements with Atomic Numbers 11 to 19*

Element	Atomic Number	Electron Configuration
Sodium	11	$1s^22s^22p^63s^1$
Magnesium	12	$1s^22s^22p^63s^2$
Aluminum	13	$1s^22s^22p^63s^23p^1$
Silicon	14	$1s^22s^22p^63s^23p^2$
Phosphorus	15	$1s^22s^22p^63s^23p^3$
Sulfur	16	$1s^22s^22p^63s^23p^4$
Chlorine	17	$1s^22s^22p^63s^23p^5$
Argon	18	$1s^22s^22p^63s^23p^6$
Potassium	19	$1s^22s^22p^63s^23p^64s^1$

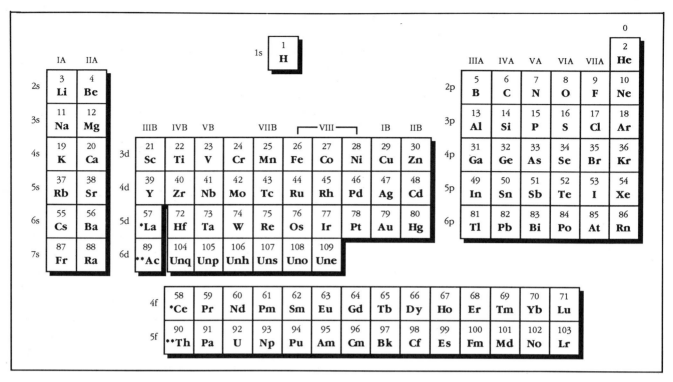

Figure 3.27
The Periodic Table divided according to the filling order of the sublevels.

Figure 3.28
A diagram for predicting the order of filling sublevels:
a) The orbital symbols are written in the pattern shown;

b) Diagonal arrows are drawn from lower left to upper right;

c) The head of one arrow is joined to the tail of the next. This gives the sequence of orbital filling; i.e., 1s, 2s, 2p, 3s, etc.

(a)
```
1s   2s   3s   4s   5s   6s   7s   8s   __
     2p   3p   4p   5p   6p   7p        __
          3d   4d   5d   6d             __  __
               4f   5f        __  __  __
                             __  __  __
```

(b)
```
1s   2s   3s   4s   5s   6s   7s   8s   __
     2p   3p   4p   5p   6p   7p        __
          3d   4d   5d   6d             __  __
               4f   5f        __  __  __
                             __  __  __
```

(c)
```
1s   2s   3s   4s   5s   6s   7s   8s   __
     2p   3p   4p   5p   6p   7p        __  __
          3d   4d   5d   6d             __  __
               4f   5f        __  __  __
                             __  __  __
```

After the 4*s* sublevel has been filled, the 3*d* sublevel will start to fill. Filling the 3*d* sublevel corresponds to the elements scandium through zinc. Filling the 4*p* sublevel corresponds to the elements gallium through krypton. The fourth row of 18 elements is thus completed.

Figure 3.27 shows the Periodic Table divided according to the filling order of the sublevels. Note that we can relate the filling of a specific sublevel to part of a row in the Periodic Table. For example, Groups IA and IIA correspond to the filling of the *s* sublevels. If you can relate the sublevel filling to the Periodic Table arrangement, writing an electron configuration is straightforward.

EXAMPLE   **3.13**   Write the electron configurations for the following elements:
a) sulfur   b) bromine

SOLUTION   a) Sulfur is in the *p* block of the third row of the Periodic Table. This means that its outermost electron must be in the 3*p* sublevel. As it is the fourth element along the *p*-block row it must have four *p* electrons. In addition, the inner sublevels must all be filled: the *s* sublevels with two electrons and the *p* sublevels with six electrons. The inner sublevels are 1*s* from the first row, 2*s* and 2*p* from the second row, and 3*s* at the beginning of the third row. The electron configuration of sulfur is therefore $1s^2 2s^2 2p^6 3s^2 3p^4$. Note that the total number of electrons must match the atomic number of the element (16).

b) Following a similar procedure, we see that bromine must have five electrons in the 5*p* sublevel. In addition, the inner filled sublevels are 1*s* (from the first row); 2*s*, 2*p* (from the second row); 3*s*, 3*p* (from the third row); and 4*s*, 3*d* (from the fourth row). The electron configuration of bromine must be $1s^2 2s^2 2p^6 3s^2 3p^6 4s^2 3d^{10} 4p^5$. Again, we can check that the total number of electrons (35) matches the atomic number.

QUESTIONS

18. Write the electron configuration for each of the following:
a) boron   b) calcium   c) iron   d) lead   e) cadmium

The Probability Model of the Atom

We usually think of particles and waves as being very different. However, the French physicist, Louis de Broglie, showed that a very small particle (such as an electron) could possess the properties of a wave. About the same time, the German physicist, Werner Heisenberg, showed that position and velocity cannot be measured simultaneously for a particle as small as an electron. This realization, known as Heisenberg's uncertainty principle, put severe limits on attempts to make the Bohr model of the atom more exact. The uncertainty in the position of a large object, such as a moving automobile, is negligible, but Heisenberg's principle indicates that for an extremely small object, such as an electron, the uncertainty is relatively large.

The implication of the work of de Broglie and Heisenberg made the Bohr theory outdated, although it is still useful to us as a model.

A new and revolutionary model of atomic structure was developed in 1926 by the German mathematician, Erwin Schrödinger. He proposed a mathematical equation that describes the electron in terms of its wave character. This complex equation has been solved with the aid of computers for the one-electron atom and two-electron atoms. Scientists are trying to solve the equation for atoms with higher numbers of electrons.

Whereas the Bohr theory accounted for the position of an electron around the nucleus, the probability (or quantum-mechanical) model (as Schrödinger's model is called) only tells us where we are most likely to find an electron. The region of high probability of finding an electron is referred to as an orbital.

Although this model is much more sophisticated than the Bohr model, we use the same symbols as we used for electron configurations to describe orbitals. The experimentally observed spectra (and energy levels) are also the same. We are just using a different mental image of the phenomenon. The solution of Schrödinger's wave equation involves sets of integers called quantum numbers. The first set is called the principal quantum number (as in the Bohr model) and relates to the volume of space around the nucleus in which we will most likely find the electron. As the principal quantum number increases, the probability volume increases. In other words, the *average* distance of the electron from the nucleus increases.

The second quantum number determines the shape of the orbital. We can relate the energy of these different orbitals to the sublevels of our simple atomic model. Thus the orbital shapes are denoted by the symbols *s*, *p*, *d*, and *f*. Examples of two orbital shapes are shown in Figure 3.29.

With the probability model of the atom, we still use electron configurations to describe electron structure, but we picture the symbols in terms of orbitals rather than sublevels.

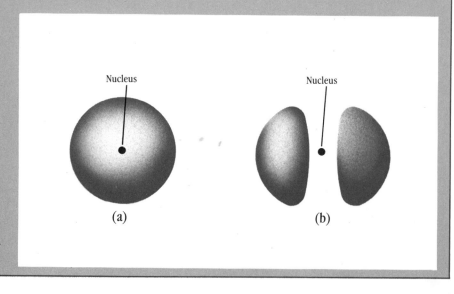

Figure 3.29
Examples of orbital shapes —
*a) the spherical shape of an **s** orbital;*
*b) the dumbbell shape of a **p** orbital.*

Summary

- The atom is composed of an extremely small central nucleus containing protons (positively charged, relative mass = 1) and neutrons (neutral, relative mass = 1) surrounded by electrons (negatively charged, relative mass = 0.0005).

- The atomic number indicates the number of protons in an atom and is unique for each element.

- In a neutral atom, the number of electrons must equal the number of protons.

- The number of neutrons in the nucleus is usually greater than the number of protons. The sum of the numbers of protons and neutrons is called the mass number.

- Atoms with the same number of protons but a different number of neutrons are called isotopes. Most elements have more than one naturally occurring isotope. The percentage of atoms that occur as a specific isotope is called the abundance of that isotope.

- In radioactive isotopes the composition of the nucleus changes over time.

- Atomic masses are based on a scale in which an atom of carbon-12 is defined as having a mass of exactly 12 u. A unified atomic mass unit (u) is $1/12$ of the mass of an atom of carbon-12.

- A mole is the amount of substance containing 6.02×10^{23} units (Avogadro's number).

- The mass of one mole of an element (its molar mass) expressed in grams has the same numerical value as the atomic mass expressed in unified atomic mass units.

- Visible light is a form of energy that makes up a small portion of the electromagnetic spectrum. Each element gives a characteristic line spectrum which can be used to identify that element.

- In the Bohr model of the atom, electrons can possess certain energies corresponding to specific distances from the nucleus. Each energy level is identified by a principal quantum number, n. As the principal quantum number increases, the energy levels become closer together.

- An electron can be forced to a higher energy level, called an excited state. When it drops back to a lower energy level the electron emits energy in the form of electromagnetic radiation.

- Electrons seek the lowest possible energy level. There is a maximum number of electrons that can be accommodated in any given energy level.

- The chemical properties of an element are determined largely by the number of valence electrons. The latter can be determined by the number of the group in which the element appears in the Periodic Table.

■ The Bohr energy levels are divided into sublevels. These are identified by the letters *s*, *p*, *d*, and *f*. Each sublevel within a given energy level has a slightly different energy. The maximum number of electrons permitted in each sublevel is 2 in an *s* sublevel, 8 in a *p* sublevel, 10 in a *d* sublevel, and 14 in an *f* sublevel.

■ The notation showing the number of electrons in each of the occupied sublevels is called the electron configuration of an element.

KEY WORDS

abundance
atom
atomic mass
atomic number
Avogadro's number
continuous spectrum
electron configuration
electron
energy level
excited state
isotope
Lewis Formula
line spectrum

mass number
mass spectrometer
molar mass
mole
neutron
nucleon
nucleus
Periodic Table
principal quantum number
proton
radioactive
unified atomic mass unit
valence electron

ANSWERS TO
SECTION QUESTIONS

1. 11p, 12n
2. 13p, 13e
3. $^{35}_{17}$Cl — 17p, 18n, 17e; $^{37}_{17}$Cl — 17p, 20n, 17e
4. $^{79}_{35}$Br and $^{81}_{35}$Br
5. $^{10}_{5}$B — 5p, 5n, 5e; $^{11}_{5}$B — 5p, 6n, 5e;   mass 10.8 u
6. 55.85 u
7. 6.00 gross
8. 1800
9. 1.66×10^{-2} mol
10. 2.50×10^{24} atoms
11. 17 g
12. 16.8 g
13. 5.3 mol
14. 5.00×10^{-3} mol
15. 0.200 g

16. 1.20×10^{23} atoms

17. a) K·   c) ·P̈·   e) ·Äl·

    b) ·N̈·   d) :Är: f) ·Ċ·

18. a) $1s^22s^22p^1$ b) $1s^22s^22p^63s^23p^64s^2$ c) $1s^22s^22p^63s^23p^64s^23d^6$

    d) $1s^22s^22p^63s^23p^64s^23d^{10}4p^65s^24d^{10}5p^66s^24f^{14}5d^{10}6p^2$

    e) $1s^22s^22p^63s^23p^64s^23d^{10}4p^65s^24d^{10}$

COMPREHENSION QUESTIONS

1. What contribution did the ancient Greeks make to the development of atomic theory?

2. On what basis did Dalton develop his atomic theory?

3. What part of Dalton's atomic theory is no longer valid

4. List the three major particles in the atom, their locations within the atom, their charges, and their relative masses.

5. Given the atomic number and mass number of an atom, how is the number of each of the following particles in an atom determined:
a) protons   b) electrons   c) neutrons

6. What is meant by the term "isotope"?

7. Define "mole".

8. What is meant by the term "molar mass"?

9. What is the difference between the spectrum produced by white light and the emission spectra produced by elements? To what use can this difference be put?

10. Explain the following terms:
a) principal quantum number   b) excited state

11. What two rules are used to place electrons into the energy levels of an atom with several electrons?

12. What is meant by the terms "valence level" and "valence electrons"? Why are valence electrons important?

13. What is a quick way of determining the number of valence electrons for a given element?

14. How many electrons can be held in each s, p, d, and f sublevel?.

PROBLEMS

15. What is the number of protons, neutrons, and electrons in an atom of
a) $^{19}_9F$ b) $^{18}_8O$ c) $^{41}_{19}K$ d) $^{238}_{92}U$

16. What is the atomic number and mass number of
a) $^{48}_{20}Ca$ b) $^{107}_{47}Ag$ c) ^4_2He

17. Using the Periodic Table, complete the following table:

Atom	Protons	Neutrons	Electrons
Cobalt-60	?	?	?
? *P 30*	? *15*	15	15
? *Br 81*	35	46	? *35*

18. Using the Periodic Table, complete the following table:

Element	Protons	Neutrons	Mass Number
Aluminum	*13*	*14*	27
Copper	*29*	36	*65*
? *I*	53	*74*	127

19. The element strontium has four naturally occurring isotopes with atomic masses of 83.91 u, 85.91 u, 86.91 u, and 87.91 u respectively. If $^{84}_{38}$Sr represents the first isotope, give the symbolic representation for the other three.

20. Boron (average atomic mass 10.811 u) consists of two isotopes: boron-10 (atomic mass 10.013 u) and boron-11 (atomic mass 11.009 u). Which of the two isotopes is more common in nature?

21. The element antimony has two isotopes, $^{121}_{51}$Sb with an atomic mass of 120.90 u and an abundance of 57.25%, and $^{123}_{51}$Sb with an atomic mass of 122.90 u. Calculate the average atomic mass of antimony.

22. Calculate the average atomic mass of lithium from the following data:

Isotope	Atomic Mass (u)	Abundance (%)
Lithium-6	6.015	7.68
Lithium-7	7.016	92.32

6.93

23. Silicon has three stable isotopes, $^{28}_{14}$Si, $^{29}_{14}$Si, and $^{30}_{14}$Si, with abundances of 92.18%, 4.71%, and 3.12%, respectively. The corresponding atomic masses are 27.98 u, 28.98 u, and 29.97 u. Calculate the average atomic mass of silicon.

24. Calculate the average atomic mass of magnesium from the following data:

Isotope	Atomic Mass (u)	Abundance (%)
Magnesium-24	23.98	78.60
Magnesium-25	24.99	10.11
Magnesium-26	25.98	11.29

25. The element copper, found in nature with an average atomic mass of 63.54 u, consists of two isotopes, copper-63 of atomic mass 62.93 u and copper-65 of atomic mass 64.93 u. Calculate the abundance of each isotope.

26. Lead has an average atomic mass of 207.19 u. There are five naturally occurring isotopes but two of them are present in very small proportions. The three major isotopes are lead-206 (atomic mass 205.98 u), lead-207 (atomic mass 206.98 u), and lead-208 (atomic mass 207.98 u). If the isotopes lead-206 and lead-207 are present in approximately equal percentages, what are the approximate percentages of lead-206, lead-207, and lead-208 in natural lead?

27. In 1981, the world population was about 4500 million people. How many moles of people were there?

28. Astronomers think that there are about 1.00×10^{11} stars in the Milky Way. How many moles of stars would this be?

29. What is the mass of 1.00 mol of each of the following:
    a) magnesium   b) argon   c) potassium

30. What is the molar mass of the following elements:
    a) copper   b) gold   c) iodine

31. Calculate the number of moles in
    a) 345 g of sulfur atoms
    b) 0.0037 g of oxygen atoms
    c) 1.07×10^4 g of gold atoms
    d) 1.00 g of helium atoms

32. How many moles are there in each of the following:
    a) 25 g of nitrogen atoms
    b) 0.348 g of chlorine atoms
    c) 15.0 kg of aluminum atoms
    d) 1.40×10^{-2} g carbon atoms

33. What is the mass of
    a) 4.75 mol of neon atoms
    b) 0.003 mol of lead atoms
    c) 3.6×10^2 mol of iodine atoms
    d) 5.11 mol of fluorine atoms

34. Calculate the mass of each of the following:
    a) 3.01×10^{-3} mol of iron atoms
    b) 10.0 mol of bromine atoms
    c) 0.105 mol of phosphorus atoms
    d) 4.2 mol of sulfur atoms

35. How many atoms are there in
    a) 5.00 mol of silver
    b) 0.0010 mol of bismuth
    c) 3×10^{-10} mol copper
    d) 21.4 mol of helium

36. How many moles of atoms are there in
    a) 1.20×10^{24} atoms of magnesium
    b) 1.00×10^{10} atoms of aluminum
    c) 3.59×10^{23} atoms of gold

37. Calculate the following:
    a) the number of atoms in 2.57 g of carbon
    b) the number of atoms in 108 g of chlorine gas
    c) the mass of 1.00×10^{20} atoms of sodium

38. Calculate
    a) the mass of 1 atom of gold
    b) the mass of 3.00×10^{22} atoms of zinc
    c) the number of atoms in 46 g of sodium
39. Describe the process by which light is emitted from an atom.
40. Explain why the Bohr model of the atom proved to be inadequate. How was the model changed to make it more consistent with experimental data?
41. If there were only four possible quantum levels for a hydrogen atom, how many lines would you expect in the emission spectrum?
42. What type of radiation is emitted when an excited electron in a hydrogen atom drops to the $n = 1$ level? What if it drops to the $n = 3$ level?
43. Draw electron-dot formulas for the following elements:
    a) lithium   b) oxygen   c) calcium
44. Draw the Lewis Formula for each of the following elements:
    a) sulfur   b) silicon   c) bromine
45. What is the highest energy level occupied in each of the following elements:
    a) magnesium   c) helium   e) cobalt
    b) nitrogen   d) cadmium
46. Formulate a rule that tells you what the highest occupied energy level is in any given atom.
47. Make a table of the groups in the Periodic Table that corresponds to the filling of the *s*, *p*, *d*, and *f* sublevels.
48. Write the electron configuration for each of the following:
    a) strontium   c) cesium   e) iodine
    b) krypton   d) nickel
49. Write the electron configuration for each of the following:
    a) zinc b) arsenic c) rubidium d) cobalt e) germanium

SUGGESTED PROJECTS

1. Using reference books, prepare a paper detailing the major advances in the development of the atomic theory from the ancient Greeks to 1950.
2. Since 1950 research has indicated that the particles in the atom, including the proton, neutron, and electron, are made up of smaller particles called quarks. Find out what you can about these particles and prepare a report.
3. Heavy water consists of two atoms of deuterium, an isotope of hydrogen, in place of the two hydrogens that normally combine with oxygen to make water. Heavy water is used in the Canadian CANDU nuclear reactor. Find out from reference books how deuterium is obtained and what its function is in the CANDU reactor.

CHAPTER 4

The Periodic Table

Chemists are always looking for patterns and trends that will help them to understand the properties and nature of matter. This is especially true in the case of chemical elements.

The observations that led to the formulation of the Periodic Law, and to the development of the Periodic Table, enabled chemists to see order among the properties of the elements. In this chapter, we will study the Periodic Table and see how it is used to identify some important trends.

The Origins of the Periodic Law

4.1

Although the 88 naturally occurring elements have been present in the crust of the earth for billions of years, most of them were only discovered during the past two hundred years. Only nine of the 88 elements were known to the ancient Greeks and Romans. These were gold, silver, copper, iron, lead, tin, mercury, sulfur, and carbon. During the Middle Ages, the alchemists were obsessed with finding ways to convert abundant metals, such as lead and iron, into gold. Although they were unsuccessful in their objective, they did, in the course of their experiments, discover the elements arsenic, antimony, bismuth, and zinc.

By the middle of the 18th century, increasingly sophisticated laboratory techniques allowed more elements to be identified, and the number of

Figure 4.1
Marguerite Perey (1909–1975), the discoverer of francium.

known elements increased from 16 in 1750 to 51 in 1825. This led chemists to speculate about the number of elements that could possibly exist. Until the internal structure of the atom was understood, chemists thought that there could be thousands of different elements! Francium, the last of the 88 naturally occurring elements, was discovered in 1939. Since then, nuclear physicists and chemists have extended the number of known elements to 107. This was accomplished by the discovery or synthesis of unstable radioactive elements that break down over time to form other, nonradioactive elements.

In 1829 Johann Dobereiner noted that some sets of three elements displayed a certain regularity in their properties. He found three such **triads** in which the middle element had an atomic mass that was about equal to the average mass of the other two. Some of the chemical and physical properties of the middle elements were also midway between those of the first and third elements. One of these triads consisted of chlorine, bromine, and iodine.

TABLE 4.1	*One of Dobereiner's Triads*	
	Atomic Mass	**Boiling Point**
Chlorine	35.5 u	−34 °C
Bromine	79.9 u	58 °C
Iodine	126.9 u	183 °C

Eighty percent of the elements known in 1829 did not fit into a triad, which suggested to most chemists that Dobereiner's observations were pure coincidence. The identification of triads was therefore not regarded as an important contribution to understanding the nature of matter.

In the early 19th century most chemists underestimated the importance of atomic mass. However, in 1864 John Newlands arranged the known elements in order of increasing atomic mass and showed that every eighth element formed part of a set of elements with similar chemical and physical properties. This **Law of Octaves**, as Newlands called it, contained each of Dobereiner's three triads. Unfortunately, because of the many discrepancies in Newlands' table of elements, most chemists again dismissed the patterns as coincidence.

It was not until 1869 that chemists accepted as meaningful the patterns observed by Dobereiner and Newlands. At that time the Russian chemist, Dmitri Ivanovitch Mendeléev, proposed the basis for the modern Periodic Table. He combined the concepts of increasing atomic mass and progressive change in valence of the elements to develop a table in which patterns in the properties of the elements could clearly be seen. Mendeléev summed up his findings in the **Periodic Law**, which states

Elements arranged in order of increasing atomic mass show a periodic repetition of properties.

Around the same time, the German chemist, Lothar Meyer, independently discovered the periodic nature of the physical and chemical properties of the elements. Mendeléev, however, is generally credited with the development of our modern Periodic Table, partly because he maintained a much higher public profile, and partly because Meyer did not pursue or use the Periodic Law to the same extent.

Mendeléev realized that arranging the elements according to their properties left some blank spaces in the Periodic Table. He predicted that these spaces would be filled by elements that had not at that time been discovered. Mendeléev also predicted the properties of these unknown elements by using the averaging concept of Dobereiner's triads. For example, in his table there was a blank space between silicon and tin. By comparing the properties of silicon and tin, Mendeléev deduced the properties of the missing element. Several years later, the element germanium, which had properties that almost exactly matched Mendeléev's predictions, was discovered. The ability to use the Periodic Table to make predictions about the elements makes it a very useful tool for chemists.

EXAMPLE   **4.1**   In the Periodic Table, strontium is directly below calcium and above barium. From the following physical properties of calcium and barium, predict some of the properties of strontium.

Element	Appearance	Density	Melting Point	Boiling Point
Calcium	Silvery metal	$1.55 \text{ g} \cdot \text{cm}^{-3}$	850 °C	1493 °C.
Strontium				
Barium	Silvery metal	$3.50 \text{ g} \cdot \text{cm}^{-3}$	710 °C	1637 °C.

SOLUTION   We would predict that the properties of strontium would be between those of calcium and barium. Therefore we would expect strontium to be a silvery metal with a density of approximately $2.5 \text{ g} \cdot \text{cm}^{-3}$. It should melt at about 780 °C and boil at about 1560 °C. (Strontium is a silvery metal with a density of $2.58 \text{ g} \cdot \text{cm}^{-3}$. Its melting point is 775 °C but its boiling point is 1367 °C. Thus, three of our four predictions are correct.)

Mendeléev realized that there were some unresolved problems in the Periodic Table. It was apparent that placing the elements strictly in order of increasing atomic mass resulted in some elements appearing in the wrong column of the table. On the basis of atomic mass only, potassium (atomic mass 39.1 u) should appear before argon (atomic mass 39.9 u), but to do this would place argon in the same column as lithium and sodium. This would obviously have been incorrect, as potassium has properties similar to those of lithium and sodium but argon does not. Similar problems arose with tellurium and iodine, and also with nickel and cobalt. Therefore, there

Mendeléev and the Periodic Table

Dmitri Ivanovich Mendeléev was born in Siberia, Russia, in 1834. Most of his life was spent in St. Petersburg (now called Leningrad). Mendeléev studied a wide range of topics, from the composition of carbon-containing compounds to the properties of gases, looking for patterns and relationships. The turning point in his career came in 1867 when he was appointed to the University of St. Petersburg.

As Mendeléev could not find a suitable text for his chemistry course, he wrote his own. Through the development of the book he clarified the concept of the Periodic Law.

At first there was opposition to Mendeléev's ideas, but the discovery of gallium by de Boisbaudran in 1875 finally brought Mendeléev fame. Nearly all the properties of gallium matched those that Mendeléev had predicted several years previously.

Mendeléev's interests included improving the Russian economy by developing oil and coal resources, and by the adoption of a more scientific approach to agriculture. Unfortunately, because of his prodemocratic sentiments, Mendeléev made many enemies in the government.

Even Mendeléev was not without scientific prejudice. He denied the existence of both the electron and radioactivity, as he thought that these concepts violated the Periodic Law.

Mendeléev died in 1907. At his funeral, students displayed a large copy of the Periodic Table as a tribute to his work. The D.I. Mendeléev Museum-Archive at the Leningrad State University is devoted to the study of his career.

Figure 4.2
Dmitri Mendeléev (1834–1907).

had to be some fundamental property, other than atomic mass, on which to base the Periodic Table.

The property that chemists had been seeking to enable them to produce a totally acceptable table was the atomic number. The concept of atomic number was developed in 1913 by the English physicist, Henry Moseley. As we saw in Chapter 3, the atomic number of an element corresponds to the number of protons in the nucleus. The modern Periodic Table represents the elements in order of increasing atomic number.

QUESTIONS

1. Predict the melting point of potassium, given that the melting point of sodium is 98 °C and that of rubidium is 39 °C.

The Modern Periodic Table

4.2 The Periodic Table contains elements arranged in order of increasing atomic number. The rows, which are called **periods**, are organized so that those elements with related properties all appear in the same column. The columns, in turn, are called **groups** or families.

1) Main group (representative) Elements IA - 8A

2) Transition Elements B groups

3) Lanthanides, Actinides

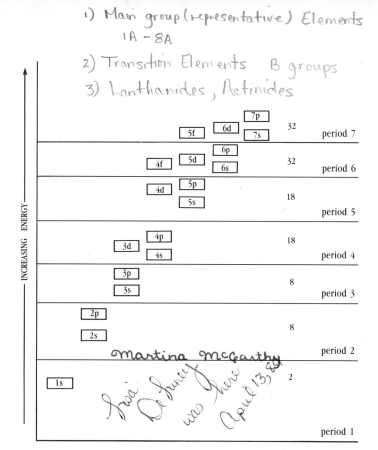

Figure 4.3
The elements in each period correspond to the order of filling of the sublevels shown.

	IA							0
1	1 **H**	IIA	IIIA	IVA	VA	VIA	VIIA	2 **He**
2	3 **Li**	4 **Be**	5 **B**	6 **C**	7 **N**	8 **O**	9 **F**	10 **Ne**
3	11 **Na**	12 **Mg**	13 **Al**	14 **Si**	15 **P**	16 **S**	17 **Cl**	18 **Ar**

Figure 4.4
The first three periods of the Periodic Table.

To see how this arrangement of the elements relates to the order of filling of the sublevels we can refer to Figure 4.3. In so doing we find that each period starts with the filling of an ***s*** sublevel and, with the exception of period number one, ends with the completion of a ***p*** sublevel.

As there is no ***p*** sublevel for the first energy level, the two elements of the first period correspond to the filling of the 1***s*** sublevel. The eight elements in the second period correspond to the step-wise filling of the 2***s*** and 2***p*** sublevels. Similarly the eight elements in the third period correspond to the filling of the 3***s*** and 3***p*** sublevels. (As we mentioned in Section 3.14, the ***d*** sublevel of one energy level does not fill until after the ***s*** sublevel of the next energy level.) The table that we can construct for the first three periods is shown in Figure 4.4.

The fourth period starts with the filling of the 4***s*** sublevel; however, the 3***d*** sublevel then fills before the 4***p*** sublevel. This period therefore contains eighteen elements. We find the same pattern is true for the fifth period, during which the 5***s***, 4***d***, and 5***p*** sublevels are filled. To accommodate the ten extra elements in each long period, the table has to be split between the Group IIA and Group IIIA elements (Figure 4.5). To show that hydrogen does not have the same properties as the Group IA elements, we have moved it into the middle of the top row.

	IA	IIA											IIIA	IVA	VA	VIA	VIIA	0
1							1 H											2 He
2	3 Li	4 Be											5 B	6 C	7 N	8 O	9 F	10 Ne
3	11 Na	12 Mg											13 Al	14 Si	15 P	16 S	17 Cl	18 Ar
4	19 K	20 Ca	21 Sc	22 Ti	23 V	24 Cr	25 Mn	26 Fe	27 Co	28 Ni	29 Cu	30 Zn	31 Ga	32 Ge	33 As	34 Se	35 Br	36 Kr
5	37 Rb	38 Sr	39 Y	40 Zr	41 Nb	42 Mo	43 Tc	44 Ru	45 Rh	46 Pd	47 Ag	48 Cd	49 In	50 Sn	51 Sb	52 Te	53 I	54 Xe

Figure 4.5
The first five periods of the Periodic Table.

With the sixth and seventh periods, we have to incorporate the ***f*** sublevels. Thus the sixth period corresponds to the filling of the 6***s***, 4***f***, 5***d***, and 6***p*** sublevels and the seventh period to the filling of the 7***s***, 5***f***, 6***d***, and 7***p*** sublevels. To incorporate these extra-long periods, we again have to split the table. This gives us the complete, long form of the Periodic Table (Figure 4.6).

To make the Periodic Table more compact, the elements 58 to 71 and 90 to 103 are usually placed below the main part of the table. The gaps between elements 57 and 72, and between elements 89 and 104 are then closed. We will be using this version of the table in subsequent discussions. (See inside front cover.)

As Mendeléev's table does not show the continuity of the atomic numbers, many people have tried to develop better ways of displaying the periodicity of the elements. A very useful format was devised by Charles Janet in 1928. Although Janet's version has many advantages over Mendeléev's, variations of Mendeléev's design are used for most purposes.

Figure 4.6
The complete Periodic Table.

	IA	IIA																									IIIA	IVA	VA	VIA	VIIA	0
1															1 H																	2 He
2	3 Li	4 Be																									5 B	6 C	7 N	8 O	9 F	10 Ne
3	11 Na	12 Mg																									13 Al	14 Si	15 P	16 S	17 Cl	18 Ar
4	19 K	20 Ca	21 Sc															22 Ti	23 V	24 Cr	25 Mn	26 Fe	27 Co	28 Ni	29 Cu	30 Zn	31 Ga	32 Ge	33 As	34 Se	35 Br	36 Kr
5	37 Rb	38 Sr	39 Y															40 Zr	41 Nb	42 Mo	43 Tc	44 Ru	45 Rh	46 Pd	47 Ag	48 Cd	49 In	50 Sn	51 Sb	52 Te	53 I	54 Xe
6	55 Cs	56 Ba	57 La	58 Ce	59 Pr	60 Nd	61 Pm	62 Sm	63 Eu	64 Gd	65 Tb	66 Dy	67 Ho	68 Er	69 Tm	70 Yb	71 Lu	72 Hf	73 Ta	74 W	75 Re	76 Os	77 Ir	78 Pt	79 Au	80 Hg	81 Tl	82 Pb	83 Bi	84 Po	85 At	86 Rn
7	87 Fr	88 Ra	89 Li	90 Th	91 Pa	92 U	93 Np	94 Pu	95 Am	96 Cm	97 Bk	98 Cf	99 Es	100 Fm	101 Md	102 No	103 Lr	104 Unq	105 Unp	106 Unh	107 Uns	108 Uno	109 Une									

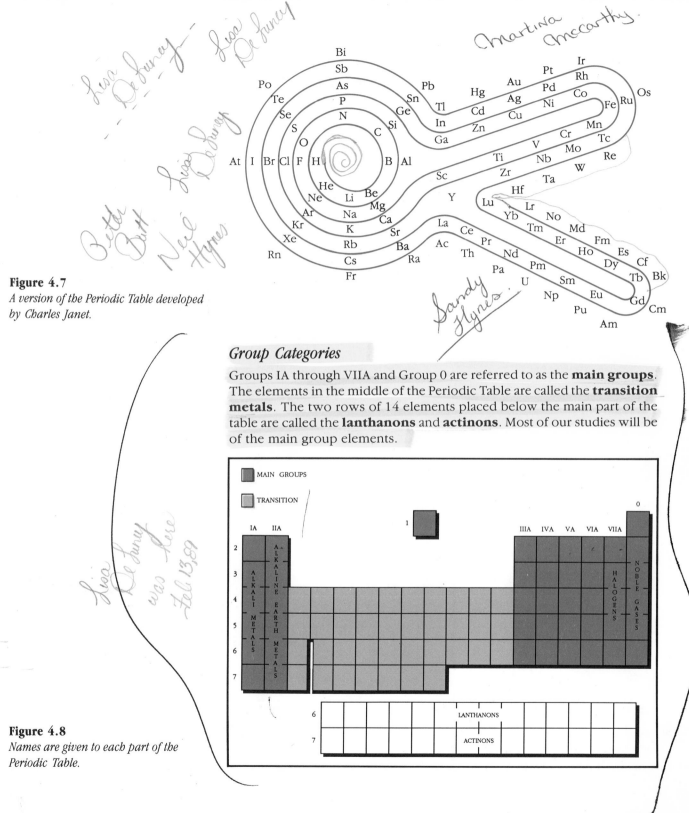

Figure 4.7
A version of the Periodic Table developed by Charles Janet.

Group Categories

Groups IA through VIIA and Group 0 are referred to as the **main groups**. The elements in the middle of the Periodic Table are called the **transition metals**. The two rows of 14 elements placed below the main part of the table are called the **lanthanons** and **actinons**. Most of our studies will be of the main group elements.

Figure 4.8
Names are given to each part of the Periodic Table.

Four of the main groups of elements have specific names: the Group IA elements are the **alkali metals**; the Group IIA elements are the **alkaline earth metals**; the Group VIIA elements are the **halogens**; and the Group 0 elements are the **noble gases**.

QUESTIONS

2. To which group (e.g. lanthanons, halogens) do each of the following elements belong:

a) lead   c) sodium   e) uranium

b) neon   d) iron   f) chlorine

The Number of Chemical Elements   4.3

It is unlikely that any more naturally occurring elements will be found in the universe. The stability of an atom is determined by the composition of its nucleus, and there appears to be a maximum number of protons that a nucleus can contain and remain stable. This upper limit seems to be 83 protons (the element bismuth). Only 81 elements have stable isotopes. Two elements with lower atomic numbers than bismuth have no stable isotopes. These are technetium (atomic number 43) and promethium (atomic number 61).

All elements with atomic numbers greater than 83 are unstable. Atoms of these elements disintegrate at a rate that is not influenced by temperature, pressure, or any other physical or chemical effect. The stability of the ele-

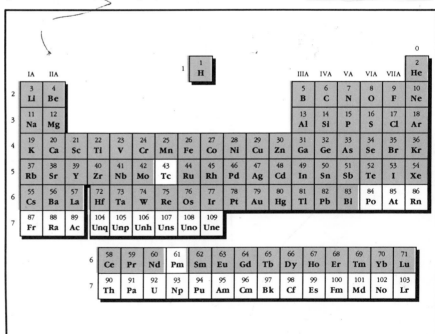

Figure 4.9

There are only 81 elements (shaded) that have stable isotopes.

ments above atomic number 88 decreases as the atomic number increases. This stability is expressed in terms of the half-life of the element. The **half-life** is the time required for half the nuclei in a sample of an element to disintegrate and form different elements. The greater the half-life, the more stable the element. The half-life of uranium-238 is 10^9 years; that of californium-249 is 360 years, and that of lawrencium-257 is eight seconds.

Nuclear physicists claim to have synthesized atoms of elements with atomic numbers as high as 109. These elements have extremely short half-lives. Because only a few atoms of most of these short-lived elements have been prepared, their chemical and physical properties have not been determined. As any elements discovered in the future will probably disintegrate at even faster rates, it is unlikely that the Periodic Table will be extended by more than a few more short-lived elements.

Names of New Elements

It is normal practice for the discoverer of an element to propose a name for it. In recent years this practice has caused difficulties, as different groups of scientists in the Soviet Union and the United States have simultaneously claimed to have synthesized identical new elements. Thus the elements with numbers 104 and 105 were named kurchatovium (Ku) and nielsbohrium (Nl) by the Soviet scientists, and rutherfordium (Rf) and hahnium (Ha) by the Americans.

An international commission has been assigned the task of deciding the official name and symbol of each newly discovered element. At the time of writing this text, the commission had not decided which claim of first discovery of elements 104 and 105 would be accepted. To prevent future problems, the commission has proposed that provisional names and symbols be given to newly synthesized elements until definitive names have been adopted. The provisional names are Latin–Greek hybrids for the atomic numbers of the elements. For example, unnilquadium (Unq) is used as the name for element 104, unnilpentium (Unp) for element 105, and unnilhexium (Unh) for element 106.

The Abundance of the Elements 4.4

Hydrogen is the most abundant element. Of all atoms in the universe, 92.5% are hydrogen atoms! In the past, this percentage may have been even higher. It is believed that all the other elements were produced from hydrogen as a result of nuclear reactions within stars. Helium is the second most abundant element, comprising 7.4% of the atoms in the universe. In general, elements become less abundant as atomic number increases. For example, the abundances of the Group VIA elements are as follows: oxygen, 6×10^{-2}%; sulfur, 1×10^{-3}%; selenium, 3×10^{-7}%; and tellurium, 2×10^{-8}%.

The abundance of an element in the earth and its atmosphere can be quite different from its abundance in the universe. Most of the low-density gases, hydrogen and helium, escaped from the earth's atmosphere millions of years ago leaving nitrogen (78%) and oxygen (21%) as the two major components of the present atmosphere. Most of the hydrogen that remains on the earth is combined with oxygen in the form of water.

If we study the earth's crust (the layers of rock in the top 10 km of the land surface) we find that the most abundant element is oxygen (60%), with silicon (20%) the next most abundant. None of the silicon exists as the pure element. Instead, it is found in combination with other elements in compounds such as silicon dioxide (sand or quartz). Many types of rocks contain oxygen, silicon, and one or more of the other most abundant elements. These elements are aluminum (6%), hydrogen (3%), magnesium (2%), calcium (2%), sodium (2%), iron (2%), and potassium (1%). These percentages are average values for the abundances of the elements in the earth's crust. If all the rarer elements were distributed uniformly throughout the crust, it would never be economical to mine them. Fortunately, many of the less abundant elements are concentrated in specific types of rock in a few locations. One of the major tasks of geologists and geochemists is to find these deposits.

Physical Properties of the Elements

4.5

Elements can be classified according to their phases at normal temperatures. The majority of the elements exist as solids. The Periodic Table in Figure 4.11 shows the phase of each element at room temperature. We see that the elements that exist as gases at this temperature are clustered in the upper right-hand corner of the Periodic Table. Only two elements, bromine and mercury, are liquids at room temperature. Three other elements, cesium and francium of Group IA, and gallium of Group IIIA, melt between 25 °C and 30 °C. Thus, depending on the definition of room temperature, it could be argued that there are as many as five liquid elements.

The elements can also be divided into metals and nonmetals. Metals are shiny and conduct heat and electricity. They can also be beaten into sheets (i.e., they are malleable) and drawn into wires (i.e., they are ductile). All the metals except mercury are solids at room temperature (20 °C).

With the exception of one form of carbon, nonmetals do not show any of the above properties. In general, the solid nonmetals are brittle and brightly colored. Several nonmetals exist as gases at room temperature.

Classifying elements as metals or nonmetals is often convenient, and a thick line is drawn on many Periodic Tables to show the division between the two classes. In reality, however, there is no sharp dividing line between metals and nonmetals. There is, instead, a border area in which we see a gradual change in the properties of elements from metallic to nonmetallic. The elements in this border area are poor conductors of electricity and are shiny and brittle. They are called **semimetals** or metalloids. You can see that the semimetals form a steplike pattern diagonally through the right side of the Periodic Table. This means that in a group such as VA, the prop-

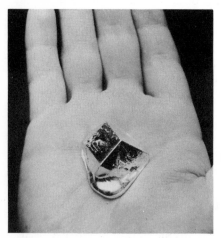

Figure 4.10
A block of gallium metal melting at body temperature. Gallium is one of the three elements with melting points between 25 °C and 30 °C.

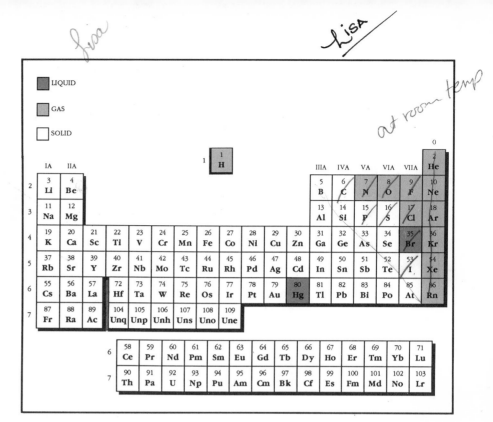

Figure 4.11
The phases of the elements at 20 °C.

Figure 4.12
Bromine, a dense, oily, reddish-brown liquid, is the only nonmetallic element in liquid form at room temperature.

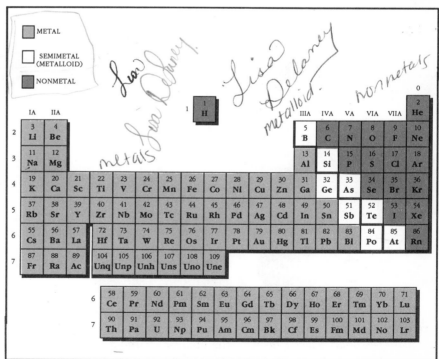

Figure 4.13
Classification of the elements into metals, semimetals (metalloids) and nonmetals. The thick black line shows the simpler division into metals and nonmetals.

erties of the elements in the group change from nonmetallic at the top (N, P), through semimetallic (As, Sb), to metallic at the bottom (Bi).

QUESTIONS

3. Of the 88 naturally occurring elements what percentage are
  a) nonmetals   b) semimetals

4. At 20 °C, what percentage of the naturally occurring elements are
  a) liquids   b) gases

Periodic Trends — Atomic Radius   4.6

The change in the properties of the elements from nonmetallic for the elements at the top right-hand corner of the table to metallic for the elements at the bottom left-hand corner is one general trend in the Periodic Table. Many other properties of the elements vary systematically as a result of the changing electron configuration across each period and down each group.

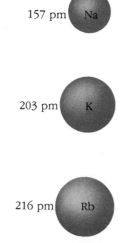

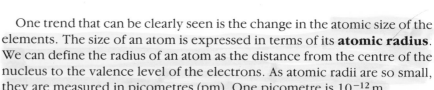

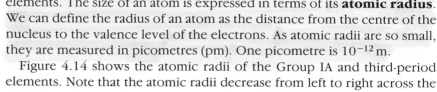

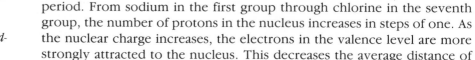

One trend that can be clearly seen is the change in the atomic size of the elements. The size of an atom is expressed in terms of its **atomic radius**. We can define the radius of an atom as the distance from the centre of the nucleus to the valence level of the electrons. As atomic radii are so small, they are measured in picometres (pm). One picometre is 10^{-12} m.

Figure 4.14 shows the atomic radii of the Group IA and third-period elements. Note that the atomic radii decrease from left to right across the period. From sodium in the first group through chlorine in the seventh group, the number of protons in the nucleus increases in steps of one. As the nuclear charge increases, the electrons in the valence level are more strongly attracted to the nucleus. This decreases the average distance of

Figure 4.14
Atomic radii of the Group IA and third-period elements.

the valence electrons from the nucleus. Consequently, there is a decrease in the size of the atoms.

As we can see from Figure 4.14, atomic radii increase as we go down Group IA. A similar trend is also observed in all the other groups. This increase in size as a group is descended can be explained in terms of the Bohr model of the atom. For example, lithium is at the top of Group IA and its only valence electron is in the second ($n = 2$) energy level. Next is sodium, with its valence electron in the third ($n = 3$) level, followed by potassium with its valence electron in the fourth ($n = 4$) level, and so on. You will recall that, as the principal quantum number increases, the energy levels are further from the nucleus. Thus, as we descend Group IA, we find that with each successive element the distance between the valence electron and the nucleus (i.e., the atomic radius) increases.

QUESTIONS

5. For each of the following pairs of atoms, predict which atom will be the larger:
   a) oxygen or sulfur   b) nitrogen or oxygen

Periodic Trends — Ionization Energy and Electron Affinity   4.7

Closely related to the size of the atom is a property known as **ionization energy**. The *first* ionization energy of an element is defined as the amount of energy required to remove the most weakly held electron from a neutral gaseous atom of that element. Using sodium as an example, we can represent this process as follows:

$$\text{Na}_{(g)} + \text{energy} \longrightarrow \text{Na}^+{}_{(g)} + e^-$$

where $\text{Na}_{(g)}$ represents a sodium atom in the gas phase, $\text{Na}^+{}_{(g)}$ represents a positively charged sodium **ion** in the gas phase, and e^- represents an electron. The second ionization energy is similarly defined as the energy required to remove a second electron, and so on. We use the SI unit the joule (symbol J), to measure energy. Ionization energy data are usually reported as the energy required to remove one electron from each atom in one mole of an element. As this is a large quantity of energy, ionization energy values are expressed in megajoules per mole ($MJ \cdot mol^{-1}$). One megajoule is 10^6 J or one million joules.

Figure 4.15 shows the first ionization energies of the elements in the third period and Group IA of the Periodic Table. From these we can make a general observation that the first ionization energies of metals are lower than those of nonmetals. Note that the ionization energy decreases down the group. The decrease is related to the increase in the size of the atoms from the top to the bottom of a group. As the atomic radius increases the valence electron removed in the ionization process is progressively further from the nucleus. The attraction between the negative electron and the

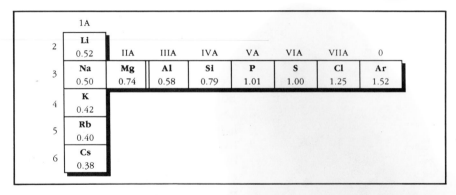

Figure 4.15

The first ionization energies of the Group IA and third period elements (MJ·mol⁻¹).

positive nucleus thus becomes weaker. meaning that less energy is required to remove the valence electron from the atom.

The general increase in ionization energy as we move from left to right across a period is caused by a decrease in atomic radius. As the atomic radius decreases, the valence electrons are more strongly attracted to the nucleus and more energy is needed to remove an electron and form an ion.

If we plot a graph of atomic number against first ionization energy for the first twenty elements, the periodic trend can be seen more clearly (Figure 4.16). The deviations from the expected general increase across a period are evidence of the energy sublevels discussed in Section 3.14. For example, the first ionization energy decrease at each Group IIIA element corresponds to the removal of a lone *p* electron. This *p* electron is in a slightly higher energy level, and will be held more weakly than the second *s* electron that has to be removed in the preceding Group IIA elements.

The ionization of oxygen and sulfur involves the removal of one of four *p* electrons. In each case, the ionization energy of each of these elements is lower than that of the preceding element (i.e. nitrogen and phosphorus, respectively). This fact can be explained by assuming that a *p* sublevel containing three electrons is more stable that a *p* sublevel containing four

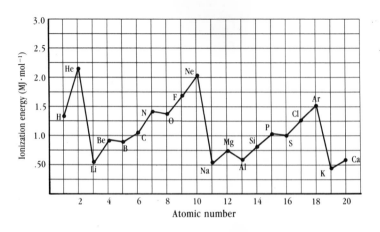

Figure 4.16

The ionization energies of the first twenty elements.

electrons. We generally associate stability with sublevels that are empty, half-filled, or full; even though half-filled sublevels are less stable than those which are full or empty.

Multiple Ionization Energies

As we mentioned at the beginning of this section, an atom has more than one ionization energy. For any atom, the number of ionization energies is the same as the number of electrons present in that atom. We can measure the energy required to remove each of the electrons in an atom. Table 4.2 shows all the ionization energies for lithium, beryllium, and boron, the elements at the beginning of the second period of the Periodic Table.

TABLE 4.2	*Ionization Energies for Lithium, Beryllium and Boron* $(MJ \cdot mol^{-1})$				
	Ionization Energies				
Element	1st	2nd	3rd	4th	5th
Lithium	0.5	7.3	11.8		
Beryllium	0.9	1.8	14.8	21.0	
Boron	0.8	2.4	3.7	25.0	32.8

As each successive electron is removed, the ionization energy increases. Notice that it is much easier to remove electrons from the valence level that it is from the inner energy levels. There is always a large difference between the amount of energy required to remove the last valence electron and that required to remove the first electron from the next highest energy level.

Electron Affinity

Just as it is possible to form a positively charged ion by removing an electron from a neutral atom, so we can form a negatively charged ion by adding an electron to an atom. Using fluorine as an example, we can represent this process as follows:

$$F_{(g)} + e^- \longrightarrow F^-_{(g)} + \text{energy}$$

Energy is usually released in this process. This energy is called the **electron affinity** of the atom.

As we go from left to right across a period in the Periodic Table, we observe that the amount of energy released when an electron is added to a neutral atom increases. In other words, the electron affinity increases. A general consequence of this fact is that the electron affinities of the metals are lower than those of the nonmetals.

We should note a subtle difference between ionization energy and electron affinity. A large value for an ionization energy indicates that the removal of an electron is difficult, and that the formation of a positive ion is unlikely to occur. On the other hand, a large value for electron affinity indicates that much energy is released when a negative ion is formed by the addition of an electron, and that such a process is very likely to occur.

QUESTIONS

6. Why do the noble gases have high first ionization energies?
7. Why does the first ionization energy for the noble gases decrease when moving down Group 0 from helium to radon?
8. Why would you expect there to be a large increase between the fourth and fifth ionization energies of carbon?

Periodic Trends 4.8 — Ionic Radius

When we form a sodium ion, Na^+, by removing the valence electron from a sodium atom, we find that the ion formed is much smaller than the parent atom (Figure 4.17). In other words, the **ionic radius** of a sodium ion is less than the atomic radius of a sodium atom. This observation is just what we would expect from the Bohr model of the atom. The outermost electrons in the sodium ion are located in the second ($n = 2$) energy level, whereas the outermost electron in a neutral sodium atom is in the third ($n = 3$) energy level. As the third energy level is further from the nucleus than the second energy level, it naturally follows that a sodium atom will be larger than a positively–charged sodium ion.

A similar observation can be made for the positive ions formed by each of the Group IA elements. A comparison of the radii of these ions shows that there is an increase in size as we go down the group (Figure 4.18). This increase can be understood if we realize that, for each successive ion in the group, the outermost occupied energy level is further from the nucleus.

Let us now compare the radii of the ions formed when we remove all the valence electrons from each of the first three members of the third period. We have already discussed sodium and have seen that the removal of its one valence electron produces an Na^+ ion. If we remove both of the valence electrons from a magnesium atom we obtain an Mg^{2+} ion. Note that the charge on this ion is +2 because it contains two more protons than electrons. Similarly, the removal of the three valence electrons from an aluminum atom produces an Al^{3+} ion.

Figure 4.17
Removing the one valence electron from a sodium atom leaves a much smaller ion.

157 pm

98 pm

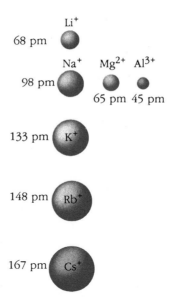

Figure 4.18
The radii of selected positive ions also show a periodic trend.

Figure 4.18 shows that, of these three ions, Na^+ is the largest and Al^{3+} is the smallest. How can this be explained? Each of the three ions, Na^+, Mg^{2+}, and Al^{3+}, contains ten electrons. However, the sodium ion contains eleven protons, the magnesium ion twelve protons, and the aluminum ion thirteen protons. Each electron in a sodium ion therefore experiences less attraction than an electron in a magnesium ion, and each electron in a magnesium ion experiences less attraction than an electron in an aluminum ion. Thus, the radius of these ions decreases in the order $Na^+ > Mg^{2+} > Al^{3+}$.

Figure 4.19
Adding an electron to the valence level of chlorine gives an ion which is much larger than the original atom.

Before we leave the subject of ionic radius, let us consider the case of chlorine. Instead of forming a positive ion by losing one or more of its valence electrons, chlorine gains an electron and forms a negatively charged ion. Chlorine does this because of its high electron affinity. The ion formed in this manner is larger than the neutral chlorine atom itself. This is because each of the *eighteen* electrons present in the ion experiences the attraction of the seventeen protons in the nucleus, whereas in the neutral atom there are only *seventeen* electrons experiencing the attraction of the same number of protons. The attraction on each electron is greater in the atom than it is in the ion. Thus, the ion has the larger radius.

9. A sulfur atom has a radius of 104 pm while that of an S^{2-} ion is 190 pm. Explain why the negative ion is larger than the neutral atom.

10. The atomic radius of a calcium atom is 197 pm, whereas the ionic radius of a Ca^{2+} ion is 99 pm. Why is the positive ion smaller than the neutral atom?

Summary

- In the Periodic Table elements are arranged in order of increasing atomic number.

- Horizontal rows of elements are called periods and vertical columns are called groups or families. Elements in the same group have similar properties.

- The group number matches the number of valence electrons possessed by each element in the group.

- Groups IA through VIIA and Group 0 are called the main groups. Elements in Groups IB through VIIB and Group VIII are called the transition metals. The two rows of elements placed below the main part of the table are called the lanthanons and actinons.

- The following groups have specific names — Group IA, alkali metals; Group IIA, alkaline earth metals; Group VIIA, halogens; and Group 0, noble gases.

- All elements with atomic numbers greater than 83 are unstable.

- All elements can be classified as either metals or nonmetals.

- The following properties show periodic variation as a result of changing electron configuration:
  a) metallic/nonmetallic character
  b) atomic and ionic radii
  c) ionization energy
  d) electron affinity

KEY WORDS

actinons	ionization energy
alkali metals	lanthanons
alkaline earth metals	Law of Octaves
atomic radius	main groups
electron affinity	noble gases
group	period
half-life	Periodic Law
halogens	semimetals
ion	transition metals
ionic radius	triad

1. By averaging the melting points of sodium and rubidium, we would predict a melting point of about 68 °C for potassium. (In fact, it is 63 °C.)

2. a) main groups   c) alkali metals   e) actinons
   b) noble gases   d) transition metals   f) halogens

3. a) 18.2%   b) 6.8%

4. a) 2.3%   b) 12.5%

5. a) sulfur   b) nitrogen

6. Because they have full p sublevels.

7. Down the group, electrons are placed in energy levels further from the nucleus. These electrons become easier to remove as their attraction to the nucleus decreases with the increase in atomic radius.

8. Because carbon has 4 valence electrons. The 5th electron comes from a full s sublevel.

9. An S^{2-} ion is larger than a neutral S atom because the addition of two electrons means that all the electrons experience less pull from the nucleus.

10. A Ca^{2+} ion is smaller than a neutral Ca atom because the outermost electrons in the Ca atom are in the fourth energy level, whereas the outermost electrons in the Ca^{2+} ion are in the third energy level.

---

1. Give the common names used to describe the following:
   a) Group IA   b) Group 0   c) The B-group elements

2. To what group of elements do each of the following belong:
   a) calcium   c) uranium
   b) iodine   d) iron

3. On what basis are the elements arranged in the modern Periodic Table?

4. What is meant by each of the following terms:
   a) period   b) group number   c) family
   d) main group elements

5. List the properties common to metals.

6. Classify each of the following elements as metals, nonmetals, or semimetals:
   a) sodium   c) oxygen   e) tellurium
   b) mercury   d) silicon   f) cerium

7. Indicate whether the following properties increase or decrease from left to right across the Periodic Table:
   a) atomic radius (excluding noble gases)
   b) first ionization energy
   c) electron affinity

8. Indicate whether the following properties increase or decrease as we descend a group in the Periodic Table:
   a) ionic radius
   b) metallic character
   c) first ionization energy

9. Name the elements that are liquid at room temperature (20 °C).

10. Name the elements that are gases at room temperature.

PROBLEMS 11. Give two reasons why it would have been difficult to develop a Periodic Table before about 1850.

12. Why did Mendeléev use atomic mass rather than atomic number to arrange the elements in his Periodic Table?

13. Which elements
    a) have a single s electron in the valence level
    b) have an s^2p^5 arrangement in the valence level
    c) correspond to the filling of the d sublevels
    d) correspond to the filling of the $4f$ sublevels

14. What is the relationship between Newlands' Law of Octaves and the modern Periodic Table? (Remember that the noble gases had not been discovered in Newlands' time.)

15. How many valence electrons are present in an atom of
    a) calcium   b) silicon   c) cesium   d) iodine

16. Give the name of an element which has
    a) three valence electrons   c) two valence electrons
    b) four valence electrons   d) seven valence electrons

17. Tellurium (atomic mass 127.6 u) is placed before iodine (atomic mass 126.9 u) in the Periodic Table. Explain the reason for this apparently anomalous order.

18. On the basis of atomic mass values, argon should be a member of the alkali metals and potassium should appear in Group 0. Explain why this is not the case.

19. Melting points and boiling points show periodic trends similar to other properties of the elements. Using the data below, what would you suggest as approximate values for the melting and boiling points of the radioactive halogen astatine?

Halogen	m.pt. (°C)	b.pt. (°C)
Fluorine	−220	−118
Chlorine	−101	−34
Bromine	−7	58
Iodine	114	183
Astatine	?	?

20. The element with atomic number 119 has not yet been isolated. To which group would it belong? Would it be a gas, liquid, or solid? A metal or nonmetal? Reactive or nonreactive? Briefly explain your reasoning.

21. Using the Periodic Table, determine the more metallic element in each of the following pairs:
    a) phosphorus and arsenic
    b) silicon and aluminum
    c) fluorine and astatine

22. Using the Periodic Table, determine which element in each of the following pairs is the least metallic:
    a) boron and carbon
    b) carbon and tin
    c) lithium and beryllium

23. For each of the following pairs, predict which element will have the larger atomic radius and which will have the higher first ionization energy:
    a) sodium and aluminum
    b) magnesium and barium
    c) hydrogen and helium

24. In general, which group of elements in each of the following pairs would have the lower first ionization energy:
    a) metals or nonmetals
    b) alkali metals or halogens
    c) noble gases or alkali metals

25. The first, second, and third ionization energies for a certain element are $0.736 \, MJ \cdot mol^{-1}$, $1.45 \, MJ \cdot mol^{-1}$, and $7.72 \, MJ \cdot mol^{-1}$, respectively.
    a) In which group of the Periodic Table would you expect to find this element? Why?
    b) Would you expect the fourth ionization energy to be greater or smaller than $7.72 \, MJ \cdot mol^{-1}$?

26. Between which ionization energies would you expect there to be a large increase for each of the following elements:
    a) potassium
    b) aluminum
    c) phosphorus

SUGGESTED PROJECTS

1. Use reference books to gather the following information about the noble gases:
   a) names, symbols, when they were discovered, and by whom
   b) physical properties
   c) reactivity
   d) where they are found
   e) their uses

2. With the help of your teacher obtain samples of as many of the elements as you possibly can. Prepare a large copy of the Periodic Table and display the elements in their proper position. Make sure that hazardous elements are properly sealed in a suitable container.

Chemical Compounds and Bonding

In the last chapter, we introduced you to the chemical elements. As we mentioned in Chapter 1, elements combine to form compounds. More than ten million different compounds have already been identified, and every week about 6000 new compounds are reported. To begin our study of chemical compounds, we will investigate the forces that hold the atoms together in a compound. These forces are called chemical **bonds**. A knowledge of the type, or types, of bonds in a compound will help us as we try to understand the behaviour and properties of the millions of chemical compounds.

A Conductivity Experiment 5.1

We can obtain information about chemical bonds by performing a simple experiment to find out what kinds of substances conduct electricity. The apparatus consists of a beaker, two electrodes (strips of metal, such as copper or aluminum), a battery, and a light bulb and holder.

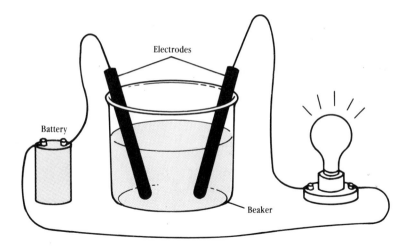

Figure 5.1

Simple apparatus for testing the conductivity of a solution.

Figure 5.2

When pure water is placed in an apparatus designed to test conductivity, the light bulb does not glow; pure water is a poor conductor of electricity.

We connect the apparatus to form a circuit similar to that shown in Figure 5.1. The circuit is not complete until we have a connection between the electrodes. First, we place pure (distilled) water in the beaker. We see that the light bulb does not glow, and from this observation we can conclude that pure water does not conduct electricity. (In fact, a very small current of electricity does flow, but it is not large enough to light the bulb.

If we next dissolve a spoonful of table salt (chemical name, sodium chloride) in the water, we see that the light bulb glows brightly. This indicates that the solution of table salt is conducting electricity. Substances that form conducting solutions are called **electrolytes**, and the solutions are called electrolytic solutions. If we repeat the experiment using a spoonful of baking soda (chemical name, sodium hydrogen carbonate), the light bulb again glows brightly. At this stage, we might be tempted to conclude that all substances, when added to water, allow an electric current to flow.

However, if we repeat the experiment by dissolving a spoonful of table sugar (chemical name, sucrose) in the water, we find that the bulb does not light up. A sugar solution does not conduct electricity: sugar is a **non-electrolyte**. Only by testing a large number of compounds can we discover what it is about a compound that determines whether it is an electrolyte or not.

Notice that the chemicals we used in our experiment all dissolved in water to form solutions. If we try to use substances such as sand (silicon dioxide) or chalk (calcium carbonate) that do not dissolve in water, we find that the light bulb does not glow. We can conclude, therefore, that in order to be an electrolyte a substance must first be able to dissolve in water.

We find that there are three categories of substances which, when dissolved in water, conduct electricity. The compounds in the first of these categories are called salts. A **salt** is usually a combination of a metallic element and one or more nonmetallic elements. We used two salts in our experiment: table salt and baking soda. The second category of compounds that behave as electrolytes consists of acids. Sulfuric acid, which is used in car batteries, and acetic acid (vinegar) are examples of acids. The third category consists of bases. An example of a base is sodium hydroxide, the compound used in oven and drain cleaners.

Substances that do dissolve in water but do not form solutions that conduct electricity include water itself, sugar, and alcohol (ethanol).

(a)

(b)

Figure 5.3

Testing the conductivity of some solutions:

a) *Placing the electrodes in a solution of table salt causes the light bulb to glow brightly; table salt is an electrolyte;*

b) *Placing the electrodes in a solution of sugar does not cause the light bulb to glow; sugar is a nonelectrolyte.*

TABLE 5.1	*Substances Classified on the Basis of Results Obtained in Conductivity Experiments*	
Electrolytes		**Nonelectrolytes**
Sodium chloride (table salt)		Water
Sodium hydrogen carbonate (baking soda)		Sucrose (table sugar)
Sulfuric acid (battery acid)		Ethanol (alcohol)
Sodium hydroxide (oven and drain cleaner)		

Ions   5.2

[handwritten: Octet Rule — element is stable with a full shell of eight e⁻]

We now need to find an explanation for the results of our conductivity experiment. What property is it that enables electrolytes to conduct electricity when they are dissolved in water? A Swedish chemist, Svante Arrhenius, first proposed what is now accepted as the explanation.

Arrhenius suggested that, when an electrolyte is dissolved in water, two types of ions are formed: one with a positive charge, called a **cation**; and one with a negative charge, called an **anion**. He further suggested that ions are responsible for carrying current when an electrolytic solution conducts electricity. A corollary to these proposals is the following:
when a non-electrolyte dissolves in water, no ions are formed.

Figure 5.4
Svante Arrhenius (1859–1927) postulated that charged ions were formed when salts, acids, or bases dissolved in water. He received the Nobel Prize for Chemistry in 1903.

As we saw in Section 4.7, ions are formed when a neutral atom either gains or loses electrons. If one or more electrons are gained, then an anion is formed; if, on the other hand, one or more electrons are lost, a cation is produced.

Immediately, a number of questions arise: Can we predict if an atom will gain or lose electrons? If so, how many electrons will it gain or lose? What is the driving force behind the gain or loss of electrons? By answering the last question we can also answer the first two.

Gilbert N. Lewis, in the United States, and Walter Kossel, in Germany, were the first to suggest that the driving force behind the formation of ions is the tendency of an atom to reach a more stable electron configuration. Stability is attained by an atom acquiring a completely full or a completely empty valence level. The most stable electron configurations are those of the elements in Group 0 (sometimes called Group VIIIA) of the Periodic Table. These elements are helium (He), neon (Ne), argon (Ar), krypton (Kr), xenon (Xe), and radon (Rn). They are known as the noble gases, and their electron configurations are often referred to as **noble-gas configurations**.

We can illustrate the importance of the noble-gas configuration by looking at the ions formed from sodium and fluorine atoms. Sodium has one valence electron. By losing this electron, the resulting sodium ion will have the same electron configuration as neon. We can represent this process using electron-dot formulas:

$$\text{Na}\cdot \longrightarrow [\text{Na}]^+ + e^-$$

Fluorine has seven valence electrons. By gaining an electron, the resulting fluorine ion, F^-, will also have the same electron configuration as neon. This process can be represented as follows:

$$:\ddot{\text{F}}\cdot + e^- \longrightarrow [:\ddot{\text{F}}:]^-$$

When naming simple anions, we change the ending of the element name to *-ide*. Thus the negative ion formed from a fluorine atom is called a fluoride ion.

Positive ions are only formed by atoms with one, two, or three valence electrons. Removal of these valence electrons produces a positive ion with an empty valence level. Negative ions are formed when an atom that has five, six, or seven valence electrons accepts additional electrons to obtain the same electron configuration as the next noble gas in the Periodic

Figure 5.5
The formation of ions from a neutral atom.

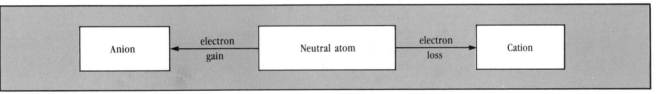

Anion		Neutral atom		Cation
	electron gain		electron loss	

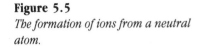

Table. Thus, a negative ion will usually have eight electrons in its valence shell and a positive ion will usually have an empty valence shell. Elements that have four or more valence electrons can also acquire a noble-gas configuration in another way, which we will describe in Section 5.5.

Hydrogen is a special case. It can give up an electron to form a cation, H^+, which is a nucleus without electrons (i.e., a proton), or it can gain an electron to form an anion H^-, which has the same electron configuration as helium.

EXAMPLE **5.1** Write the electron-dot formulas for the ions that are most likely to be formed by

a) oxygen   b) magnesium

SOLUTION a) As oxygen is a Group VIA element, we can immediately say that it has six valence electrons. By *gaining* two electrons, it can acquire the same electron configuration as neon, the nearest noble gas. We can represent this acquisition as follows:

$$\cdot \ddot{O} \cdot + 2\,e^- \longrightarrow [:\ddot{O}:]^{2-}$$

b) As magnesium is a Group IIA element, it has two valence electrons. By *losing* two electrons, it can also acquire the electron configuration of neon. We can represent the process by

$$\cdot Mg \cdot \longrightarrow [Mg]^{2+} + 2\,e^-$$

We can represent the formula of an ion more compactly by simply writing the charge on the ion to the upper right of the symbol for the element. Thus the ions of sodium, magnesium, fluorine, and oxygen can be written as Na^+, Mg^{2+}, F^-, and O^{2-} (if the charge is $+1$ or -1, the number "1" is omitted).

QUESTIONS

1. In general, which elements will tend to form positive ions? Which tend to form negative ions?

2. Indicate whether the following elements would tend to gain or lose electrons to form an ion. How many electrons would be gained or lost in each case:
   a) sulfur   c) aluminum   e) rubidium
   b) barium   d) nitrogen   f) bromine

3. Write the electron-dot formulas for the ions formed by each of the following:
   a) chlorine   c) aluminum   e) sulfur
   b) calcium   d) potassium   f) phosphorus

Ions and our Health

Some of the ions we have discussed are essential for maintaining good health. The sodium ion (Na^+) and chloride ion (Cl^-) are both major components of blood plasma. The combined total mass of these two ions in the human body is about 200 g. A daily intake of about 5 g of sodium and chlorine ions (as sodium chloride) is required to maintain this level. Sodium and chloride ions are lost from the body through perspiration, and therefore in hot climates it is often necessary for people to take salt pills to restore the balance of these ions in their bodies. It is, however, believed that the diets of many people who live in temperate climates are too rich in sodium, as most prepared foods contain salt as a flavour enhancer. An excess of sodium chloride is implicated as a cause of high blood pressure and hypertension. Sodium chloride can also cause water retention, which results in swelling and a puffy appearance.

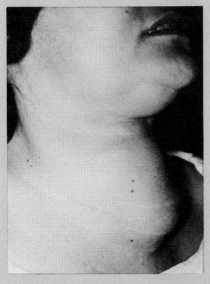

Figure 5.6
A lack of the iodide ion in the diet causes goitre.

The body also requires large quantities (about 1.5 to 4.5 g per day) of potassium ion (K^+). The main sources of potassium are vegetables and fruits, particularly bananas. Coffee also has a very high potassium content.

In the body the potassium ion is concentrated in the cells, whereas the sodium ion is concentrated in the blood plasma. Cells have a sodium-potassium "pump" to keep the potassium in and the sodium out, but the way in which this pump works is still not well understood. During transmission of a nerve impulse, potassium ions leave the cells while sodium ions flood in. Some antibiotics seem to work partly by helping to transport potassium ions into the cells.

The calcium ion (Ca^{2+}) is vital in the formation of bones and teeth. Most of the 0.8 g of calcium ion that is required daily by the body can be obtained from milk and milk products. A major cause of bone brittleness in older people is loss of calcium ion. It is therefore very important for people to maintain an adequate calcium intake throughout their lives.

Many other ions are important for our survival. For example, we require about 0.1 mg of iodide ion (I^-) every day to prevent goitre, a disease that results in enlargement of the thyroid gland. Our main sources of iodide ion are seafood and iodized salt.

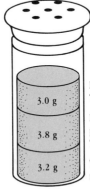

3.0 g	Naturally occurring in meat, eggs, milk, etc. This is unavoidable salt.
3.8 g	From foods to which salt is added during preparation e.g. bread, butter, margarine, cheese. This salt is avoidable only by changing our diet.
3.2 g	Table salt. This is purely discretionary and added merely as flavouring.

Figure 5.7
Dietary sources of salt. Although we require only about 5 g of salt per day, the average intake is about 10 g.

Introduction to Chemical Bonding   ## 5.3

If elements existed only as free atoms, the earth would be a lifeless conglomeration of iron, oxygen, silicon, and so on. This has not happened because atoms of different elements join together by means of chemical bonds to form compounds.

A chemical bond can be formed in two ways. The first, involving the *transfer* of electrons and the formation of ions, results in an **ionic bond**. Compounds formed in this manner are called ionic compounds. Their structure consists of ions arranged in a three-dimensional array called a **crystal lattice**.

In the second method of chemical bond formation, atoms *share* electrons to form **covalent bonds**. The compounds formed are called covalent compounds. The smallest unit of a covalent compound that retains all its chemical properties is called a **molecule**.

Ionic Bonding   ## 5.4

When a compound is formed from elements by the transfer of electrons, one element will lose electrons to form a cation and the other element will gain these electrons to form an anion. The (negative) anion and (positive) cation are then attracted to each other by electrostatic forces. We can illustrate this process by looking at the formation of sodium chloride from atoms of sodium and chlorine.

Sodium Chloride

As we saw in Section 5.2, the sodium atom can most easily acquire a noble-gas configuration by losing its one valence electron to give an ion with a $+1$ charge, that is, Na^+. The chlorine atom can most easily acquire a noble-gas configuration by adding one more electron to its seven valence electrons to give a chloride ion with a -1 charge, that is, Cl^-.

We can represent the formation of the ionic compound sodium chloride using electron-dot formulas:

$$Na\cdot + \cdot \ddot{\underset{..}{Cl}}\!: \longrightarrow [Na]^+ \; [:\ddot{\underset{..}{Cl}}\!:]^-$$

Note that when we write the electron-dot formula of an ionic compound, we must show that electron transfer has occurred. A space must be left between the symbols for the cation and anion, and the dots representing the electrons, including the transferred electrons, should be written close to the symbol of the element that forms the anion.

The Crystal Lattice.   A solid ionic compound, such as sodium chloride, consists of a three-dimensional array of positive and negative ions. This type of array is known as a crystal lattice.

Lithium (Li).

Sodium (Na) stored under oil.

Cesium (Cs).

Sodium Chloride (NaCl)
— halite.

Barium sulfate (BaSO$_4$)
crystals — barite.

The Group IA and IIA Elements

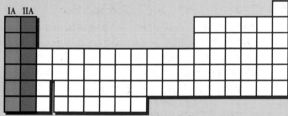

Calcium carbonate (CaCO$_3$)
crystals — calcite.

Magnesium (Mg) crystals.

Calcium (Ca).

Strontium (Sr).

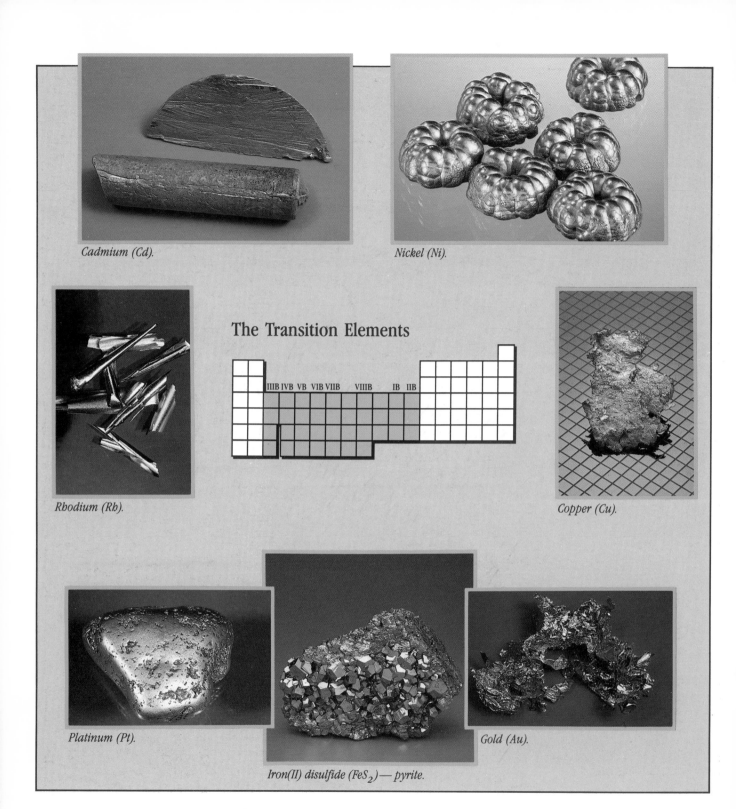

Cadmium (Cd).

Nickel (Ni).

The Transition Elements

| | IIIB | IVB | VB | VIB | VIIB | | VIIIB | | IB | IIB |

Rhodium (Rh).

Copper (Cu).

Platinum (Pt).

Gold (Au).

Iron(II) disulfide (FeS_2) — pyrite.

PLATE 2 — THE TRANSITION ELEMENTS

Silver (Ag).

Cobalt (Co).

Zinc (Zn).

Molybdenum (Mo).

Titanium (Ti).

Hydrated manganese oxide
— a seafloor "nodule".

Scandium (Sc).

Vanadium (V).

Niobium (Nb).

Chromium (Cr).

Boron (B).

Boron (B).

Indium (In).

The Group IIIA and IVA Elements

IIIA IVA

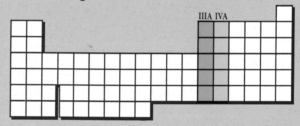

Aluminum oxide (Al$_2$O$_3$) — bauxite.

Gallium (Ga).

PLATE 4 — GROUP IIIA

Carbon (C) — diamond.

Carbon (C) — graphite.

Tin (Sn).

Lead (Pb).

Lead(II) sulfide (PbS) — galena.

Germanium (Ge).

Silicon dioxide (SiO$_2$) crystals — quartz.

Silicon (Si).

Diarsenic trisulfide (As$_2$S$_3$) — orpiment.

Antimony (Sb).

The Group VA and VIA Elements

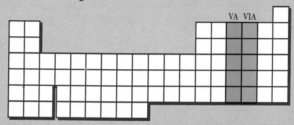

Bismuth (Bi).

White phosphorus (P) under water.

Arsenic (As).

PLATE 6 — GROUP VA

Sulfur (S).

Sulfur mining.

Sulfur (S) — rhombic crystals.

Selenium (Se).

Sulfur (S) — monoclinic crystals.

Tellurium (Te).

Iodine (I) vapour and crystals.

Bromine (Br) liquid and vapour.

Calcium fluoride (CaF$_2$) crystals — fluorite.

The Group VIIA and O (VIIIA) Elements

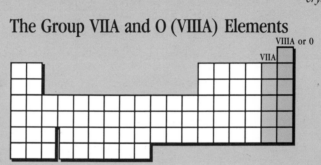

Krypton (Kr) lasers.

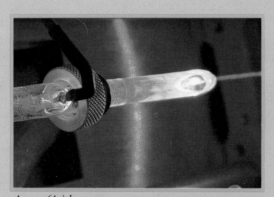

Argon (Ar) laser.

Neon (Ne) discharge tube.

PLATE 8 — GROUPS VIIA & O (VIIIA)

If we look closely at the sodium chloride lattice, we see that each sodium ion has six chloride ions equidistant from it and, similarly, each chloride ion has six sodium ions equidistant from it. Thus, it is impossible to say that a given chloride ion "belongs with" any specific sodium ion. All we can say is that sodium chloride contains equal numbers of sodium and chloride ions. Alternatively, we could say that the sodium and chloride ions are present in a 1:1 ratio.

Ionic compounds do not all have the same crystal lattice as the one shown. This is only one of many possible arrangements of ions in a crystal lattice.

The Formula of Sodium Chloride. In the ionic compound sodium chloride, the sodium and chloride ions are present in a 1:1 ratio. We can indicate this using a chemical formula. In the formula of an ionic compound, we use the symbols of each of the elements present to indicate the ratio of the ions in the crystal lattice. Thus, for sodium chloride we use the formula NaCl to tell us that there are equal numbers of sodium and chloride ions present.

Because ionic compounds do not exist as molecules, chemists use the **formula unit** to represent the smallest unit of an ionic compound that would still have the properties of that compound. Thus, one formula unit of sodium chloride consists of one chloride ion and one sodium ion. We use the formula NaCl to represent this unit. In practice, a formula unit of sodium chloride could not exist independently.

Figure 5.8
In a sodium chloride crystal, the sodium ions alternate with the chloride ions.

Calcium Chloride

Many elements require the loss or gain of more than one electron to form an ion with a stable electron configuration. One example is calcium, Ca, an element in Group IIA of the Periodic Table. Let us now see what happens in terms of electron configuration when a compound is formed between calcium and chlorine.

As calcium is located in Group IIA of the Periodic Table, it has two valence electrons. To acquire the same electron configuration as argon, the nearest noble gas, a calcium atom must lose the two electrons in its valence level to form a Ca^{2+} ion. Chlorine in Group VIIA, has seven valence electrons and only needs to gain one additional electron to complete the valence level and form a Cl^- ion. If a compound is formed by calcium and chlorine, two chlorine atoms will be required to accept the two electrons provided by the calcium atom. Therefore, in the compound calcium chloride, the Ca^{2+} and Cl^- ions will be present in a 1:2 ratio, and we write the formula as $CaCl_2$. Thus, a formula unit of calcium chloride consists of one calcium ion and two chloride ions.

The above process may be summarized as follows:

$$:\ddot{Cl}\cdot + \cdot Ca \cdot + \cdot \ddot{Cl}: \longrightarrow [:\ddot{Cl}:]^- [Ca]^{2+} [:\ddot{Cl}:]^-$$

Aluminum Oxide

Let us now consider a more complicated example and see what ionic compound might be formed by the combination of aluminum and oxygen. Aluminum is in Group IIIA and has three valence electrons. Oxygen, in Group VIA, has six valence electrons.

To achieve a noble-gas configuration, an aluminum atom would have to lose three electrons to form the cation, Al^{3+}. On the other hand, an oxygen atom would have to gain two electrons to form the anion, O^{2-}. How can all the electrons produced in the formation of Al^{3+} be used up in the production of O^{2-}? The answer is that a formula unit of aluminum oxide consists of two aluminum ions and three oxygen ions. The six electrons released during the formation of two Al^{3+} ions are captured by the three oxygen atoms to form three O^{2-} ions (called oxide ions). Thus the formula of the compound formed is Al_2O_3, indicating a 2:3 ratio of aluminum and oxide ions. The formation of aluminum oxide can be represented as follows:

$$\cdot \ddot{O} \cdot + \cdot \dot{Al} \cdot + \cdot \ddot{O} \cdot + \cdot \dot{Al} \cdot + \cdot \ddot{O} \cdot \longrightarrow [:\ddot{O}:]^{2-} [Al]^{3+} [:\ddot{O}:]^{2-} [Al]^{3+} [:\ddot{O}:]^{2-}$$

EXAMPLE **5.2** Predict the formula of the compound formed by magnesium and bromine.

SOLUTION Magnesium, in Group IIA, has two valence electrons. Bromine, in Group VIIA, has seven valence electrons. Each magnesium atom will lose two electrons to give an Mg^{2+} cation, and each bromine atom will gain one electron to give a Br^- anion. Two bromide anions can be formed for each magnesium cation produced. Thus, the chemical formula for this ionic compound is $MgBr_2$.

EXAMPLE **5.3** Draw the electron-dot formula for $MgBr_2$.

SOLUTION By forming Mg^{2+}, the magnesium atom has emptied its valence level, and by forming Br^-, the bromine atom has filled its valence level. The electron-dot formula will therefore be

$$[:\ddot{Br}:]^- [Mg]^{2+} [:\ddot{Br}:]^-$$

An ionic compound is not formed between any two arbitrarily selected elements. The formation of an ionic bond requires that one of the elements involved has relatively few valence electrons (usually 1, 2, or 3), while the other element should only require 1, 2, or 3 additional electrons to complete its valence level. The former condition is usually met by metals and the latter by nonmetals. Therefore, you can assume that a compound formed by a metal and a nonmetal will be ionic.

We can also interpret the formation of ionic compounds in terms of energy changes. As we discussed in Section 4.7, less energy is required to ionize a metal than a nonmetal. We also mentioned that nonmetals usually release more energy than metals when forming negative ions. Thus, if we regard the competition for valence electrons as a kind of tug-of-war between atoms, we will find that nonmetals win by pulling valence electrons from metals.

QUESTIONS

4. Write the chemical formula and electron-dot formula of the compound formed between each of the following pairs of elements:
   a) lithium and iodine   c) calcium and phosphorus
   b) sodium and sulfur

5. In what ratio would you expect the following pairs of elements to combine:
   a) potassium and fluorine   c) lithium and nitrogen
   b) lithium and oxygen   d) barium and chlorine

Covalent Bonding

5.5

The second type of chemical bonding, called covalent bonding, results from electrons being shared by atoms rather than being transferred from one atom to another. Compounds containing only this type of bonding are called covalent compounds. The driving force behind the formation of a covalent bond is the tendency for an atom to obtain a stable electron configuration, which is usually a full valence level. In covalent compounds, a full valence level is achieved by atoms sharing two or more electrons; the shared electrons are then considered as simultaneously belonging to the valence levels of both the atoms involved. The shared electrons constitute the covalent bond. Covalent bonds are formed between two nonmetallic elements, that is, between elements whose valence levels are at least half full.

The Hydrogen Molecule

As we mentioned in Section 5.2, a hydrogen atom can lose its valence electron to give the cation, H^+, or it can gain an electron to give the anion, H^- The H^- ion has the same electron configuration as the noble gas, helium.

A hydrogen atom can also acquire the same electron configuration as helium by sharing electrons with another atom. The simplest case occurs when two hydrogen atoms share their electrons with each other. We can represent this using electron-dot formulas:

$$\mathbf{H\cdot + \cdot H \longrightarrow H{:}H}$$

The shared electrons are simultaneously attracted by the nuclei of both atoms and this attraction holds the two atoms together.

When a molecule consists of just two atoms joined together, as in the case of hydrogen, the molecule can be more precisely described as **diatomic**. When we write the formula for the hydrogen molecule, we want to show that this element exists as diatomic molecules rather than as individual atoms. We therefore write H_2 instead of H. The subscript placed to the lower right of the symbol indicates the presence of two hydrogen atoms in the molecule.

The Chlorine Molecule

Like the hydrogen molecule, the chlorine molecule is diatomic. It consists of two chlorine atoms joined by a covalent bond. Each atom originally has seven electrons in its valence level and acquires a noble-gas configuration by obtaining a share of the valence electrons belonging to the other atom:

$$\mathbf{{:}\ddot{C}l\cdot + \cdot \ddot{C}l{:} \longrightarrow {:}\ddot{C}l{:}\ddot{C}l{:}}$$

We can represent the chlorine molecule as Cl_2. Several other nonmetallic elements form *polyatomic* molecules. Of these, sulfur and phosphorus are the only non-diatomic examples. Molecules of these elements are often written without their subscripts.

TABLE 5.2	*Diatomic and Polyatomic Elements*		
	Group VA	Group VIA	Group VIIA
H_2	N_2	O_2	F_2
	P_4	S_8	Cl_2
			Br_2
			I_2

The Hydrogen Chloride Molecule

In the two examples of covalent bonding just discussed, the two atoms sharing electrons were identical. We will now extend the idea of electron sharing to molecules containing two or more different atoms.

Hydrogen chloride is a compound formed by hydrogen and chlorine. A hydrogen atom has just one valence electron. By sharing an additional electron it can acquire the same electron configuration as helium. Chlorine has seven valence electrons and requires one more electron to fill its valence level. The requirements of both atoms can be satisfied if they share the valence electron of hydrogen and one of the valence electrons of chlorine:

$$\text{H·} + \text{·}\overset{\cdot\cdot}{\underset{\cdot\cdot}{\text{Cl}}}\text{:} \longrightarrow \text{H:}\overset{\cdot\cdot}{\underset{\cdot\cdot}{\text{Cl}}}\text{:}$$

The Water Molecule

As you probably know, water is a compound of hydrogen and oxygen. Oxygen, which has six valence electrons, requires two additional electrons to fill its valence level. This can be achieved if two hydrogen atoms share their valence electrons with the oxygen atom. In return, each hydrogen atom shares one of the oxygen atom's valence electrons:

$$\text{H·} + \text{·}\overset{\cdot\cdot}{\underset{\cdot\cdot}{\text{O}}}\text{·} + \text{·H} \longrightarrow \text{H:}\overset{\cdot\cdot}{\underset{\cdot\cdot}{\text{O}}}\text{:H}$$

Note that if only one atom of an element is present in the molecule, no subscript is used after the symbol of that element in the chemical formula. Thus we represent the water molecule by H_2O rather than by H_2O_1. The formula of a covalent compound tells us exactly how many atoms of each element are contained in one molecule of that compound.

EXAMPLE   **5.4**   Give the electron-dot formula for each of the following:

a) NH_3 b) CCl_4

SOLUTION   a) NH_3 is the formula for ammonia. The ammonia molecule is formed in a fashion similar to that for water. The nitrogen atom has five valence electrons and needs to share the electrons from three hydrogen atoms to attain a noble-gas configuration:

$$\text{H·} + \text{·}\overset{\cdot\cdot}{\text{N}}\text{·} + \text{·H} \longrightarrow \text{H:}\overset{\cdot\cdot}{\text{N}}\text{:H}$$
$$+ \qquad\qquad\qquad \text{H}$$
$$\overset{\cdot}{\text{H}}$$

In the process, three covalent bonds are formed between hydrogen and nitrogen.

b) CCl_4 is the formula for carbon tetrachloride. Carbon has four valence electrons and requires four more electrons to fill its valence level. Chlorine, as we have already seen, has seven valence electrons and requires only one more electron to attain a noble-gas configuration. Thus, four covalent bonds are formed:

$$
\begin{array}{c}
:\ddot{\underset{..}{C}}l: \\
+ \\
:\ddot{\underset{..}{C}}l\cdot + \cdot\dot{\underset{.}{C}}\cdot + \cdot\ddot{\underset{..}{C}}l: \longrightarrow :\ddot{\underset{..}{C}}l:\ddot{\underset{..}{C}}:\ddot{\underset{..}{C}}l: \\
+ \\
:\ddot{\underset{..}{C}}l:
\end{array}
$$

The Carbon Dioxide Molecule

The covalent bonds we have discussed so far have all been formed by atoms sharing one pair of electrons. A bond that consists of just one shared pair of electrons is known as a **single bond**. Many molecules, however, have covalent bonds that consist of two or three electron pairs shared by two atoms. If two pairs of electrons (i.e. a total of four electrons) are shared by two atoms, the bond formed is called a **double bond**.

An example of a molecule containing double bonds is carbon dioxide. The carbon dioxide molecule consists of a central carbon atom and two oxygen atoms. Carbon has four valence electrons and hence needs four more to attain a noble-gas configuration. Oxygen has six valence electrons and therefore needs two more to fill its valence level. For all the atoms to be satisfied, each oxygen atom must share two of its electrons with the carbon atom. At the same time, carbon must share two of its electrons with each oxygen. Thus we have

$$\cdot\ddot{\underset{..}{O}}\cdot + \cdot\dot{\underset{.}{C}}\cdot + \cdot\ddot{\underset{..}{O}}\cdot \longrightarrow \ddot{\underset{..}{O}}::C::\ddot{\underset{..}{O}}$$

The compound formed is called carbon dioxide. The prefix *di-* in the word ''dioxide'' indicates the presence of two oxygen atoms.

EXAMPLE   *5.5*   Write the electron-dot formula for H_2CO. This molecule contains a double bond between the carbon and oxygen atoms, and a single bond between the carbon atom and each hydrogen atom.

SOLUTION   As we are told exactly what bonds to form, it is relatively easy to draw the correct electron-dot formula:

$$
\begin{array}{c}
H. \\
\,\overset{..}{\underset{.}{C}}::\ddot{\underset{..}{O}} \\
H^{\cdot}
\end{array}
$$

Note that the presence of a double bond allows both carbon and oxygen to achieve filled valence levels.

The Existence of Covalent Bonds

Do covalent bonds really exist? Strong evidence of their existence can be obtained by using an instrument called an infrared spectrometer. If we shine a beam of infrared light through a sample of a covalent compound, we find that certain wavelengths of light are absorbed by the sample. Since each covalent compound absorbs light at different sets of wavelengths, we can use this technique to identify a covalent compound. As well, by studying the absorption pattern, we can relate the wavelength of absorption to the bonded atoms. For example, a compound containing a carbon-fluorine bond absorbs light of wavelength 8.3 μm (8.3 $\times$ 10^{-6} m).

The wavelength of the infrared light absorbed by a given bond depends on the strength of that bond and on the mass of each of the atoms involved. We can imagine that a covalent bond behaves very much like a spring that is attached to two balls. If we stretch the spring and then let go, the balls will vibrate (Figure 5.10). How frequently they will vibrate depends on their mass and on the strength of the spring. Similarly, the frequency of vibration of two atoms joined by a covalent bond depends on both the mass of the atoms and on the strength of the bond. Thus, because a double bond is stronger than a single bond, those atoms joined by a double bond vibrate at a higher frequency than the same two atoms joined by the single bond. In addition, the lower the atomic mass of the atoms involved, the greater the frequency of vibration.

How is the vibration of the atoms in a bond related to the absorption of infrared light? Absorption occurs when the energy of the light matches the energy of the vibrating bond. In simple terms, the lower the energy (i.e. frequency) of the vibration, the longer the wavelength of the absorbed light. Thus, because a carbon–oxygen double bond is stronger than a carbon–oxygen single bond, the former typically absorbs light with a wavelength of 5.5 to 6.0 μm, whereas the latter typically absorbs light with a wavelength of 8.7 to 9.5 μm. As you can see, the infrared spectrometer allows us to obtain detailed information about the bonding in a covalent compound.

Figure 5.9
An infrared spectrometer is used to study covalent bonds.

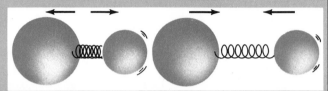

Figure 5.10
We can picture a covalent bond as being like a spring, with the atoms vibrating back and forth.

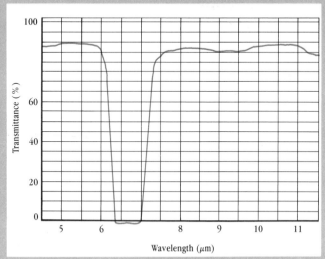

Figure 5.11
The covalent compound, CS_2, absorbs infrared light of wavelength 6.7 μm.

The Nitrogen Molecule

When six electrons are shared by two atoms, a **triple bond** is formed. The diatomic nitrogen molecule, the major component of air, is an example of a molecule with a triple bond. A nitrogen atom has five valence electrons, which is three electrons short of a noble-gas configuration. We can picture the bonding as a three-step process: pairing of two electrons (1), then of four electrons (2), then of six electrons (3) to form the three bonding electron pairs that represent the triple covalent bond:

$$:\dot{N}\cdot + \cdot\dot{N}: \xrightarrow{(1)} :\dot{N}\!:\!\dot{N}: \xrightarrow{(2)} :\dot{N}\!::\!\dot{N}: \xrightarrow{(3)} :N\!:::\!N:$$

QUESTIONS

6. Write the electron-dot formula for each of the following:
   a) OF_2 b) ClF c) H_2S d) SiH_4 e) CS_2
7. How many electrons are shared in forming each of the following:
   a) a single bond   b) a double bond   c) a triple bond

Coordinate Covalent Bonds

5.6

Although equal sharing of electrons can be used to explain the bonding in most simple covalent compounds, the concept cannot be successfully applied to all cases. In 1923 Nevil Sidgwick, a British chemist, showed that covalent bond formation could involve the sharing of an electron pair donated by only one of the two atoms. This situation occurs in the formation of the ammonium ion (NH_4^+) from ammonia (NH_3) and the H^+ ion:

$$\begin{array}{c} H \\ H\!:\!\ddot{N}\!: \\ \ddot{H} \end{array} + H^+ \longrightarrow \left[\begin{array}{c} H \\ H\!:\!\ddot{N}\!:\!H \\ \ddot{H} \end{array}\right]^+$$

In the ammonia molecule, the nitrogen has three bonding electrons plus one **lone pair** of electrons that is not involved in bonding. The H^+ ion, which is the nucleus of a hydrogen atom, has no electrons. It has a positive charge and is attracted by the lone pair of electrons of the nitrogen atom. The resulting single covalent bond is, in all respects, equivalent to the other three covalent bonds between the nitrogen and hydrogen atoms. In this case, however, both of the electrons involved in bond formation come from the nitrogen atom. Sidgwick called this type of bond a **coordinate covalent bond.**

In the ammonium ion, the positive charge is spread out over the entire ion. This is represented by writing the electron-dot formula inside square brackets with the net ionic charge shown as a superscript.

EXAMPLE	**5.6**	Draw the electron-dot formula of F_3NO. The compound has a central nitrogen atom.
SOLUTION		Let us approach this problem in a stepwise manner. First, the nitrogen atom has five valence electrons:

The fluorine atoms each share one of their electrons with the nitrogen atom:

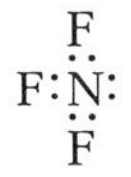

$$\begin{matrix} & F & \\ F : & \ddot{N} : & \\ & F & \end{matrix}$$

The nitrogen atom now has a complete valence level. The oxygen atom, which is to be added, has six valence electrons. If this oxygen atom shares the free electron pair on the nitrogen atom to form a coordinate covalent bond, it will also obtain a noble-gas configuration:

QUESTIONS

8. Draw the electron-dot formula of each of the following compounds. Each compound has at least one coordinate covalent bond:

a) SO_3 b) $SOCl_2$

Structural Formulas

5.7 You may have found drawing electron-dot formulas for compounds rather time-consuming, especially if there are several atoms in the molecule. Chemists overcome this by drawing **structural formulas**, in which a solid line is used to represent each pair of bonding electrons. Below you can see how ammonia, NH_3, and the ammonium ion, NH_4^+, are represented by this method:

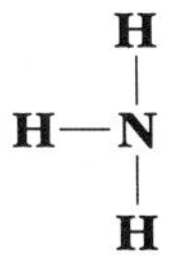

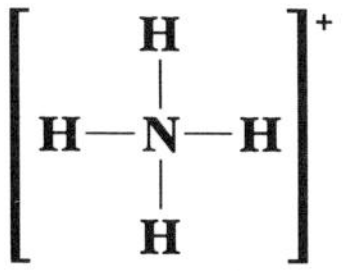

$$\begin{matrix} & H & \\ & | & \\ H - & N & \\ & | & \\ & H & \end{matrix} \qquad \left[\begin{matrix} & H & \\ & | & \\ H - & N & - H \\ & | & \\ & H & \end{matrix}\right]^+$$

If a double or triple bond is present in the molecule, we still use one solid line for each bonding pair of electrons. Thus, carbon dioxide and nitrogen are represented as follows:

$$O = C = O \qquad N \equiv N$$

One disadvantage of such formulas is that they do not show the valence electrons that are not involved in covalent bonding. A modified version of the structural formula can be used to show these lone pairs of electrons. The modified formula for the ammonia molecule, which has one lone pair of electrons, is shown below:

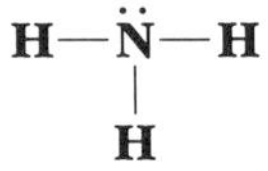

$$H - \overset{\cdot\cdot}{N} - H$$
$$|$$
$$H$$

QUESTIONS

9. Draw the electron-dot formula and the structural formula for each of the compounds listed below. The central atoms are N, C, and O, respectively:

   a) NI_3 b) CS_2 c) Cl_2O

Comparison of Ionic and Covalent Compounds
5.8

We have seen that ionic compounds are formed between a metal and a nonmetal, and that covalent compounds are formed between nonmetals. The differences in the physical properties of ionic and covalent compounds are quite marked. In general, ionic substances have high melting and boiling points, whereas the melting and boiling points of covalent compounds are much lower.

TABLE 5.3	Comparison of an Ionic Compound with a Covalent Compound	
Compound	$MgCl_2$	SCl_2
Bonding type	Ionic	Covalent
Melting point	714 °C	−122 °C
Boiling point	1417 °C	60 °C

A better way of distinguishing between ionic and covalent compounds is to test the electrical conductivity of a solution of each compound, as described in Section 5.1. An ionic compound that dissolves in water will produce free ions (cations and anions) that will conduct an electric current through the solution. Covalent compounds, with the exception of the acid-forming compounds, e.g. HCl, do not form ions in solution. Their neutral molecules do not conduct electricity.

We also find that molten ionic compounds conduct electricity. When an ionic compound melts the ions are no longer held in the crystal lattice, but become free to move around, just as they do in a solution. To illustrate the conductivity of a molten ionic compound, we can do an electrical conductivity test similar to that described in Section 5.1.

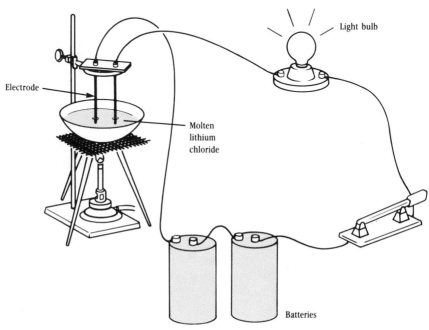

Figure 5.12

A molten ionic compound will conduct electricity.

QUESTIONS

10. Compound X melts at $-57\,°C$ and boils at $126\,°C$. Compound Y melts at $640\,°C$ and boils at $1304\,°C$.

  a) Which of the two compounds is most likely to be ionic?

  b) Of the two compounds, which is most likely to consist of two or more nonmetals?

  c) Could either compound be an electrolyte?

Polyatomic Ions

5.9 The ammonium ion, NH_4^+, which we discussed in Section 5.6, is an example of an ion that is composed of more than one atom. Ionic species of this type are quite common and are known as **polyatomic ions**. Some frequently encountered polyatomic ions and their chemical formulas are listed in Table 5.4. With the exception of the ammonium ion, which is a cation, all the ions listed are polyatomic anions. Polyatomic ions have dual-bonding characteristics. The bonds within the polyatomic ion are covalent or coordinate covalent bonds, but the polyatomic ions themselves form ionic bonds with other ionic species. For example, ammonium fluoride (NH_4F) is an ionic compound consisting of NH_4^+ and F^- ions. However, as we have already seen, within the NH_4^+ ion there is covalent bonding between the nitrogen and hydrogen atoms.

TABLE 5.4	*The Most Common Polyatomic Ions*		
Name	Formula	Name	Formula
Ammonium	NH_4^+	Nitrate	NO_3^-
Carbonate	CO_3^{2-}	Sulfate	SO_4^{2-}
Hydroxide	OH^-		

Calcium carbonate ($CaCO_3$), which exists naturally as chalk, marble, or limestone, is another example of an ionic compound in which a polyatomic ion, CO_3^{2-}, is involved. The Ca^{2+} and CO_3^{2-} ions are held together by an ionic bond, but in the CO_3^{2-} ion, covalent bonds are formed between the carbon and oxygen atoms.

Each polyatomic ion can be represented by an electron-dot formula. When writing the formula, we must always indicate the charge on the ion. For example, the hydroxide ion, OH^-, has one more electron than the sum of the oxygen and hydrogen valence electrons. We can represent this ion as follows:

$$[:\ddot{O}:H]^-$$

The sulfate ion can be represented as

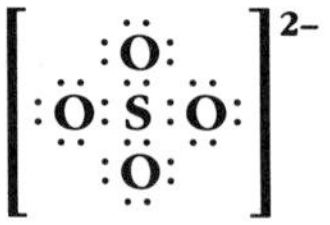

$$\left[:\ddot{O}:\overset{\displaystyle :\ddot{O}:}{\underset{\displaystyle :\ddot{O}:}{S}}:\ddot{O}:\right]^{2-}$$

An ionic compound containing a polyatomic ion will dissolve in water to give cations and anions, just as a simple ionic compound will. However, the polyatomic ion itself will remain intact. For example, the compound, NaOH, will dissolve in water to give sodium ions (Na^+) and hydroxide ions (OH^-).

The Bonding Continuum

5.10

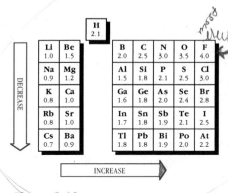

Figure 5.13
Electronegativity values for the elements in the main groups of the Periodic Table, as assigned by Linus Pauling.

We have discussed chemical bonding in terms of two models: ionic and covalent. In doing so, we have assumed that the bond between two atoms is always exclusively one or the other. This picture is rather simplistic. A closer examination of the bond in hydrogen chloride (HCl), described in Section 5.5 as a covalent bond between the hydrogen and chlorine atoms, will clarify this statement:

$$\mathbf{H \!:\! \ddot{\underset{\cdot\cdot}{Cl}} \!:}$$

This formula suggests that the pair of electrons that constitutes the covalent bond is shared equally between the hydrogen and the chlorine atoms. This is not the case. The electrons forming a covalent bond are only shared equally when the two atoms involved are identical, as for example, in molecules of hydrogen or chlorine. In hydrogen chloride the chlorine atom exercises a stronger attractive force on the bonding electron pair than the hydrogen atom does.

The **electronegativity** of an atom is a measure of the tendency of that atom to attract electrons toward itself when forming a covalent bond. Linus Pauling, an American chemist, proposed numerical values for the electronegativities of the elements. Figure 5.13 shows these values for the elements of the left and right-hand portions of the Periodic Table. Note the increase in electronegativity as we go from left to right in a period and the decrease in electronegativity as we descend a group. The two trends combine to give fluorine (F) the highest and cesium (Cs) the lowest electronegativities.

When we apply the electronegativity concept to the hydrogen chloride molecule, we see from Figure 5.13 that the value for chlorine (3.0) is greater than the value for hydrogen (2.1). In a covalent bond formed between these two atoms, the bonding electrons will be closer to the more electronegative atom (i.e., chlorine). This means the portion of the molecule in which the hydrogen atom is located has a slight positive electrical charge whereas the portion of the atom in which the chlorine atom resides is slightly negative. This is often illustrated by placing the Greek letter δ (delta) with a plus or minus sign over the appropriate portions of the molecule in the structural formula:

$$\overset{\delta +}{\mathbf{H}}\!-\!\overset{\delta -}{\mathbf{Cl}}$$

Because these charges are smaller than the charges that we find in ionic compounds, hydrogen chloride is sometimes described as being partially ionic. Another name for this characteristic is **polar covalent bonding**.

We can assign a numerical value to the ionic character of a bond by using the information in Figure 5.14. If we know the difference in electronegativity of the two atoms in the bond, we can determine its percentage ionic character.

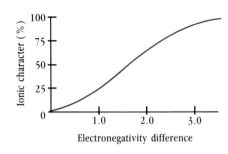

Figure 5.14
The relation between the difference in electronegativity and ionic character.

Pauling — A Worker For Chemistry and Peace

Linus Pauling was born in Portland, Oregon, in 1901. His scientific career has been connected almost entirely with the California Institute of Technology in Pasadena, California. The central theme of Pauling's work was relating the properties of chemical substances to their structures. The culmination of his work was the book, ''The Nature of the Chemical Bond'', which was published in 1939. This is still regarded as the classic text on the subject. Pauling was awarded the Nobel Prize for Chemistry in 1954 for his work on chemical bonds and molecular structure.

Pauling then turned his attention to biochemistry. His earlier work on the structure of protein molecules led him to investigate the relationship between molecular abnormalities and hereditary diseases. He championed the idea of using large doses of vitamins to treat both physical and mental illness. He wrote an important paper on orthomolecular psychiatry, a controversial field that promotes the use of vitamins in the treatment of mental illnesses such as schizophrenia. He has also conducted studies that suggest a high intake of vitamin C can be used to combat the common cold.

Pauling became very active in nuclear disarmament campaigns long before nuclear disarmament became a popular cause. He spoke out about the danger of nuclear war and the necessity for multilateral disarmament. In 1958 he presented to the United Nations a petition urging the end of nuclear weapons tests. The petition was signed by 11 021 scientists from around the world. Pauling's prodisarmament work caused him great difficulties with the U.S. Government, including two denials of a passport. He was awarded the Nobel Peace Prize for 1962. The announcement of the Peace Prize was made on October 10, 1963, the day that a partial nuclear test ban went into effect.

Figure 5.15
Linus Pauling (1901–   ).

For hydrogen chloride, the difference in electronegativity between hydrogen and chlorine is $3.0 - 2.1$, or 0.9; this corresponds to a bond with 19% ionic character (and thus 81% covalent character). In the compound cesium fluoride, CsF, the difference is $4.0 - 0.7$, or 3.3, which corresponds to a bond with 94% ionic character. There appears to be no sharp dividing line between ionic and covalent bonds. Instead, there is a continuous range from totally nonpolar covalent bonds through those with partial ionic character (such as the bonds in hydrogen chloride, HCl, and hydrogen fluoride, HF), to bonds that are generally regarded as being fully ionic (such as those found in cesium fluoride, CsF).

EXAMPLE   **5.7** The following molecules contain polar covalent bonds. Indicate which atom(s) are slightly positive and which are slightly negative:
a) HBr   b) CO_2

SOLUTION First we must draw the structural formula of each compound. We will then refer to Figure 5.14 to determine the relative electronegativities of the atoms and label them accordingly:

a)
$$\overset{\delta+\quad\delta-}{H—Br}$$
(H 2.1, Br 2.8)

b)
$$\overset{\delta-\quad\delta+\quad\delta-}{O=C=O}$$
(C 2.5, O 3.5)

Although we have just shown that there is no true dividing line between ionic and covalent bonds, we usually regard compounds with greater than 50% ionic character as being ionic. Similarly, compounds with less than 50% ionic character are considered to be covalent. The arbitrary assignment of compounds to one of these two classes will continue to be useful in our studies of chemistry.

QUESTIONS

11. Identify which of the following molecules have polar covalent bonds. Indicate which of the atoms within the molecules you have identified are slightly positive and which are slightly negative:
   a) Cl_2 b) NH_3 c) CO d) H_2O e) OF_2

Summary

■ When an electrolyte is dissolved in water it produces a solution that conducts electricity. Salts, acids, and bases are electrolytes.

■ If nonelectrolytes are dissolved in water the resulting solutions do not conduct electricity.

■ Electricity is conducted through solutions by the movement of charged particles called ions. These are formed when a neutral atom gains or loses electrons. If a neutral atom gains electrons, a negative ion (anion) is formed. If electrons are lost, a positive ion (cation) is formed.

■ An anion generally has eight electrons in its valence level and a cation usually has an empty valence level.

■ Ionic bonds are formed by the transfer of electrons from a metallic element to a nonmetallic element.

■ Covalent bonds are formed by nonmetallic elements sharing two or more electrons.

■ Covalent bonds can be single (one shared pair of electrons), double (two shared pairs), or triple (three shared pairs).

■ In coordinate covalent bonds the shared electron pair is donated entirely by one atom.

- The smallest unit of a covalent compound is a molecule.

- Ionic compounds have high melting and boiling points. Covalent compounds generally have low melting and boiling points.

- Bonds within polyatomic ions are covalent or coordinate covalent, but polyatomic ions form ionic bonds with other ionic species.

- The electronegativity of an atom is a measure of the tendency of that atom to attract electrons towards itself when forming a covalent bond. Electronegativity increases from left to right across a period and decreases down a group.

- There is a continuous range from the totally nonpolar covalent bond, through polar covalent bonds, to ionic bonds. The position of any particular bond along this continuum is determined by the electronegativity difference between the elements.

KEY WORDS

anion	ionic bond
bond	lone pair
cation	molecule
coordinate covalent bond	noble-gas configuration
covalent bond	nonelectrolyte
crystal lattice	polar covalent bonding
diatomic molecule	polyatomic ion
double bond	salt
electrolyte	single bond
electronegativity	structural formula
formula unit	triple bond

ANSWERS TO SECTION QUESTIONS

1. Metallic elements form positive ions; nonmetallic elements form negative ions.

2. a) gain 2   c) lose 3   e) lose 1
   b) lose 2   d) gain 3   f) gain 1

3. a) $[:\ddot{\text{Cl}}:]^-$ c) $[\text{Al}]^{3+}$ e) $[:\ddot{\text{S}}:]^{2-}$

   b) $[\text{Ca}]^{2+}$ d) $[\text{K}]^+$ f) $[:\ddot{\text{P}}:]^{3-}$

4. a) LiI, $[\text{Li}]^+[:\ddot{\text{I}}:]^-$

   b) Na_2S, $[\text{Na}]^+[:\ddot{\text{S}}:]^{2-}[\text{Na}]^+$

   c) Ca_3P_2, $[\text{Ca}]^{2+}[:\ddot{\text{P}}:]^{3-}[\text{Ca}]^{2+}[:\ddot{\text{P}}:]^{3-}[\text{Ca}]^{2+}$

5. a) 1:1   b) 2:1   c) 3:1   d) 1:2

6. a)  $:\ddot{F}:\ddot{O}:\ddot{F}:$ **d)** 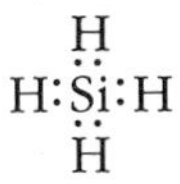   H
                        H:$\ddot{Si}$:H
b) $:\ddot{Cl}:\ddot{F}:$ H

c) H:$\ddot{S}$:H

                       e) 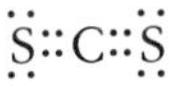 $\ddot{S}::C::\ddot{S}$

7. a) two   **b)** four   **c)** six

8. a)  $:\ddot{O}:S:\ddot{O}:$ **b)**  $:\ddot{Cl}:\ddot{S}:\ddot{Cl}:$
        $:\ddot{O}:$ $:\ddot{O}:$

9. a)  $:\ddot{I}:\ddot{N}:\ddot{I}:$,   I—N—I
         $:\ddot{I}:$ |
                       I

b) 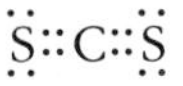 $\ddot{S}::C::\ddot{S}$,   S=C=S

c) $:\ddot{Cl}:\ddot{O}:\ddot{Cl}:$,   Cl—O—Cl

10. a) Y   **b)** X   **c)** Y could be

11. a) nonpolar
b) polar, N slightly −, H slightly +
c) polar, C slightly +, O slightly −
d) polar, H slightly +, O slightly −
e) polar, O slightly +, F slightly −

COMPREHENSION QUESTIONS

1. How are positive ions formed from neutral atoms?
2. How are negative ions formed from neutral atoms?
3. In a solid conductor such as copper, electricity is conducted through the metal by a flow of electrons. How is electricity conducted through an electrolytic solution?
4. How many electrons are generally found in the valence shell of the following:
   a) a positive ion   b) a negative ion
5. Name the anion that is formed from each of the following elements:
   a) oxygen   b) bromine   c) iodine
6. Where do the electrons come from when a neutral atom forms an anion?
7. What is meant by the term "formula unit"?
8. Why are molecules not present in the solid phase of ionic compounds?
9. Why are covalent compounds generally not considered to be electrolytes?
10. List three important differences between ionic and covalent compounds.
11. What is meant by the term "coordinate covalent bond"?

12. In the compound sodium sulfate, Na_2SO_4, is the bonding ionic, covalent, or both? Explain.

13. Approximately what electronegativity difference corresponds to 50% ionic character?

14. What is the least electronegativity difference possible between two atoms involved in a bond? What type of bonding is involved? Give an example.

PROBLEMS

15. Predict whether each of the following compounds would be predominantly ionic or covalent:
   a) KCl
   b) $C_6H_{12}O_6$
   c) BaS
   d) $CrCl_3$
   e) NO_2
   f) CCl_4

16. Indicate whether the following compounds are predominantly ionic or covalent:
   a) H_2S
   b) CaF_2
   c) AgBr
   d) C_6H_6
   e) HCN
   f) K_2S

17. Predict the usual ionic charge on the ions of the following atoms:
   a) Rb   b) Sr   c) Xe   d) S   e) I   f) H

18. Predict the usual ionic charge on the ions of the following atoms:
   a) He   b) Br   c) Se   d) Ba   e) Cs   f) N

19. Identify the ions that have the following atomic structures:

	Protons	Electrons
a)	11	10
b)	15	18
c)	20	18
d)	29	28
e)	53	54

20. How many protons and electrons do each of the following species have:
   a) Fe^{3+} b) O^{2-} c) Kr   d) Zn^{2+} e) Br^-

21. Write the electron configuration for each of the following ions and in each case identify the inert gas that has the same electron configuration:
   a) Li^+ b) Mg^{2+} c) Cl^- d) S^{2-}

22. Two species that have the same electronic structure are said to be isoelectronic. Identify an ion that is:
   a) isoelectronic with Ne and has a charge of -1
   b) isoelectronic with Ne and has a charge of $+3$
   c) isoelectronic with Ne and has a charge of $+1$
   d) isoelectronic with Kr and has a charge of $+1$
   e) isoelectronic with V and has a charge of $+3$

23. In Chapter 3 we saw how isotopes can be represented by including the atomic number and the mass number when we write the symbol

for a given element, for example, ^7_3Li. Deduce the number of protons, neutrons, and electrons present in each of the following ions:

a) $^7_3Li^+$ b) $^{35}_{17}Cl^-$ c) $^{32}_{16}S^{2-}$ d) $^{27}_{13}Al^{3+}$

24. Complete the table shown below. The first line serves as an example:

Symbol	Atomic Number	Number of Electrons	Mass Number	Number of Neutrons	Net Ionic Charge
$^{37}_{17}Cl^-$	17	18	37	20	1−
$^1_1H^-$					
	55		133		1+
		78	—	120	2+
		36	80		1−

25. Write the electron-dot formula for each of the following atoms and ions:

a) B   b) Mg   c) Ar   d) I   e) Ca^{2+} f) N^{3-} g) Br^-

26. Write the electron-dot formula for each of the following atoms and ions:

a) Si   b) P   c) Cs   d) S   e) Mg^{2+} f) Sc^{3+} g) O^{2-}

27. Draw the electron-dot formulas for each of the following ionic compounds:

a) NaI   b) K_2S c) Ca_3N_2

28. Draw the electron-dot formulas for each of the following compounds:

a) Li_2O b) $BaCl_2$ c) AlF_3

29. An unknown compound A is a solid at room temperature and does not melt when heated in a bunsen flame. Its solution in water is a good conductor of electricity. Is the compound likely to be ionic or covalent? Would you expect it to conduct electricity if it was melted?

30. Explain why the electronegativity scale is useful when trying to predict whether the bonding in a compound is ionic or covalent.

31. Write the electron-dot formula for each of the following molecules, which may contain single, double, or triple bonds:

a) CS_2 b) HCN   c) PCl_3

32. Each of the following covalent compounds contains at least one double or triple bond. Draw the electron-dot formula for each molecule. Hint: The molecules in b) and c) each contain a coordinate covalent bond:

a) N_2 b) SO_2 c) O_3, ozone

33. Draw the structural formula for each of the following:

a) Br_2 b) PH_3 c) CBr_4 d) H_2S e) CS_2 f) HCN   g) SO_3

34. Draw the structural formula for each of the following covalent substances:

a) F_2 b) OF_2 c) NCl_3 d) SiH_4 e) N_2 f) SO_2 g) O_3

35. Using the electronegativity table, indicate which atoms in the following molecules carry a partial positive charge ($\delta+$) and which carry a partial negative charge ($\delta-$):

a) H—I

b) H—S—H

c)
$$Cl—\underset{\underset{Cl}{|}}{\overset{\overset{Cl}{|}}{C}}—Cl$$

36. Indicate the polar nature of the covalent bonds in the following compounds:

a) I—Cl

b)
$$Cl—\underset{\underset{Cl}{|}}{P}—Cl$$

c)
$$H—\underset{\underset{H}{|}}{N}—H$$

37. Each of the following compounds contains a polyatomic ion. Draw the electron-dot formula for each compound:

a) Na_2CO_3 b) NH_4OH c) KNO_3

38. Draw the electron-dot formula for each of the following polyatomic anions. In each case, the central atom appears first in the formula:

a) ClO_3^- (chlorate)   b) PO_4^{3-} (phosphate)

39. Describe the differences in conductivity of ionic and covalent compounds in the solid and liquid phase, and when dissolved in water. What are the reasons for these differences?

40. Why do the elements in Group VIIA, the halogens, form diatomic molecules?

SUGGESTED PROJECTS

1. Look up the crystal structure of some common ionic compounds, such as sodium chloride, and cesium chloride. Draw a diagram of the arrangement of ions in the crystal and/or construct a model of the structure. Find out all you can about other types of crystal systems.

2. Look up information on infrared spectroscopy (the study of how infrared light is absorbed by compounds). How does an infrared spectrometer work? What wavelengths of absorption correspond to bonds between different elements? If possible, visit a nearby college or university and run an infrared spectrum of a compound.

3. What is the structure of covalent compounds in the solid phase? How do they differ from ionic compounds? Does this difference help to explain why covalent compounds generally have much lower melting points than ionic compounds?

4. There is a third type of bonding called metallic bonding. Find out how this type of bonding differs from ionic or covalent bonding. Give some examples of substances that contain metallic bonds.

The Names and Formulas of Chemical Compounds

When we describe a chemical compound, we use both its name *and* its formula. The formula tells us the ratio of the elements in an ionic compound, or the number of atoms of each element in a molecule of a covalent compound. Different compounds can have the same formula, but when they do the ions or atoms within the ionic or molecular structure of each compound are arranged differently. However, every chemical compound has a unique name. Therefore, when you see a bottle labelled NaCl, you should refer to its contents as "sodium chloride", not as "en-ay-see-ell".

In this chapter we will discuss the naming system for chemical compounds. We will also see how to name a chemical compound from its formula and how to derive the formula of a chemical compound from its name.

The Origins of Our Naming System

6.1

Until the late 18th century there was no systematic method of assigning names to chemical compounds. Some substances, such as Epsom salts, were named after places; some, such as Glauber's salt, after people; and some were given names related to the appearance of the substance, as for example, oil of vitriol and butter of arsenic. Many compounds were known by more than one name, which caused some confusion. Some of the old names, such as muriatic acid, quicklime, and methyl hydrate, are still in use today, and still cause confusion.

In 1787, Guyton de Morveau, a French chemist, devised a systematic approach to naming compounds. His **classical system of nomenclature** named compounds using words from Greek and Latin, two languages that could be understood by scholars and scientists throughout Europe. The name of a compound gave specific information about the chemical composition of that compound, with a key part of the name being the word ending (the suffix). A large proportion of our current chemical naming system is based on the rules devised by de Morveau.

As more and more compounds were discovered, it became apparent that the classical system had reached the limits of its capabilities. In 1919 therefore, Alfred Stock, a Prussian chemist, devised a new system of naming chemical compounds, which became known as the **Stock system**.

When the International Union of Pure and Applied Chemistry (IUPAC) was organized in 1920, one of its objectives was to obtain international agreement on a system for naming chemical compounds. The IUPAC still meets periodically to make recommendations about the names of chemical compounds, and published its latest complete set of *Definitive Rules* in 1970. Although the rules allow some flexibility in the use of the classical and Stock systems, the latter system is generally preferred. In North America we use parts of both systems, but in some countries, such as the United Kingdom, the Stock system is used almost exclusively. Many industries and some chemical supply companies still use the classical system.

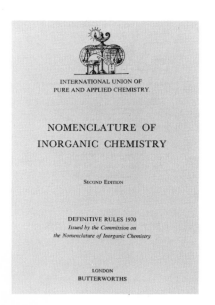

Figure 6.1
The rules for naming compounds are made by the International Union of Pure and Applied Chemistry.

The Names and Charges of Common Ions

6.2

In Section 5.2 we saw that, when forming compounds, elements with one, two, or three valence electrons (the metals) lose their electrons and form positive ions. For example, a potassium atom will lose its one valence electron to give the K^+ ion. We previously represented this process using an electron-dot formula, as follows:

$$K\cdot \longrightarrow [K]^+ + e^-$$

The name of a cation is usually the name of the element followed by the word *ion*. Thus the K^+ ion is referred to as the potassium ion.

When forming compounds, elements with five, six, or seven valence electrons (the nonmetals) gain electrons to form negative ions. For example, an oxygen atom, which has six valence electrons, will gain two electrons to fill its valence level. We can represent this process as:

$$\cdot\ddot{O}\cdot + 2\,e^- \longrightarrow [:\ddot{O}:]^{2-} \cdot$$

The name of a simple anion *always* has the suffix *-ide*, but the element name is sometimes shortened. Thus, the O^{2-} ion is called the oxide ion and the N^{3-} ion is called the nitride ion.

The charges on most of the ions we will be discussing can be found using the same method that we used to determine the charges on the potassium and oxide ions. Some common examples are shown in Figure 6.2. You may find yourself referring to this figure quite often as we proceed through this chapter.

The Main Group Elements

The charges on the ions formed by the elements in the main groups of the Periodic Table can usually be predicted (Table 6.1).

TABLE 6.1	*The Ionic Charges of the Main Group Elements*					
Group	IA	IIA	IIIA	VA	VIA	VIIA
Charge	+1	+2	+3	−3	−2	−1

Figure 6.2

Names and charges of some common anions and cations.

Groups 0 and IVA have been omitted from this table for several reasons. First, the Group 0 elements do not form simple ions, as they already have

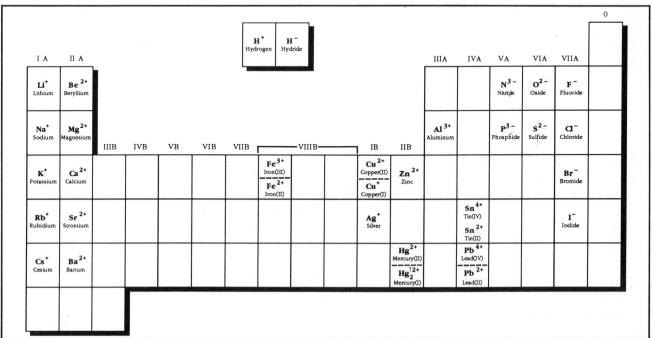

a full valence level. Second, the higher members of Group IVA (i.e. carbon, silicon, and germanium) form covalent rather than ionic compounds. Lastly, Figure 6.2 shows that the two bottom members of Group IVA (i.e. tin and lead) can both form ions of charge +2 and +4. An ionic charge of +4 is to be expected as this corresponds to an empty valence level. Why a lead or tin ion can have a charge of +2 is more difficult to explain and is beyond the scope of this discussion. To differentiate between ions of the same element that have different charges, the name of the element is written followed by the charge in Roman numerals enclosed in parentheses. Thus

Pb^{4+} is called lead(IV)

Pb^{2+} is called lead(II)

The Stock System

The Transition Elements

The transition elements iron, copper, silver, zinc, and mercury will be used in several examples throughout this text. The charges on the ions of these metals cannot be predicted from simple atomic theory. Iron, copper, and mercury each form two ions with different charges. For example, iron forms an Fe^{2+} ion, iron(II), and an Fe^{3+} ion, iron(III). Mercury forms a simple Hg^{2+} ion and another ion which is written as Hg_2^{2+}. The latter is a *diatomic* ion that contains two mercury atoms bonded together. Although this diatomic ion is often written as Hg^+, in this text we will use the symbol Hg_2^{2+}.

The Classical System

In many industries, the classical system for naming ions is still used extensively. The metals that can have more than one ion are referred to by their Latin names, and suffixes are used to identify the charge on the ion. The suffix *-ic* is used for ions with the higher charge and *-ous* for ions with the lower charge.

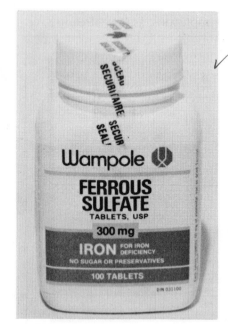

Figure 6.3
Classical names are still used in medicine.

Ferrous Sulfate 300 mg.

TABLE 6.2	*Classical Names Used to Distinguish Different Ions of the Same Metal*	
Metal	Ion of Lower Charge	Ion of Higher Charge
Iron	Ferrous, Fe^{2+}	Ferric, Fe^{3+}
Copper	Cuprous, Cu^+	Cupric, Cu^{2+}
Tin	Stannous, Sn^{2+}	Stannic, Sn^{4+}
Lead	Plumbous, Pb^{2+}	Plumbic, Pb^{4+}
Mercury	Mercurous, Hg_2^{2+}	Mercuric, Hg^{2+}

(handwritten top margin) SN^{4+} SN^{2+} Pb^{2+} P^{4+} CO^{2+} CO^{3+} Hg_2^{2+} Hg^{2+} Fe^{3+} Fe^{2+}

QUESTIONS

1. Write the names and symbols of the ions formed by the following elements:
   a) magnesium   c) iodine   e) nitrogen
   b) silver   d) copper (two)   f) tin (two)

(handwritten) STANNOUS!

The Names and Formulas of Binary Ionic Compounds

6.3

When you have become familiar with the names and charges of the ions, you will find that it is relatively easy to derive the formulas and names of the compounds formed from them. Compounds resulting from the combination of two elements are referred to as **binary compounds.**

The basic principles in the formation of ionic compounds are as follows:

1. **Positive ions (cations) will combine with negative ions (anions).**
2. **Cations and anions will only combine in ratios that will result in electrically neutral compounds.**

Let us derive the formula and name of the compound formed by potassium and chlorine. Potassium forms the potassium ion, K^+, and chlorine forms the chloride ion, Cl^-. To form a neutral compound, the ions must combine in a 1:1 ratio; that is, only one chloride ion can combine with each potassium ion. The formula for the compound will be KCl. The name of the compound, potassium chloride, is obtained by combining the names of the cation and the anion. NOTE: the name and symbol of the metal always precedes that of the nonmetal.

If an element can form two different cations, it can in principle form two different compounds with any given anion.

EXAMPLE   **6.1**   What is the formula and name of the compound formed by magnesium and iodine?

SOLUTION   From Figure 6.2, we see that magnesium forms the magnesium ion, Mg^{2+}, and iodine forms the iodide ion, I^-. To balance the charges, we will need two iodide ions (each with a -1 charge) to balance the charge of $+2$ on the magnesium ion. The formula will therefore be MgI_2, and the name of the compound will be magnesium iodide.

EXAMPLES   **6.2**   What is the formula and name of each of the two compounds formed between lead and oxygen?

SOLUTION   a) From Figure 6.2, we see that lead forms the lead(II) ion, Pb^{2+}, and the lead(IV) ion, Pb^{4+}. Oxygen forms the oxide ion, O^{2-}.

        b) The lead(II) ion, (Pb^{2+}) can combine with the oxide ion (O^{2-}) in a 1:1 ratio because the ions have equal but opposite charges. The formula of the compound formed will be PbO and its name will be lead(II) oxide (the Roman "two" tells us that this lead ion has a +2 charge).

c) To balance the +4 charge of the lead(IV) ion, we will need two oxide ions, each with a −2 charge. The formula of the compound formed will be PbO_2 and its name will be lead(IV) oxide.

QUESTIONS

2. Derive the formulas and names of the compounds formed between
  a) lithium and sulfur   c) zinc and oxygen
  b) aluminum and fluorine   d) calcium and phosphorus

3. Derive the names and formulas for the compounds formed between
  a) iron and chlorine   b) copper and sulfur   c) mercury and oxygen

---

The Names and Formulas of Polyatomic Ions   6.4

non-metal + oxygen

C
N
P
S
Cl

In Section 5.9, we introduced you to some common polyatomic ions. The ability to recognize each combination of atoms and to assign a net ionic charge and correct name to each of these ions is very important. With the exception of the ammonium ion (NH_4^+), the cyanide ion (CN^-), and the acetate ion ($CH_3CO_2^-$), all the polyatomic ions that we will be discussing are negatively charged and contain oxygen and only one other element. These oxygen-containing ions are called **oxyanions**.

Formulas and Names of Some Oxyanions

To assist you in learning the names and formulas of the oxyanions, we will point out a few patterns that relate to them. Figure 6.4 shows some of the oxyanions within the framework of the Periodic Table. Note that the formulas in the second row of the table (CO_3^{2-}, NO_3^-) have three oxygen atoms combined with one atom of another element, whereas those in the

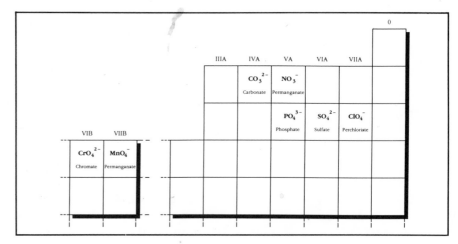

Figure 6.4
Some common oxyanions.

-ate & -ic / -ite & -ous
HIGH # / LOW #

Stock and Chemical Names

Alfred Stock was born in 1876 in Danzig, East Prussia (now Gdansk, Poland). Although he is best known for devising the modern system of naming chemical compounds, Stock's main interest was in preparing new compounds containing boron and hydrogen, or silicon and hydrogen. As most compounds formed by these combinations of elements can only exist in the absence of air, Stock had to devise novel types of apparatus to prepare and study them. The preparation of new chemical compounds was one of his chief joys in life.

Unfortunately, Stock's health deteriorated after he obtained his Doctoral degree. He suffered from headaches, numbness, and loss of hearing and memory. These were all traced to mercury poisoning, caused by prolonged exposure to mercury vapour in poorly ventilated laboratories. After the cause of his illness had been identified, Stock began a program of research into the hazards of working with mercury, and on its toxic effects. In doing so, he devised a method of detecting quantities of mercury as small as 10^{-8} g. Stock also suggested steps that could be taken to prevent mercury poisoning. He died in 1943.

Figure 6.5
Alfred Stock (1876–1943).

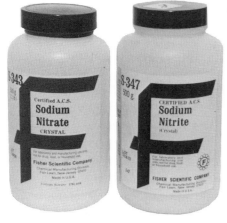

Figure 6.6
Although the names of these two compounds are very similar, their chemical properties are quite different. You must be particularly careful in identifying the names and formulas of common oxyanions.

third row (PO_4^{3-}, SO_4^{2-}, ClO_4^-) have four oxygen atoms combined with one atom of another element. Also note that the charge on the ions decreases in steps of one unit from left to right across a period.

These oxyanions all contain oxygen and a nonmetal. Figure 6.4 also includes two oxyanions that contain metal atoms. These are the chromate (CrO_4^{2-}) and the permanganate (MnO_4^-) ions. There are some similarities between these two ions and the nonmetal oxyanions. Chromium, in Group VIB of the Periodic Table, like sulfur in Group VIA, forms an oxyanion of the type XO_4^{2-}. (Thus we have CrO_4^{2-} and SO_4^{2-}). Similarly, manganese in Group VIIB forms the permanganate ion (MnO_4^-), and chlorine, in Group VIIA, forms the perchlorate ion (ClO_4^-).

The names of these oxyanions are based on the name of the element other than oxygen: carbonate contains carbon, sulfate contains sulfur, and so on. You have probably noticed that each of the names has the ending *-ate*. Some elements can form more than one oxyanion. When only two oxyanions are formed by a nonmetal, the suffix *-ate* is reserved for the oxyanion with the higher number of oxygen atoms. The ions with the lower number of oxygen atoms are given the suffix *-ite* and the rest of the name remains unchanged. Thus, in addition to forming the nitrate ion (NO_3^-), nitrogen and oxygen can also combine to give the nitrite ion (NO_2^-). Note that although the nitrite ion contains one less oxygen atom than the nitrate ion, the net ionic charge (-1) is the same for both ions.

A few nonmetallic elements can form more than two oxyanions. For these we use prefixes to identify oxyanions that contain more oxygen atoms than the *-ate* ion or fewer oxygen atoms than the *-ite* ion. To indicate one more oxygen atom than the *-ate* ending, we use the prefix *per-* together with the ending *-ate*. To indicate one less oxygen atom than the *-ite* ending, we use the prefix *hypo-* together with the ending *-ite*.

TABLE 6.3	*Names and Formulas of Common Oxyanions*		
Formula	**Name**	**Formula**	**Name**
CO_3^{2-}	Carbonate	ClO_4^-	Perchlorate
NO_3^-	Nitrate	ClO_3^-	Chlorate
NO_2^-	Nitrite	ClO_2^-	Chlorite
PO_4^{3-}	Phosphate	ClO^-	Hypochlorite
SO_4^{2-}	Sulfate	CrO_4^{2-}	Chromate
SO_3^{2-}	Sulfite	$Cr_2O_7^{2-}$	Dichromate
		MnO_4^-	Permanganate

The Names and Formulas of Compounds Containing Polyatomic Ions

6.5

The formula for a compound containing a polyatomic ion is derived in the same way as the formula for a binary ionic compound. We combine the cations and anions in a ratio that will balance the charges and give us a neutral compound.

For example, a compound formed by the sodium ion (Na^+) and the sulfate ion (SO_4^{2-}) must contain twice as many sodium ions as sulfate ions for the charges to balance. The formula of the compound will therefore be Na_2SO_4.

For some combinations of ions, more than one polyatomic ion is required to balance the charges. To show this, the formula of the polyatomic ion is placed in parentheses, with the number of ions written as a subscript. For example, the compound formed by the calcium ion (Ca^{2+}) and the nitrate ion (NO_3^-) requires two nitrate ions to balance the charge on the calcium ion. Therefore, its formula is $Ca(NO_3)_2$.

Naming Compounds Containing Polyatomic Ions

To name compounds containing polyatomic ions, we simply combine the name of the cation with the name of the anion. Thus the compound formed by the sodium ion and the sulfate ion is called sodium sulfate. Similarly, the compound $Ca(NO_3)_2$ is calcium nitrate.

You must be able to identify compounds that contain polyatomic ions from their formulas. For example, when you see the formula, Na_2SO_4, you should be able to identify it as a compound that is composed of sodium ions and sulfate ions, *not* just as a compound of sodium, sulfur, and oxygen.

| EXAMPLE | **6.3** | Write the names of each of the following ionic compounds (each contains a polyatomic ion): |

a) K_2CO_3 b) $Pb(NO_3)_2$ c) NH_4Cl

SOLUTION

a) This compound contains potassium ions and carbonate ions. Its name is therefore potassium carbonate.

b) Lead can form two cations: lead(II), Pb^{2+}; and lead(IV), Pb^{4+}. The polyatomic anion in this compound is the nitrate ion, NO_3^-. As the compound contains two nitrate ions for each lead ion, the charge on the lead ion must be $+2$. The name of the compound will be lead(II) nitrate.

c) Here the cation is the polyatomic ion, ammonium (NH_4^+), and the anion is chloride (Cl^-). The name of the compound will be ammonium chloride.

To derive the formula of a compound from its name, we always need to know the charges on the ions before we can decide how many of each are required.

| EXAMPLE | **6.4** | Write the formula of each of the following compounds: |

a) magnesium perchlorate   b) iron(III) sulfate

SOLUTION

a) Magnesium forms the ion Mg^{2+}, and the perchlorate ion has the formula ClO_4^-. To obtain a neutral compound, two perchlorate ions are needed for each magnesium ion. The formula is therefore $Mg(ClO_4)_2$.

b) Iron(III) is the name of the Fe^{3+} ion. Sulfate is the SO_4^{2-} ion. To balance the charges in this compound, we will need three sulfate ions for every two iron(III) ions. The formula must therefore be $Fe_2(SO_4)_3$.

Hydrated Salts

Many salts form crystals that contain molecules of water within the crystal structure. Such salts are called **hydrated salts**. For example, if we analyze

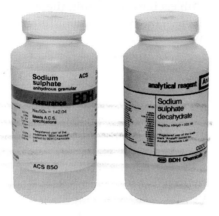

Figure 6.7
Many salts exist in hydrated form, with water molecules being part of their structure.

some blue copper(II) sulfate crystals, we find that for each copper(II) sulfate unit in the crystal there are five water molecules. The presence of the water molecules in crystalline compounds is indicated by including the word "hydrate" in the name of the compound. Therefore the blue copper(II) sulfate is sometimes called hydrated copper(II) sulfate. Greek prefixes are attached to the word "hydrate" to show the exact number of water molecules per formula unit (see Table 6.4). Thus the correct name for hydrated copper(II) sulfate is copper(II) sulfate pentahydrate. When writing the formula of a hydrated salt, a raised dot is used to separate the formula of the salt from the formula for water. The number of water molecules per formula unit is given in front of the formula for water. Therefore, the formula of copper(II) sulfate pentahydrate is written as $CuSO_4 \cdot 5H_2O$.

TABLE 6.4   *Greek Prefixes*

Greek Prefix	Number	Greek Prefix	Number
Mono-	1	Hexa-	6
Di-	2	Hepta-	7
Tri-	3	Octa-	8
Tetra-	4	Ennea- (or nona-)	9
Penta-	5	Deca-	10

Know

EXAMPLE   **6.5**   Write the name of the hydrated salt, $MgSO_4 \cdot 6H_2O$.

SOLUTION   Without any water molecules in the compound, the salt would be called magnesium sulfate. As the hydrate has six molecules of water associated with each formula unit, the word hexahydrate must be added to the salt's name. The hydrated salt's full name, therefore, is magnesium sulfate hexahydrate.

Sulfuric acid = H_2SO_4

TABLE 6.5   *Some Acid Anions*

Formula	Name
HCO_3^-	Hydrogen carbonate
HSO_4^-	Hydrogen sulfate ANION
HSO_3^-	Hydrogen sulfite
HS^-	Hydrogen sulfide
HPO_4^{2-}	Hydrogen phosphate
$H_2PO_4^-$	Dihydrogen phosphate

ie.

sometimes took paper (bi bisulfate)

Acid Salts

Acid when dissolved in water will release Hydrogen protons. H^+

In addition to normal salts, there is a family of salts whose anions contain one or more covalently bonded hydrogen atoms. These salts are called **acid salts** and the anions are called acid anions. Acid anions combine with cations in the same way as normal anions. Thus the sodium cation, Na^+, will combine with the hydrogen carbonate anion, HCO_3^- to give sodium hydrogen carbonate, $NaHCO_3$. This compound is also known as sodium bicarbonate, or baking soda.

Nitric Acid → Nitrate

Acid + Base → salt + water
HCl + NaOH → NaCl + H_2O

QUESTIONS

4. Write the formula of the compounds formed between the following:
   a) the potassium ion and the carbonate ion
   b) the calcium ion and the perchlorate ion
   c) the aluminum ion and the sulfate ion
   d) the zinc ion and the chromate ion
   e) the iron(III) ion and the nitrate ion
   f) the ammonium ion and the phosphate ion

5. What ions are present in each of the following compounds:
   a) potassium sulfate   c) calcium nitrate
   b) ammonium carbonate

6. Write the formula for each of the following compounds:
   a) aluminum nitrate   d) potassium chlorite
   b) copper(II) nitrate   e) calcium permanganate
   c) ammonium carbonate   f) tin(IV) sulfate

7. Name the following compounds:
   a) $CaSO_3$ c) $NaClO_3$ e) $Hg(CN)_2$
   b) Li_3PO_4 d) $SnSO_4$ f) $PbCrO_4$

8. Write the name of each of these hydrated salts:
   a) $CaCl_2 \cdot 2H_2O$ b) $Na_2CO_3 \cdot 10H_2O$

9. Name each of the following acid salts:
   a) $KHSO_4$ b) $Ca(HCO_3)_2$ c) $(NH_4)HS$

The Formulas of Binary Covalent Compounds

6.6

As we saw in Section 6.3, predicting the formulas of binary ionic compounds is easy if we know the charges on each of the ions involved. Covalent compounds present more of a problem. In Section 5.5 we showed how to write the electron-dot formulas of covalent compounds. We can now use the electron-dot method to predict the formula of a compound formed between two or more nonmetals.

EXAMPLE   **6.6** Predict the formula of the compound formed by oxygen and fluorine.

SOLUTION The electron-dot formula of oxygen is $\cdot \ddot{O} \cdot$, and that of fluorine is $: \ddot{F} \cdot$.

The oxygen atom needs two electrons to acquire a full valence level and the fluorine atom needs one. Both requirements can be met if the oxygen atom shares two of its valence electrons, one with each of two fluorine atoms. In return, each fluorine atom shares one of its valence electrons with the oxygen atom. Hence, the electron-dot formula is $: \ddot{F} : \ddot{O} : \ddot{F} :$ and the formula is OF_2.

A Look at Labels

Although you are only just beginning your study of chemistry, you will find that you will be able to recognize the names of the components of many consumer items. For example, many household products contain compounds of sodium. Pharmaceutical products also contain chemical compounds that you should recognize.

If you look carefully at product labels, you will see that, in addition to the main ingredients, many of them list very small quantities of other chemical compounds. These chemicals are called additives, and have been included in the product for purposes such as flavouring or food preservation.

When you are at the supermarket, check the ingredients listed on the packages of products and try to identify some of the additives. Then try to find out what purposes they serve.

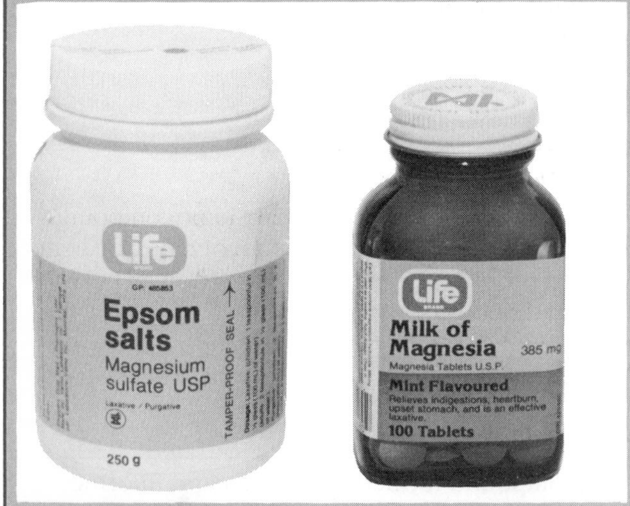

Figure 6.8
Two common pharmaceutical products containing the magnesium ion:
a) Epsom salts is magnesium sulfate, $MgSO_4$.
b) Milk of Magnesia is magnesium hydroxide, $Mg(OH)_2$.

TABLE 6.6   *Household Products Containing Sodium*

Name	Formula	Use
Sodium hydroxide	NaOH	Oven and drain cleaner
Sodium phosphate	Na_3PO_4	Grease remover in kitchen cleansers
Sodium hypochlorite	NaClO	Bleach
Sodium hydrogen sulfate	$NaHSO_4$	Toilet bowl cleaner
Sodium hydrogen carbonate	$NaHCO_3$	Baking soda

TABLE 6.7   *Common Pharmaceutical Chemicals*

Name	Formula	Use
Calcium carbonate	$CaCO_3$	Antacid
Magnesium hydroxide	$Mg(OH)_2$	Antacid
Lithium carbonate	Li_2CO_3	Antidepressant drug
Iron(II) sulfate	$FeSO_4$	Iron supplements
Zinc oxide	ZnO	Skin ointments

TABLE 6.8   *Additives in Consumer Products*

Name	Formula	Use
Sodium chloride	NaCl	Flavour enhancer
Sodium fluoride	NaF	Toothpaste additive (prevents cavities)
Potassium iodide	KI	Table salt additive (prevents goitre)
Potassium nitrate	KNO_3	Meat preservative
Iron(III) phosphate	$FePO_4$	Iron supplement in foods
Sodium hydrogen sulfite	$NaHSO_3$	Food preservative

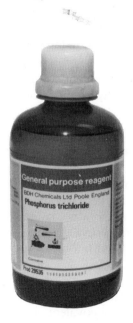

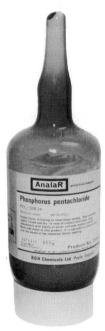

Figure 6.9

The existence of compounds like phosphorus pentachloride, PCl₅, requires us to modify our simple model of covalent bonding.

In Example 6.6, we were very careful to ask you to *predict* the formula of the compound. To find out if the prediction is correct, we would have to try to synthesize the compound in the laboratory. One of the most exciting challenges in chemistry is the preparation of new compounds. Chemists often find that compounds formed during experiments are not those that they had predicted. When this happens, ideas and theories have to be modified to explain the unexpected results.

Let us look at the compound formed between phosphorus and chlorine. We can easily construct an electron-dot formula. A phosphorus atom has five valence electrons and a chlorine atom has seven. Thus phosphorus requires three electrons to fill its valence level. It can do this by sharing one electron with each of three chlorine atoms:

$$:\ddot{C}l : \ddot{P} : \ddot{C}l: \qquad \text{phosphorus}$$
$$\qquad :\ddot{C}l: \qquad\qquad\quad \text{trichlorate}$$

The compound PCl_3 is known to exist. However, phosphorus and chlorine also form another compound, PCl_5. Other examples of compounds that would not be predicted from electron-dot formulas are SF_6 and IF_7. How can we explain the existence of these compounds?

Expansion of the Valence Level

We find that for elements of the third (and subsequent) periods, more than 8 electrons can occupy the valence level when a covalent compound is formed. From our knowledge of the chemical formulas of known compounds, it appears that phosphorus can expand its valence level to hold a maximum of 10 electrons, sulfur a maximum of 12 electrons, and chlorine a maximum of 14 electrons. In each case, the "normal" value of eight is only exceeded when the atom is in the centre of a polyatomic molecule.

For PCl_5, we can construct an electron-dot structure with the phosphorus atom sharing a pair of electrons with each chlorine atom. When we do this, phosphorus acquires 10 electrons in its valence level.

$$\quad :\ddot{C}l: \ :\ddot{C}l:$$
$$:\ddot{C}l : \ddot{P} : \ddot{C}l:$$
$$\qquad :\ddot{C}l:$$

These exceptions do not invalidate the rule that valence levels can contain a maximum of 8 electrons. The formulas of most covalent compounds do appear to fit the "rule-of-eight", as it is sometimes called. The elements in the second period *never* have more than 8 electrons in the valence level. However, the exceptions for the later periods are important because they suggest that many compounds can be prepared which *do not fit the rule-of-eight*.

QUESTIONS

10. Draw the electron-dot formula for each of the following compounds:

    a) SF_2 b) SF_4 c) SF_6

11. Oxygen is in the same group as sulfur, but oxygen and fluorine combine to form only the compound OF_2. Why do they not also form OF_4 and OF_6?

Naming Binary Covalent Compounds   6.7

When we described the method of naming binary ionic compounds, we said that the first element in the formula (the metal) kept its own name, but that the ending of the second element (the nonmetal) was changed to *-ide*. When the metal could form two different cations, as in Fe^{2+} and Fe^{3+}, and could therefore form two different compounds with a given nonmetal, we used the Stock system of nomenclature.

As we saw in the previous section, it is also possible for two nonmetals to combine to form more than one compound. Although the Stock system can be modified to distinguish between such binary covalent compounds, in Canada, we use the classical naming system for this purpose. When using the classical system, we change the ending of the name of the second element in the formula to *-ide*. To indicate the number of atoms of each element present, we use the same Greek prefixes that we used when naming hydrated salts (Table 6.4). Thus, the two compounds of phosphorus and chlorine (PCl_3 and PCl_5) are called phosphorus trichloride and phosphorus pentachloride, respectively.

If there is no prefix before the first name, as in the two examples just given, we assume there is only one atom of that element in the compound. The prefix *mono-* is attached to the name of the second element in a compound when only one atom of the second element is present in the molecule.

EXAMPLE   **6.7**

Give the name of each of the following covalent compounds:

    a) CO_2 b) CO c) N_2O_4

SOLUTION
a) carbon dioxide
b) carbon monoxide (The name monooxide is shortened to monoxide for easier pronunciation)
c) dinitrogen tetraoxide

QUESTIONS

12. Give the names of the following binary covalent compounds:

a) SO_3	c) Cl_2O	e) N_2O	g) NO_2
b) XeF_6	d) P_4O_{10}	f) NO	h) N_2O_5

dinitrogen monoxide

The Order of Symbols in a Chemical Formula

6.8

You have now seen many examples of chemical formulas and are familiar with the use of numerical subscripts to indicate the numbers of each type of atom present in a compound. When writing formulas, we also need to know the order in which to indicate the elements in the compound. For example, why is water written as H_2O rather than OH_2? Why is sodium chloride written as NaCl rather than ClNa?

In ionic compounds, the cation is always written first. In binary covalent compounds, the less electronegative element is usually written first. (The compound NH_3 is one of the few exceptions).

cation first / least electronegative.
ionic *covalent.*

EXAMPLE

6.8

Identify the correct way to write the formula of the following compounds:
a) KCl or ClK   b) SH_2 or H_2S

SOLUTION

a) This compound contains a metal and a nonmetal. The metal (K) forms the cation and is therefore written first. Thus, KCl is the correct formula.

b) Since both sulfur and hydrogen are nonmetals, the compound is covalent. The electronegativity of hydrogen is less than that of sulfur, and therefore hydrogen is written first. The correct formula is H_2S.

QUESTIONS

13. Which formula is correct in each of the following:
a) CaS or SCa   b) NF_3 or F_3N

Periodic Trends — Chemical Formulas

6.9

Patterns in chemical formulas provided Mendeléev with his most powerful argument for periodicity. If, for example, we consider the oxides of the third period elements (Table 6.9), we note that from left to right across a period, the number of oxygen atoms that combine with one atom of the other element steadily increases. We find a similar trend with the third period fluorides (Table 6.10).

TABLE 6.9 *Formulas of Some Third Period Oxides*

Element	Na	Mg	Al	Si	P	S	Cl
Oxide formula	Na_2O	MgO	Al_2O_3	SiO_2	P_4O_{10}	SO_3	Cl_2O_7
Ratio of element:oxygen	1:0.5	1:1	1:1.5	1:2	1:2.5	1:3	1:3.5

TABLE 6.10 *Formulas of Some Third Period Fluorides*

Element	Na	Mg	Al	Si	P	S	Cl
Fluoride formula	NaF	MgF_2	AlF_3	SiF_4	PF_5	SF_6	ClF_5
Ratio of element:fluorine	1:1	1:2	1:3	1:4	1:5	1:6	1:5

In the fluoride series, the number of fluorine atoms in the compounds increases steadily until we reach chlorine. With chlorine, we would expect a compound with the formula ClF_7. However, ClF_7 is not known, and there are several reasons (beyond the level of this text) why it may never be prepared. Thus, even periodicity has limitations.

It is important to remember that the type of bonding also changes across a period. For example, NaF, MgF_2, and AlF_3 contain ionic bonds; whereas SiF_4, PF_5, SF_6, and ClF_5 contain covalent bonds.

Within a specific group, we generally find a strong similarity in the formulas of the compounds. We can see this similarity in the fluorides of the alkali metals (Group IA) (Table 6.11).

TABLE 6.11 *Formulas of the Group IA Fluorides*

Element	Li	Na	K	Rb	Cs
Fluoride formula	LiF	NaF	KF	RbF	CsF

When looking at the Group VA fluorides, we find that two different sets of compounds are usually formed (Table 6.12).

TABLE 6.12 *Formulas of the Group VA Fluorides*

Element	N	P	As	Sb	Bi
Fluoride formula	NF_3	PF_3	AsF_3	SbF_3	BiF_3
	—	PF_5	AsF_5	SbF_5	BiF_5

As we mentioned in Section 6.6, nonmetals of the third and subsequent periods can acquire more than 8 valence electrons through covalent bonding. As nitrogen is in the second period, it is limited to 8 valence electrons and can form only one fluoride.

The Need for Scientists to Have Open Minds

Scientists have sometimes been guilty of ignoring the results of experiments or research if the results do not fit current theories. For example, when the noble gases were first identified at the end of the nineteenth century, several unsuccessful attempts were made to combine them with other elements. Chemists explained the lack of reactivity by using the concept of the stability of the noble-gas electron configuration. Generations of chemistry students were told that it was impossible to form compounds containing the noble gases because the atoms of these elements already had full sets of valence electrons.

However, many covalent compounds do have a central atom with more than 8 electrons in its valence level. Sulfur hexafluoride, SF_6, for example, has 12 electrons around the central sulfur atom. Chemists were so obsessed with the concept of the stability of the noble-gas configuration (the ''rule-of-eight'' or ''octet rule''), that they ignored the evidence provided by the many compounds that were exceptions to the rule.

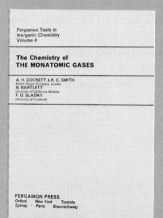

Figure 6.10
So many compounds of the noble (monatomic) gases are known that whole books, such as this one, are devoted to their study.

When compounds of xenon were first prepared in 1962, many chemists concluded that their existence contradicted the concept of periodicity. However, if we look at two of the known compounds of xenon, xenon trioxide (XeO_3), and

xenon difluoride (XeF_2), we see that their formulas are quite compatible with periodic concepts. The table below gives the formulas of some of the fifth period oxides. As you can see, xenon trioxide completes the trend across the period.

TABLE 6.13	Formulas of Some Fifth Period Oxides			
Element	Sb	Te	I	Xe
Oxide formula	Sb_2O_3	TeO_2	I_2O_5	XeO_3
Ratio of element:oxygen	1:1.5	1:2	1:2.5	1:3

Another way to look at periodicity is to study series of molecules in which the central atom is surrounded by the same number of electrons. We find that the later fifth period fluorides form a series in which each central atom has 10 valence electrons.

TABLE 6.14	Formulas of Some Fifth Period Fluorides			
Element	Sb	Te	I	Xe
Fluoride formula	SbF_5	TeF_4	IF_3	XeF_2
Ratio of element:fluoride	1:5	1:4	1:3	1:2

We have seen that the existence of xenon compounds reinforces, rather than contradicts, the usefulness of the periodicity concept. On the other hand, we should not fall into the trap of assuming a compound has to exist, just to fit a periodic trend. Many factors are involved in the existence of compounds and part of the excitement of chemistry is to understand what these factors are. Scientists must keep open minds and be receptive to new ideas and to evidence that disproves current theories.

Periodic Properties — Oxidation Numbers

VOID

6.10

We have learned how to determine chemical formulas by using electron-dot diagrams. In addition, we have found that there are patterns to these chemical formulas. It is possible to develop a simple way of predicting chemical formulas by using the concept of oxidation numbers. As the tables below show, patterns also occur in oxidation numbers.

We can begin our discussion of oxidation numbers by stating that the **oxidation number** of an atom in its pure form, as an element, is *always zero*. Thus, the oxidation number of magnesium in magnesium metal is zero, and the oxidation number of fluorine in diatomic fluorine gas (F_2) is also zero. In an ionic compound, however, the oxidation number of each element is equal to the charge on the ion. Thus, the oxidation number of magnesium in $MgCl_2$ is $+2$, because the Mg^{2+} ion is present. Similarly, the oxidation number of chlorine in $MgCl_2$ is -1. The oxidation number for certain elements can vary from one compound to another. For example, iron has an oxidation number of $+3$ in $FeCl_3$, but $+2$ in $FeCl_2$.

When we studied ionic compounds we learned that the sum of the charges on the ions in such compounds equaled zero. The same relationship is true for oxidation numbers. Thus, in an ionic compound the sum of the oxidation numbers is equal to zero. In a polyatomic ion, on the other hand, the sum of the oxidation numbers is equal to the charge on the ion.

The assignment of oxidation numbers to elements in covalent compounds is not as simple. Because we are no longer dealing with ions, we cannot simply set oxidation numbers as being equal to ionic charges. However, chemists have been able to develop a set of rules to overcome this problem. These rules are best understood by first examining several periods of the Periodic Table.

TABLE 6.15	*Common Oxidation Numbers of the Second Period Elements*						
Group	IA	IIA	IIIA	IVA	VA	VIA	VIIA
Element	Li	Be	B	C	N	O	F
Common Oxidation numbers	+1	+2	+3	+4 −4	+5,+3 −3	−2	−1

As you can see from Table 6.15, oxidation numbers increase as we move from Group IA through VA, and again from IVA through VIIA. Also, the highest oxidation number of any element with a positive oxidation number is equal to the group number. Where the oxidation number is negative, we find that the oxidation number is equal to the group number minus eight. For oxygen, which is in Group VIA, subtracting eight from six gives minus two (-2), the most common oxidation number for oxygen. Similar trends are shown by the elements in the third period. In this period, there is a range of oxidation numbers for the nonmetals, particularly sulfur and chlorine.

TABLE 6.16 *Common Oxidation Numbers of the Third Period Elements*

Group	IA	IIA	IIIA	IVA	VA	VIA	VIIA
Element	Na	Mg	Al	Si	P	S	Cl
Common Oxidation Numbers	+1	+2	+3	+4	+3,+5	+2,+4,+6	+1,+3,+5,+7
				−4	−3	−2	−1

When using oxidation numbers to predict the formulas of binary covalent compounds, the more electronegative element *always* has a negative oxidation number. To illustrate this fact, let's examine the two compounds formed between phosphorus and chlorine.

Since both elements are nonmetals, any compounds formed between them are likely to be covalent. By examining Figure 5.13 we can see that chlorine is more electronegative than phosphorus ($Cl = 3.0$, $P = 2.1$). We therefore assign a negative oxidation number of −1 to chlorine. Table 6.16 shows two positive oxidation numbers for phosphorus. It also shows a −3 oxidation number that we need not consider, as both elements cannot have negative oxidation numbers. In order to obtain a compound in which the sum of the oxidation numbers is zero, phosphorus and chlorine can combine in ratios of 1:3 and 1:5. Thus, the formulas for the two compounds are PCl_3 and PCl_5. Both of these compounds are known to exist.

EXAMPLE 6.9

Use oxidation numbers to predict the formulas for the compounds formed between nitrogen and oxygen.

SOLUTION

Since nitrogen and oxygen are nonmetals, any compounds formed between them will be covalent. As oxygen is the more electronegative element, it is assigned an oxidation number of −2. Next, we identify from Table 6.15 the possible *positive* oxidation numbers of nitrogen.

a) When nitrogen has an oxidation number of +3, we need two nitrogen atoms and three oxygen atoms to ensure than the sum of the oxidation numbers is zero. The formula of this compound will be N_2O_3.

b) If nitrogen is assigned an oxidation number of +5, we need two nitrogen atoms and five oxygen atoms to obtain a compound in which the sum of the oxidation numbers is zero. This compound has the formula N_2O_5. Both compounds, N_2O_3 and N_2O_5, are known to exist.

We can now summarize the key rules for assigning oxidation numbers as follows:

ELEMENTS

The oxidation number of an atom is zero.

IONIC COMPOUNDS

For monatomic ions, the oxidation number matches the charge on the ion.

In polyatomic ions, the sum of the individual oxidation numbers must equal the charge on the ion.

In ionic compounds, the sum of the oxidation numbers equals zero.

COVALENT COMPOUNDS

The more electronegative element is always assigned a negative oxidation number.

The sum of the oxidation numbers equals zero.

There are a number of other rules for assigning oxidation numbers, but most are reserved for more advanced study. Two additional guidelines that will be useful for you now are the following:

The most common oxidation number for hydrogen is + 1.
The most common oxidation number for oxygen is − 2.

One final point deserves our attention. Although oxidation numbers serve a very useful purpose in helping us find the formulas of chemical compounds, not all the compounds predicted by this method are known to exist.

QUESTIONS

14. Assign the correct oxidation number to each element in the following compounds:
   a) SF_6 b) $NiCl_2$ c) CO_2 d) H_2O

15. Using the concept of oxidation numbers, predict the formula(s) of the compound(s) formed between each of the following:
   a) lithium and nitrogen   d) carbon and chlorine
   b) sulfur and chlorine   e) phosphorus and oxygen
   c) aluminum and sulfur

Summary

- There are two main systems of naming compounds: the classical system and the Stock system.

- When naming an ionic compound by the Stock system, the name of the element forming the cation comes first, followed by the name of the anion. If the cation can have more than one charge, the charge on the ion is shown in Roman numerals, in brackets, after the name. In the classical system, metals that can have more than one charge are referred to by their Latin names with the ending *-ic* used for the ion of higher charge and the ending *-ous* used for the ion of lower charge.

- In binary ionic compounds, positive ions combine with negative ions in ratios that result in electrically neutral compounds. The name and symbol of the metal is always given first.

- Most common polyatomic ions contain oxygen and one other element. These are called oxyanions, and their names are based on the element other than oxygen that is present. Prefixes and suffixes are used to distinguish between different oxyanions formed by the same element.

- Cations and polyatomic anions combine to give neutral compounds. When naming these compounds, the name of the cation is followed by the name of the anion.

- The presence of water molecules in a crystal structure is indicated by the word hydrate in the name of the compound. Greek prefixes indicate the number of water molecules per formula unit.

- Acid salts contain one or more hydrogen atoms covalently bonded to an anion. The name of the anion is preceded by the word "hydrogen" when such compounds are named.

- The formulas of binary covalent compounds can be predicted by drawing electron-dot formulas. Nonmetallic elements of the third and subsequent periods can have more than 8 electrons in the valence level if the atom is in the centre of a polyatomic molecule.

- In the names and formulas of binary covalent compounds, the less electronegative element is usually written first.

- There is a periodic trend in the formulas of oxides and fluorides in going from left to right across the Periodic Table.

- Oxidation numbers can be used to predict the formulas of binary, ionic, and covalent compounds.

KEY WORDS

acid salt
binary compound
classical system of nomenclature
hydrated salt

oxidation number
oxyanion
Stock system

1. a) magnesium *(names)* ion, Mg^{2+} *(Symbols)*
   b) silver ion, Ag^+
   c) iodide ion, I^-
   d) copper(I) ion or cuprous ion, Cu^+
      copper(II) ion or cupric ion, Cu^{2+}
   e) nitride ion, N^{3-}
   f) tin(II) ion or stannous ion, Sn^{2+}
      tin(IV) ion or stannic ion, Sn^{4+}

Formulas

2. a) Li_2S, lithium sulfide   c) ZnO, zinc oxide
   b) AlF_3, aluminum fluoride   d) Ca_3P_2, calcium phosphide

3. a) $FeCl_2$, iron(II) chloride; $FeCl_3$, iron(III) chloride
   b) Cu_2S, copper(I) sulfide; CuS, copper(II) sulfide
   c) Hg_2O, mercury(I) oxide; HgO, mercury(II) oxide

Formulas

4. a) K_2CO_3 d) $ZnCrO_4$
   b) $Ca(ClO_4)_2$ e) $Fe(NO_3)_3$
   c) $Al_2(SO_4)_3$ f) $(NH_4)_3PO_4$

5. a) K^+, SO_4^{2-} b) NH_4^+, CO_3^{2-} c) Ca^{2+}, NO_3^-

6. a) $Al(NO_3)_3$ c) $(NH_4)_2CO_3$ e) $Ca(MnO_4)_2$
   b) $Cu(NO_3)_2$ d) $KClO_2$ f) $Sn(SO_4)_2$

7. a) calcium sulfite   d) tin(II) sulfate
   b) lithium phosphate   e) mercury(II) cyanide
   c) sodium chlorate   f) lead(II) chromate

8. a) calcium chloride dihydrate
   b) sodium carbonate decahydrate

9. a) potassium hydrogen sulfate
   b) calcium hydrogen carbonate
   c) ammonium hydrogen sulfide

10. a) $:\!\ddot{F}\!:\!\ddot{S}\!:\!\ddot{F}\!:$

    c)

    b) $:\!\ddot{F}\!:\ \ddot{S}\ :\!\ddot{F}\!:$
       $:\!\ddot{F}\!:\ :\!\ddot{F}\!:$

11. Oxygen is in the second period and cannot have more than eight electrons in its valence level.

12. a) sulfur trioxide   e) dinitrogen monoxide
    b) xenon hexafluoride   f) nitrogen monoxide
    c) dichlorine monoxide   g) nitrogen dioxide
    d) tetraphosphorus decaoxide h) dinitrogen pentaoxide

13. a) CaS b) NF_3

14. a) $F = -1$, $S = +6$ c) $C = +4$, $O = -2$
    b) $Ni = +2$, $Cl = -1$ d) $O = -2$, $H = +1$

15. a) Li_3N b) SCl_2, SCl_4, SCl_6 c) Al_2S_3 d) CCl_4 e) P_2O_3, P_2O_5

1. How are the following ions named:
   a) a simple metal cation
   b) a simple nonmetal anion
   c) a cation that has more than one possible charge
   d) a polyatomic ion with one fewer oxygen atom than the -*ate* form
   e) a polyatomic ion with one more oxygen atom than the -*ate* form
   f) a polyatomic ion with two fewer oxygen atoms than the -*ate* form

2. How are the following compounds named:
   a) a binary ionic compound
   b) a binary covalent compound (classical method)
   c) a binary ionic compound where the cation has more than one possible charge (Stock method)
   d) a hydrated salt
   e) an acid salt

3. In a binary ionic compound, which element is written first in the formula?

4. In a binary covalent compound, which element is written first in the formula?

5. Give the formula of the following oxyanions:
   a) carbonate   c) perchlorate
   b) chlorite   d) dichromate

6. Give the name of each of the following:
   a) NO_2^- c) MnO_4^- e) CrO_4^{2-} g) HSO_4^-
   b) ClO^- d) HS^- f) SO_3^{2-} h) ClO_3^-

7. What is meant by the term "acid salt"? Give the name and formula of an example.

8. What is meant by the term "hydrated salt"? Name and give the formula of an example.

9. How many electrons are normally in the valence level of a cation? How many are in the valence level of an anion?

10. How many electrons are normally in the valence level of a covalently bonded atom? Can it have more? If so, give an example.

11. What is the trend in the oxidation numbers within a family of elements?

12. What is the trend in oxidation numbers across a period in the Periodic Table?

13. Which element in a binary compound has the positive oxidation number?

14. Briefly describe the major contribution made by each of the following chemists towards the development of a systematic method for naming compounds:
    a) Guyton de Morveau
    b) Alfred Stock

Handwritten notes:

KI potassium iodide

Ba F Barium Flouride

Sn Cl$_4$ SnCl$_2$

Li$_2$O

Zn S

15. Predict the formula of the binary compound that is likely to be formed by each of the following pairs of metals and nonmetals, and give an acceptable name for each compound:
a) potassium and iodine
b) barium and fluorine
c) tin and chlorine (two possibilities)
d) lithium and oxygen
e) zinc and sulfur

16. Predict the formula of the binary compound most likely to be formed by the following pairs of metals and nonmetals, naming the compound in each case:
a) sodium and sulfur
b) aluminum and oxygen
c) lead and chlorine (two possibilities)
d) calcium and bromine
e) silver and iodine

17. State both the formula and the name of the compound formed between the following pairs of ions:
a) calcium and sulfate
b) sodium and sulfide
c) lead(II) and phosphate
d) aluminum and chloride
e) mercury(I) and nitrate

18. State the formula and name of the compound formed between the following pairs of ions:
a) lithium and nitride
b) copper(II) and phosphide
c) magnesium and oxide
d) tin(IV) and phosphate
e) potassium and dichromate

19. Name the following compounds:
a) KBr   b) BaF$_2$ c) NaNO$_3$ d) Ca(NO$_2$)$_2$ e) Na$_2$SO$_4 \cdot$7H$_2$O

20. Name the following compounds:
a) LiCl   b) NH$_4$Br   c) Na$_2$S   d) Mg$_3$(PO$_4$)$_2$ e) Na$_2$CO$_3 \cdot$10H$_2$O

21. Write an acceptable name for each of the following compounds:
a) CO$_2$ b) BaCl$_2$ c) Cl$_2$O$_7$ d) SnCl$_2$ e) Al$_2$O$_3$

22. Write an acceptable name for each of the following binary compounds:
a) SO$_2$ b) CaF$_2$ c) P$_2$O$_5$ d) PbCl$_4$ e) Rb$_2$SO$_4$

23. Write the formula for each of the following:
a) boron trifluoride
b) potassium oxide
c) dinitrogen tetraoxide
d) mercury(II) bromide
e) silicon dioxide

24. Write the formula for each of the following:
a) silicon tetrafluoride
b) calcium oxide
c) diiodine pentaoxide
d) iron(III) oxide
e) mercury(I) bromide

25. Name the polyatomic ion present in each of the following:
a) BaSO$_4$
b) KCN
c) Al(OH)$_3$
d) Ag$_2$Cr$_2$O$_7$
e) Zn(CH$_3$CO$_2$)$_2$

26. Name the acid anion present in each of the following:
    a) $NaHCO_3$ c) LiH_2PO_4
    b) KHS   d) $Ca(HSO_3)_2$

27. The following compounds each have more than 8 electrons around their central atoms:
    a) XeO_2 b) SF_6
    Draw electron-dot formulas for each. Name each compound.

28. Draw electron-dot formulas for each of the following compounds:
    a) IF_5 b) XeO_3
    Name each compound.

29. Name the following compounds:
    a) $CaSO_4$ c) $Cu(CH_3CO_2)_2$ e) $Al(OH)_3$ g) NH_4ClO_4 i) $Mg(NO_3)_2$
    b) $Pb(NO_3)_2$ d) Na_3PO_4 f) $ZnSO_3$ h) $LiClO$ j) $Mg(NO_2)_2$

30. Name each of the following compounds:
    a) Li_2CO_3 c) $(NH_4)_2S$ e) $Ca(OH)_2$ g) $Pb(CO_3)_2$ i) $AgClO$
    b) $Fe_2(SO_4)_3$ d) $Sn_3(PO_4)_2$ f) $FeSO_4$ h) $AgClO_4$ j) $Ca(ClO_2)_2$

31. Write the formula for each of the following:
    a) potassium sulfate   f) sodium chlorate
    b) sodium cyanide   g) ammonium phosphate
    c) lead(II) chromate   h) zinc perchlorate
    d) iron(III) hydroxide   i) iron(II) sulfite
    e) ammonium nitrate   j) magnesium hypochlorite

32. Write the formula for each of the following:
    a) ammonium sulfate   f) sodium perchlorate
    b) barium acetate   g) silver sulfide
    c) sodium dichromate   h) tin(II) hypochlorite
    d) tin(IV) nitrate   i) iron(III) perchlorate
    e) potassium permanganate   j) calcium phosphate

33. Write the formula for each of the following salts and identify each as being either an acid salt or hydrated salt:
    a) barium chloride dihydrate   c) zinc chloride tetrahydrate
    b) potassium hydrogen sulfate   d) calcium hydrogen carbonate

34. Name the following salts and indicate whether each is an acid salt or a hydrated salt:
    a) $SnCl_2 \cdot 5H_2O$ c) $BaHPO_4$
    b) $NaHSO_4$ d) $FePO_4 \cdot 3H_2O$

35. The following minerals are all found in nature and are commonly known by the names given. Supply a systematic name in each case:
    a) PbS, galena   b) SiO_2, quartz   c) $CaSO_4 \cdot 2H_2O$, gypsum

36. Provide a systematic name for each of the following naturally occurring minerals:
    a) HgS, cinnabar   c) $Al_2O_3 \cdot 2H_2O$, bauxite
    b) Fe_2O_3, hematite

37. The following are named after people, places, or the appearance of the substance. Provide IUPAC names for each of them:
    a) Epsom salts, $MgSO_4 \cdot 7H_2O$ c) butter of arsenic, $AsCl_3$
    b) Glauber's salt, $Na_2SO_4 \cdot 10H_2O$

38. Give the IUPAC name for each of the following compounds:
    a) butter of tin, $SnCl_4 \cdot 5H_2O$ c) saltpetre, KNO_3
    b) calomel, Hg_2Cl_2 d) green vitriol, $FeSO_4$

39. Give the formula and IUPAC name for each of the following classical names:
    a) ferrous sulfate   b) stannous chloride   c) cupric nitrate

40. The following names are on the bottles of chemicals obtained from the chemical storeroom:
    a) plumbic bromide   b) mercurous sulfate   c) stannic fluoride
    What is the correct IUPAC name of each? Write the formula for each compound.

41. In Britain, the Stock system is used for covalent compounds as well as ionic compounds. Determine the formula and classical name for each of the following compounds:
    a) sulfur(VI) fluoride   b) nitrogen(IV) oxide   c) iodine(V) oxide

42. Change each of the following Stock names for covalent compounds into the commonly used classical name:
    a) chlorine(VII) oxide   c) xenon(VI) oxide
    b) phosphorus(V) sulfide

43. Use the concept of oxidation numbers to write the formulas and names for all the possible compounds that could be formed between sulfur and each of the elements of the second period.

44. Use oxidation numbers to predict the formulas of all the possible compounds that could be formed between nitrogen and the elements of the third period (sodium through chlorine). Name each compound.

45. Oxygen has an oxidation number of -2. Name each of the following compounds and determine the oxidation number of the nonoxygen element in each.
    a) WO_3 b) V_2O_5 c) CdO d) Mn_2O_7 e) Co_2O_3

46. The halogens can have an oxidation number of -1 when combined with metals. Name each of the following compounds and determine the oxidation number of the metal in each:
    a) $AuCl_3$ b) $MoCl_5$ c) WF_6 d) $PtCl_4$ e) UF_4

SUGGESTED PROJECTS

1. Many of the chemicals used in fertilizers are simple ionic compounds. Some of these chemicals have already been mentioned in this chapter. Look at the labels on some bags of fertilizer and see what they contain. Use reference books to find out why plants need these chemicals.

2. Sodium fluoride can be used to help prevent cavities in teeth. Where there is not enough natural fluoride in drinking water, sodium fluoride may be added to the water by local authorities. Compounds containing fluoride are also added to some toothpastes and mouthwashes. Yet fluoridation is still a controversial topic. Use reference books and articles from newspapers and magazines to find out more about this subject. Try to find out where the authorities in your area stand on this issue.

3. Many of the transition metal ions are brightly coloured. Check the transition metal compounds in your school laboratory and list the colours commonly associated with each metal ion. Use reference books to look up information on the chemistry of these elements and their compounds.

The Mole and Chemical Compounds

In the last two chapters, we described how to derive the names and formulas of chemical compounds. However, we cannot be certain that a specific compound can actually exist until we go into the laboratory and try to make that compound. When we have prepared a compound, how do we determine its formula? To do this we make use of the mole concept, a topic introduced in Sections 3.7 and 3.8.

A Review of the Mole

7.1

In the laboratory we have to work with very large numbers of atoms because they have extremely small masses. We count atoms in groups of 6.02×10^{23}. This number is known as Avogadro's number, and is the number of atoms in a mole. The conversion-factor method can be used to convert between moles and the number of atoms.

EXAMPLE **7.1** Calculate the number of moles in 1.00×10^{23} atoms.

SOLUTION Since we want our answer to be in moles, our conversion factor will be the inverted or reciprocal form of 6.02×10^{23} atoms·mol^{-1}. This is written as

$$\frac{1 \text{ mol}}{6.02 \times 10^{23} \text{ atoms}}$$

Therefore

$$\text{Number of moles} = 1.00 \times \cancel{10^{23} \text{ atoms}} \times \frac{1 \text{ mol}}{6.02 \times \cancel{10^{23} \text{ atoms}}}$$

$$= 0.166 \text{ mol}$$

To measure a specific number of moles of atoms, we first need to know the mass of one mole. We calculate this mass by using another conversion factor, the molar mass. The molar mass has the same numerical value as the atomic mass, but is expressed in grams per mole.

EXAMPLE   **7.2**   Calculate the mass of 2.50 mol of lead.

SOLUTION   From the Periodic Table, we see that the molar mass of lead is $207.2 \text{ g} \cdot \text{mol}^{-1}$. We will use this as our conversion factor.

$$\text{Mass of lead} = 2.50 \; \cancel{\text{mol Pb}} \times \frac{207.2 \text{ g Pb}}{1 \; \cancel{\text{mol Pb}}}$$

$$= 518 \text{ g Pb}$$

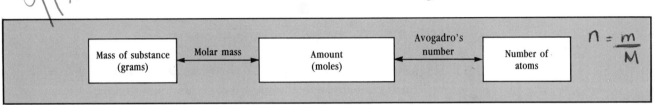

$$n = \frac{m}{M}$$

Figure 7.1
The relationship between mass and number of atoms.

Figure 7.1 shows us how we can use the mole as a way of relating the mass of a substance to the number of atoms present in that substance. The following example shows both a strategy and the steps involved in such a calculation. When solving problems of a similar nature you should design a strategy using Figure 7.1.

EXAMPLE   **7.3**   How many atoms are there in 24 g of carbon?

SOLUTION

> **STRATEGY**
> 1. Mass $\longrightarrow$ Moles
> 2. Moles $\longrightarrow$ Atoms

STEP 1: First, we convert from mass of carbon to moles of carbon using the molar mass of carbon as the conversion factor. From the Periodic Table, we find a value of $12.0 \text{ g} \cdot \text{mol}^{-1}$ for the molar mass of carbon. To obtain an answer in moles, we invert the factor and multiply:

$$\text{Number of moles of carbon} = 24 \; \cancel{\text{g C}} \times \frac{1 \text{ mol C}}{12.0 \; \cancel{\text{g C}}}$$

$$= 2.0 \text{ mol C}$$

STEP 2: We can now use Avogadro's number as our second conversion factor to determine the number of atoms present:

$$\text{Number of atoms of carbon} = 2.0 \text{ mol C} \times \frac{6.02 \times 10^{23} \text{ atoms C}}{1 \text{ mol C}}$$

$$= 1.2 \times 10^{24} \text{ atoms C}$$

Note that the same *masses* of different elements contain different numbers of atoms. Just as we know that 100 g of quarters will contain fewer coins than 100 g of dimes because each dime has a smaller mass than a quarter, so it is with elements. Every element has a different atomic mass. Therefore if we have the same mass of two elements, we will have more atoms of the one with the lower atomic mass than of the one with the higher atomic mass.

If we want to measure the same number of atoms of different elements, we must measure the mass of each element that corresponds to a specific number of moles.

QUESTIONS

1. Calculate the mass of 0.320 mol of copper.
2. Find the number of moles of silver in 2.63 g of the element.
3. Find the mass (in grams) of 1.0×10^6 atoms of helium.
4. Which contains more atoms, 1.0 g of aluminum or 1.0 g of lead?

Molecular Mass, Formula Mass, and Molar Mass 7.2

So far, all our examples of mole calculations have been carried out using elements. Mole calculations can also be performed with compounds. To do this we need to introduce two new terms, molecular mass and formula mass. We can then relate these two new terms to molar mass.

Molecular Mass

The term **molecular mass** applies to covalent compounds. It is the mass of one molecule of such a compound, expressed in unified atomic mass units. To calculate molecular mass we simply add the atomic masses of all the atoms present in the molecule in question.

EXAMPLE 7.4 Calculate the molecular mass of water (H_2O).

SOLUTION

$$2 \times (\text{Atomic mass of H}) = 2 \times 1.01 \text{ u} = 2.02 \text{ u}$$
$$1 \times (\text{Atomic mass of O}) = 1 \times 16.0 \text{ u} = \underline{16.0 \text{ u}}$$
$$\text{Molecular mass of } H_2O = 18.0 \text{ u}$$

Formula Mass

As we mentioned in Section 5.4, the smallest grouping of an ionic compound is a formula unit. The mass of this unit is called the **formula mass** of the compound. The calculation for the formula mass is exactly the same as that for molecular mass.

EXAMPLE   **7.5**   Calculate the formula mass of sodium sulfate, Na_2SO_4.

SOLUTION

$$2 \times \text{(Atomic mass of Na)} = 2 \times 23.0\,u = 46.0\,u$$
$$1 \times \text{(Atomic mass of S)} = 1 \times 32.1\,u = 32.1\,u$$
$$4 \times \text{(Atomic mass of O)} = 4 \times 16.0\,u = \underline{64.0\,u}$$
$$\text{Formula mass of } Na_2SO_4 = 142.1\,u$$

EXAMPLE   **7.6**   Calculate the formula mass of calcium nitrate, $Ca(NO_3)_2$.

SOLUTION   Here we must remember that the parentheses in $Ca(NO_3)_2$ indicate that we have two nitrate ions present in each formula unit. Thus, we have a total of one calcium atom, two nitrogen atoms, and six oxygen atoms. The formula mass is found by adding the atomic masses of all the atoms present. Thus

$$1 \times \text{(Atomic mass of Ca)} = 1 \times 40.1\,u = 40.1\,u$$
$$2 \times \text{(Atomic mass of N)} = 2 \times 14.0\,u = 28.0\,u$$
$$6 \times \text{(Atomic mass of O)} = 6 \times 16.0\,u = \underline{96.0\,u}$$
$$\text{Formula mass of } Ca(NO_3)_2 = 164.1\,u \quad \text{Molar Mass}$$

Molar Mass

Molar mass.

The mass of one mole of a substance is referred to as its molar mass. In Section 3.8 we saw that the mass of one mole of atoms, expressed in grams, is numerically equal to the atomic mass, expressed in unified atomic mass units. The same relationship holds true between the mass of one mole of a compound and the compound's molecular or formula mass. If the compound is ionic, we can convert its formula mass in unified atomic mass units to molar mass in $g \cdot mol^{-1}$. Similarly, when the compound is covalent, we can convert its molecular mass to molar mass, provided that we change the units accordingly. The following examples should make this point clear.

> For the *covalent* compound, carbon disulfide, CS_2, the molecular mass is 76.2 u; thus, the molar mass is 76.2 $g \cdot mol^{-1}$.

> For the *ionic* compound, sodium chloride, NaCl, the formula mass is 58.5 u; thus, the molar mass is 58.5 $g \cdot mol^{-1}$.

Since both the formula mass and the molecular mass can be converted to molar mass, it makes sense to adopt a system that allows us to add the masses of the moles of each element in a compound. The following example does just that.

(Handwritten notes in margin: "Back at ya!", "Hiya Dude", "Molecular mass", "Molar mass (in g)", "Martina McCarthy")

| EXAMPLE | 7.7 | Calculate the molar mass of calcium chloride dihydrate, $CaCl_2 \cdot 2H_2O$. |

SOLUTION We have to take note of the fact that this hydrated compound has two molecules of water associated with each formula unit.

$$
\begin{array}{rcl}
1 \times \text{(Mass of 1 mol of Ca)} = 1 \times 40.1 \text{ g} = & 40.1 \text{ g} \\
2 \times \text{(Mass of 1 mol of Cl)} = 2 \times 35.5 \text{ g} = & 71.0 \text{ g} \\
4 \times \text{(Mass of 1 mol of H)} = 4 \times 1.01 \text{ g} = & 4.04 \text{ g} \\
2 \times \text{(Mass of 1 mol of O)} = 2 \times 16.0 \text{ g} = & \underline{32.0 \text{ g}} \\
\text{Mass of 1 mol of } CaCl_2 \cdot 2H_2O = & 147.1 \text{ g}
\end{array}
$$

Since molar mass is expressed as mass *per mole*, our answer is $147.1 \text{ g} \cdot \text{mol}^{-1}$.

QUESTIONS

5. Calculate the following:
   a) the molecular mass of CF_2Cl_2
   b) the formula mass of $MgCO_3$
   c) the molar mass of $(NH_4)_3PO_4$
   d) the molar mass of $C_{12}H_{22}O_{11}$

Mole Calculations for Compounds

7.3 Mole calculations for compounds are essentially the same as those for elements. However, before we can perform these calculations we must first find the molar mass of the compound. Having done this, we can then determine the number of moles present in a specified mass of a given compound. Conversely, we can determine the mass of a given compound that corresponds to a specified number of moles of that compound.

| EXAMPLE | 7.8 | A chemist wishes to conduct an experiment with 0.200 mol of calcium carbonate ($CaCO_3$). What mass of calcium carbonate must be used? |

SOLUTION Using the method introduced in Example 7.7, the mass of one mole of $CaCO_3$ is found to be

$$40.1 \text{ g} + 12.0 \text{ g} + 3(16.0 \text{ g}) = 100.1 \text{ g}$$

We then use the molar mass, which is $100.1 \text{ g} \cdot \text{mol}^{-1}$, as our conversion factor:

$$\text{Mass of } CaCO_3 = 0.200 \text{ mol } CaCO_3 \times \frac{100.1 \text{ g } CaCO_3}{1 \text{ mol } CaCO_3}$$

$$= 20.0 \text{ g } CaCO_3$$

We can also determine the number of molecules present in a given mass of a covalent compound. This involves a two-step calculation.

EXAMPLE	7.9	Calculate the number of molecules of water in an ice cube of mass 12.6 g.

SOLUTION

STRATEGY

1. Mass ⟶ Moles
2. Moles ⟶ Molecules

SANDY

STEP 1: The mass of one mole of water is
$$2(1.01 \text{ g}) + 16.0 \text{ g} = 18.0 \text{ g}$$

The molar mass is therefore $18.0 \text{ g} \cdot \text{mol}^{-1}$. The reciprocal is used as our conversion factor.

$$\text{Number of moles of water} = 12.6 \text{ g H}_2\text{O} \times \frac{1 \text{ mol H}_2\text{O}}{18.0 \text{ g H}_2\text{O}}$$
$$= 0.700 \text{ mol H}_2\text{O}$$

STEP 2: Since we have Avogadro's number of water molecules in each mole of water, our second conversion factor is 6.02×10^{23} molecule$\cdot$mol^{-1}. Thus

Number of molecules of H_2O

$$= 0.700 \text{ mol H}_2\text{O} \times \frac{6.02 \times 10^{23} \text{ molecules H}_2\text{O}}{1 \text{ mol H}_2\text{O}}$$
$$= 4.21 \times 10^{23} \text{ molecules H}_2\text{O}$$

By adding one more step to the calculation carried out in Example 7.9, it is possible to determine the number of hydrogen and oxygen atoms present in the ice cube. We know that each molecule of water contains two atoms of hydrogen and one atom of oxygen. Therefore, by multiplying the answer in Example 7.9 by a factor of two we will derive the number of hydrogen atoms. Since there is only one oxygen atom in each water molecule, the number of oxygen atoms in the ice cube is the same as the number of water molecules in the ice cube. Example 7.10 shows the details of a similar calculation.

EXAMPLE	7.10	Nitrogen is the major component of our atmosphere. Calculate the number of atoms present in 1.00 g of nitrogen.

SOLUTION

STRATEGY

1. Mass ⟶ Moles
2. Moles ⟶ Molecules
3. Molecules ⟶ Atoms

STEP 1: Nitrogen forms diatomic molecules. Therefore, the mass of one mole of nitrogen gas is determined by multiplying the atomic mass of nitrogen found in the Periodic Table by two. Thus

$$\text{Mass of one mole of } N_2 = 2(14.0 \text{ g}) = 28.0 \text{ g}$$

$$\text{Number of moles of } N_2 = 1.00 \text{ g } N_2 \times \frac{1 \text{ mol } N_2}{28.0 \text{ g } N_2}$$

$$= 3.57 \times 10^{-2} \text{ mol } N_2$$

STEP 2: Number of N_2 molecules

$$= 3.57 \times 10^{-2} \text{ mol } N_2 \times \frac{6.02 \times 10^{23} \text{ molecules } N_2}{1 \text{ mol } N_2}$$

$$= 2.15 \times 10^{22} \text{ molecules } N_2$$

STEP 3: Since each nitrogen molecule contains two atoms

Number of nitrogen atoms

$$= 2.15 \times 10^{22} \text{ molecules } N_2 \times \frac{2 \text{ atoms } N}{1 \text{ molecule } N_2}$$

$$= 4.30 \times 10^{22} \text{ atoms } N$$

EXAMPLE   **7.11**

Calcium chloride ($CaCl_2$) is an ionic compound that finds considerable use in the laboratory because of its ability to absorb moisture from the air. Calculate the number of chloride ions in 22.2 g of calcium chloride.

SOLUTION

> **STRATEGY**
> 1. Mass ⟶ Moles
> 2. Moles ⟶ Formula units
> 3. Formula units ⟶ Number of ions

STEP 1: The mass of one mole of $CaCl_2$ = 40.1 g + 2(35.5 g)

$$= 111.1 \text{ g}$$

$$\text{Moles of } CaCl_2 = 2.22 \text{ g } CaCl_2 \times \frac{1 \text{ mol } CaCl_2}{111.1 \text{ g } CaCl_2}$$

$$= 2.00 \times 10^{-2} \text{ mol } CaCl_2$$

STEP 2: As there are 6.02×10^{23} formula units of $CaCl_2$ per mole of $CaCl_2$ then

Number of formula units of $CaCl_2$

$$= 2.00 \times 10^{-2} \text{ mol } CaCl_2 \times \frac{6.02 \times 10^{23} \text{ formula units } CaCl_2}{1 \text{ mol } CaCl_2}$$

$$= 1.20 \times 10^{22} \text{ formula units } CaCl_2$$

STEP 3: Each formula unit of $CaCl_2$ consists of one Ca^{2+} ion and two Cl^- ions:

Number of Cl^- ions

$$= 1.20 \times 10^{22} \text{ formula units } CaCl_2 \times \frac{2 \text{ } Cl^- \text{ ions}}{1 \text{ formula unit } CaCl_2}$$

$$= 2.40 \times 10^{22} \text{ } Cl^- \text{ ions.}$$

QUESTIONS

6. If a spoonful of sugar (sucrose, $C_{12}H_{22}O_{11}$) contains 4.87 g of the compound, find
   a) the number of sugar molecules in each spoonful
   b) the number of carbon atoms in each spoonful
7. Find the number of sodium ions in 6.81 g of sodium sulfate.

The Composition of a Compound

7.4

In 1799, the French chemist, Joseph Proust, showed that copper(II) carbonate always had the same chemical composition, irrespective of its method of preparation. This discovery laid the foundation for an important principle of chemistry, the Law of Constant Composition.

The Law of Constant Composition

We can express this law as follows:

A specific compound has the same composition anywhere in the universe.

For example, a molecule of water always contains two hydrogen atoms and one oxygen atom. This is true anywhere on the earth, on another planet, or at any location in the universe. We can also state the law in terms of mass ratios as follows:

A specific compound always contains the same elements in the same fixed mass ratio.

For example, water always contains 8 g of oxygen for every 1 g of hydrogen.

The Law of Multiple Proportions

In some cases, a pair of elements can combine to form more than one compound. John Dalton (Section 3.1) showed that when this happened, the compositions of the different compounds were related by the **Law of Multiple Proportions**, as stated below:

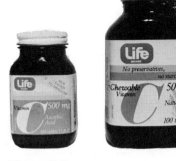

Figure 7.2
A molecule of vitamin C has the formula $C_6H_8O_6$ whether it is synthesized by a living plant or in a chemical laboratory.

When two elements can combine to form more than one compound, the masses of one element that will combine with a fixed mass of the other element are in small, whole-number ratios.

We already mentioned that water contains 8 g of oxygen for every 1 g of hydrogen. Hydrogen and oxygen can also combine in different proportions to form a second compound, hydrogen peroxide, which has very different properties from those of water. In hydrogen peroxide, for every 1 g of hydrogen there are 16 g of oxygen. Therefore, if we have a sample of water and a sample of hydrogen peroxide that contain the same mass of hydrogen, the mass of oxygen in the sample of hydrogen peroxide will be twice the mass of oxygen in the sample of water.

Figure 7.3

Water and hydrogen peroxide both contain hydrogen and oxygen. The differences in their properties result from the greater proportion of oxygen in hydrogen peroxide.

EXAMPLE   *7.12*   Sulfur and oxygen can combine to form two compounds. Compound A contains 1.0 g of oxygen for every 1.0 g of sulfur and Compound B contains 1.5 g of oxygen for every 1.0 g of sulfur. Show that these results are consistent with the Law of Multiple Proportions.

SOLUTION   Consider the mass of oxygen that is combined with 1.0 g of sulfur in each compound. In compound A this mass is 1.0 g, while in compound B it is 1.5 g. The ratio of these two masses of oxygen is 1.0 : 1.5, or 2 : 3 when expressed in whole numbers. This is in clear agreement with the Law of Multiple Proportions.

Percentage Composition

Instead of expressing the composition of a compound in terms of the actual mass of each element present, it is often more convenient to use the percentage composition by mass.

Let us consider a simple analogy. Suppose that, for your lunch, you have an apple of mass 90.0 g and an orange of mass 60.0 g. You might say that because your lunch consists of one apple and one orange, the percentage composition is 50% oranges and 50% apples. However, if we think in terms of mass, the total mass of the lunch is $90.0\,g + 60.0\,g = 150.0\,g$.

Hence

$$\text{Percent of orange by mass} = \frac{60.0\,g}{150.0\,g} \times 100\% = 40.0\%$$

$$\text{Percent of apple by mass} = \frac{90.0\,g}{150.0\,g} \times 100\% = 60.0\%$$

Now let us consider a chemical example. We know that 1.00 mol of carbon monoxide contains 6.02×10^{23} molecules, and that each molecule is composed of one carbon atom and one oxygen atom. Therefore, in 6.02×10^{23} molecules of CO, we must have 6.02×10^{23} atoms of carbon and 6.02×10^{23} atoms of oxygen. Thus we see that 1.00 mol of CO is made up of 1.00 mol of carbon atoms and 1.00 mol of oxygen atoms.

$$\text{The mass of one mole of CO} = 12.0\,g + 16.0\,g$$
$$= 28.0\,g$$

Thus, in one mole of carbon monoxide, we can calculate that

$$\text{Percent of carbon by mass} = \frac{12.0\,g}{28.0\,g} \times 100\% = 42.9\%$$

$$\text{Percent of oxygen by mass} = \frac{16.0\,g}{28.0\,g} \times 100\% = 57.1\%$$

EXAMPLE   **7.13**   Determine the percentage composition (by mass) of table sugar (sucrose), which has the formula $C_{12}H_{22}O_{11}$.

SOLUTION   The mass of one mole of $C_{12}H_{22}O_{11} = 12(12.0\,g) + 22(1.01\,g)$
$$+ 11(16.0\,g)$$
$$= 144\,g + 22.2\,g + 176\,g$$
$$= 342\,g$$

Considering 1.00 mol of sugar, we can write

$$\text{Percent of carbon} = \frac{144\,g}{342\,g} \times 100\% = 42.1\%$$

$$\text{Percent of hydrogen} = \frac{22.2\,g}{342\,g} \times 100\% = 6.49\%$$

$$\text{Percent of oxygen} = \frac{176\,g}{342\,g} \times 100\% = 51.5\%$$

NOTE: The sum of the percentages should ideally be 100%, but errors introduced by rounding give us a total of 100.1%.

8. Calculate the percentage of nitrogen, *by mass*, in each of the following compounds:

a) N_2O_5 b) $Ca(NO_3)_2$ c) NH_4NO_2

Empirical and Molecular Formulas   7.5

If not specified always assume 100 g

Note

In the last section, we learned how to determine the percentage composition of a compound from its formula. From a practical point of view the reverse procedure, i.e. determining the chemical formula of a compound from its percentage composition, is more important.

The determination of a chemical formula from experimentally obtained data involves several steps, one of which is to find the empirical formula from the percentage composition. The **empirical formula** of a compound tells us the simplest whole-number ratio of the atoms (or ions) in the compound. This is in contrast to the **molecular formula**, which tells us the actual number of atoms of each element in one molecule of the compound.

EXAMPLE   **7.14**

Note

molecular formula first requires empirical formula

A compound consists of 40.1% sulfur and 59.9% oxygen (by mass). What is its empirical formula?

SOLUTION   Let us assume that we have 100.0 g of the compound. Our first step is to determine the mass of each element present:

$$\text{Mass of sulfur} = 100.0\,g \times \frac{40.1}{100.0} = 40.1\,g$$

$$\text{Mass of oxygen} = 100.0\,g \times \frac{59.9}{100.0} = 59.9\,g$$

The next step is to convert mass to moles:

mass : mass RATIO

$$\text{Moles of sulfur atoms} = 40.1\,g\,S \times \frac{1\text{ mol S}}{32.1\,g\,S} = 1.25\text{ mol S}$$

$$\text{Moles of oxygen atoms} = 59.9\,g\,O \times \frac{1\text{ mol O}}{16.0\,g\,O} = 3.74\text{ mol O}$$

Thus the mole ratio of sulfur to oxygen is $1.25:3.74$. As a mole of sulfur atoms and a mole of oxygen atoms each contain the same number of atoms (6.02×10^{23}), we can say that the ratio of sulfur atoms to oxygen atoms in the compound under investigation is also $1.25:3.74$. However, this is not a whole-number ratio. To find the whole-number ratio we divide both numbers by the smaller of the two. Thus

$$S:O = 1.25:3.74 = \frac{1.25}{1.25}:\frac{3.74}{1.25}$$

$$= 1.00:2.99$$

Remembering that the percentage composition will have been determined by experiment, we are quite justified in rounding off this ratio to $1:3$. Thus the empirical formula of the compound is SO_3.

Although knowing the empirical formula of a compound is useful, it still does not provide us with complete information about the compound. For example, acetylene, the gas used in oxyacetylene torches, and benzene, a liquid used in the chemical industry, both have the empirical formula CH. However, a molecule of acetylene contains two carbon atoms and two hydrogen atoms, and has a molecular formula of C_2H_2; whereas a molecule of benzene contains six carbon and six hydrogen atoms and has a molecular formula of C_6H_6.

In order to determine the molecular formula of a compound we must know both its empirical formula and its molar mass.

EXAMPLE   **7.15**   A student has determined that the empirical formula for a compound of sulfur and chlorine is SCl. If the known molar mass of this compound is $135\,g \cdot mol^{-1}$, what is its molecular formula?

SOLUTION   First, we calculate the mass that corresponds to one mole of the substance as indicated by the empirical formula, SCl. We call this the empirical-formula mass:

$$\text{Empirical-formula mass of SCl} = 32.1\,g + 35.5\,g = 67.6\,g$$

From the molar mass, which was given, we know that the mass of one mole of the substance is really 135 g. We also know that the molecular formula is always some multiple of the empirical formula. We can find this multiple by dividing the mass of one mole of the substance by the empirical-formula mass. Therefore

$$\frac{\text{Known mass of one mole}}{\text{Empirical-formula mass}} = \frac{135\,g}{67.5\,g} = 2.00$$

$$\text{Molecular formula} = 2 \times \text{empirical formula}$$
$$= (SCl)_2 = S_2Cl_2$$

Using a combination of the calculations shown in Examples 7.14 and 7.15, we can obtain the molecular formula of a compound from its percentage composition and molar mass.

EXAMPLE   **7.16**   A compound contains 40.0% carbon, 6.7% hydrogen, and 53.3% oxygen by mass. The mass of one mole of the compound is 90.1 g. Determine the molecular formula of the compound.

SOLUTION   First, we find the empirical formula of the compound. If we assume we have 100.0 g of the compound then, as in Example 7.14, we can show that this 100.0 g contains 40.0 g of carbon, 6.7 g of hydrogen, and 53.3 g of oxygen. By using the reciprocal of the molar mass, we can find the number of moles of each element:

$$\text{Moles of carbon atoms} \quad = \quad 40.0\,g\,C \times \frac{1\ \text{mol C}}{12.0\,g\,C} = 3.33\ \text{mol C}$$

$$\text{Moles of hydrogen atoms} = \quad 6.7\,g\,H \times \frac{1\ \text{mol H}}{1.01\,g\,H} = 6.6\ \text{mol H}$$

$$\text{Moles of oxygen atoms} \quad = \quad 53.3\,g\,O \times \frac{1\ \text{mol O}}{16.0\,g\,O} = 3.33\ \text{mol O}$$

Therefore

$$\text{Ratio C} : \text{H} : \text{O} = 3.33 : 6.6 : 3.33$$
$$= \frac{3.33}{3.33} : \frac{6.6}{3.33} : \frac{3.33}{3.33}$$
$$= 1.00 : 2.0 : 1.00$$

Thus the empirical formula is CH_2O.

To find the molecular formula, we need the empirical-formula mass, i.e.

$$12.0\ g + 2(1.01\ g) + 16.0\ g = 30.0\ g$$

Dividing the known mass of one mole of the substance by the empirical-formula mass we obtain

$$\frac{\text{Known mass of one mole}}{\text{Empirical-formula mass}} = \frac{90.1\ g}{30.0\ g} = 3.00$$

$$\text{Molecular formula} = 3 \times \text{empirical formula}$$
$$= (CH_2O)_3 = C_3H_6O_3$$

QUESTIONS

9. Calculate the empirical formula for compounds with the following percentage composition:
   a) 59.3% lead, 40.6% chlorine
   b) 50.1% sulfur, 49.9% oxygen
   c) 44.9% potassium, 18.4% sulfur, 36.7% oxygen

10. A compound of empirical formula P_2O_3 has a molar mass of $220\ g \cdot mol^{-1}$. What is its molecular formula?

11. Determine the molecular formula of a compound containing 85.7% carbon and 14.3% hydrogen by mass. The molar mass of the compound is $84\ g \cdot mol^{-1}$.

Determining the Formula of a Compound

7.6

How do we set about finding the formula of a given compound? There are many different ways, but one of the simplest involves breaking down (or decomposing) a known mass of a compound and measuring the mass

of the elements obtained. We will use an example to illustrate this method.

Silver and oxygen combine to form a compound. From chemical studies it is found that heating the compound releases the oxygen (as oxygen gas) and leaves the silver metal. To determine the formula of this compound, we take a known mass of the compound and heat it strongly in a crucible (Figure 7.4). Heating decomposes the compound, releasing the oxygen and leaving a small button of silver metal in the crucible. We then measure the mass of silver metal. Subtracting this mass from the original mass of the compound gives us the mass of oxygen released. The empirical formula of the compound can then be determined.

EXAMPLE **7.17** After a 4.626 g sample of silver oxide is heated, 4.306 g of silver metal remains. What is the empirical formula of the compound?

SOLUTION

$$\text{Mass of silver} = 4.306\,\text{g}$$

$$\text{Mass of oxygen} = \text{mass of silver oxide} - \text{mass of silver}$$

$$= 4.626\,\text{g} - 4.306\,\text{g} = 0.320\,\text{g}$$

$$\text{Moles of silver atoms} = 4.306\,\text{g Ag} \times \frac{1\,\text{mol Ag}}{107.9\,\text{g Ag}}$$

$$= 3.991 \times 10^{-2}\,\text{mol Ag}$$

$$\text{Moles of oxygen atoms} = 0.320\,\text{g O} \times \frac{1\,\text{mol O}}{16.0\,\text{g O}}$$

$$= 2.00 \times 10^{-2}\,\text{mol O}$$

Thus

$$\text{Ag} : \text{O} = 3.991 \times 10^{-2} : 2.00 \times 10^{-2}$$

We now divide both of these numbers by the smaller of the two.

$$= \frac{3.991 \times 10^{-2}}{2.00 \times 10^{-2}} : \frac{2.00 \times 10^{-2}}{2.00 \times 10^{-2}}$$

$$= 2.00 : 1.00$$

This indicates that there are twice as many silver atoms as there are oxygen atoms in the compound. Therefore the empirical formula can be written as Ag_2O.

Determining an Empirical Formula Graphically

If we have several sets of experimental data, we can obtain a more reliable result by plotting the data on a graph. There are a number of reasons why different results are sometimes obtained when we repeat an experiment.

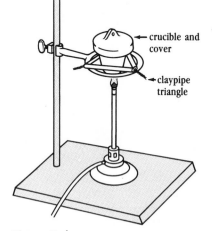

Figure 7.4
The apparatus for heating a crucible.

These include inaccuracies in taking measurements, impurities in the compounds, or allowing insufficient time for the reaction to be completed. If we repeat an experiment a number of times and plot the results on a graph, we can then draw the straight line that fits the data best. The slope of this line will give us the most reliable value for the empirical formula.

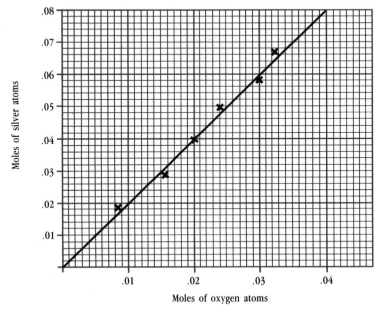

Figure 7.5

Plotting data to determine the empirical formula of silver oxide.

Figure 7.5 shows six sets of results for the silver oxide experiment described above. Within experimental error, the points lie on a straight line. This means that there is a fixed relationship between the number of moles of silver and the number of moles of oxygen, and hence between the numbers of atoms of each element. This is evidence for the Law of Constant Composition.

If we determine the slope of the line, we find it has a value of 2.00. This result is the same as that calculated in Example 7.17. For every mole of oxygen there are two moles of silver, which gives us a formula of Ag_2O.

Formula of a Hydrated Salt

As we discussed in Section 6.5, the salts of some metals have molecules of water in their crystalline structures. If we take a known mass of hydrated salt, heat it so that the water of crystallization is released, and then determine the mass of the anhydrous salt that remains, we can calculate the formula of the hydrate.

EXAMPLES   **7.18**   When 5.742 g of hydrated magnesium sulfate (Epsom salts) is heated until all the water has been released, 2.801 g of anhydrous magnesium sulfate remains. What is the formula of hydrated magnesium sulfate?

mole : mole RATIO.

SOLUTION   Mass of H_2O released

$$= \text{mass of hydrated salt} \ - \ \text{mass of anhydrous salt}$$
$$= 5.742\,\text{g} \ - \ 2.801\,\text{g} \ = \ 2.941\,\text{g}$$

Using the Periodic Table we can determine the following molar masses:

Molar mass of $MgSO_4$ = $120.4\,\text{g·mol}^{-1}$
Molar mass of H_2O = $18.0\,\text{g·mol}^{-1}$

These can be used as conversion factors to find the number of moles of water released and anhydrous magnesium sulfate remaining, as follows:

$$\text{Moles of anhydrous } MgSO_4 \ = \ 2.801\,\text{g MgSO}_4 \times \frac{1\,\text{mol } MgSO_4}{120.4\,\text{g MgSO}_4}$$

$$= \ 0.02326\,\text{mol } MgSO_4$$

$$\text{Moles of } H_2O \ = \ 2.941\,\text{g H}_2\text{O} \times \frac{1\,\text{mol } H_2O}{18.0\,\text{g H}_2\text{O}}$$

$$= \ 0.163\,\text{mol } H_2O$$

Thus

$$MgSO_4 \ : \ H_2O \ = \ 0.02326 \ : \ 0.163$$

To simplify, we divide by the smaller of the two numbers:

$$= \ \frac{0.02326}{0.02326} \ : \ \frac{0.163}{0.02326}$$

$$= \ 1.000 \ : \ 7.01$$

Therefore, the formula of the hydrate is $MgSO_4 \cdot 7H_2O$.

Carbon-Hydrogen Analysis

To determine the empirical formula of a compound containing carbon and hydrogen, we use a technique called combustion analysis. We burn a known mass of the compound and collect the water and carbon dioxide produced. From the mass of each of these, we can calculate the mass of carbon and hydrogen in the original compound, and hence determine the empirical formula. The instrument that we use is shown in Figure 7.6.

A simplified diagram of the interior of a carbon-hydrogen analyzer is shown in Figure 7.8. A current of dry oxygen gas is passed over a heated sample of the compound. As the compound burns the oxygen combines with the carbon to form carbon dioxide, and with the hydrogen to form water vapour. The carbon dioxide-water vapour mixture is passed through a tube containing anhydrous magnesium perchlorate. This chemical absorbs the water vapour from the mixture. The remaining carbon dioxide is passed through a second tube. This tube contains sodium hydroxide which absorbs

Figure 7.6
A carbon-hydrogen analyzer is used to find the empirical formula of a compound containing these two elements.

Quantitative Analysis and Lead Pollution

Since 2500 B.C., lead has been used for a variety of purposes, including pottery glazes, water pipes (until recently), and roof coverings. Lead-covered roofs have been popular in Europe for at least two thousand years. In Canada, almost one million tonnes of lead are used annually. About 40 % of this lead is used in automobile batteries and about 20 % is used to make tetraethyl lead, an additive for gasoline.

Lead is a very poisonous element. Most of our lead intake is in the form of lead compounds. The average amount of lead absorbed by adult Canadians is 31 μg per day, which is about one-third of the level that causes symptoms of lead poisoning. Smokers usually have significantly higher levels of lead intake, as about 1 μg of lead is absorbed by the lungs from each cigarette consumed. As our lead intake is so close to toxic levels, it is very important that our air, water, and food is carefully analyzed for lead content.

Maximum allowable levels of lead have been established for a number of products, including paint and food products. In addition, drinking water must not contain more than 50 μg of lead per litre.

Early symptoms of lead poisoning can include stomach ache, weakness, and irritability (these symptoms fit many other disorders). A major problem is high lead levels in young children. *Acute* lead poisoning in children causes mental retardation, and lower lead levels result in smaller reductions in intelligence. In ancient Rome, the people in the higher levels of society suffered from *chronic* lead poisoning (which causes infertility and insanity) as a result of using lead(II) acetate to sweeten wine (the compound used to be called sugar of lead).

Although some of the lead in the environment occurs naturally, between one-quarter and one-half of our lead intake comes from automobile exhaust gases. Most of our intake of lead is through the lungs. When we breathe the polluted air, our lungs absorb the lead it contains. This is obviously a much greater hazard for people who live in cities than for those who live in rural areas. Crops that grow close to main highways also absorb lead emissions. It is therefore very important for food crops to be analyzed for lead content to prevent lead-rich food from reaching our stores.

Lead pollution could be greatly reduced if we stopped using tetraethyl lead in gasoline. Some types of engines run on lead-free gasoline but others need tetraethyl lead to function properly. A number of European countries, including West Germany and the United Kingdom, have taken steps to ban lead in gasoline. Although there are plans to lower the allowable levels of lead in gasoline sold in Canada, as yet there is no deadline for a complete ban on leaded gasoline. You should be able to get more information about the problems of lead poisoning from your teacher or from a public library. Your local Member of Parliament should be able to tell you about any proposed Federal legislation on lead limits in gasoline, food, or water.

Figure 7.7
Leaded gasoline is a major source of our lead intake.

the carbon dioxide. The increase in mass of the first tube enables us to calculate the mass of water produced. The increase in mass of the second tube is equal to the mass of the carbon dioxide formed.

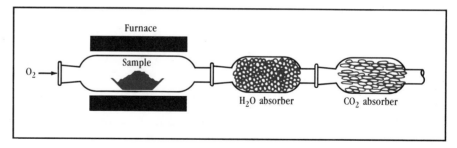

Figure 7.8
A simplified diagram of a carbon-hydrogen analyzer.

EXAMPLE *7.19* When a sample of a compound containing only carbon and hydrogen is burned in a carbon-hydrogen analyzer, 3.94 g of water and 9.62 g of carbon dioxide are produced. Find the empirical formula of the compound. If the measured molar mass of the compound is 84 g·mol⁻¹, what is its molecular formula?

SOLUTION First, we calculate the number of moles of water and carbon dioxide as follows:

$$\text{Moles of water} = 3.94 \text{ g H}_2\text{O} \times \frac{1 \text{ mol H}_2\text{O}}{18.0 \text{ g H}_2\text{O}}$$

$$= 0.219 \text{ mol H}_2\text{O}$$

$$\text{Moles of carbon dioxide} = 9.62 \text{ g CO}_2 \times \frac{1 \text{ mol CO}_2}{44.0 \text{ g CO}_2}$$

$$= 0.219 \text{ mol CO}_2$$

We can then find the number of moles of carbon and hydrogen:

$$\text{Moles of hydrogen atoms} = 0.219 \text{ mol H}_2\text{O} \times \frac{2 \text{ mol H}}{1 \text{ mol H}_2\text{O}}$$

$$= 0.438 \text{ mol H}$$

$$\text{Moles of carbon atoms} = 0.219 \text{ mol CO}_2 \times \frac{1 \text{ mol C}}{1 \text{ mol CO}_2}$$

$$= 0.219 \text{ mol C}$$

Thus

$$\text{C : H} = 0.219 : 0.438$$

$$= \frac{0.219}{0.219} : \frac{0.438}{0.219}$$

$$= 1.00 : 2.00$$

This gives us an empirical formula of CH_2, for which the empirical-formula mass is $14.0\,g$. Therefore

$$\frac{\text{Known mass of one mole}}{\text{Empirical-formula mass}} = \frac{84\,g}{14.0\,g} = 6.0$$

Thus, the molecular formula $\quad = 6 \times$ empirical formula

$$= (CH_2)_6 = C_6H_{12}$$

QUESTIONS

12. In addition to Ag_2O, silver forms a second compound with oxygen. If $3.862\,g$ of the second compound is heated, $3.363\,g$ of silver remains. What is the empirical formula of the second compound?

13. When $8.72\,g$ of iron is heated in an atmosphere of chlorine gas, $25.36\,g$ of a compound of iron and chlorine is formed. What is the empirical formula of this compound?

14. When $3.62\,g$ of anhydrous calcium chloride, $CaCl_2$, is left open to the air, $1.17\,g$ of water is absorbed. What is the formula of the hydrated compound formed?

15. A sample of a compound containing only carbon and hydrogen is burned to give $6.29\,g$ of carbon dioxide and $3.86\,g$ of water. The molar mass of the compound is found to be $30\,g\cdot mol^{-1}$. Calculate the molecular formula of the compound.

16. A sample of a compound containing carbon, hydrogen, and lead is burned at a high temperature. As a result, $37.8\,g$ of carbon dioxide, $23.2\,g$ of water, and $44.5\,g$ of lead are produced. What is the empirical formula of the compound?

Avogadro's Hypothesis

7.7 In the last section, we described how empirical formulas are determined experimentally. We also learned that, in order to find the molecular formula of a compound, we need to know its molar mass as well as its empirical formula. There is a simple way of finding the molar mass of a gas. The method is based on a hypothesis proposed in 1811 by the Italian scientist, Amadeo Avogadro. **Avogadro's hypothesis** states that

> **Equal volumes of all gases, measured at the same temperature and pressure, contain the same number of molecules.**

Thus, according to this hypothesis, if we have a $1.00\,L$ sample of oxygen gas and a $1.00\,L$ sample of chlorine gas (or any other gas) at the same temperature and pressure, both samples will contain the same number of molecules.

If gases contain equal numbers of molecules, then they will also contain equal numbers of moles. We can therefore modify Avogadro's hypothesis as follows:

Equal volumes of all gases, measured at the same temperature and pressure, contain the same number of moles.

To find the molar mass of an unknown gas, we measure the mass of a particular volume of a known gas and the mass of an equal volume of the unknown gas at the same temperature and pressure. From the first measurement we can calculate the number of moles of the known gas. According to Avogadro's hypothesis, this quantity must equal the number of moles of unknown gas. Knowing both the mass and the number of moles of the unknown gas allows us to calculate its molar mass.

Example 7.20
Example 7.20

EXAMPLE   **7.20**   An 8.99×10^{-2} g sample of hydrogen gas has a volume of 1.00 L at a certain temperature and pressure. A mass of 1.78 g of an unidentified noble gas occupies the same volume at the same temperature and pressure. Determine the molar mass of the gas and identify it.

SOLUTION

> **STRATEGY**
> 1. Mass of A $\longrightarrow$ Moles of A
> 2. Moles of A $\longrightarrow$ Moles of B
> 3. Moles of B $\longrightarrow$ Molar Mass of B

STEP 1:   Moles of hydrogen gas $= 8.99 \times 10^{-2} \text{ g H}_2 \times \dfrac{1 \text{ mol H}_2}{2.02 \text{ g H}_2}$

$$= 4.45 \times 10^{-2} \text{ mol H}_2$$

STEP 2:   According to Avogadro's hypothesis

$$\text{Moles of noble gas} = \text{moles of hydrogen gas}$$

$$= 4.45 \times 10^{-2} \text{ mol}$$

STEP 3:   Molar mass of noble gas $= \dfrac{1.78 \text{ g}}{4.45 \times 10^{-2} \text{ mol}}$

$$= 40.0 \text{ g} \cdot \text{mol}^{-1}$$

The noble gas with this molar mass is argon.

EXAMPLE   **7.21**   Hydrazine is a compound that can be used as a component of rocket fuel. Analysis of a sample of hydrazine shows that it consists of 87.4% nitrogen and 12.6% hydrogen by mass. Additional experiments show that, at a certain temperature and pressure, 1.00 L of hydrazine gas has a mass of 1.43 g and that 1.00 L of helium gas, at the same temperature and pressure, has a mass of 0.178 g. Find the molecular formula of hydrazine.

SOLUTION   First, we need to find the empirical formula. Assuming 100.0 g of hydrazine, we have 87.4 g of nitrogen and 12.6 g of hydrogen. Thus

$$\text{Moles of nitrogen atoms} = 87.4 \, g\,N \times \frac{1 \text{ mol N}}{14.0 \, g\,N} = 6.24 \text{ mol N}$$

$$\text{Moles of hydrogen atoms} = 12.6 \, g\,H \times \frac{1 \text{ mol H}}{1.01 \, g\,H} = 12.5 \text{ mol H}$$

$$\text{N : H} = 6.24 : 12.5 = \frac{6.24}{6.24} : \frac{12.5}{6.24} = 1.00 : 2.00$$

$$\text{Empirical formula} = NH_2$$

Before we can determine the molecular formula, we have to calculate the molar mass:

$$\text{Moles of helium gas} = 0.178 \, g \text{ He} \times \frac{1 \text{ mol He}}{4.00 \, g \text{ He}}$$

$$= 4.45 \times 10^{-2} \text{ mol He}$$

According to Avogadro's hypothesis

$$\text{Moles of hydrazine} = \text{moles of helium} = 4.45 \times 10^{-2} \text{ mol}$$

$$\text{Molar mass of hydrazine} = \frac{1.43 \, g}{4.45 \times 10^{-2} \text{ mol}}$$

$$= 32.1 \, g \cdot mol^{-1}$$

Finally, we can find the molecular formula:

$$\text{Empirical-formula mass of } NH_2 = 16.0 \, g$$

$$\frac{\text{Measured mass of one mole}}{\text{Empirical-formula mass}} = \frac{32.1 \, g}{16.0 \, g} = 2.01$$

$$\text{Therefore the molecular formula} = (NH_2)_2 = N_2H_4$$

QUESTIONS

17. A sample of 4.05 g of phosphorus is heated to 300 °C, at which temperature it is a gas. At the same temperature and pressure, an equal volume of nitrogen gas has a mass of 0.915 g.
   a) What is the molar mass of gaseous phosphorus?
   b) Calculate the number of atoms present in each molecule of gaseous phosphorus.

18. A gas consists of 30.4% nitrogen and 69.6% oxygen. A 5.14 g sample of the gas occupies the same volume as 2.46 g of carbon dioxide gas at the same temperature and pressure. Determine the molecular formula of the gas.

Avogadro — The Intuitive Chemist

Amadeo Avogadro was born in Turin, Italy in 1776. He originally trained to be an ecclesiastical lawyer, but became interested in the work on electricity that was being conducted by his compatriot, Alessandro Volta.

Avogadro's only claim to fame is the hypothesis named after him. A French scientist, Gay-Lussac, had shown that gases combined in simple volume ratios. Avogadro proposed his hypothesis as a means of explaining Gay-Lussac's law. Dalton had considered such a hypothesis, but had rejected it as being inconsistent with his atomic theory.

For a variety of reasons, Avogadro's hypothesis was neglected by the vast majority of chemists until about 1870. Avogadro was a modest and obscure physicist, geographically separated from the mainstream of scientific discovery in London and Paris, and was regarded by some of his contemporaries as a careless experimenter. This reputation harmed his credibility. He published the work on his hypothesis in small-circulation Italian and French science journals, and therefore few people read about his work. In addition, the interpretation of his results required the known gaseous elements to exist as diatomic molecules (for example, oxygen as O_2). Most chemists of that era, including Dalton, believed that all elements consisted of free atoms. It was therefore necessary for the existence of diatomic molecules to be accepted before Avogadro's hypothesis could be recognized.

Avogadro will be remembered as an intuitive, speculative, and theoretical scientist.

Figure 7.9
Amadeo Avogadro (1776–1856).

Summary

- Molecular mass is the mass of one molecule of a covalent compound.

- Formula mass is the mass of one formula unit of an ionic compound.

- Molecular mass and formula mass are usually expressed in unified atomic mass units.

- Molar mass is the mass of one mole of a substance. It is expressed in $g \cdot mol^{-1}$.

- The Law of Constant Composition states that in any given compound, the mass ratio of the elements is always the same.

- The Law of Multiple Proportions states that when two elements combine to form more than one compound, the masses of one element that combine with a fixed mass of the other elements are in small, whole-number ratios.

- The empirical formula of a compound indicates the simplest whole-number ratio of the atoms (or ions) in the compound. The molecular formula indicates the actual number of atoms in each molecule of a compound. The empirical formula is determined from the percentage composition of the compound.

- Avogadro's hypothesis states that equal volumes of all gases, measured at the same temperature and pressure, contain the same number of molecules and hence equal numbers of moles.

KEY WORDS

Avogadro's hypothesis	Law of Multiple Proportions
empirical formula	molecular formula
formula mass	molecular mass
Law of Constant Composition	

ANSWERS TO
SECTION QUESTIONS

1. 20.3 g
2. 2.44×10^{-2} mol Ag
3. 6.6×10^{-18} g
4. 1.0 g of aluminum
5. a) 121 u   c) 149.1 g·mol^{-1}
   b) 84.3 u   d) 342.2 g·mol^{-1}
6. a) 8.57×10^{21} sugar molecules
   b) 1.03×10^{23} carbon atoms
7. 5.77×10^{22} sodium ions
8. a) 25.9% N   b) 17.1% N   c) 43.8% N
9. a) $PbCl_4$ b) SO_2 c) K_2SO_4
10. P_4O_6
11. C_6H_{12}
12. AgO
13. $FeCl_3$
14. $CaCl_2 \cdot 2H_2O$
15. C_2H_6
16. PbC_4H_{12}
17. a) 124 g·mol^{-1} b) 4
18. N_2O_4

1. How is the molecular mass of a covalent compound computed?
2. How is the formula mass of an ionic compound computed?
3. State the Law of Constant Composition.
4. What is the Law of Multiple Proportions?
5. What is the difference between the molecular mass and the molar mass of a compound?
6. What is the difference between the empirical formula and the molecular formula of a compound?
7. Summarize the steps followed in determining the empirical formula of a compound from its percentage composition.
8. What additional information is necessary to find the molecular formula if the empirical formula is known?
9. What is Avogadro's hypothesis?
10. How can Avogadro's hypothesis be used to determine the molar mass of an unknown gas?
11. What method is used to find the empirical formula of a compound containing carbon and hydrogen?
12. Make a diagram, similar to Figure 7.1, showing the relationship between the mass of a compound and the number of molecules present.

PROBLEMS

13. Calculate the molar mass of each of the following:
    a) $Mg_3(PO_4)_2$ b) $AgClO_4$ c) $(NH_4)_2S$ d) $BaHPO_4$ e) $NaNO_3$
14. Calculate the molar mass of the following compounds:
    a) P_2O_5 b) LiH_2PO_4 c) $Cu(CH_3CO_2)_2$ d) IF_5 e) $SnCl_2 \cdot 5H_2O$
15. Calculate the number of moles in each of the following:
    a) 55.3 g of Zn   c) 27 mg of $FeSO_4$
    b) 1.24×10^3 g $AgNO_3$ d) 90.0 g of H_2O
16. How many moles of substance are there in each of the following:
    a) 1.00×10^2 g of Cl_2 c) 284 g Na_2SO_4
    b) 0.100 mg of NaF   d) 1.00 g of CO_2
17. A bag of sugar ($C_{12}H_{22}O_{11}$) has a mass of 1.0×10^1 kg. How many moles of sugar does it contain?
18. How many moles of salt are present in a 1.0 kg packet of table salt (sodium chloride)?
19. Silver nitrate, $AgNO_3$, costs $99.50 for a 1.00×10^2 g bottle. What is the cost per mole of this chemical?
20. A Canadian maple leaf gold coin with a mass of 28.0 g costs $450. What is the cost of purchasing one mole of gold in this way?

21. Calculate the number of moles in
   a) 3.00×10^{23} atoms of magnesium
   b) 8.72×10^{15} molecules of carbon dioxide
   c) 5.0×10^{24} formula units of sodium chloride

22. Calculate the number of moles in
   a) 7.08×10^{24} molecules of sugar
   b) 1.59×10^{22} atoms of sulfur
   c) 8.82×10^{10} formula units of calcium phosphate

23. What is the mass of 0.250 mol of each of the following:
   a) potassium   d) nitrogen gas
   b) phosphorus trichloride   e) water
   c) iron(III) sulfate

24. What is the mass of each of the following:
   a) 2.50 mol of aluminum
   b) 0.500 mol of calcium carbonate
   c) 6.47×10^{-2} mol of nitrogen dioxide
   d) 8.8×10^{-5} mol of hydrogen gas

25. What is the mass of each of the following:
   a) 1.15×10^{20} formula units $LiNO_3$
   b) 6.02×10^{30} atoms of mercury
   c) 1.0×10^{10} molecules of iodine pentachloride

26. Calculate the number of molecules in 1.00 g of each of the following:
   a) UF_6 b) $FeSO_4$ c) N_2 d) C_6H_6

27. In each of the following examples, determine which contains the larger number of atoms or molecules:
   a) 11.5 g sodium or 8.1 g of boron
   b) 4.40 g of carbon dioxide or 0.200 mol of sulfur dioxide
   c) 186 g of water or 1.00 kg of urea, $(NH_2)_2\,CO$

28. Calculate the mass in grams of one formula unit of each of the following:
   a) $KClO_2$ b) $(NH_4)_2SO_3$ c) $FePO_4 \cdot 3H_2O$

29. Water and acetone (C_3H_6O) can be mixed in any proportion to give a solution. Suppose that you are asked to prepare 20.0 g of a mixture containing equal numbers of moles of water and acetone. What mass of each substance would you use?

30. A chemist wishes to carry out a chemical reaction in which potassium bromide (KBr) and silver nitrate ($AgNO_3$) are used.
   a) Calculate the molar mass of each of these substances.
   b) What mass of each would be required if the chemist wanted to use 2.00×10^{-2} moles of each compound?

31. Calculate the number of
   a) atoms in 2.56 mol of hydrogen gas
   b) chloride ions in 0.41 mol of calcium chloride
   c) atoms of oxygen in 22.5 g of aluminum nitrate

$2.56 \, mol \, H_2 \times \dfrac{6.02 \times 10^{23} \, atoms}{1 \, mol}$

$1.54 \times 10^{24} \, atoms$

$0.41 \, mol \, CaCl_2 \times 6.02 \times 10^{23} \, for.$

$= 2.47 \times 10^{23} \, for \times \dfrac{2Cl^-}{1 \, mol} \times \dfrac{1 \, mol}{1 \, A}$

$= 4.94 \times 10^{23} \, ions$

$Al(NO_3)_3$

$22.5g \times \dfrac{1 \, mol}{144g} = 0.156 \, mol \, O$

$0.156 \, mol \times 6.02 \times 10^{23} \dfrac{formula}{1 \, mol}$

32. Calculate the number of
    a) molecules in 1.00 g of oxygen
    b) atoms of sulfur in 3.08 mol of sulfur dioxide
    c) nitrite ions in 3.99 g of aluminum nitrite

33. Magnetite (Fe_3O_4) is a commonly occurring iron ore.
    a) Calculate the percentage composition of magnetite.
    b) How many iron atoms are present in 1.0 mg of Fe_3O_4?

34. The amino acid glycine has the formula $C_2H_5O_2N$.
    a) Calculate the percentage composition of glycine.
    b) What mass of glycine contains 1.50 g of nitrogen?

35. The following chemicals are used extensively in most chemical laboratories. Find the percentage composition of each:
    a) sodium dichromate ($Na_2Cr_2O_7$)
    b) potassium permanganate ($KMnO_4$)
    c) magnesium sulfate ($MgSO_4$)

36. The following chemicals are used as colourants for ceramic glazes. Find the percentage composition of each:
    a) cobalt(II) carbonate ($CoCO_3$), which produces a blue glaze colour
    b) barium chromate ($BaCrO_4$), which produces colours in the yellow to light-green range
    c) iron(III) chloride hexahydrate ($FeCl_3 \cdot 6H_2O$), which produces an iridescent gold colour

37. Determine the empirical formula that corresponds to each of the following percentage compositions:
    a) 48.0% zinc, 52.0% chlorine
    b) 25.9% iron, 74.1% bromine
    c) 62.6% lead, 8.5% nitrogen, 29.0% oxygen

38. Determine the empirical formula that corresponds to each of the following percentage compositions:
    a) 7.2% phosphorus, 92.8% bromine
    b) 19.0% tin, 81.0% iodine
    c) 36.5% sodium, 25.4% sulfur, 38.1% oxygen

39. Diethyl ether, a medical anesthetic, contains 64.9% carbon, 13.5% hydrogen, and 21.6% oxygen by mass. Find the molecular formula of diethyl ether, given that its molar mass is $74.1\ g \cdot mol^{-1}$.

40. Acetylsalicylic acid (aspirin) has a molar mass of $180\ g \cdot mol^{-1}$ and contains 60.02% carbon, 4.44% hydrogen, and 35.54% oxygen by mass. Find the molecular formula of this substance.

41. Boron and hydrogen form a series of compounds called boranes, some of which have been used as rocket fuels. The percentage composition and molar mass of a number of these compounds are given in the table below. Find the empirical formula and molecular formula of each compound.

Compound	Boron (% by mass)	Hydrogen (% by mass)	Molar Mass $(g \cdot mol^{-1})$
1	78.3	21.7	27.7
2	81.2	18.8	53.3
3	85.7	14.3	63.1
4	88.5	11.5	122

42. The alkanes are a group of compounds containing only carbon and hydrogen. Some alkanes form the main constituents of natural gas and gasoline. From the percentage composition and molar mass data for the alkanes in the table below, derive the empirical formula and the molecular formula of each compound.

Compound	Carbon (% by mass)	Hydrogen (% by mass)	Molar Mass $(g \cdot mol^{-1})$
1	74.87	25.13	16.0
2	79.89	20.11	30.1
3	81.71	18.29	44.1
4	84.12	15.88	114.2

43. When 7.59 g of an oxide of manganese is heated, 3.76 g of manganese metal is obtained. What is the empirical formula of this compound?

44. When 3.76 g of hydrated iron(III) phosphate was heated to drive off the water of crystallization, 2.77 g of anhydrous salt remained. What is the formula of the hydrated salt?

45. A sample of a compound containing only carbon and hydrogen was burned to produce 1.36 g of water and 5.22 g of carbon dioxide. Calculate the empirical formula of the compound.

46. A compound containing only carbon and hydrogen was burned and the water produced was condensed and collected. From a 0.436 g sample of the compound, 0.478 g of water was obtained, together with an undetermined amount of carbon dioxide. What is the empirical formula of the compound? If the molar mass of the compound is 82.1 $g \cdot mol^{-1}$, what is its molecular formula?

47. Under certain conditions, the mass of 2.00 L of hydrogen gas is 1.80 g. Calculate the mass of 2.00 L of ammonia (NH_3) under identical conditions.

48. Carbon monoxide (CO) is a toxic gas formed by the incomplete combustion of coal; it has a density of 1.25 $g \cdot L^{-1}$ at 0 °C and one atmosphere pressure. Calculate the density of nitrogen monoxide (NO), an air pollutant found in automotive exhaust fumes, under these conditions.

49. a) The mass of 1.00 L of oxygen under certain conditions is 1.43 g. The mass of an equal volume of an unknown gas under identical conditions is 2.86 g. Calculate the molar mass of the unknown gas.

   b) The unknown gas in part (a) is found to contain 49.9% oxygen and 50.1% sulfur by mass. Find the empirical formula of the compound and then calculate its molecular formula using the molar mass determined in part (a).

50. A mixture of two nitrogen-containing gases, A and B, acts as an efficient rocket fuel. Under identical conditions, the mass of a certain volume of gas A is 15.89 times greater than the mass of an equal volume of hydrogen, whereas the mass of a given volume of gas B is 45.61 times greater than the mass of the same volume of hydrogen. The percentage compositions of the two compounds by mass are as follows:

   A: 87.43% N, 12.57% H
   B: 30.45% N, 69.55% O

   Determine the molar mass, empirical formula, and molecular formula of each compound.

SUGGESTED PROJECTS

1. In mining, the composition of an ore is an important factor in determining whether mining operations would be economical. The analysis of an ore's composition is called an assay. Prepare a report on how an assay is done for at least one type of ore.

2. Water (H_2O) and hydrogen peroxide (H_2O_2) are compounds that illustrate the Law of Multiple Proportions. Prepare a report comparing their properties and uses.

Chemical Reactions

To this point, we have been concerned with understanding the nature of matter. We are now ready to look at changes that matter can undergo. This is the study of chemical reactions, one of the most fascinating aspects of chemistry.

The Importance of Chemical Reactions

8.1

Many chemical reactions occur naturally, although some take place so slowly that we do not notice them. Some of our sources of energy, for example coal and petroleum, are the products of chemical reactions that have taken place beneath the earth over a very long period. Many other mineral deposits are the results of slow interactions among various chemicals in the earth. The natural chemical reactions that we observe occurring in living things are known as **biochemical reactions**.

Biochemical Reactions

A vast number of chemical reactions take place continuously inside our bodies. Many chemists and biochemists study these reactions to try to

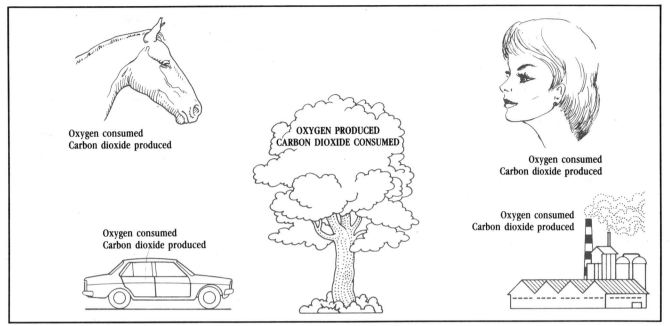

Oxygen consumed
Carbon dioxide produced

OXYGEN PRODUCED
CARBON DIOXIDE CONSUMED

Oxygen consumed
Carbon dioxide produced

Oxygen consumed
Carbon dioxide produced

Oxygen consumed
Carbon dioxide produced

Figure 8.1

The importance of photosynthesis in maintaining an adequate level of oxygen in the earth's atmosphere.

$CO_2 + H_2O \rightarrow STARCH$ & O_2

understand how and why they occur. The knowledge thus acquired assists us in the study of nutrition and in the study of disease.

One important biochemical reaction is **photosynthesis**. This is the process by which plants convert carbon dioxide and water to starch and oxygen. Photosynthesis is vital in order to provide the animals on this planet with the oxygen that they need. Adequate levels of oxygen production can only occur if we maintain a substantial quantity of vegetation on the earth.

A major portion of the oxygen required to maintain animal life is produced as a result of photosynthesis in tropical forests. Unfortunately, these forests are being destroyed at a rapid rate, particularly in South America, to make room for farms, highways, and cities to accommodate rapidly expanding populations.

Manufacture of Important Chemicals

We cannot rely on nature to produce all the chemicals we need in industry and agriculture, as we often need more of a specific type of chemical than nature provides. For example, although there are many natural fertilizers, they do not occur in large enough quantities to fulfil the demands of agriculture. Thus millions of tonnes of fertilizer must be manufactured each year to meet our requirements.

Equally important is the manufacture of materials that do not exist in nature. Many of these have become essential in our modern lifestyles. In this category we can include cement, plastics, synthetic textiles, and pharmaceuticals. The development of the chemical industry has been a

Figure 8.2

The Polysar plant in Sarnia, Ontario, converts simple compounds of carbon and hydrogen into complex polymers.

major reason for our progress in the last two hundred years and chemists are still striving to make new materials with properties that are better than, or different from, those of currently available materials.

Production of Energy

Chemical reactions are also important in producing energy. In the process known as combustion, natural gas, kerosene, fuel oil, coal, or wood react with the oxygen in the air to produce heat energy. Combustion of gasoline, diesel fuel, or aviation fuel is used to provide the energy of motion (kinetic energy) for our various modes of transportation.

Chemical reactions are also used to produce electrical energy in batteries. Chemists are currently trying to develop more efficient and longer-lasting batteries.

Recognizing a Chemical Reaction   8.2

aqueous
— includes
water

When two or more substances have been mixed together, how do we know if a chemical reaction has taken place? When a chemical reaction occurs, we usually observe at least one of a number of changes. Examples of these changes are described below.

Change in Colour

When a solution of potassium dichromate (orange) is added to a solution of sodium hydrogen sulfite (colourless), the resulting solution is green (Figure 8.4).

Figure 8.3
The launch of a U.S. space shuttle. In this dramatic chemical reaction, enough energy is produced to propel the vehicle into space.

Figure 8.4
Example of a chemical reaction in which a change of colour is observed.

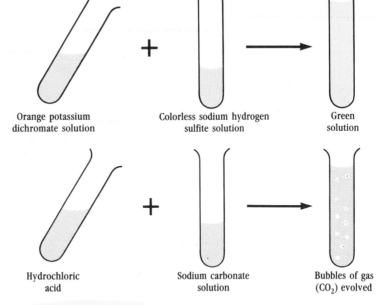

Orange potassium dichromate solution + Colorless sodium hydrogen sulfite solution → Green solution

Figure 8.5
Example of a chemical reaction in which a gas is formed.

Hydrochloric acid + Sodium carbonate solution → Bubbles of gas (CO_2) evolved

Formation of a Gas

If hydrochloric acid is added to a solution of sodium carbonate, we see bubbles of gas (carbon dioxide) escaping from the resulting solution (Figure 8.5).

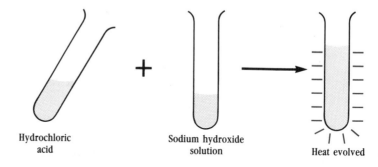

Calcium chloride
solution

Potassium carbonate
solution

White solid
forms

Formation of a Solid

When a clear solution of calcium chloride is added to a clear solution of potassium carbonate, a white solid (calcium carbonate) is produced (Figure 8.6). A solid formed in such a way is called a **precipitate**.

Although the disappearance of a solid can indicate that a chemical reaction has taken place, a solid can sometimes disappear without a chemical reaction occurring. For example, when a solution of ammonia is added to solid silver chloride, the solid dissolves because a chemical reaction occurs between the two chemicals. However, when water is added to solid sodium chloride and the solid disappears, no chemical reaction occurs. Instead we simply witness the formation of a solution of sodium chloride. Care must therefore be exercised in using the disappearance of a solid as justification for saying that a chemical reaction has occurred.

Hydrochloric
acid

Sodium hydroxide
solution

Heat evolved

Figure 8.7

Example of a chemical reaction in which heat is released.

Release or Absorption of Heat

When hydrochloric acid is added to a solution of sodium hydroxide, heat is released and the reaction vessel becomes warm (Figure 8.7).

Again, we cannot always assume that a chemical reaction has occurred when heat is absorbed or released. Many substances release or absorb heat when they are mixed together, even though no reaction takes place. For example, when solid sodium hydroxide is added to water, heat is released but no chemical reaction occurs. The heat results from the sodium hydroxide dissolving in water to give a solution of aqueous sodium hydroxide.

Writing Chemical Equations

8.3

In mathematics, instead of writing long sentences to convey information we use equations. Thus, instead of writing the sentence: "When two is added to two the total is four", we use the equation

$$2 + 2 = 4$$

This equation is understood not only by mathematicians, but also by most of the general public.

Chemists use **chemical equations** to convey information about chemical reactions to each other. As with mathematical equations, a chemical equation condenses a large amount of information into a short expression. Let us look at a few examples of chemical equations and see how they differ from mathematical equations.

The Word Equation

Suppose we want to write an equation for the chemical reaction described by the following sentence:

Carbon burns in oxygen to produce carbon dioxide.

First, we can represent the reaction by a **word equation**, as follows:

Carbon + Oxygen ⟶ Carbon dioxide

In a word equation we write the names of the species that undergo a chemical reaction, the **reactants**, on the left of the arrow. The names of the species that are formed in the reaction, the **products**, are written on the right of the arrow. The arrow points towards the product side and is a symbol that implies "produces" or "yields".

The Molecular Equation

Because the names of compounds are often long, we can condense the word equation even further by replacing the names of the reactants and products by the corresponding chemical formulas. In this way we obtain a **molecular equation** or, as it is sometimes called, a **formula equation**. To do this, we need to know the symbol or formula of each of the elements or compounds involved in the reaction. Thus, to write the molecular equation for the reaction between carbon and oxygen, we need to know that the symbol for carbon is C, and that the formula for carbon dioxide is CO_2. We must also remember that oxygen exists as diatomic molecules, and that in any chemical equation we write elemental oxygen as O_2 rather than O. This also applies to nitrogen (N_2) and hydrogen (H_2), and to the four members of Group VIIA fluorine (F_2), chlorine (Cl_2), bromine (Br_2), and iodine (I_2). The molecular equation now becomes

$$C + O_2 \longrightarrow CO_2$$

Finally, we usually indicate the physical states of the reactants and products. This can be done by adding the appropriate symbol, in parentheses, as a subscript after the formula of the substance to which it refers. The four symbols used are (s) for solid, (ℓ) for liquid, (g) for gas, and (aq) for aqueous (meaning dissolved in water). We can now rewrite our molecular equation for the reaction of carbon with oxygen as

$$C_{(s)} + O_{2\,(g)} \longrightarrow CO_{2\,(g)}$$

The information conveyed by this equation is: solid carbon reacts with oxygen gas to produce gaseous carbon dioxide.

Balancing Chemical Equations

The above equation is very simple as it did not require **balancing**. By "balancing a chemical equation" we mean multiplying some of the reactants or products by a coefficient that will ensure that equal numbers of each atom are on both sides of the equation. Although this may sound complicated, it is quite easy to do.

Suppose we wish to write a balanced chemical equation for the reaction in which solid sodium combines with chlorine gas to produce solid sodium chloride. First, we can write a word equation:

$$\textbf{Sodium} + \textbf{Chlorine} \longrightarrow \textbf{Sodium chloride}$$

To write a molecular equation, we will need to know the formula of each of the reactants (Na and Cl_2) and of the product (NaCl). Following our earlier example, we write

$$\textbf{Na} + \textbf{Cl}_2 \longrightarrow \textbf{NaCl}$$

This equation is not yet balanced. On the reactant side of the equation we have a chlorine molecule consisting of two chlorine atoms, whereas on the product side of the equation we have only one chlorine atom (actually one chloride ion). As it is not possible for one of the chlorine atoms to just disappear, we must balance our equation so that we have two chlorines on the product side of the equation. We cannot do this by writing $NaCl_2$ as the formula for sodium chloride, because the formula of a compound cannot be altered to balance an equation. We must therefore place the coefficient 2 in front of the NaCl to give 2 NaCl as the product:

$$\textbf{Na} + \textbf{Cl}_2 \longrightarrow \textbf{2 NaCl}$$

The 2 in front of the NaCl implies two formula units of sodium chloride, each one consisting of one sodium ion and one chloride ion. Our equation is still not balanced, because we now have two sodium atoms on the product side but only one on the reactant side. We must therefore add another sodium atom to the reactant side of the equation to obtain a chemical balance:

$$\textbf{2 Na} + \textbf{Cl}_2 \longrightarrow \textbf{2 NaCl}$$

We now add symbols to indicate the physical states of the species in this reaction: solid sodium, chlorine gas, and solid sodium chloride. The completed molecular equation now becomes

$$2\,Na_{(s)} + Cl_{2\,(g)} \longrightarrow 2\,NaCl_{(s)}$$

It is quite easy to write a chemical equation if we know the correct formulas for each of the substances involved in the reaction. After the correct formulas have been written they cannot be altered in any way. Remember that to balance the equation we can change the coefficients, but we cannot change the formulas.

EXAMPLE   **8.1**   When water is added to liquid silicon tetrachloride, solid silicon dioxide and hydrogen chloride gas are produced. Write a balanced molecular equation for the reaction.

SOLUTION   First, we can write a word equation as follows:

Silicon tetrachloride + Water $\longrightarrow$

Silicon dioxide + Hydrogen chloride

We can then substitute formulas for names:

$$SiCl_4 + H_2O \longrightarrow SiO_2 + HCl$$

As there are four chlorines on the reactant side but only one on the product side, we need four hydrogen chloride molecules on the product side:

$$SiCl_4 + H_2O \longrightarrow SiO_2 + 4\,HCl$$

We now find there are two hydrogen atoms on the reactant side but four on the product side. We will therefore need two water molecules as reactant to give a balanced equation:

$$SiCl_4 + 2\,H_2O \longrightarrow SiO_2 + 4\,HCl$$

The final step is to add the phase of each species:

$$SiCl_{4\,(\ell)} + 2\,H_2O_{(\ell)} \longrightarrow SiO_{2\,(s)} + 4\,HCl_{(g)}$$

Reactions in Solution

One of the symbols used to indicate the physical state of a chemical taking part in a reaction is (aq). This tells us that the substance is dissolved in water.

EXAMPLE   **8.2**   When an aqueous solution of sodium chloride is added to an aqueous solution of silver nitrate a precipitate of silver chloride is formed. The other product, sodium nitrate, remains dissolved in water. Write a balanced molecular equation for this reaction.

SOLUTION   The word equation for the reaction is

Silver nitrate + Sodium chloride $\longrightarrow$

Silver chloride + Sodium nitrate

Substituting formulas for names gives us

$$AgNO_3 + NaCl \longrightarrow AgCl + NaNO_3$$

As this equation is already balanced, we need only add the appropriate symbols to indicate the states:

$$AgNO_{3\,(aq)} + NaCl_{(aq)} \longrightarrow AgCl_{(s)} + NaNO_{3\,(aq)}$$

Reactions that Require Heat

Many reactants have to be heated in order for a reaction to occur. We indicate this by writing a small triangle above the arrow in the chemical equation.

EXAMPLE   **8.3**   The 18th century chemists prepared oxygen by heating solid mercury(II) oxide. The other reaction product was shiny globules of mercury metal. Write the equation for this reaction.

SOLUTION   First, we write the word equation and then the molecular equation:

$$\text{Mercury(II) oxide} \xrightarrow{\text{heat}} \text{Mercury} + \text{Oxygen}$$
$$HgO \xrightarrow{\text{heat}} Hg + O_2$$

As we have two oxygens on the right side, we must place a 2 in front of the HgO on the left side. We also replace the word "heat" by the symbol for heat, Δ:

$$2\,HgO \xrightarrow{\Delta} Hg + O_2$$

Now the mercury is not balanced. We need 2 Hg on the right side. Thus

$$2\,HgO \xrightarrow{\Delta} 2\,Hg + O_2$$

Finally, we put in the symbols for the states, remembering that metallic mercury is a liquid:

$$2\,HgO_{(s)} \xrightarrow{\Delta} 2\,Hg_{(\ell)} + O_{2\,(g)}$$

You will sometimes see a temperature (or pressure) written above (or below) the arrow in a chemical equation, as in the following equation for the industrial preparation of calcium oxide (quicklime):

$$CaCO_{3\,(s)} \xrightarrow{850\,°C} CaO_{(s)} + CO_{2\,(g)}$$

The temperature (or pressure) indicates the conditions under which the reaction is carried out — in this case, at a temperature of 850 °C.

Reactions that Require a Catalyst

Many reactions take place very slowly and require a long time to produce the maximum quantity of products. In the teaching laboratory or in industry we cannot afford to wait hours, days, or months to obtain reaction products. Therefore a catalyst is often added to the reactants to speed up a reaction. A **catalyst** is a substance that increases the rate of a chemical reaction, but is itself unchanged at the end of the reaction.

A catalyst is not consumed during a reaction. It is therefore neither a reactant nor a product. Its presence is indicated by writing its symbol or formula above the arrow. Thus, you will see equations such as

$$2\ H_2O_{2\ (aq)} \xrightarrow{\ MnO_2\ } 2\ H_2O_{(\ell)}\ +\ O_{2\ (g)}$$

This equation tells us that hydrogen peroxide solution decomposes to form water and oxygen gas. Without a catalyst the reaction proceeds so slowly that you cannot see it occurring. If manganese(IV) oxide is added, the reaction proceeds at a much faster rate. The hydrogen peroxide solution bubbles and froths as oxygen is produced (Figure 8.8).

We find that most of the chemical reactions that take place in our bodies occur very slowly if we try to duplicate them in the laboratory. However, our body cells produce a large variety of catalysts, called **enzymes**, that speed up the reactions in our bodies and allow us to function at a reasonable rate. Enzymes are often very complex molecules.

Figure 8.8
The decomposition of hydrogen peroxide:
a) Hydrogen peroxide decomposes very slowly on its own.
b) Some manganese(IV) oxide catalyst is added.
c) Very rapid decomposition of the hydrogen peroxide occurs.

Equilibrium Reactions

In some reactions, the reactants do not change completely to products even if the reactants are left for years. In these reactions, referred to as **equilibrium reactions**, there is always a mixture of products and reactants present. Equilibrium reactions are identified by the presence of a double arrow in the equation to indicate that both the forward and reverse processes occur.

Although we will mention a few examples of equilibrium reactions later in this text, we will not study them in detail.

EXAMPLE   **8.4**   When carbon dioxide gas comes into contact with water, an equilibrium is established with a solution of carbonic acid (H_2CO_3) as the product. Write a balanced equation for this equilibrium.

SOLUTION   The word equation is

$$\text{Carbon dioxide} + \text{Water} \rightleftharpoons \text{Carbonic acid}$$

The molecular equation is

$$CO_2 + H_2O \rightleftharpoons H_2CO_3$$

As this is already balanced, we just need to add the symbols for the states:

$$CO_{2\ (g)} + H_2O_{(\ell)} \rightleftharpoons H_2CO_{3\ (aq)}$$

Balancing More Complicated Equations

You will find that balancing equations becomes easier with practice. When balancing complicated equations, it is usually best to start with atoms that occur only once on the reactant side and once on the product side. It is easier to balance atoms that occur more than twice in the equation at a later stage of the balancing process.

Spectator ions
ions that do not React.

EXAMPLE   **8.5**   Many hikers and campers use stoves that use propane as a fuel. When propane gas burns (i.e., reacts with oxygen), the products are carbon dioxide gas and water vapour. Write a balanced chemical equation for this reaction. The formula for propane is C_3H_8.

SOLUTION   The unbalanced equation is

$$C_3H_8 + O_2 \longrightarrow CO_2 + H_2O$$

We have to balance three elements: carbon, hydrogen, and oxygen. Of these, carbon and hydrogen occur only twice in the equation, whereas oxygen occurs three times. Thus, it would be best to balance either carbon or hydrogen first and leave oxygen until the end of the balancing process. If we arbitrarily decide to balance carbon first, we would write

$$C_3H_8 + O_2 \longrightarrow 3\,CO_2 + H_2O$$

Next, we balance hydrogen. As we have eight hydrogen atoms on the left-hand side, we need four water molecules on the right:

$$C_3H_8 + O_2 \longrightarrow 3\,CO_2 + 4\,H_2O$$

Finally, we balance the oxygen. Oxygen occurs in three species: O_2, CO_2, and H_2O. At this stage of the balancing process it would be unwise to alter the coefficients in front of CO_2 and H_2O. The preferred species for balancing oxygen is O_2. We find a total of ten oxygen atoms on the right-hand side of the equation; thus, we will need five molecules of oxygen on the left. After adding symbols for the states, we obtain the following equation:

$$C_3H_{8\,(g)} + 5\,O_{2\,(g)} \longrightarrow 3\,CO_{2\,(g)} + 4\,H_2O_{(g)}$$

EXAMPLE   **8.6**   Balance the following equation:

$$2\,Al + 3\,H_2SO_4 \longrightarrow Al_2(SO_4)_3 + 3\,H_2$$

SOLUTION   Of the four elements present, only hydrogen is already balanced. Let us balance aluminum next. Thus

$$2\,Al + H_2SO_4 \longrightarrow Al_2(SO_4)_3 + H_2$$

Both sulfur and oxygen occur once on the product side and once on the reactant side. We notice that for both H_2SO_4 and $Al_2(SO_4)_3$, sulfur and oxygen occur in the polyatomic sulfate anion SO_4^{2-}. Within this ion, the S:O ratio is constant and equal to 1:4. Balancing sulfur will therefore automatically balance oxygen and vice versa. Instead of balancing sulfur and oxygen separately, we balance the sulfate anion by placing a 3 in front of the H_2SO_4 to give us

$$2\,Al + 3\,H_2SO_4 \longrightarrow Al_2(SO_4)_3 + H_2$$

During this process we unbalanced hydrogen. We can restore the hydrogen balance by inserting a 3 in front of H_2. When the symbols for the states are added, the final equation becomes

$$2\,Al_{(s)} + 3\,H_2SO_{4\,(aq)} \longrightarrow Al_2(SO_4)_{3\,(aq)} + 3\,H_{2\,(g)}$$

Our discussion so far has focussed on the mechanical aspects of equation writing. However, chemists are interested in much more than this. They want to know why a reaction does or does not occur, and they also want to be able to predict whether previously unknown reactions are possible.

The first step towards these goals is to study as many chemical reactions as possible to see if there are any detectable patterns. If patterns can be found, we can then group together reactions of the same type. Doing this, we find that most reactions fit into one of four basic categories. In the following sections we will discuss each of these categories.

QUESTIONS

1. Write a balanced molecular equation for each of the reactions below.
   a) When gaseous carbon dioxide is passed over solid calcium oxide, solid calcium carbonate is formed.
   b) Solid carbon burns in fluorine gas to give gaseous carbon tetrafluoride.
   c) Aluminum metal burns in oxygen gas to give solid aluminum oxide.
2. When sodium sulfate solution is added to barium chloride solution, a white precipitate of barium sulfate is produced while sodium chloride remains in solution. Write a balanced molecular equation for this reaction.
3. Sulfur dioxide gas reacts with oxygen gas in the presence of a platinum catalyst at 200 °C to give gaseous sulfur trioxide. Write a balanced molecular equation for this reaction.
4. Balance the following equations:
   a) $NH_{3\,(g)} + O_{2\,(g)} \longrightarrow NO_{(g)} + H_2O_{(g)}$
   b) $Li_{(s)} + H_2O_{(\ell)} \longrightarrow LiOH_{(aq)} + H_{2\,(g)}$
   c) $Al_4C_{(s)} + H_2O_{(\ell)} \longrightarrow CH_4 + Al(OH)_{3\,(s)}$
   d) $C_4H_{10\,(g)} + O_{2\,(g)} \longrightarrow CO_{2\,(g)} + H_2O_{(g)}$
   e) $CuFeS_{2\,(s)} + O_{2\,(g)} \longrightarrow Cu_{(s)} + FeO_{(s)} + SO_{2\,(g)}$

Combination Reactions

8.4

A **combination reaction** occurs when two or more simple substances combine to produce a more complex substance. There are four types of combination reaction.

Combination Reactions of Elements

The most common type of combination reaction involves two elements reacting together to form a compound. We have already encountered two combination reactions in this chapter. The first was the reaction of oxygen gas with solid carbon to produce carbon dioxide gas:

$$C_{(s)} + O_{2\,(g)} \longrightarrow CO_{2\,(g)}$$

The second was the reaction of metallic sodium with chlorine gas to produce solid sodium chloride:

$$2\,Na_{(s)} + Cl_{2\,(g)} \longrightarrow 2\,NaCl_{(s)}$$

The oxides and chlorides of many elements can be prepared by reacting the element with oxygen or chlorine gas respectively. Other pairs of elements can also combine in chemical reactions, but it is often difficult to make predictions about which pairs will actually react with each other.

Combination Reactions that Produce Acids

We can sometimes combine two relatively simple compounds to produce a more complicated compound. The product of this type of reaction is often an acid. An example is the reaction of sulfur trioxide with water to form sulfuric acid:

$$SO_{3\,(s)} + H_2O_{(\ell)} \longrightarrow H_2SO_{4\,(aq)}$$

Many nonmetal oxides will combine with water to form an acid in this way. Another example is the reaction between dinitrogen pentaoxide and water to produce nitric acid:

$$N_2O_{5\,(s)} + H_2O_{(\ell)} \longrightarrow 2\,HNO_{3\,(aq)}$$

Nonmetal oxides, such as sulfur trioxide and dinitrogen pentaoxide, that react with water to form acids are called **acidic oxides**.

Combination Reactions that Produce Bases

Several metal oxides will combine with water to form bases. For example, solid lithium oxide reacts with water to give a solution of lithium hydroxide:

$$Li_2O_{(s)} + H_2O_{(\ell)} \longrightarrow 2\,LiOH_{(aq)}$$

Similarly, solid barium oxide reacts with water to give a solution of barium hydroxide:

$$BaO_{(s)} + H_2O_{(\ell)} \longrightarrow Ba(OH)_{2\,(aq)}$$

Metal oxides that react with water to form bases are called **basic oxides**.

Combination Reactions that Produce Salts

Acidic oxides and basic oxides can react with each other in a combination reaction to form a salt. For example, solid calcium oxide (a basic oxide) reacts with carbon dioxide gas (an acidic oxide) to give the salt known as calcium carbonate:

$$CaO_{(s)} + CO_{2\,(g)} \longrightarrow CaCO_{3\,(s)}$$

Another example is the reaction that occurs when solid barium oxide is heated with solid sulfur trioxide. In this case the product is solid barium sulfate:

$$BaO_{(s)} + SO_{3\,(s)} \xrightarrow{\Delta} BaSO_{4\,(s)}$$

5. Complete and balance the following combination reactions:
   a) $Zn_{(s)} + Cl_{2 (g)} \longrightarrow$ c) $Li_2O_{(s)} + CO_{2 (g)} \longrightarrow$
   b) $CaO_{(s)} + H_2O_{(\ell)} \longrightarrow$ d) $Mg_{(s)} + O_{2 (g)} \longrightarrow$

6. For each reaction in question 5, identify whether the product is an acid, a base, a salt, an acidic oxide, or a basic oxide.

Decomposition Reactions

8.5

A **decomposition reaction** can be considered as the reverse of a combination reaction. In a decomposition reaction, a complicated substance is broken down into two or more simpler substances. Decomposition reactions that occur as a result of heating are called **thermal decompositions**. The classification scheme used for decomposition reactions is similar to that used for combination reactions.

Decomposition Reactions that Produce Elements

Decomposition reactions in which elements are produced are quite rare. One example that we have already discussed is the decomposition of solid mercury(II) oxide into mercury metal and oxygen gas:

$$2 \, HgO_{(s)} \xrightarrow{\Delta} 2 \, Hg_{(\ell)} + O_{2 (g)}$$

The thermal decomposition of silver oxide into silver metal and oxygen gas is another example:

$$2 \, Ag_2O_{(s)} \xrightarrow{\Delta} 4 \, Ag_{(s)} + O_{2 (g)}$$

Decomposition of Acids

We can decompose a few acids to form acidic oxides and water. In the equilibrium reaction that we encountered in Section 8.3, carbonic acid was on the products side of an equilibrium reaction:

$$CO_{2 (g)} + H_2O_{(\ell)} \rightleftharpoons H_2CO_{3 (aq)}$$

In an equilibrium reaction we always have a mixture of reactants and products present in the system. It is possible, however, to alter the ratio of reactants to products by changing the conditions of the reaction. In the present example, heating the mixture will cause some of the carbonic acid to decompose into carbon dioxide gas and water:

$$H_2CO_{3 (aq)} \xrightleftharpoons{heat} CO_{2 (g)} + H_2O_{(\ell)}$$

Decomposition of Bases

Although it is quite rare for acids to decompose to form acidic oxides and water, most bases decompose on heating to form a basic oxide and water. Thus, strong heating of calcium hydroxide produces calcium oxide and water vapour:

$$Ca(OH)_{2\ (s)} \xrightarrow{\Delta} CaO_{(s)} + H_2O_{(g)}$$

Decomposition of Salts

Several salts can be thermally decomposed to form an acidic oxide and a basic oxide. For example, strong heating of solid iron(III) sulfate decomposes the salt into solid iron(III) oxide and sulfur trioxide gas:

$$Fe_2(SO_4)_{3\ (s)} \xrightarrow{\Delta} Fe_2O_{3\ (s)} + 3\ SO_{3\ (g)}$$

In the reverse of one of the combination reactions studied earlier, solid calcium carbonate is heated to give solid calcium oxide and carbon dioxide gas:

$$CaCO_{3\ (s)} \xrightarrow{\Delta} CaO_{(s)} + CO_{2\ (g)}$$

Other Decomposition Reactions

It is not always easy to make predictions about the products that will be formed in a decomposition reaction. For example, if solid ammonium nitrate is heated, water vapour and dinitrogen oxide gas are produced:

$$NH_4NO_{3\ (s)} \xrightarrow{\Delta} 2\ H_2O_{(g)} + N_2O_{(g)}$$

Ammonium nitrate is used as both a fertilizer and an explosive and must be handled carefully. Some disastrous explosions have occurred when bulk quantities of ammonium nitrate have been accidentally heated by the flames of a fire. One example was a harbour explosion in 1947 in Texas City, Texas, in which over 600 people were killed.

Sometimes a decomposition can be better understood if we consider it as occurring in two steps. A good example is the decomposition of silver carbonate, in which the products are silver metal, carbon dioxide, and oxygen:

$$2\ Ag_2CO_{3\ (s)} \xrightarrow{\Delta} 4\ Ag_{(s)} + 2\ CO_{2\ (g)} + O_{2\ (g)}$$

This reaction is easier to understand if we consider that the silver carbonate first breaks down into silver oxide and carbon dioxide:

$$2\ Ag_2CO_{3\ (s)} \xrightarrow{\Delta} 2\ Ag_2O_{(s)} + 2\ CO_{2\ (g)}$$

The decomposition of silver carbonate into an acidic oxide (carbon dioxide) and a basic oxide (silver oxide) is the same type of reaction as that of calcium carbonate decomposing to form carbon dioxide and calcium oxide.

However, we have also seen that silver oxide decomposes on heating to form silver metal and oxygen gas:

$$2\ Ag_2O_{(s)} \xrightarrow{\Delta} 4\ Ag_{(s)} + O_{2\ (g)}$$

Thus, the silver oxide produced in the first step of the reaction is decomposed to form silver metal and oxygen gas. By considering the reaction as a two-step process, we can account for the three reaction products. If we add together the equations for the two steps we find that the $2\ Ag_2O_{(s)}$ cancels to give us a final equation that describes the overall reaction, as follows:

$$2\ Ag_2CO_{3\ (s)} \xrightarrow{\Delta} 2\ \cancel{Ag_2O}_{(s)} + 2\ CO_{2\ (g)}$$

$$2\ \cancel{Ag_2O}_{(s)} \xrightarrow{\Delta} 4\ Ag_{(s)} + O_{2\ (g)}$$

$$\overline{2\ Ag_2CO_{3\ (s)} \xrightarrow{\Delta} 4\ Ag_{(s)} + 2\ CO_{2\ (g)} + O_{2\ (g)}}$$

QUESTIONS

7. Complete and balance the following decomposition reactions:

    a) $AgCl_{(s)} \xrightarrow{\Delta}$ b) $MgCO_{3\ (s)} \xrightarrow{\Delta}$ c) $Mg(OH)_{2\ (s)} \xrightarrow{\Delta}$

8. For each reaction in question 7, identify whether an acid, base, or salt is being decomposed.

Single Displacement Reactions

8.6

In a **single displacement reaction** one element replaces another element in a compound. An example of industrial importance involves the addition of scrap iron to a copper(II) sulfate solution to displace the more valuable copper metal:

$$Fe_{(s)} + CuSO_{4\ (aq)} \longrightarrow FeSO_{4\ (aq)} + Cu_{(s)}$$

A second example, also of industrial importance, is the production of bromine from seawater (brine) containing bromide ions. After the brine has been concentrated by evaporating some of the water, chlorine gas is added. The chlorine displaces the bromide ion to produce bromine. Hence

$$Cl_{2\ (aq)} + 2\ NaBr_{(aq)} \longrightarrow 2\ NaCl_{(aq)} + Br_{2\ (aq)}$$

Figure 8.9
A copper recovery plant. In this patented process, solutions of copper ions are passed down towers filled with scrap steel. The iron displaces the copper from its solution to give solid copper. The towers are periodically opened and the copper metal is removed for subsequent smelting.

The Activity Series

We can usually predict when a single displacement reaction is likely to occur by referring to the activity series. The **activity series** (or electro-chemical, or electromotive series, as it is also called) consists of a table of

Each metal will displace any metal ion that appears below it in the series.

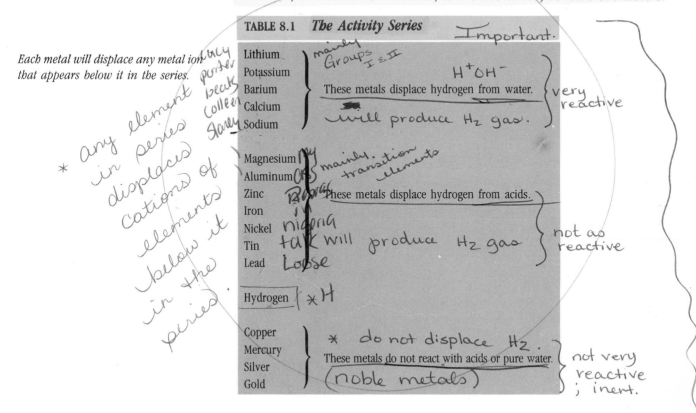

TABLE 8.1 *The Activity Series*

Lithium	
Potassium	
Barium	These metals displace hydrogen from water.
Calcium	
Sodium	
Magnesium	
Aluminum	
Zinc	These metals displace hydrogen from acids.
Iron	
Nickel	
Tin	
Lead	
Hydrogen	
Copper	
Mercury	These metals do not react with acids or pure water.
Silver	
Gold	

Handwritten annotations:

Important.

mainly Groups I & II

H^+OH^-

very reactive

will produce H_2 gas.

mainly transition elements

not as reactive

* do not displace H_2.

(noble metals)

not very reactive ; inert.

* Any element in series displaces cations of elements below it in the series.

metallic elements (plus hydrogen). Any element in the table will displace ions of the elements below it from aqueous solutions of their salts. Thus, as we have seen, iron is able to displace copper from an aqueous solution of copper(II) sulfate because iron is above copper in the series. The reverse reaction does not occur because copper is below iron in the series.

$$Cu_{(s)} + FeSO_{4\ (aq)} \longrightarrow \text{no reaction}$$

Notice that the nonmetal, hydrogen, is included in the activity series. This allows us to predict that zinc metal will displace hydrogen gas from hydrochloric acid as zinc comes above hydrogen in the series. This prediction proves to be correct. The following reaction is an excellent method for the small-scale preparation of hydrogen.

$$Zn_{(s)} + 2\ HCl_{(aq)} \longrightarrow ZnCl_{2\ (aq)} + H_{2\ (g)}$$

Metals Very High in the Activity Series

The metals that are very high in the activity series can not only displace hydrogen from an acid, but can also displace hydrogen from water. For example, sodium metal reacts violently with water to give hydrogen gas and a solution of sodium hydroxide:

$$2\ Na_{(s)} + 2\ H_2O_{(\ell)} \longrightarrow 2\ NaOH_{(aq)} + H_{2\ (g)}$$

We can understand this reaction if we think of water as H–OH ("hydrogen hydroxide"). Thus, the sodium atom displaces the "H" of H–OH to form NaOH, and the displaced hydrogen atoms combine to form H_2 molecules (hydrogen gas). The only metals in the activity series that are capable of reacting with water are the top five: lithium, potassium, barium, calcium and sodium.

The Halogen Displacement Series

Each element in the **halogen displacement series** can displace the ions of any element below it from an aqueous solution of one of its salts. Thus, as we saw previously, chlorine will displace bromine from a sodium bromide solution, but the reverse reaction does not occur because bromine is below chlorine in this series.

$$Br_{2\ (aq)} + 2\ NaCl_{(aq)} \longrightarrow \text{no reaction}$$

TABLE 8.2

The Halogen Displacement Series

Each halogen will displace any halide ion that appears below it.	Fluorine Chlorine Bromine Iodine

---

EXAMPLE *8.7* Which of the following reactions will *not* occur:

a) $Zn_{(s)} + NiCl_{2\ (aq)} \longrightarrow Ni_{(s)} + ZnCl_{2\ (aq)}$

b) $I_{2\ (aq)} + 2\ KF_{(aq)} \longrightarrow F_{2\ (aq)} + 2\ KI_{(aq)}$

c) $Cu_{(s)} + 2\ AgNO_{3\ (aq)} \longrightarrow Cu(NO_3)_{2\ (aq)} + 2\ Ag_{(s)}$

SOLUTION In each case we just need to check the appropriate series. In (a) zinc is above nickel in the activity series and in (c) copper is above silver in the same series. Both of these reactions proceed as shown by the equations. In (b), however, we find that iodine is below fluorine in the displacement series for the halogens, hence the reaction shown does not take place. The reverse reaction should be possible. Thus

$$F_{2\,(aq)} + 2\,KI_{(aq)} \longrightarrow I_{2\,(aq)} + 2\,KF_{(aq)}$$

The Activity Series in Mining

When we study the deposits of metallic elements in the earth, we find that only a few elements actually occur in the elemental state. Gold is always found as the element, and some deposits of metallic silver, mercury, and copper are known. However, these latter three elements are more often found as silver sulfide, mercury(II) sulfide, and copper(II) sulfide. All the other metals only occur in nature as compounds.

Note the location of gold, silver, mercury, and copper in the activity series. They are all near the bottom of the series, with gold at the lowest point. Only the least active metals can be found as free elements in nature. If any of the metals above hydrogen in the activity series are exposed to acids, such as the naturally occurring humic acids in the soil, a reaction leading to the formation of a compound will occur. Thus it is impossible to find elemental deposits of metals such as sodium, aluminum, or zinc.

We also have to pay attention to the activity series when we extract metals from their ores. We can never use an aqueous process to extract any of the metals high in the activity series from their compounds because, as we showed earlier, as soon as the metal is formed, it will react immediately with water.

QUESTIONS

9. In which of the following cases does a reaction occur?
   a) $Cl_{2\,(aq)} + NaI_{(aq)} \longrightarrow$
   b) $Ca_{(s)} + H_2O_{(\ell)} \longrightarrow$
   c) $Pb_{(s)} + HCl_{(aq)} \longrightarrow$
   d) $Zn_{(s)} + CuCl_{2\,(aq)} \longrightarrow$
   e) $Br_{2\,(aq)} + CaCl_{2\,(aq)} \longrightarrow$

   Where reactions occur, complete and balance the equations.

Double Displacement Reactions

8.7

In a **double displacement reaction** (which always involves two ionic compounds) the cation of one compound changes place with the cation of the second compound. The overall effect is that the positive ions exchange their negative partners. An example is the precipitation of iron(II) sulfide when aqueous solutions of iron(II) sulfate and ammonium sulfide are mixed. The other product of this reaction, ammonium sulfate, remains

Coinage and the Activity Series

Coins first appeared in the 6th century B.C. Their use appears to have originated independently in Greece and China. One of the factors that led to prosperity in the early Roman Empire was the stability of the currency. The value of the coins remained almost unchanged for over two centuries. The lowest value coin, the *sestertius*, was made of bronze, which is a mixture of 80% copper and 20% tin. The *denarius* (worth four sestertii) was made of silver, and the *aureus* (worth one hundred sestertii) was made of gold. You can see that these higher value coins were made from the metals that are lowest in the activity series.

Copper, silver, and gold have formed the basis of almost every coinage system. One reason for this is that these metals are lowest in the activity series and thus are the least likely to corrode. Other metals, including platinum, tin, zinc, and aluminum, have been used for coinage in various parts of the world.

In Canada, as in most other countries, the coin with the lowest value (the cent) is made of copper. As the price of copper has risen, the mass of the cent has decreased from 3.24 g in 1964 to 2.8 g in 1980 to 2.5 g in 1982. This decrease in mass has prevented the coin from costing more than one cent to make! (In the U.S., the current cent contains a zinc core, as zinc is less expensive than copper.)

The metal used most in coin production in Canada is nickel. Although nickel is between iron and tin on the activity scale, its hardness, low cost, and high lustre make it a convenient choice. Nickel was first used in 1922 for the five cent coin (hence the name, nickel).

Because of wartime shortages of nickel, a mixture of 88% copper and 12% zinc was used to manufacture nickels in 1942 and 1943. Nickel-chromium plated iron was used to make nickels in 1944 and 1945, and again from 1951 to 1954. All other Canadian coinage in general circulation (10¢, 25¢, 50¢, and $1) is made of nickel. In addition, there are "silver" dollars that are really 50% silver and 50% copper, $100 gold coins, and $50 gold "maple-leaf" coins. The gold maple leaf is minted primarily for gold collectors, and the silver dollar and $100 gold coin for coin collectors. None of the three are true coinage as their purchase price is much higher than their face value.

Figure 8.10
The 1951 nickel, commemorating the first isolation of nickel in 1751 by the Swedish chemist, A.F. Cronstedt.

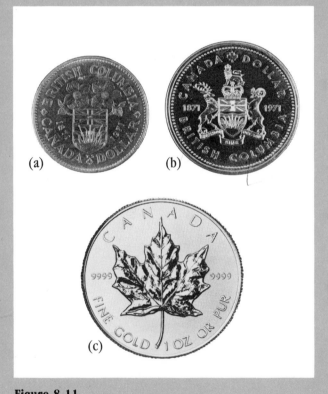

(a)   (b)

(c)

Figure 8.11
a) A nickel dollar
b) A "silver" dollar
c) A $50 gold "maple-leaf" coin

in solution but can be isolated by evaporating the water. The balanced equation for this reaction is

$$(NH_4)_2S_{(aq)} \; + \; FeSO_{4\,(aq)} \longrightarrow \; FeS_{(s)} \; + \; (NH_4)_2SO_{4\,(aq)}$$

In this reaction, we can clearly see the "change of partners" in operation. Initially the iron(II) ion is combined with the sulfate ion in the compound iron(II) sulfate and the ammonium and sulfide ions are combined in the compound, ammonium sulfide. When aqueous solutions of the two compounds are mixed, the iron(II) ion combines with the sulfide ion to form a precipitate of iron(II) sulfide and the ammonium and sulfide ions remain in solution.

How can we predict when a double displacement reaction will occur? Such reactions usually result in the formation of a precipitate, a gas, or water. We shall look at each of these situations in turn.

Reactions in Which Precipitates are Formed

To predict if a precipitate might be formed by a double displacement reaction, we need to know if the ionic compounds that could be produced in the reaction are soluble or insoluble in water. For this information, we can refer to the solubility rules summarized in Table 8.3. Remember that, if a substance produced in a reaction is insoluble in water, it will be obtained as a precipitate. If it is soluble, it will remain in solution.

TABLE 8.3   *Solubilities: Rules and Exceptions*

Rule	Important Exceptions
Nitrates (NO_3^-) are soluble	None
Halides (Cl^-, Br^-, I^-) are soluble	Ag^+, Hg_2^{2+}, Cu^+, Pb^{2+}
Sulfates (SO_4^{2-}) are soluble	Ca^{2+}, Sr^{2+}, Ba^{2+}, Pb^{2+}, Hg_2^{2+}, Ag^+
Sulfides (S^{2-}) are insoluble	NH_4^+ and ions of the Group IA and IIA elements
Carbonates (CO_3^{2-}) are insoluble	NH_4^+ and ions of the Group IA elements
Phosphates (PO_4^{3-}) are insoluble	NH_4^+ and ions of the Group IA elements
Hydroxides (OH^-) are insoluble	Ba^{2+}, Sr^{2+}, and ions of the Group IA elements

If we check the products of the ammonium sulfide–iron(II) sulfate reaction, that is, ammonium sulfate and iron(II) sulfide, we see that iron(II) sulfide is insoluble and that, in general, sulfates are soluble. Thus, it is possible to predict the products of this reaction correctly as a precipitate of iron(II) sulfide and an aqueous solution of ammonium sulfate. As we can predict the formation of the iron(II) sulfide precipitate, we know that when we mix aqueous solutions of iron(II) sulfate and ammonium sulfide a reaction will occur.

Figure 8.12

An X-ray photograph of a patient's intestine. X-rays like this are taken to assist in diagnosing ulcers and tumours. The patient is given a suspension of barium sulfate. As barium absorbs X-rays, the intestine appears on this photograph as the white area. Because the barium ion in solution is very poisonous, insoluble barium sulfate must be used. This compound passes harmlessly through the patient's system.

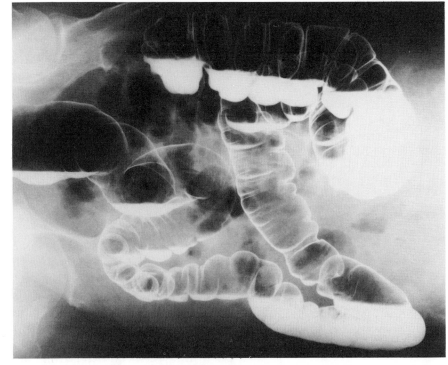

Figure 8.13

A general view of a plant for extracting magnesium from seawater. The circular tanks on the right contain the magnesium hydroxide that precipitated when hydroxide ions were added to seawater.

A double displacement reaction is used to extract magnesium from sea-water. The sea contains about 0.13% of magnesium ion by mass. This is much less than the percentage of sodium (1.08%) in seawater. To extract the magnesium ion, we need to find an anion that will form an insoluble salt with magnesium while forming soluble salts with sodium and the other alkali metal (Group IA) cations. If you check Table 8.3, you will see that magnesium forms an insoluble hydroxide, whereas the hydroxides of the alkali metals are all soluble.

In practice, calcium hydroxide is added to large tanks of seawater (Figure 8.13). As the mixture is stirred, a white precipitate of magnesium hydroxide forms. This precipitate is filtered off from the solution. We can represent the reaction as

$$MgCl_{2\ (aq)}\ +\ Ca(OH)_{2\ (aq)}\ \longrightarrow\ Mg(OH)_{2\ (s)}\ +\ CaCl_{2\ (aq)}$$

EXAMPLE   **8.8**   When an aqueous solution of barium chloride is added to an aqueous solution of potassium sulfate, a precipitate is obtained. Write a balanced molecular equation for this reaction.

SOLUTION   The (unbalanced) equation for the reaction is

$$BaCl_2\ +\ K_2SO_4\ \longrightarrow\ KCl\ +\ BaSO_4$$

This can be balanced by inserting the coefficient 2 in front of KCl:

$$BaCl_2\ +\ K_2SO_4\ \longrightarrow\ 2\ KCl\ +\ BaSO_4$$

Referring to Table 8.3, we see that potassium chloride is not listed as one of the three insoluble chlorides and that barium sulfate is one of the few insoluble sulfates. Thus, the potassium chloride will remain in solution and barium sulfate will form as a precipitate. The equation should therefore be written as

$$BaCl_{2\ (aq)}\ +\ K_2SO_{4\ (aq)}\ \longrightarrow\ BaSO_{4\ (s)}\ +\ 2\ KCl_{(aq)}$$

Reactions that Produce Gases

A double displacement reaction is also likely to occur if there is a possibility of a gas being formed. An example is the reaction between sodium carbonate solution and hydrochloric acid. As we have classified the reaction as double displacement, we would expect the following exchange of ions to take place:

$$Na_2CO_{3\ (aq)}\ +\ 2\ HCl_{(aq)}\ \longrightarrow\ 2\ NaCl_{(aq)}\ +\ H_2CO_{3\ (aq)}$$

We can certainly regard this equation as representing a first reaction. However, as we saw in Example 8.4, carbonic acid (H_2CO_3) is in equilibrium with carbon dioxide gas and water:

$$H_2CO_{3\ (aq)}\ \rightleftharpoons\ CO_{2\ (g)}\ +\ H_2O_{(\ell)}$$

Thus, many of the carbonic acid molecules produced in the first reaction will decompose immediately to give carbon dioxide gas and water. We can add these two steps together to obtain the overall reaction:

$$Na_2CO_{3\,(aq)} + 2\,HCl_{(aq)} \longrightarrow 2\,NaCl_{(aq)} + \cancel{H_2CO_3}_{\,(aq)}$$

$$\cancel{H_2CO_3}_{\,(aq)} \rightleftharpoons CO_{2\,(g)} + H_2O_{(\ell)}$$

$$Na_2CO_{3\,(aq)} + 2\,HCl_{(aq)} \longrightarrow 2\,NaCl_{(aq)} + H_2O_{(\ell)} + CO_{2\,(g)}$$

Let us look at two similar reactions in which gases are produced. The first is the reaction of sodium sulfite solution with hydrochloric acid. We can break this reaction down into two stages. One product of the first stage is sulfurous acid, which then decomposes into sulfur dioxide and water in the second stage:

$$Na_2SO_{3\,(aq)} + 2\,HCl_{(aq)} \longrightarrow 2\,NaCl_{(aq)} + \cancel{H_2SO_3}_{\,(aq)}$$

$$\cancel{H_2SO_3}_{\,(aq)} \rightleftharpoons SO_{2\,(g)} + H_2O_{(\ell)}$$

If we add these two equations together and cancel the $H_2SO_{3\,(aq)}$ we find that the overall equation for the process is

$$Na_2SO_{3\,(aq)} + 2\,HCl_{(aq)} \longrightarrow 2\,NaCl_{(aq)} + H_2O_{(\ell)} + SO_{2\,(g)}$$

The second reaction to be considered here is the one that occurs between ammonium chloride solution and sodium hydroxide. Again, we can consider this as a two-stage reaction. The ammonium hydroxide solution produced in the first stage is in equilibrium with ammonia gas and water:

$$NH_4Cl_{(aq)} + NaOH_{(aq)} \longrightarrow NaCl_{(aq)} + \cancel{NH_4OH}_{\,(aq)}$$

$$\cancel{NH_4OH}_{\,(aq)} \rightleftharpoons NH_{3\,(g)} + H_2O_{(\ell)}$$

Following the same procedure as before, we find that adding the two equations gives us

$$NH_4Cl_{(aq)} + NaOH_{(aq)} \longrightarrow NaCl_{(aq)} + H_2O_{(\ell)} + NH_{3\,(g)}$$

One gas-producing reaction that can be written directly as a double displacement reaction occurs between sodium sulfide solution and hydrochloric acid. Hydrogen sulfide is produced as a gas, with the other product being a solution of sodium chloride:

$$Na_2S_{(aq)} + 2\,HCl_{(aq)} \longrightarrow 2\,NaCl_{(aq)} + H_2S_{(g)}$$

The only double displacement reactions of this type that you will encounter in this text will be those that produce either carbon dioxide, sulfur dioxide, ammonia, or hydrogen sulfide.

EXAMPLE   **8.9**   Write a balanced molecular equation for the double displacement reaction between solid calcium carbonate and nitric acid.

SOLUTION   The two products should be calcium nitrate and carbonic acid. We can therefore construct the following equation remembering that all nitrates are soluble:

$$CaCO_{3\,(s)} + 2\,HNO_{3\,(aq)} \longrightarrow Ca(NO_3)_{2\,(aq)} + H_2CO_{3\,(aq)}$$

The carbonic acid will decompose, as in the example above, to give carbon dioxide gas and water:

$$H_2CO_3 \rightleftharpoons CO_{2\,(g)} + H_2O_{(\ell)}$$

We combine the two equations as before to give the overall equation:

$$CaCO_{3\,(s)} + 2\,HNO_{3\,(aq)} \longrightarrow Ca(NO_3)_{2\,(aq)} + H_2O_{(\ell)} + CO_{2\,(g)}$$

Reactions that Produce Water

Both types of double displacement reactions that we have discussed involved the removal of ions from solution. This was accomplished in the first type by the formation of a solid ionic compound, and in the second type by the formation of a covalently bonded gas. The reactions we will now discuss also involve the removal of ions from solution, this time by the formation of covalently bonded water molecules.

Because this type of double displacement reaction is so important, it is given the special name of **neutralization reaction**. A neutralization reaction involves the reaction of an acid with a base to produce a salt plus water. For example, the reaction between nitric acid and potassium hydroxide gives potassium nitrate (which remains in solution because all nitrates are soluble) and water:

$$HNO_{3\,(aq)} + KOH_{(aq)} \longrightarrow KNO_{3\,(aq)} + H_2O_{(\ell)}$$

Martina McCarthy.

EXAMPLE   **8.10**   Write the balanced molecular equation for the reaction between hydrochloric acid and barium hydroxide solution.

SOLUTION   First, we can predict that the products will be a solution of barium chloride and water:

$$HCl_{(aq)} + Ba(OH)_{2\,(aq)} \longrightarrow BaCl_{2\,(aq)} + H_2O_{(\ell)}$$

Then we have to balance the equation:

$$2\,HCl_{(aq)} + Ba(OH)_{2\,(aq)} \longrightarrow BaCl_{2\,(aq)} + 2\,H_2O_{(\ell)}$$

In our discussion of combination reactions (Section 8.4) we introduced the terms *acidic oxide* and *basic oxide*. These oxides can also undergo neutralization reactions. We can react zinc oxide (a basic oxide) with nitric acid to give zinc nitrate solution (a salt) and water:

$$ZnO_{(s)} + 2\,HNO_{3\,(aq)} \longrightarrow Zn(NO_3)_{2\,(aq)} + H_2O_{(\ell)}$$

Similarly, we can react sodium hydroxide solution with an acidic oxide, carbon dioxide, to give sodium carbonate solution and water:

$$2\,NaOH_{(aq)} + CO_{2\,(g)} \longrightarrow Na_2CO_{3\,(aq)} + H_2O_{(\ell)}$$

Because this last reaction occurs readily, it is important to keep solutions of sodium hydroxide in stoppered containers; otherwise the trace amounts of carbon dioxide in the air will react with the solution.

We have seen that acids are neutralized by bases, that acidic oxides are neutralized by bases, and that basic oxides are neutralized by acids. A logical question would be, "Can acidic oxides be neutralized by basic oxides?" The answer is a qualified "yes". Acidic oxides do react with basic oxides, as we have seen in Section 8.4, where we discussed the reaction between carbon dioxide (an acidic oxide) and calcium oxide (a basic oxide):

$$CaO_{(s)} + CO_{2\,(g)} \longrightarrow CaCO_{3\,(s)}$$

However, this reaction could not be classified as a double displacement reaction as defined above because there is clearly no "change of partners". As we have said that neutralization reactions are really special examples of double displacement reactions, excluding this reaction from the neutralization category could be justified. Nevertheless, many chemists would argue that as the reaction involves an acidic substance and a basic substance, it should be regarded as a neutralization.

QUESTIONS

10. The following reactions produce precipitates:

a) $CaCl_{2\,(aq)} + Na_2SO_{4\,(aq)} \longrightarrow$ c) $MgSO_{4\,(aq)} + NaOH_{(aq)} \longrightarrow$

b) $AgNO_{3\,(aq)} + NaI_{(aq)} \longrightarrow$

Write a balanced equation in each case.

11. The following reactions produce gases:

a) $(NH_4)_2SO_{4\,(aq)} + KOH_{(aq)} \longrightarrow$ c) $CaS_{(aq)} + H_2SO_{4\,(aq)} \longrightarrow$

b) $K_2CO_{3\,(aq)} + HNO_{3\,(aq)} \longrightarrow$

Write a balanced equation in each case.

12. The following reactions produce water:

a) $H_2SO_{4\,(aq)} + LiOH_{(aq)} \longrightarrow$ c) $KOH_{(aq)} + SO_{2\,(g)} \longrightarrow$

b) $Fe_2O_{3\,(s)} + HCl_{(aq)} \longrightarrow$

Write a balanced equation in each case.

Identifying Classes of Chemical Reactions

8.8

In the last four sections we discussed the four main classes of chemical reactions: combination, decomposition, single displacement, and double displacement. Let us now see how we can assign a given reaction to one of these classes. Knowing the class to which a reaction belongs helps us to predict the products that will be formed. We can summarize these reactions and classes as follows:

1. **Combination reactions**
   a) Combination of two elements
   b) Combination of an acidic oxide with water to give an acid
   c) Combination of a basic oxide with water to give a base
   d) Combination of a basic oxide with an acidic oxide to give a salt

2. **Decomposition reactions**
   a) Decomposition of a compound into its elements
   b) Decomposition of an acid into water and an acidic oxide
   c) Decomposition of a base into water and a basic oxide
   d) Decomposition of a salt into a basic oxide and an acidic oxide

3. **Single displacement reactions**
   a) Single displacement of one metal by another
   b) Single displacement of one halogen by another

4. **Double displacement reactions**
   a) Double displacement to give a precipitate
   b) Double displacement to produce a gas
   c) Double displacement to produce water (neutralization)

EXAMPLE

8.11

To which reaction class do each of the following belong:

a) $Zn_{(s)} + S_{(s)} \longrightarrow ZnS_{(s)}$ comb.

b) $Zn_{(s)} + CuSO_{4\,(aq)} \longrightarrow Cu_{(s)} + ZnSO_{4\,(aq)}$ SR

c) $Ba(NO_3)_{2\,(aq)} + Na_2SO_{4\,(aq)} \longrightarrow BaSO_{4\,(s)} + 2\,NaNO_{3\,(aq)}$ DR

d) $2\,PbO_{(s)} \longrightarrow 2\,Pb_{(s)} + O_{2\,(g)}$ Dec

SOLUTION

a) This is a reaction between two elements to form a compound. It is therefore a combination reaction.

b) A reaction between a metal and a salt where one metal ion is substituted by another must be a single displacement reaction.

c) The reaction is between two salts to give two other salts, one of which is insoluble. A double displacement reaction is taking place.

d) This is a decomposition reaction producing two elements. It is the easiest class of reaction to identify, as only a single reactant is involved.

To identify the products of a reaction, first decide upon the class of reaction taking place. You can then use the information in the last four sections to predict the probable products.

EXAMPLE   **8.12**   Complete the following equations:

a) $Zn_{(s)} + Pb(NO_3)_{2\,(aq)} \longrightarrow$

b) $Na_2O_{(s)} + H_2O_{(\ell)} \longrightarrow$

c) $Cu(OH)_{2\,(s)} \longrightarrow$

d) $NaOH_{(aq)} + HClO_{4\,(aq)} \longrightarrow$

e) $CaCl_{2\,(aq)} + Na_2CO_{3\,(aq)} \longrightarrow$

SOLUTION   a) This is a reaction between a metal and a salt. It must be a single displacement reaction. The products will be zinc nitrate and lead metal:

$$Zn_{(s)} + Pb(NO_3)_{2\,(aq)} \longrightarrow Zn(NO_3)_{2\,(aq)} + Pb_{(s)}$$

NOTE: A check of the activity series given in Table 8.1 shows that zinc will indeed displace lead(II) ion from its salts.

b) Here we have a reaction between a basic oxide and water. This combination reaction will give a base (sodium hydroxide):

$$Na_2O_{(s)} + H_2O_{(\ell)} \longrightarrow 2\,NaOH_{(aq)}$$

c) A reaction involving a single reactant is easy to classify. It must be a decomposition reaction. The reactant is a base, and it is unlikely to decompose into its elements. It is more probable that a basic oxide and water will be formed.

$$Cu(OH)_{2\,(s)} \longrightarrow CuO_{(s)} + H_2O_{(\ell)}$$

d) A reaction between a base and an acid is called a neutralization reaction. The products would be a salt, sodium perchlorate, and water:

$$NaOH_{(aq)} + HClO_{4\,(aq)} \longrightarrow NaClO_{4\,(aq)} + H_2O_{(\ell)}$$

e) Here we have a reaction between two salts. This should be a double displacement reaction leading to the precipitation of a salt. The two products would be calcium carbonate and sodium chloride. According to the solubility rules, one of the products (sodium chloride) is soluble in water and the other (calcium carbonate) is insoluble. The equation for the reaction will therefore be

$$CaCl_{2\,(aq)} + Na_2CO_{3\,(aq)} \longrightarrow CaCO_{3\,(s)} + 2\,NaCl_{(aq)}$$

QUESTIONS

13. Complete and balance the following equations:

a) $ZnCl_{2\,(aq)} + Na_2S_{(aq)} \longrightarrow$

b) $KOH_{(aq)} + H_2SO_{4\,(aq)} \longrightarrow$

c) $Ba_{(s)} + S_{(s)} \longrightarrow$

d) $Pb(NO_3)_{2\,(aq)} + Mg_{(s)} \longrightarrow$

e) $NaI_{(aq)} + Br_{2\,(aq)} \longrightarrow$

f) $FeS_{(s)} + HCl_{(aq)} \longrightarrow$

Net Ionic Equations

8.9

Chemists use molecular equations to convey information about chemical reactions in a clear, concise manner. When we are discussing reactions in aqueous solution we often use **net ionic equations**, which are even more concise than molecular equations.

In Section 5.1 we described an experiment in which we examined the conductivity of certain solutions. We saw that, in general, solutions of ionic compounds conduct electricity, whereas solutions of covalent compounds usually do not. This happens because a solution will only conduct electricity if it contains ions. In general, solutions of ionic compounds contain ions, whereas solutions of covalent compounds do not.

Ionic Compounds in Solution

When an ionic compound dissolves in water its constituent ions, which were held in place within the crystal, become free to move among the surrounding water molecules in the solution. Thus solid potassium bromide dissolves in water to give potassium ions and bromide ions. We can represent this as follows:

$$KBr_{(s)} \xrightarrow[\text{in water}]{\text{dissolve}} K^+_{(aq)} + Br^-_{(aq)}$$

Similarly, when magnesium sulfate is dissolved in water, we obtain magnesium ions and sulfate ions. Note that the polyatomic sulfate ion remains as a single unit:

$$MgSO_{4\,(s)} \xrightarrow[\text{in water}]{\text{dissolve}} Mg^{2+}_{(aq)} + SO_4^{2-}_{(aq)}$$

Calcium chloride likewise dissolves in water to give calcium ions and chloride ions. Because the formula of calcium chloride is $CaCl_2$, two chloride ions will be produced for each calcium ion:

$$CaCl_{2\,(s)} \xrightarrow[\text{in water}]{\text{dissolve}} Ca^{2+}_{(aq)} + 2\,Cl^-_{(aq)}$$

Net Ionic Equations for Reactions in Solution

In Example 8.2 we said that if a solution of sodium chloride is added to a solution of silver nitrate, a precipitate of silver chloride is formed. The molecular equation that represents this process is

$$AgNO_{3\,(aq)} + NaCl_{(aq)} \longrightarrow AgCl_{(s)} + NaNO_{3\,(aq)}$$

Instead of thinking in terms of adding a solution of sodium chloride to a solution of silver nitrate, we can think in terms of adding a solution containing sodium ions and chloride ions to a solution containing silver ions and nitrate ions. From the molecular equation we see that, of the two products, sodium nitrate remains dissolved in the water and silver chloride is obtained as a solid. We say that silver chloride is insoluble in water, which means that it does not dissolve in water to any appreciable extent (Figure 8.14). Thus there are no silver ions or chloride ions in solution when the reaction is complete, and we may regard the products of this reaction as being solid silver chloride plus a solution containing sodium ions and nitrate ions. Let us now try to express this in a chemical equation. We write

$$Na^{+}_{(aq)} + Cl^{-}_{(aq)} + Ag^{+}_{(aq)} + NO_{3}^{-}_{(aq)} \longrightarrow$$
$$AgCl_{(s)} + Na^{+}_{(aq)} + NO_{3}^{-}_{(aq)}$$

This equation is an example of a **total ionic equation** because every species that dissociates into ions when it is dissolved in water has been written in ionic form.

If you look at the above equation you will see that the sodium ions and nitrate ions are unchanged by the reaction and are written in exactly the same way on each side of the equation. These ions, called **spectator ions**, are omitted when writing the net ionic equation. Thus, the net ionic equation for the reaction between silver nitrate and sodium chloride is

$$Ag^{+}_{(aq)} + Cl^{-}_{(aq)} \longrightarrow AgCl_{(s)}$$

NOTE: We cannot avoid using compounds containing spectator ions because it is impossible to obtain bottles containing only silver ions or chloride ions.

(handwritten margin note: solids do not carry charges)

Figure 8.14
The reaction between aqueous sodium chloride and aqueous silver nitrate. The sodium and nitrate ions are spectator ions.

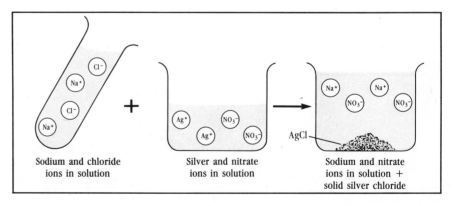

| Sodium and chloride ions in solution | Silver and nitrate ions in solution | Sodium and nitrate ions in solution + solid silver chloride |

EXAMPLE   **8.13**   Write the net ionic equation for the reaction that occurs when a solution of silver nitrate is added to a solution of barium chloride. The products of the reaction are barium nitrate, which remains in solution, and solid silver chloride.

SOLUTION   The molecular equation is

$$2 \, AgNO_{3 \, (aq)} + BaCl_{2 \, (aq)} \longrightarrow 2 \, AgCl_{(s)} + Ba(NO_3)_{2 \, (aq)}$$

Writing all the ionic compounds that are present in the solution as ions, we obtain the following total ionic equation:

$$2 \, Ag^+_{(aq)} + 2 \, NO_3^-{}_{(aq)} + Ba^{2+}{}_{(aq)} + 2 \, Cl^-{}_{(aq)} \longrightarrow$$
$$2 \, AgCl_{(s)} + Ba^{2+}{}_{(aq)} + 2 \, NO_3^-{}_{(aq)}$$

Elimination of the spectator ions, Ba^{2+} and NO_3^-, simplifies this equation to:

$$2 \, Ag^+_{(aq)} + 2 \, Cl^-{}_{(aq)} \longrightarrow 2 \, AgCl_{(s)}$$

This can be further simplified by dividing by 2 to give the net ionic equation:

$$Ag^+_{(aq)} + Cl^-{}_{(aq)} \longrightarrow AgCl_{(s)}$$

    You can see that the net ionic equation obtained in Example 8.13 is exactly the same as that obtained for the reaction between sodium chloride and silver nitrate. In fact, any solution containing chloride ions will produce a precipitate of silver chloride when mixed with a solution of silver ions. In all these reactions, the net ionic equation will be the same. Thus, a net ionic equation can often convey all the necessary information about a reaction. In these cases, there is no advantage in writing the full, or molecular, equation.

Guidelines for Writing Net Ionic Equations

The hints below will help you when writing net ionic equations.
1. Write in *ionic* form
   a) hydrochloric acid ($HCl_{(aq)}$), nitric acid ($HNO_{3 \, (aq)}$), sulfuric acid ($H_2SO_{4 \, (aq)}$), perchloric acid ($HClO_{4 \, (aq)}$)
   b) the Group IA and IIA hydroxides (e.g. NaOH, $Ca(OH)_2$)
   c) soluble salts, including such compounds as copper(II) sulfate, potassium nitrate, and ammonium chloride
2. Write in *molecular* form all the substances that do not fit into any of the categories listed above. These include
   a) insoluble salts, such as silver chloride
   b) other acids, such as acetic acid
   c) other bases, such as ammonia
   d) gases, such as hydrogen or oxygen
   e) liquids, such as water
   f) covalent solids, such as sugar

Net Ionic Equations for Reactions Involving Covalent Molecules

Covalently bonded molecules, such as water and carbon dioxide, must also be written in molecular form. The following example illustrates this point.

EXAMPLE   **8.14**   Write (a) the balanced molecular equation, (b) the total ionic equation, and (c) the net ionic equation for the reaction that occurs when hydrochloric acid is added to a solution of sodium carbonate. The products are carbon dioxide gas, water, and sodium chloride; the latter remains in solution.

SOLUTION   a) The molecular equation is

$$2\, HCl_{(aq)} + Na_2CO_{3\,(aq)} \longrightarrow 2\, NaCl_{(aq)} + CO_{2\,(g)} + H_2O_{(\ell)}$$

b) The total ionic equation is

$$2\, H^+_{(aq)} + 2\, Cl^-_{(aq)} + 2\, Na^+_{(aq)} + CO_3^{2-}_{(aq)} \longrightarrow$$
$$2\, Na^+_{(aq)} + 2\, Cl^-_{(aq)} + CO_{2\,(g)} + H_2O_{(\ell)}$$

c) The net ionic equation is

$$2\, H^+_{(aq)} + CO_3^{2-}_{(aq)} \longrightarrow H_2O_{(\ell)} + CO_{2\,(g)}$$

QUESTIONS

14. Write equations to show the process that occurs when the following compounds dissolve in water:
   a) sodium sulfide
   b) ammonium chloride
   c) calcium nitrate
   d) sodium phosphate
   e) ammonium carbonate
   f) aluminum sulfate

15. Write the net ionic equation for each of the following reactions:
   a) When aqueous sodium carbonate solution is added to a solution of calcium chloride, solid calcium carbonate is formed and sodium chloride remains in solution.
   b) When solid zinc metal is added to a solution of copper(II) chloride, solid copper metal is formed, leaving a solution of zinc chloride.
   c) When sodium iodide solution is mixed with aqueous lead(II) nitrate, a yellow lead(II) iodide precipitate is formed, leaving a solution of sodium nitrate.

16. Write the net ionic equation for each of the following reactions (remember that you must first write the balanced molecular equation and then the total ionic equation):
   a) An aqueous solution of sodium sulfide reacts with hydrochloric acid to produce hydrogen sulfide gas and a solution of sodium chloride.
   b) An aqueous solution of potassium hydroxide reacts with sulfuric acid to give a solution of potassium sulfate and water.

Double Displacement Reactions in Qualitative Analysis

8.10

The qualitative analysis of an ionic compound involves identifying the ions present. To do this, we dissolve the compound in water (assuming the compound is soluble) and then perform a set of simple double displacement reactions as tests. These tests enable us to determine which of certain groups of ions are present. We can then perform other specific tests in order to identify the ions positively.

Let us first consider the tests that we carry out in order to identify anions. For the sake of simplicity, we will consider only the following anions: carbonate, sulfite, sulfide, choride, bromide, iodide, sulfate, and nitrate.

Anion Identification

In Section 8.7 we saw that some anions (carbonate, sulfite, and sulfide) react with acids to release a gas. Thus, if we wish to identify the anion present in an ionic compound, our first step is to add acid to its solution. If a gas is released, we know that a carbonate, sulfite, or sulfide is present and we must then carry out a specific test for each one. For example, if we added a lead(II) ion solution to some of the unknown solution we might obtain a precipitate of lead(II) carbonate (white), lead(II) sulfite (white), or lead(II) sulfide (black). If the precipitate is black, we know the anion in the unknown substance is sulfide. If it is white, then we must find a different test that distinguishes between carbonate ions and sulfite ions.

Suppose that no gas was released when we added acid to the unknown solution. In such an event our next step is to test for the presence of a halide ion (chloride, bromide, or iodide). We could do this by taking a fresh sample of the solution and adding some silver nitrate solution to it. If a precipitate appears, we know that the unknown compound contains either chloride, bromide, or iodide. We can then determine which of these three ions is present by making use of the halogen replacement series (Section 8.6). If aqueous chlorine is added to the solution, there will be no reaction if the anion is chloride, but bromide or iodide will produce the brown colour of aqueous bromine or iodine respectively. To distinguish between bromide and iodide, we can add aqueous bromine to a fresh sample of the solution. No reaction will occur with bromide (or chloride) ions, but a brown liquid (aqueous iodine) will form if iodide ions are present.

What happens if a solution of the unknown compound produces neither a gas when acid is added, nor a precipitate with silver nitrate? The next step is to add a solution of barium chloride to a fresh sample of the unknown solution. The formation of a precipitate indicates the presence of sulfate ions in the original compound.

If no reaction is observed in any of the above tests, we would conclude that by the process of elimination, the anion present is nitrate. Figure 8.19 summarizes these procedures in the form of a flowchart.

Of course, if we had to consider a wider range of possible anions (for example, chromate, chlorate, phosphate, nitrite), then a more complex system of analysis would be needed.

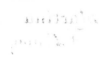

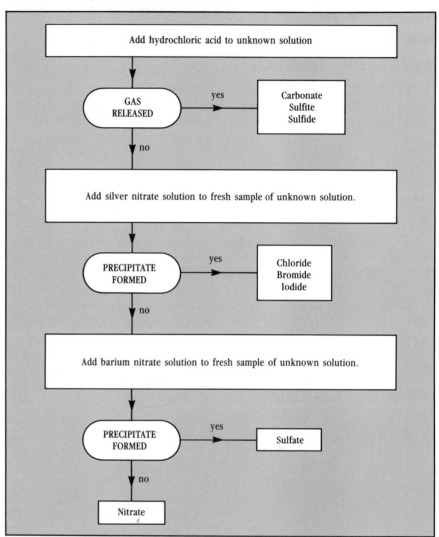

Figure 8.15

A sample flowchart for identifying the anion present in a simple ionic compound.

Cation Identification

We can identify the cation present in an unknown ionic compound by using a procedure similar to the one used to identify anions. Let us assume that the cation is one of the following: silver, lead(II), magnesium, calcium, barium, sodium, or potassium. By referring to the solubility rules in Table 8.3, we can set up a series of precipitation tests that will enable us to eliminate a number of these possibilities. This is shown in the form of a flowchart in Figure 8.16.

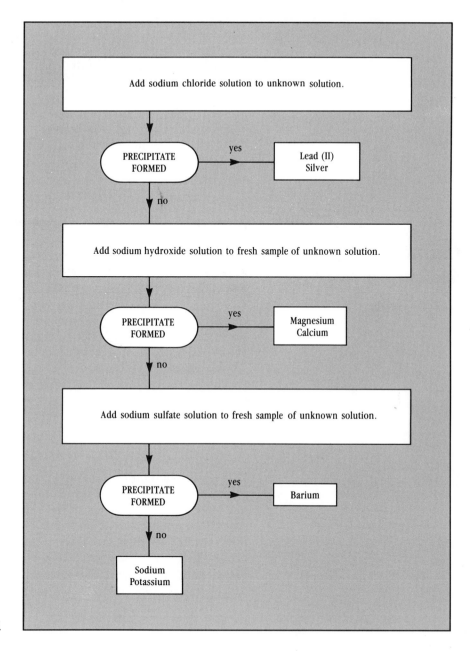

Figure 8.16
A sample flowchart for identifying the cation present in a simple ionic compound.

Once the number of possibilities has been reduced, we can use a specific test for each cation in order to confirm its presence or absence in the compound. For example, we can distinguish between sodium and potassium by using the flame test (Section 3.11).

The schemes shown in Figures 8.15 and 8.16 can be modified to allow analysis of mixtures as well as individual ionic compounds.

17. Write a balanced net ionic equation for the reaction between
    a) hydrogen ion (from hydrochloric acid) and sulfide ion
    b) hydrogen ion and carbonate ion
    c) silver ion and chloride ion
    d) barium ion and sulfate ion
    e) lead(II) ion and sulfide ion
    f) aqueous chlorine and iodide ion

18. Write a balanced net ionic equation for the reaction between
    a) lead(II) ion and chloride ion
    b) calcium ion and hydroxide ion

Oxidation–Reduction (Redox) Reactions

8.11

Void.

In many chemical reactions two or more of the atoms involved undergo a change in oxidation number. Reactions of this type are called **oxidation–reduction**, or more simply, **redox** reactions. These reactions usually belong to either the combination, decomposition, or single displacement categories. All single displacement reactions are redox reactions, but only some combination and decomposition reactions fall into this category. Double displacement reactions are *never* redox reactions.

In Section 6.10 we learned that, in all compounds, the sum of the oxidation numbers equals zero. We also learned that the oxidation number of an atom of a pure element is always zero, even when the element exists as diatomic molecules. Let us now look at the changes in oxidation number that occur when hydrogen gas reacts with oxygen gas to form water.

$$2\ H_{2\,(g)}\ +\ O_{2\,(g)} \longrightarrow 2\ H_2O_{(\ell)}$$

In the hydrogen molecule each hydrogen atom has an oxidation number of zero; similarly, the oxidation number of each oxygen atom in an oxygen molecule is zero. However, in the compound water, oxygen has its usual oxidation number of -2, and each of the hydrogen atoms has an oxidation number of $+1$. During the reaction, the oxidation number of hydrogen increases from 0 to $+1$, while the oxidation number of oxygen decreases from 0 to -2. This change can be represented as follows:

OXIDATION

$$2\ H_{2\,(g)}\ +\ O_{2\,(g)} \longrightarrow 2\ H_2O_{(\ell)}$$
   0   0   +1 −2

REDUCTION

We use the term **reduction** for the process in which an oxidation number decreases and **oxidation** for the process during which an oxidation number increases. You should note that it is not possible to have a reaction in which only oxidation or reduction occurs. The two processes always occur simultaneously.

In Example 8.7, we discussed the reaction between metallic zinc and a solution of nickel(II) chloride. The molecular equation for this reaction is

$$Zn_{(s)} + NiCl_{2\,(aq)} \longrightarrow Ni_{(s)} + ZnCl_{2\,(aq)}$$

For reactions in solution, it is usually easiest to identify species that are undergoing a change in oxidation number by looking at the net ionic equation. For the zinc–nickel(II) chloride reaction this is:

$$Zn_{(s)} + Ni^{2+}_{\ (aq)} \longrightarrow Ni_{(s)} + Zn^{2+}_{\ (aq)}$$

During this reaction the $Ni^{2+}_{\ (aq)}$ ions gain two electrons to form nickel metal, and in so doing undergo a decrease in oxidation number from +2 to 0. At the same time, the zinc metal loses two electrons to form $Zn^{2+}_{\ (aq)}$ ions and undergoes an increase in oxidation number from 0 to +2:

OXIDATION

$$Zn_{(s)} + Ni^{2+}_{\ (aq)} \longrightarrow Ni_{(s)} + Zn^{2+}_{\ (aq)}$$

$$0 \qquad\qquad +2 \qquad\qquad\qquad 0 \qquad\qquad +2$$

REDUCTION

Thus zinc metal is being *oxidized* and nickel ions are being *reduced*.

EXAMPLE   **8.15**   In the reaction between aqueous chlorine and a solution of sodium bromide discussed in Section 8.6, which species is being oxidized and which is being reduced?

SOLUTION   The molecular equation for this reaction is

$$Cl_{2\,(aq)} + 2\,NaBr_{(aq)} \longrightarrow 2\,NaCl_{(aq)} + Br_{2\,(aq)}$$

This may be rewritten as the total ionic equation

$$Cl_{2\,(aq)} + 2\,Na^{+}_{\ (aq)} + 2\,Br^{+}_{\ (aq)} \longrightarrow 2\,Na^{+}_{\ (aq)} + 2\,Cl^{-}_{\ (aq)} + Br_{2\,(aq)}$$

or as the net ionic equation

$$Cl_{2\,(aq)} + 2\,Br^{-}_{\ (aq)} \longrightarrow Br_{2\,(aq)} + 2\,Cl^{-}_{\ (aq)}$$

NOTE: We write $Cl_{2\,(aq)}$ and $Br_{2\,(aq)}$, which indicates that although chlorine and bromine are dissolved in water, they do not dissociate into ions. Aqueous chlorine and bromine (like these elements in their pure state — chlorine gas and bromine liquid) are molecular species, in which the bonding is purely covalent.

Chlorine has an oxidation number of 0 in $Cl_{2\,(aq)}$ and an oxidation number of -1 in $Cl^{-}_{\ (aq)}$. Bromine has an oxidation number of -1 in $Br^{-}_{\ (aq)}$ and 0 in $Br_{2\,(aq)}$. The change in oxidation numbers can be illustrated as follows:

OXIDATION

$$Cl_{2\,(aq)} + 2\,Br^{-}_{\ (aq)} \longrightarrow Br_{2\,(aq)} + 2\,Cl^{-}_{\ (aq)}$$

$$0 \qquad\qquad -1 \qquad\qquad\qquad 0 \qquad\qquad -1$$

REDUCTION

The oxidation number for chlorine decreases and that for bromine increases. We therefore say that in this reaction chlorine gas is reduced to chloride ions and bromide ions are oxidized to molecular bromine.

Careful study of the reactions discussed in this chapter will reveal several other examples of redox reactions. Among them is the following decomposition reaction:

$$\overbrace{2\ HgO_{(s)} \xrightarrow{\ \Delta\ } 2\ Hg_{(\ell)} + O_{2\ (g)}}^{\text{OXIDATION}}$$

with oxidation numbers $+2\ -2$ for $HgO_{(s)}$, 0 for $Hg_{(\ell)}$, and 0 for $O_{2\ (g)}$, and REDUCTION bracketing HgO to Hg.

in which Hg^{2+} ions are reduced to Hg, and O^{2-} ions are oxidized to O_2.

Another example of a redox reaction is the single displacement reaction in which zinc reacts with hydrochloric acid to form hydrogen gas and zinc chloride solution, as follows:

$$\overbrace{Zn_{(s)} + 2\ HCl_{(aq)} \longrightarrow H_{2\ (g)} + ZnCl_{2\ (aq)}}^{\text{OXIDATION}}$$

with oxidation numbers 0 for $Zn_{(s)}$, $+1\ -1$ for $HCl_{(aq)}$, 0 for $H_{2\ (g)}$, and $+2\ -1$ for $ZnCl_{2\ (aq)}$, and REDUCTION bracketing.

In this reaction, $H^+_{(aq)}$ ions are reduced to H_2 gas and Zn is oxidized to $Zn^{2+}_{(aq)}$ ions. Note that the oxidation number of the Cl^- ions (the spectator ions) remains unchanged.

QUESTIONS

19. In each of the following reactions indicate the species that are oxidized or reduced:

    a) $Mg_{(s)} + 2\ AgNO_{3\ (aq)} \longrightarrow 2\ Ag_{(s)} + Mg(NO_3)_{2\ (aq)}$

    b) $S_{(s)} + O_{2\ (g)} \longrightarrow SO_{2\ (g)}$

    c) $2\ Ag_2O_{(s)} \longrightarrow 4\ Ag_{(s)} + O_{2\ (g)}$

    d) $Br_{2\ (aq)} + CaI_{2\ (aq)} \longrightarrow CaBr_{2\ (aq)} + I_{2\ (aq)}$

    For the atoms concerned, determine the oxidation number in both the oxidized and reduced form.

VOID.

Reactions in Which Heat is Absorbed or Released

8.12

Sometimes the energy released in a chemical reaction is more important than the chemical products. A reaction accompanied by the release of energy in the form of heat is called an **exothermic reaction**, whereas a reaction that absorbs heat from the surroundings is called an **endothermic reaction**. There is an easy way of showing that a reaction is exothermic:

$$2\ Na_{(s)} + Cl_{2\ (g)} \longrightarrow 2\ NaCl_{(s)} + Heat$$

Sometimes we wish to be more specific and say exactly how much heat is released. For example, when one mole of methane gas (CH_4) is burned with two moles of oxygen to give one mole of carbon dioxide gas and two moles of water vapour, 890 kJ of energy is produced. Thus, we may write

$$CH_{4\,(g)} + 2\,O_{2\,(g)} \longrightarrow CO_{2\,(g)} + 2\,H_2O_{(g)} + 890\,kJ$$

Each of the four substances involved in this reaction contains a certain quantity of energy, which we usually call the **enthalpy** (symbol H) of that substance. In the example above, 890 kJ of energy was released as heat. This means that one mole of carbon dioxide gas plus two moles of water vapour must contain 890 kJ less energy than one mole of methane gas plus two moles of oxygen gas. Because the products possess 890 kJ less energy than the reactants, we say that the enthalpy change (symbol ΔH) of the reaction is −890 kJ. A more usual way of indicating the enthalpy change that accompanies a particular reaction is as follows:

$$CH_{4\,(g)} + 2\,O_{2\,(g)} \longrightarrow CO_{2\,(g)} + 2\,H_2O_{(g)} \qquad \Delta H = -890\,kJ$$

If heat is absorbed during the reaction, the enthalpy of the products will be greater than that of the reactants. The enthalpy change of an endothermic reaction will therefore have a positive sign. An example of such a reaction is

$$2\,HgO_{(s)} \longrightarrow 2\,Hg_{(\ell)} + O_{2\,(g)} \qquad \Delta H = +181.7\,kJ$$

The study of the energy changes that take place during chemical reactions is called **thermochemistry**.

Summary

% composition

Sr(OH)₂ · 8H₂O

18H − 18.18
1 Sr − 87.62
10 O − 16.00
─────────────
265.8 g·mol⁻¹

find % of H

$\%\ of\ H = \dfrac{18.18}{265.8} \times 100\,\%$

$= 6.839\,\%$

- A chemical reaction is often indicated by a change in colour, by the formation of a gas or solid, or by the release or absorption of heat.

- Reactions can be represented by an equation, with the reactants (species that undergo the reaction) on the left side of an arrow and the products (species formed in the reaction) on the right. The equation can be either a word equation or, more commonly, a formula equation.

- The physical state of each reactant and product is indicated by an (s) for solid, (ℓ) for liquid, (g) for gas, or (aq) for aqueous solution.

- An equation is balanced by multiplying some of the reactants and/or products by coefficients so that equal numbers of each atom are on both sides of the equation. The formulas of the reactants and products cannot be changed when balancing an equation.

- When balancing complicated equations, it is best to start with atoms that occur only once on the reactant side and once on the product side.

- If heat is required for a reaction to occur, it is indicated in the chemical equation by a small triange (Δ) above the arrow. Specific conditions of temperature or pressure can also be written above or below the arrow.

- A catalyst is a substance that increases the rate of a chemical reaction but is unchanged at the end of the reaction. Its presence is indicated by writing its symbol or formula above the arrow.

- In some reactants we do not obtain the complete conversion of the reactants into products. A mixture of reactants and products is present at all times. Such reactions are called equilibrium reactions, and they are indicated by the presence of a double arrow ($\rightleftharpoons$) in the equation.

- Most reactions can be classified as belonging to one of four types: combination, decomposition, single displacement, or double displacement.

- A combination reaction occurs when two or more simple substances combine to produce a more complex substance.

- Decomposition reactions are those in which a complicated substance is broken down into two or more simpler substances.

- In a single displacement reaction, one element replaces another element in a compound. We can usually predict when a single displacement reaction is likely to occur by referring to the activity series for metals or halogens.

- Double displacement reactions always involve two ionic compounds. The cation of one compound changes place with the cation of the second compound. These reactions usually result in the formation of a precipitate, a gas, or water.

- A neutralization reaction involves the reaction of an acid with a base to produce a salt plus water. Acidic and basic oxides can also undergo neutralization reactions.

- In a total ionic equation, every species that dissociates into ions in solution is written in ionic form. Ions that are unchanged and written in exactly the same way on both sides of the equation are called spectator ions. A net ionic equation does not include the spectator ions. Covalently bonded molecules, insoluble salts, gases, and liquids such as water, must be written in molecular form.

- Qualitative analysis involves identifying the ions present in a compound. This can be done by dissolving the compound in water and performing a series of tests involving simple double displacement reactions.

- In oxidation–reduction (redox) reactions, two or more of the species involved undergo changes in their oxidation numbers. Reduction is a process in which the oxidation number of a species atom decreases. Oxidation is a process in which the oxidation number of a species increases. Oxidation and reduction always occur together.

- A reaction accompanied by the release of energy in the form of heat is called an exothermic reaction. A reaction that absorbs heat from the surroundings is called an endothermic reaction.

KEY WORDS

activity series
acidic oxide
balancing equations
basic oxide
biochemical reaction
catalyst
chemical equation
combination reaction
decomposition reaction
double displacement reaction
endothermic reaction
enthalpy
enzyme
equilibrium reaction
exothermic reaction
formula equation
halogen displacement series

molecular equation
net ionic equation
neutralization reaction
oxidation
oxidation–reduction reaction
photosynthesis
precipitate
product
reactant
redox reaction
reduction
single displacement reaction
spectator ion
thermal decomposition
thermochemistry
total ionic equation
word equation

ANSWERS TO SECTION QUESTIONS

1. a) $CO_{2\,(g)} + CaO_{(s)} \longrightarrow CaCO_{3\,(s)}$
   b) $C_{(s)} + 2\,F_{2\,(g)} \longrightarrow CF_{4\,(g)}$
   c) $4\,Al_{(s)} + 3\,O_{2\,(g)} \longrightarrow 2\,Al_2O_{3\,(s)}$

2. $Na_2SO_{4\,(aq)} + BaCl_{2\,(aq)} \longrightarrow BaSO_{4\,(s)} + 2\,NaCl_{(aq)}$

3. $2\,SO_{2\,(g)} + O_{2\,(g)} \xrightarrow[200\,°C]{Pt} 2\,SO_{3\,(g)}$

4. a) $4\,NH_{3\,(g)} + 5\,O_{2\,(g)} \longrightarrow 4\,NO_{(g)} + 6\,H_2O_{(g)}$
   b) $2\,Li_{(s)} + 2\,H_2O_{(\ell)} \longrightarrow 2\,LiOH_{(aq)} + H_{2\,(g)}$
   c) $Al_4C_{3\,(s)} + 12\,H_2O_{(\ell)} \longrightarrow 3\,CH_{4\,(g)} + 4\,Al(OH)_{3\,(s)}$
   d) $2\,C_4H_{10\,(g)} + 13\,O_{2\,(g)} \longrightarrow 8\,CO_{2\,(g)} + 10\,H_2O_{(g)}$
   e) $2\,CuFeS_{2\,(s)} + 5\,O_{2\,(g)} \longrightarrow 2\,Cu_{(s)} + 2\,FeO_{(s)} + 4\,SO_{2\,(g)}$

5. a) $Zn_{(s)} + Cl_{2\,(g)} \longrightarrow ZnCl_{2\,(s)}$
   b) $CaO_{(s)} + H_2O_{(\ell)} \longrightarrow Ca(OH)_{2\,(aq)}$
   c) $Li_2O_{(s)} + CO_{2\,(g)} \longrightarrow Li_2CO_{3\,(s)}$
   d) $2\,Mg_{(s)} + O_{2\,(g)} \longrightarrow 2\,MgO_{(s)}$

6. a) salt   c) salt
   b) base   d) basic oxide

7. a) $2 \ AgCl_{(s)} \xrightarrow{\Delta} 2 \ Ag_{(s)} + Cl_{2 \ (g)}$

b) $MgCO_{3 \ (s)} \xrightarrow{\Delta} MgO_{(s)} + CO_{2 \ (g)}$

c) $Mg(OH)_{2 \ (s)} \xrightarrow{\Delta} MgO_{(s)} + H_2O_{(g)}$

8. a) salt   b) salt   c) base

9. a) $Cl_{2 \ (aq)} + 2 \ NaI_{(aq)} \longrightarrow 2 \ NaCl_{(aq)} + I_{2 \ (aq)}$

b) $Ca_{(s)} + 2 \ H_2O_{(\ell)} \longrightarrow Ca(OH)_{2 \ (aq)} + H_{2 \ (g)}$

c) $Pb_{(s)} + 2 \ HCl_{(aq)} \longrightarrow PbCl_{2 \ (s)} + H_{2 \ (g)}$

d) $Zn_{(s)} + CuCl_{2 \ (aq)} \longrightarrow ZnCl_{2 \ (aq)} + Cu_{(s)}$

e) no reaction

10. a) $CaCl_{2 \ (aq)} + Na_2SO_{4 \ (aq)} \longrightarrow CaSO_{4 \ (s)} + 2 \ NaCl_{(aq)}$

b) $AgNO_{3 \ (aq)} + NaI_{(aq)} \longrightarrow AgI_{(s)} + NaNO_{3 \ (aq)}$

c) $MgSO_{4 \ (aq)} + 2 \ NaOH_{(aq)} \longrightarrow Mg(OH)_{2 \ (s)} + Na_2SO_{4 \ (aq)}$

11. a) $(NH_4)_2SO_{4 \ (aq)} + 2 \ KOH_{(aq)} \longrightarrow K_2SO_{4 \ (aq)} + 2 \ NH_{3 \ (g)} + 2 \ H_2O_{(\ell)}$

b) $K_2CO_{3 \ (aq)} + 2 \ HNO_{3 \ (aq)} \longrightarrow 2 \ KNO_{3 \ (aq)} + CO_{2 \ (g)} + H_2O_{(\ell)}$

c) $CaS_{(aq)} + H_2SO_{4 \ (aq)} \longrightarrow CaSO_{4 \ (s)} + H_2S_{(g)}$

12. a) $H_2SO_{4 \ (aq)} + 2 \ LiOH_{(aq)} \longrightarrow Li_2SO_{4 \ (aq)} + 2 \ H_2O_{(\ell)}$

b) $Fe_2O_{3 \ (s)} + 6 \ HCl_{(aq)} \longrightarrow 2 \ FeCl_{3 \ (aq)} + 3 \ H_2O_{(\ell)}$

c) $2 \ KOH_{(aq)} + SO_{2 \ (g)} \longrightarrow K_2SO_{3 \ (aq)} + H_2O_{(\ell)}$

13. a) $ZnCl_{2 \ (aq)} + Na_2S_{(aq)} \longrightarrow ZnS_{(s)} + 2 \ NaCl_{(aq)}$

b) $2 \ KOH_{(aq)} + H_2SO_{4 \ (aq)} \longrightarrow K_2SO_{4 \ (aq)} + 2 \ H_2O_{(\ell)}$

c) $Ba_{(s)} + S_{(s)} \longrightarrow BaS_{(s)}$

d) $Pb(NO_3)_{2 \ (aq)} + Mg_{(s)} \longrightarrow Mg(NO_3)_{2 \ (aq)} + Pb_{(s)}$

e) $2 \ NaI_{(aq)} + Br_{2 \ (aq)} \longrightarrow 2 \ NaBr_{(aq)} + I_{2 \ (aq)}$

f) $FeS_{(s)} + 2 \ HCl_{(aq)} \longrightarrow FeCl_{2 \ (aq)} + H_2S_{(g)}$

14. a) $Na_2S_{(s)} \longrightarrow 2 \ Na^+_{(aq)} + S^{2-}_{(aq)}$

b) $NH_4Cl_{(s)} \longrightarrow NH_4^+_{(aq)} + Cl^-_{(aq)}$

c) $Ca(NO_3)_{2 \ (s)} \longrightarrow Ca^{2+}_{(aq)} + 2 \ NO_3^-_{(aq)}$

d) $Na_3PO_{4 \ (s)} \longrightarrow 3 \ Na^+_{(aq)} + PO_4^{3-}_{(aq)}$

e) $(NH_4)_2CO_{3 \ (s)} \longrightarrow 2 \ NH_4^+_{(aq)} + CO_3^{2-}_{(aq)}$

f) $Al_2(SO_4)_{3 \ (s)} \longrightarrow 2 \ Al^{3+}_{(aq)} + 3 \ SO_4^{2-}_{(aq)}$

15. a) $Ca^{2+}_{(aq)} + CO_3^{2-}_{(aq)} \longrightarrow CaCO_{3 \ (s)}$

b) $Zn_{(s)} + Cu^{2+}_{(aq)} \longrightarrow Zn^{2+}_{(aq)} + Cu_{(s)}$

c) $Pb^{2+}_{(aq)} + 2 \ I^-_{(aq)} \longrightarrow PbI_{2 \ (s)}$

16. a) $2 \ H^+_{(aq)} + S^{2-}_{(aq)} \longrightarrow H_2S_{(g)}$

b) $H^+_{(aq)} + OH^-_{(aq)} \longrightarrow H_2O_{(\ell)}$

17. a) $2 \ H^+_{(aq)} + S^{2-}_{(aq)} \longrightarrow H_2S_{(g)}$

b) $2 \ H^+_{(aq)} + CO_3^{2-}_{(aq)} \longrightarrow H_2O_{(\ell)} + CO_{2 \ (g)}$

c) $Ag^+_{(aq)} + Cl^-_{(aq)} \longrightarrow AgCl_{(s)}$

d) $Ba^{2+}_{(aq)} + SO_4{}^{2-}_{(aq)} \longrightarrow BaSO_{4\,(s)}$

e) $Pb^{2+}_{(aq)} + S^{2-}_{(aq)} \longrightarrow PbS_{(s)}$

f) $Cl_{2\,(aq)} + 2\,I^-_{(aq)} \longrightarrow 2\,Cl^-_{(aq)} + I_{2\,(aq)}$

18. a) $Pb^{2+}_{(aq)} + 2\,Cl^-_{(aq)} \longrightarrow PbCl_{2\,(s)}$

b) $Ca^{2+}_{(aq)} + 2\,OH^-_{(aq)} \longrightarrow Ca(OH)_{2\,(s)}$

19. a)

$$Mg_{(s)} + 2\,Ag^+_{(aq)} \longrightarrow 2\,Ag_{(s)} + Mg^{2+}_{(aq)}$$

  (0)   (+1)   (0)   (+2)

  oxidized   reduced

b)

$$S_{(s)} + O_{2\,(g)} \longrightarrow SO_{2\,(g)}$$

  (0)   (0)   (+4) (−2)

  oxidized   reduced

c)

$$2\,Ag_2O_{(s)} \longrightarrow 4\,Ag_{(s)} + O_{2\,(g)}$$

  (+1) (−2)   (0)   (0)

  Ag reduced O oxidized   oxidized

d)

$$Cl_{2\,(aq)} + CaBr_{2\,(aq)} \longrightarrow CaCl_{2\,(aq)} + Br_{2\,(aq)}$$

  (0)   (+2) (−1)   (+2) (−1)   (0)

  reduced   Br oxidized

COMPREHENSION QUESTIONS

1. What is the name given to chemical reactions that occur in living things?

2. Describe the four ways in which we can identify when a chemical reaction has occurred.

3. Explain the following terms as applied to chemical reactions:
   a) reactants   c) word equation   e) formula equation
   b) products   d) coefficient

4. What is meant by "balancing an equation"?

5. Explain the meaning of the following symbols:
   a) (aq)   b) (g)   c) (ℓ)

6. What does the symbol above the arrow mean in each of the following:
   a) $\xrightarrow{\ \Delta\ }$ b) $\xrightarrow{\ Fe\ }$ c) $\xrightarrow{\ 250°C\ }$

7. What is a catalyst? Give an example.

8. What is an enzyme?

9. What are the four main types of chemical reactions? Briefly describe each one.

10. Explain and give an example of
    a) an acidic oxide   b) a basic oxide

11. Explain and give an example of
    a) an equilibrium reaction   c) a redox reaction
    b) a neutralization reaction

12. What is meant by the term "activity series"?

13. Explain the difference between a total ionic equation and a net ionic equation. Illustrate your answer with an example.

14. What are spectator ions?

15. What is qualitative analysis?

16. Explain each of the following terms:
    a) reduction   b) oxidation   c) exothermic   d) endothermic

17. What is meant by the term "enthalpy"?

18. Is the change in enthalpy positive or negative for an endothermic reaction?

PROBLEMS

19. Write a word equation for
    a) $Cu_{(s)} + S_{(s)} \longrightarrow CuS_{(s)}$
    b) $Zn_{(s)} + 2\ HCl_{(aq)} \longrightarrow ZnCl_{2\ (aq)} + H_{2\ (g)}$

20. Write a balanced molecular equation for each of the following:
    a) Potassium chlorate $\longrightarrow$ Potassium chloride + Oxygen (catalyst: manganese(IV) oxide)
    b) Calcium carbonate $\longrightarrow$ Calcium oxide + Carbon dioxide (when heated)

21. Balance the equation for each of the following:
    a) the reaction used for the industrial preparation of ammonia
    $N_{2\ (g)} + H_{2\ (g)} \xrightarrow{\Delta} NH_{3\ (g)}$
    b) a reaction that can be used to produce nitrogen in the laboratory
    $NaN_{3\ (s)} \xrightarrow{\Delta} Na_{(\ell)} + N_{2\ (g)}$
    c) the overall reaction occurring in a blast furnace
    $Fe_2O_{3\ (s)} + C_{(s)} \xrightarrow{\Delta} Fe_{(s)} + CO_{2\ (g)}$
    d) a method for preparing ammonia in the laboratory
    $Mg_3N_{2\ (s)} + 6\ H_2O_{(\ell)} \longrightarrow Mg(OH)_{2\ (s)} + 2\ NH_{3\ (g)}$
    e) a step in the industrial preparation of nitric acid
    $H_2O_{(\ell)} + NO_{2\ (g)} \longrightarrow HNO_{3\ (aq)} + NO_{(g)}$

22. Balance the equations that describe the following processes:
    a) photosynthesis—plants use this process to produce simple sugars that may then be converted to starch or cellulose

    $CO_{2\ (g)} + H_2O_{(\ell)} \xrightarrow[\text{sunlight}]{\text{chlorophyll}} C_6H_{12}O_{6\ (s)} + O_{2\ (g)}$

    b) the extraction of phosphorus from the ore, apatite
    $Ca_3(PO_4)_{2\ (s)} + SiO_{2\ (s)} + C_{(s)} \longrightarrow P_{4\ (s)} + CaSiO_{3\ (s)} + CO_{2\ (g)}$
    c) the neutralization reaction between stomach acid (HCl) and the active ingredient in some antacids, sodium aluminum dihydroxide carbonate

$NaAl(OH)_2CO_{3\ (s)} + HCl_{(aq)} \longrightarrow NaCl_{(aq)} + AlCl_{3\ (aq)} + H_2O_{(\ell)} + CO_{2\ (g)}$

d) the reaction that occurs when dynamite explodes

$$C_7H_5N_3O_{6\,(s)} + O_{2\,(g)} \longrightarrow CO_{2\,(g)} + H_2O_{(\ell)} + N_{2\,(g)}$$

e) the reaction that occurs to produce energy in a nickel–cadmium rechargeable dry cell

$$NiO(OH)_{(s)} + H_2O_{(\ell)} + Cd_{(s)} \longrightarrow Ni(OH)_{2\,(s)} + Cd(OH)_{2\,(s)}$$

23. Write a balanced molecular equation for each of the following reactions, and indicate the physical state of the species involved whenever possible:
   a) When magnesium metal is heated in nitrogen gas, the product is magnesium nitride.
   b) Bubbling hydrogen sulfide gas into a solution of copper(II) sulfate in water produces a precipitate of copper(II) sulfide and a solution of sulfuric acid.
   c) Chlorine gas can be made by reacting solid manganese(IV) oxide with hydrochloric acid. The other products are water and manganese(II) chloride.
   d) Barium metal reacts with water to give barium hydroxide solution and hydrogen gas.

24. For each of the reactions described below, write a balanced molecular equation indicating the physical state of each species:
   a) When ammonia gas and hydrogen chloride gas are mixed, a white solid, ammonium chloride, is formed.
   b) If carbon dioxide gas is passed into a solution of calcium hydroxide in water, a precipitate of calcium carbonate is obtained. The other product of the reaction is water.
   c) Metallic zinc reacts with a solution of lead(II) nitrate. Solid lead metal is formed together with a solution of zinc nitrate.
   d) Heating solid copper(II) nitrate trihydrate produces solid copper(II) oxide, nitrogen dioxide gas, oxygen gas, and water vapour.

25. Write equations to show the dissociation of the following compounds in water:
   a) solid potassium hydroxide
   b) solid magnesium bromide
   c) liquid nitric acid (HNO_3)
   d) solid aluminum nitrate
   e) solid copper(II) sulfate

26. Write the equation to show the process that occurs when each of the following compounds dissolves in water:
   a) solid zinc sulfate
   b) solid iron(III) nitrate
   c) solid ammonium phosphate
   d) solid strontium hydroxide
   e) solid mercury(I) nitrate

27. Using the activity series, decide whether the following reactions will occur:
   a) $2\,Fe_{(s)} + Al_2(SO_4)_{3\,(aq)} \longrightarrow 2\,Al_{(s)} + Fe_2(SO_4)_{3\,(aq)}$
   b) $Mg_{(s)} + Zn(NO_3)_{2\,(aq)} \longrightarrow Mg(NO_3)_{2\,(aq)} + Zn_{(s)}$

c) $Sn_{(s)} + 2\ HCl_{(aq)} \longrightarrow SnCl_{2\ (aq)} + H_{2\ (g)}$

28. According to the activity series, which of the following reactions will take place:

a) $Ag_{(s)} + NaNO_{3\ (aq)} \longrightarrow AgNO_{3\ (aq)} + Na_{(s)}$

b) $2\ K_{(s)} + 2\ H_2O_{(\ell)} \longrightarrow 2\ KOH_{(aq)} + H_{2\ (g)}$

c) $Cu_{(s)} + 2\ HCl_{(aq)} \longrightarrow CuCl_{2\ (aq)} + H_{2\ (g)}$

29. In which of the following cases will a reaction *not* occur? For the reactions that you predict will occur, complete and balance the equations.

a) $Al_{(s)} + H_2O_{(\ell)} \longrightarrow$

b) $Cu_{(s)} + Hg(NO_3)_{2\ (aq)} \longrightarrow$

c) $Br_{2\ (aq)} + MgI_{2\ (aq)} \longrightarrow$

30. Indicate which of the following reactions will occur and balance the equations.

a) $Au_{(s)} + FeSO_{4\ (aq)} \longrightarrow$

b) $Al_{(s)} + ZnSO_{4\ (aq)} \longrightarrow$

c) $Sn_{(s)} + AgNO_{3\ (aq)} \longrightarrow$

31. For each of the following reactions, indicate whether a precipitate will be formed and name it.

a) $CaCl_{2\ (aq)} + K_2CO_{3\ (aq)} \longrightarrow CaCO_{3(?)} + 2\ KCl_{(?)}$

b) $3\ Ba(OH)_{2\ (aq)} + Fe_2(SO_4)_{3\ (aq)} \longrightarrow 2\ Fe(OH)_{3(?)} + 3\ BaSO_{4(?)}$

c) $3\ NH_4Cl_{(aq)} + Na_3PO_{4\ (aq)} \longrightarrow (NH_4)_3PO_{4(?)} + 3\ NaCl_{(?)}$

32. For each of the following equations, indicate the physical state of each of the products formed. If the product(s) are precipitates, name them.

a) $Cu(NO_3)_{2\ (aq)} + H_2S_{(g)} \longrightarrow CuS_{(?)} + 2\ HNO_{3(?)}$

b) $2\ KOH_{(aq)} + MgCl_{2\ (aq)} \longrightarrow 2\ KCl_{(?)} + Mg(OH)_{2(?)}$

c) $Hg_2(NO_3)_{2\ (aq)} + 2\ NaCl_{(aq)} \longrightarrow Hg_2Cl_{2(?)} + 2\ NaNO_{3(?)}$

33. Complete and balance the following combination reactions. Identify each product as an acid, a base, a salt, an acidic oxide, or a basic oxide.

a) $S_{(s)} + O_{2\ (g)} \xrightarrow{\Delta}$ c) $Li_2O_{(s)} + CO_{2(g)} \longrightarrow$

b) $CaO_{(s)} + H_2O_{(\ell)} \longrightarrow$

34. For each of the following combination reactions, write the formula of the product and balance the equation. Classify the products as acids, bases, salts, acidic oxides, or basic oxides.

a) $Mg_{(s)} + S_{(s)} \longrightarrow$ c) $Li_2O_{(s)} + H_2O_{(\ell)} \longrightarrow$

b) $Na_2O_{(s)} + SO_{2\ (g)} \longrightarrow$

35. For each of the following decomposition reactions, predict the products that you expect to be formed and balance the equation:

a) $CuSO_{4\ (s)} \longrightarrow$ b) $Zn(OH)_{2\ (s)} \longrightarrow$ c) $PbCO_{3(s)} \longrightarrow$

36. Which of the following salts are not soluble:
    a) ammonium carbonate
    b) lead(II) sulfate
    c) barium hydroxide
    d) silver iodide
    e) mercury(II) nitrate
    f) lead(IV) sulfate
    g) copper(II) bromide
    h) aluminum phosphate
    i) silver sulfate
    j) potassium hydroxide

37. Complete and balance the equation for the following double displacement reactions. In each case, indicate whether a precipitate will be formed, a gas will be produced, or neutralization will occur.
    a) $Mg(OH)_{2 (s)} + H_2SO_{4 (aq)} \longrightarrow$
    b) $Na_2CO_{3 (aq)} + H_3PO_{4 (aq)} \longrightarrow$
    c) $Pb(NO_3)_{2 (aq)} + KCl_{(aq)} \longrightarrow$
    d) $(NH_4)_2S_{(aq)} + FeSO_{4 (aq)} \longrightarrow$

38. Complete and balance the following equations:
    a) $(NH_4)_2SO_{4 (aq)} + Ba(OH)_{2 (aq)} \longrightarrow$
    b) $AgNO_{3 (aq)} + Na_2S_{(aq)} \longrightarrow$
    c) $Al(OH)_{3 (s)} + HCl_{(aq)} \longrightarrow$
    d) $MgCl_{2 (aq)} + NaOH_{(aq)} \longrightarrow$

39. Indicate which of the reactions below involve oxidation and reduction. Identify the species that are being oxidized and reduced, and determine the oxidation number in both the oxidized and reduced forms:
    a) $2 Al_{(s)} + 3 S_{(s)} \longrightarrow Al_2S_{3 (s)}$
    b) $HCl_{(aq)} + NaOH_{(aq)} \longrightarrow NaCl_{(aq)} + H_2O_{(\ell)}$
    c) $CuSO_{4 (aq)} + Zn_{(s)} \longrightarrow ZnSO_{4 (aq)} + Cu_{(s)}$
    d) $NH_4NO_{3 (s)} \longrightarrow N_2O_{(g)} + 2 H_2O_{(\ell)}$
    (NOTE: The two nitrogen atoms in ammonium nitrate have different oxidation numbers.)

40. Which of the following are redox reactions? In each case, show the change in the oxidation number and identify which species is reduced and which is oxidized.
    a) $2 Fe_{(s)} + O_{2(g)} + 2 H_2O_{(\ell)} \longrightarrow 2 Fe(OH)_{2 (s)}$
    b) $Zn_{(s)} + 2 AgNO_{3 (aq)} \longrightarrow Zn(NO_3)_{2 (aq)} + 2 Ag_{(s)}$
    c) $NaCl_{(s)} + NaHSO_{4 (s)} \longrightarrow HCl_{(g)} + Na_2SO_{4 (s)}$
    d) $NH_4NO_{2 (s)} \longrightarrow N_{2 (g)} + 2 H_2O_{(g)}$

41. Classify each of the following as a combination, decomposition, single or double displacement reaction.
    a) $KOH_{(aq)} + HNO_{3 (aq)} \longrightarrow KNO_{3 (aq)} + H_2O_{(\ell)}$
    b) $Ni_{(s)} + CuSO_{4 (aq)} \longrightarrow NiSO_{4 (aq)} + Cu_{(s)}$
    c) $2 NaNO_{3 (s)} \xrightarrow{\Delta} 2 NaNO_{2 (s)} + O_{2 (g)}$
    d) $Al(NO_3)_{3 (aq)} + 3 LiOH_{(aq)} \longrightarrow 3 LiNO_{3 (aq)} + Al(OH)_{3 (s)}$
    e) $2 Zn_{(s)} + O_{2 (g)} \longrightarrow 2 ZnO_{(s)}$

42. To which of the above categories of reaction does each of the following belong? Indicate which are redox reactions.
    a) $CaO_{(s)} + SO_{2 (g)} \longrightarrow CaSO_{3 (s)}$
    b) $Cl_{2 (aq)} + CaBr_{2 (aq)} \longrightarrow CaCl_{2 (aq)} + Br_{2 (aq)}$

c) $2 KNO_{3 (s)} \xrightarrow{\Delta} 2 KNO_{2 (s)} + O_{2 (g)}$

d) $Ca(OH)_{2 (aq)} + 2 HNO_{3 (aq)} \longrightarrow Ca(NO_3)_{2 (aq)} + 2 H_2O_{(\ell)}$

e) $2 Al_{(s)} + 3 Cl_{2 (g)} \longrightarrow 2 AlCl_{3 (s)}$

43. Determine whether each of the following reactions should be described as exothermic or endothermic:

a) $Fe_2O_{3 (s)} + 3 CO_{(g)} \longrightarrow 2 Fe_{(s)} + 3 CO_{2 (g)} + 27.6 kJ$

b) $N_2O_{3 (g)} \longrightarrow NO_{(g)} + NO_{2 (g)} \qquad \Delta H = +39.7 kJ$

c) $C_{(s)} + H_2O_{(g)} \longrightarrow CO_{(g)} + H_{2 (g)} \qquad \Delta H = +1313 kJ$

d) $NH_{3 (g)} + HCl_{(g)} \longrightarrow NH_4Cl_{(s)} \qquad \Delta H = -176.9 kJ$

44. Which of the following reactions are endothermic and which are exothermic:

a) $N_{2 (g)} + O_{2 (g)} + 90.37 kJ \longrightarrow 2 NO_{(g)}$

b) $C_3H_{8 (g)} + 5 O_{2 (g)} \longrightarrow 3 CO_{2 (g)} + 4 H_2O_{(g)} \qquad \Delta H = -2043.9 kJ$

c) $2 H_{2 (g)} + O_{2 (g)} \longrightarrow 2 H_2O_{(g)} + 241.8 kJ$

d) $2 Fe_2O_{3 (s)} \longrightarrow 4 Fe_{(s)} + 3 O_{2 (g)} \qquad \Delta H = +1644.4 kJ$

SUGGESTED PROJECTS

1. Many biochemical reactions occurring within our bodies only proceed at a reasonable rate because of the presence of enzymes. Most of these enzymes have very specific functions (i.e. have specific reactions that they catalyze). Use reference books to identify some of these enzymes and their functions.

2. In addition to magnesium, many other elements can be extracted from sea water (brine). The dissolved salts can also be removed to produce fresh water for irrigation, or for drinking. Write a report on either the extraction of chemicals from sea water or the production of fresh water from brine. Try to build a working model that demonstrates one of these processes.

3. According to the United Nations Food and Agricultural Organization, more than eleven million hectares of tropical rainforest are being destroyed annually. Investigate the importance of the tropical rainforests and the severe effects that any accelerated depletion might have on our atmosphere.

The Chemistry of Selected Elements

Chemistry is the study of the chemical elements and the compounds they form. In a book of this size, it is impossible to describe all the elements and their millions of compounds. Instead, we will select some of the more interesting elements and study their properties. We will also see how some of them can be prepared, and introduce you to a few of the important compounds they form. We will also discuss some of the reactions these elements undergo. Most of the reactions will belong to one of the categories discussed in Chapter 8. You should try to identify the category into which each reaction fits.

A Review of Periodicity

9.1 In Chapter 4, we saw that if the elements are arranged in a format known as the Periodic Table, patterns in their properties become apparent. These patterns do not occur by chance, but are a consequence of the systematic differences in the electron configurations of neighbouring elements.

Most of the elements are metals. The few nonmetals are located in the upper right-hand corner of the Periodic Table. However, there is no sharp dividing line between metals and nonmetals. Instead, the elements on the metal–nonmetal border in the Periodic Table exhibit properties that are between those of a metal and a nonmetal. These elements are referred to as semimetals.

Several physical properties of the atoms change systematically across or down the Periodic Table. For example, in Section 4.6 we saw that the atomic radius of atoms decreases from left to right across a period, but increases down a group. In Section 5.10, we introduced the concept of electronegativity and noted that electronegativity values increase towards the top right-hand corner of the Periodic Table. This means that the nonmetals have higher electronegativities (i.e., a greater tendency to form negative ions) than metals. Additional trends were shown in Chapter 6 for both formulas and oxidation numbers. Although the concept of periodicity is important in chemistry, and can help us in making predictions about the properties of the elements, each element is unique and many of its chemical properties are often unpredictable.

Group IA (The Alkali Metals)

9.2 We saw in Section 4.5 that metals are shiny, malleable, and ductile. Most metals, such as iron, lead, and gold, have high densities and are relatively unreactive. The alkali metals, however, have certain properties that make them distinctly different from most other metals.

Compounds of sodium and potassium have been known since ancient times. The name alkali comes from the Arabic *al kali*, meaning 'the ashes', because the burned remains of vegetation were a good source of sodium and potassium compounds.

Physical Properties

Lithium, sodium, and potassium are all less dense than water. Lithium, the least dense of the group, is about half as dense as water.

From the top to the bottom of the group there is a steady decrease in melting point, ranging from 180 °C for lithium to 27 °C for francium. Cesium (melting point 28 °C) and francium are sometimes listed in Periodic Tables as liquids because of their low melting points. The alkali metals are all quite soft and become softer down the group. Thus, lithium can be cut by a sharp knife, whereas potassium has a consistency more like soft butter.

TABLE 9.1 *Properties of the Group IA Elements*

Element	Phase at 20 °C	Appearance	Classification
Lithium	Solid	Silvery	Metal
Sodium	Solid	Silvery	Metal
Potassium	Solid	Silvery	Metal
Rubidium	Solid	Silvery	Metal
Cesium	Solid	Silvery	Metal

Chemical Properties

One important property of the Group IA metals is their high chemical reactivity, which increases down the group. All compounds formed by the alkali metals are ionic, and the metal always forms a cation with a +1 charge.

Oxygen reacts very rapidly with the alkali metals, making it difficult to appreciate their beautiful lustre unless they are stored under oil. If an alkali metal is exposed to air, its surface becomes white and powdery. The powder is an oxide formed as the result of a reaction between the metal and the oxygen in the air. This reaction can be very spectacular and dangerous. If a piece of sodium is heated in a test tube in a current of oxygen, the heat from the brilliant flame that is produced usually cracks the glass tube. The product of this reaction is not sodium oxide (Na_2O), but sodium peroxide (Na_2O_2):

$$2\,Na_{(s)} \;+\; O_{2\,(g)} \longrightarrow Na_2O_{2\,(s)}$$

If sodium is heated until it melts, and is then placed in a jar of chlorine gas, a white smoke forms. The white powder that settles after the smoke subsides is sodium chloride (NaCl), the compound commonly known as table salt:

$$2\,Na_{(\ell)} \;+\; Cl_{2\,(g)} \longrightarrow 2\,NaCl_{(s)}$$

A similar reaction occurs with any combination of an alkali metal and a Group VIIA element (fluorine, chlorine, bromine, or iodine). Thus, rubidium reacts violently with fluorine gas to give rubidium fluoride (RbF):

$$2\,Rb_{(s)} \;+\; F_{2\,(g)} \longrightarrow 2\,RbF_{(s)}$$

As we discussed in Chapter 8, all the salts of the alkali metals are soluble in water. To test for the presence of an alkali metal, we can use a flame test

(handwritten margin notes)
3) Very reactive as you more down
4) all form 1+ cations
6) quite electro-negative. Cs is the most electro- of all elements

$$K + O_2 \longrightarrow K[O_2]^-$$

(Section 3.10) as each of the alkali metals gives a very distinctive colour to the flame. These colours are crimson (lithium), yellow (sodium), violet (potassium), red-violet (rubidium), and blue (cesium). The name cesium comes from the Latin word for 'sky blue'.

You may have noticed that we have not discussed francium, the lowest member of the alkali metals. This is because all the isotopes of francium are radioactive (Section 3.4) and relatively unstable. The chemistry of francium has rarely been studied as only small quantities of the element have ever been prepared. We will not discuss the properties of francium or of any other element that exists only in radioactive form.

Reaction With Water

The alkali metals all react with water to produce hydrogen gas and a solution of the metal hydroxide. Lithium reacts fairly slowly with water. During the reaction, bubbles of hydrogen gas are given off:

$$2 \, Li_{(s)} \; + \; 2 \, H_2O_{(\ell)} \longrightarrow 2 \, LiOH_{(aq)} \; + \; H_{2 \, (g)}$$

The reaction of sodium with water is much faster and during the reaction so much heat is produced that the sodium melts and a little molten ball of sodium metal skates around on the surface of the water:

$$2 \, Na_{(s)} \; + \; 2 \, H_2O_{(\ell)} \longrightarrow 2 \, NaOH_{(aq)} \; + \; H_{2 \, (g)}$$

If a large enough piece of sodium is used, sufficient heat is released to ignite the hydrogen gas. When potassium, which is even more reactive than sodium, is added to water, the heat produced is easily sufficient to set the hydrogen alight:

$$2 \, K_{(s)} \; + \; 2 \, H_2O_{(\ell)} \longrightarrow 2 \, KOH_{(aq)} \; + \; H_{2 \, (g)}$$
$$2 \, H_{2 \, (g)} \; + \; O_{2 \, (g)} \longrightarrow 2 \, H_2O_{(g)}$$

Rubidium and cesium explode when they come into contact with water. Cesium will even react with a block of ice that has been cooled to $-100 \, °C$. The reactions between the alkali metals and water illustrate the increase in reactivity of the alkali metals down Group IA.

The reactivity of the alkali metals prevented their isolation until 1807, when the brilliant young English chemist, Humphry Davy, devised an electrochemical method for isolating potassium and sodium.

Why are the alkali metals so reactive? Each of these elements has one valence electron which is very easily lost to form a cation with a noble gas configuration. The alkali metals lose their valence electrons more readily than elements of the other groups because the ionization energy (the energy needed to form positive ions) is less for the alkali metals than for any other group (see Section 4.7)

Figure 9.1
Lithium compounds are used in high-quality greases.

Sodium Chloride

Sodium compounds are widespread in nature. Sodium chloride can be obtained from seawater, but there are also vast underground deposits of this compound in different regions of the world. Sodium chloride is used as a reactant in the manufacture of other sodium-containing compounds. For example, sodium chloride reacts with sulfuric acid to produce sodium sulfate, which is used in the Kraft process for making brown wrapping paper and corrugated boxes. The equation for this reaction is as follows:

$$2\ NaCl_{(aq)} + H_2SO_{4\ (aq)} \longrightarrow Na_2SO_{4\ (aq)} + 2\ HCl_{(g)}$$

Sodium hydroxide is usually prepared by passing an electric current through a solution of sodium chloride:

$$2\ NaCl_{(aq)} + 2\ H_2O_{(\ell)} \xrightarrow[\text{current}]{\text{electric}} 2\ NaOH_{(aq)} + H_{2\ (g)} + Cl_{2\ (g)}$$

QUESTIONS

1. Write the formula of the compound formed by lithium and
   a) iodine   b) oxygen
2. Write a balanced molecular equation for the reaction between
   a) potassium metal and bromine   b) rubidium metal and water
3. Which of the alkali metals (except francium)
   a) is the hardest?   c) has the largest atomic radius?
   b) has the highest melting point?   d) is the most reactive?

Figure 9.2

The Goderich, Ontario, salt mine. Much of the sodium chloride used in Canada is mined from underground deposits. The ceiling, walls, and floor of the mine are all pure salt.

Davy, The Discoverer of Sodium

Sir Humphry Davy was born in 1778 in Penzance, England. His first studies in chemistry were on the properties of the gas, dinitrogen oxide, which is often called nitrous oxide or laughing gas. Before Davy's time, it had been thought that dinitrogen oxide was poisonous. However, by using himself as a subject, Davy showed that the gas was not poisonous. In addition, he discovered that the gas had anesthetic properties and suggested that it be used in minor surgical operations.

In Davy's time, chemistry was regarded as a great popular entertainment. Up to 1000 people at a time would flock to see public experiments and to hear about new research work, just as they would go to a circus today. One of the highlights of Davy's lectures, illustrated in Figure 9.3, was his demonstration using a hand bellows filled with laughing gas. Unfortunately, during the 20th century science and the general public

have moved apart, partly because of the increasing complexity of science, but also because scientists in general have not made enough effort to describe their work to the population at large.

In 1807 Davy first tried to apply an electric current to liquid salts. This work proved to be very successful, and he was able to isolate sodium, potassium, magnesium, calcium, strontium, and barium by passing an electric current through the appropriate metal salts. Davy's fame became so great that a rhyme about his work was passed from generation to generation of British students.

> *Sir Humphry Davy*
> *Abominated gravy*
> *Lived in the odium*
> *Of having discovered sodium*

In the early 19th century there had been a number of large explosions in coal mines. These were caused by a gas that Davy identified as methane, CH_4. The miners in those days carried lamps with open flames to light their way through the mines. Davy developed a safety lamp that could be used in the mines without igniting the methane.

Davy was a good experimentalist, but his theories were not usually based on firm grounds and were speculative and sometimes confusing. He believed (as he often wrote) that the only value of hypotheses was that they led to new experiments.

Figure 9.3
A 19th century public chemistry lecture. Davy (holding the bellows) is giving a lecture on the properties of gases.

Group IIA (The Alkaline Earth Metals)

9.3 The alkaline earth metals are all harder and denser than the alkali metals. The melting points of the Group IIA metals are also much higher than those of the Group IA metals, but follow the same general trend of decreasing down the group. For example, the melting point of beryllium is 1283 °C and that of barium is 725 °C. The alkaline earth metals form predominantly ionic compounds in which the metal ion has a +2 charge.

Important

TABLE 9.2 *Properties of the Group IIA Elements*

Element	Phase at 20 °C	Appearance	Classification
Beryllium	Solid	Silvery	Metal
Magnesium	Solid	Silvery	Metal
Calcium	Solid	Silvery	Metal
Strontium	Solid	Silvery	Metal
Barium	Solid	Silvery	Metal

The Group IIA elements all burn in air to form the corresponding oxide. Thus, magnesium forms magnesium oxide (MgO):

$$2\ Mg_{(s)}\ +\ O_{2\ (g)}\ \longrightarrow\ 2\ MgO_{(s)}$$

When magnesium burns in oxygen, an eye-searing white light is produced. Before the invention of the flashbulb, burning magnesium was used by photographers as a light source.

Although they are not as reactive as the alkali metals, the alkaline earth metals are quite reactive when compared to metals such as lead and tin. Like the metals in Group IA, the Group IIA metals will react with water to produce the metal hydroxide and hydrogen gas. For example

$$Ba_{(s)}\ +\ 2\ H_2O_{(\ell)}\ \longrightarrow\ Ba(OH)_{2\ (s)}\ +\ H_{2\ (g)}$$

The oxides of the alkaline earth metals also react with water to form solutions of the metal hydroxide. The reaction between calcium oxide (quicklime) and water is quite violent and produces, in addition to calcium hydroxide, a large amount of heat and light:

$$CaO_{(s)}\ +\ H_2O_{(\ell)}\ \longrightarrow\ Ca(OH)_{2\ (aq)}$$

In the past, the light emitted by this reaction was used for lighting theatre stages — hence the term "limelight."

Calcium

Calcium is the fifth most abundant element in the earth's crust. Most of it is found as calcium carbonate, the major constituent of marble, limestone, and chalk.

The shells of marine creatures, such as oysters and coral, are composed of calcium carbonate. Most calcium carbonate deposits were formed from the shells of marine organisms that lived in earlier geological periods. Egg shells are also composed of calcium carbonate.

When rainwater containing dissolved carbon dioxide percolates through limestone rocks, some of the calcium carbonate dissolves to form soluble calcium hydrogen carbonate. This results in the slow formation of caves and explains why caves are found mainly in chalk or limestone areas. The equation for the reaction is as follows:

$$CaCO_{3\,(s)} + CO_{2\,(g)} + H_2O_{(\ell)} \longrightarrow Ca(HCO_3)_{2\,(aq)}$$

If some of the water from a solution of calcium hydrogen carbonate evaporates, the reverse of the above reaction occurs and solid calcium carbonate is formed. This is the process by which stalagmites and stalactites are formed.

Another important calcium-containing compound is calcium sulfate dihydrate, also known as gypsum. This compound is used in the production of Portland cement and gypsum wallboard. Plaster of Paris, $(CaSO_4)_2 \cdot H_2O$, is formed by gently heating gypsum:

$$2\,CaSO_4 \cdot 2\,H_2O_{(s)} \xrightarrow{\Delta} (CaSO_4)_2 \cdot H_2O_{(s)} + 3\,H_2O_{(\ell)}$$

QUESTIONS

4. Write the formula for the compound formed between calcium and
   a) chlorine   b) oxygen

5. Write a balanced molecular equation for the reaction between
   a) calcium metal and water   c) barium oxide and water
   b) barium metal and oxygen

6. Which of the alkaline earth metals
   a) has the lowest melting point?   c) is the most abundant in nature?
   b) has the smallest atomic radius?

Figure 9.4
Carlsbad Caverns, New Mexico. These magnificent cave formations consist of almost pure calcium carbonate.

Group IIIA   9.4

Compared to the Group IA and IIA elements, the elements in Group IIIA display a much greater variety of physical and chemical properties. The elements range from boron (a hard, black, inert semimetal) to thallium (a soft, reactive metal). At room temperature, none of the members of this group react with air or water.

Important

TABLE 9.3 *Properties of the Group IIIA Elements*

Element	Phase at 20 °C	Appearance	Classification
Boron	Solid	Black	Semimetal
Aluminum	Solid	Silvery	Metal
Gallium	Solid	Silvery	Metal
Indium	Solid	Silvery	Metal
Thallium	Solid	Silvery	Metal

The Essential Trace Elements of Life

Most living matter consists of the elements carbon, hydrogen, nitrogen, oxygen, and sulfur. To survive and grow, we need to ingest large quantities of these elements every day. We also require daily quantities, ranging from 1 g to 0.1 g, of sodium, magnesium, phosphorus, chlorine, potassium, and calcium. These serve as structural components of tissues and, as constituents of body fluids, are essential for the function of all cells.

In addition, we require very small quantities, in the range of milligrams or micrograms per day, of at least fourteen other elements. These are known as the essential trace elements. It is suspected that a number of other elements might also fall into this category (Figure 9.5).

Each of the essential trace elements has a vital function in our bodies. For example, a lack of zinc results in poor growth, loss of appetite, loss of taste sensation, and abnormal births. Unfortunately, it is mainly the "luxury foods", such as meat and oysters, that contain large quantities of zinc and low-income families are the most likely to experience zinc deficiency.

You may be surprised to see that poisonous elements, such as arsenic, selenium, and chromium, are essential for maintaining our health. There is, in fact, a safe range of daily intake for each element. This concept, known as Bertrand's Rule, is illustrated in Figure 9.6. Too little or too much of any element can be equally dangerous. For example, to maintain good health, we need between about 50 and 200 μg of chromium per day. A North American study showed that the chromium intake of many people is less than this. Lack of sufficient chromium has been related to certain types of diabetes and to high cholesterol levels.

Identifying and studying trace elements in human nutrition is a major field of research. One difficulty in relating illness to a trace metal deficiency (or excess) is measuring the very small quantities of an element in a patient. Research is therefore being conducted to find new methods of measuring trace elements in humans.

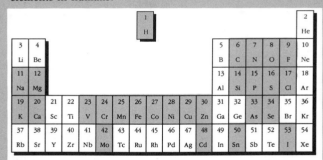

Figure 9.5
Part of the Periodic Table, showing all the elements that are accepted as being essential (shaded).

TABLE 9.4 *Adult Daily Requirement of Selected Trace Elements*

Element	Daily Requirement (mg/day)
Iron (males)	10
Iron (females)	18
Zinc	15
Manganese	2.5 to 5.0
Fluorine	1.5 to 4.0
Copper	2.0 to 3.0
Molybdenum	0.15 to 0.5
Iodine	0.15
Chromium	0.05 to 0.2
Selenium	0.05 to 0.2
Arsenic	0.03

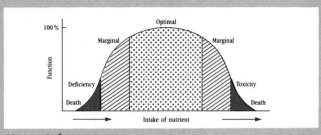

Figure 9.6
This graph shows how our body responds to varying intake of a particular trace element.

Figure 9.7
To save weight, the superstructures of some British warships were constructed of an aluminum-magnesium alloy instead of steel. This alloy of two reactive metals burns spectacularly, as shown in this photograph taken during the Falkland Islands war.

Similarity in formulas does not necessarily mean similarity in properties. For example, although boron and aluminum form chlorides with similar formulas, BCl_3 and $AlCl_3$, the properties of these two compounds are quite different. Boron trichloride is a gas at room temperature, whereas aluminum chloride is a solid. Since covalently bonded compounds have low boiling points, we could predict that the bonding in BCl_3 is covalent. This prediction is correct; in BCl_3 a semimetal and a nonmetal combine to form a covalent compound. The other members of Group IIIA are metals and should form ionic compounds.

Aluminum

The most abundant member of Group IIIA is aluminum. Aluminum is a fairly reactive metal, but when it is exposed to air a thin, protective layer of the relatively inert oxide (Al_2O_3) forms over its surface. This oxide protects the aluminum from further attack by air or water. If the surface of the metal is scratched the oxide "skin" immediately reforms and gives the impression that aluminum is unreactive.

The oxide "skin" on the surface of aluminum metal is the normal oxide of aluminum that is formed when aluminum is burned in oxygen:

$$4\ Al_{(s)}\ +\ 3\ O_{2\,(g)}\ \longrightarrow\ 2\ Al_2O_{3\,(g)}$$

This oxide is almost totally insoluble in water (unlike the oxides of the Group IA and IIA metals) and exists naturally in the form of rubies and sapphires. The colour of these stones is caused by traces of chromium (Cr^{3+}), iron (Fe^{3+}), and titanium (Ti^{4+}) ions.

QUESTIONS

7. Write the formula of the compound formed between aluminum and sulfur.

8. Which of the Group IIIA elements
   a) is a poor conductor of electricity?
   b) has the lowest melting point?

9. Draw the electron-dot structure of
   a) BCl_3 (NOTE: Boron forms several compounds in which the boron atom has only six electrons in its valence level.)
   b) $AlCl_3$ (NOTE: Remember that this is an ionic compound.)

Group IVA **9.5**

This family of elements provides the most striking changes in properties from one member to the next. Carbon is a nonmetal, silicon and germanium are semimetals, and tin and lead are metals.

TABLE 9.5	*Properties of the Group IVA Elements*		
Element	Phase at 20 °C	Appearance	Classification
Carbon	Solid	Black	Nonmetal
Silicon	Solid	Shiny grey	Semimetal
Germanium	Solid	Shiny yellow-grey	Semimetal
Tin	Solid	Silvery grey	Metal
Lead	Solid	Dark grey	Metal

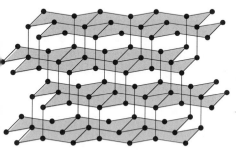

The diamond lattice. The structure is a three-dimensional network with identical bonds in all directions.

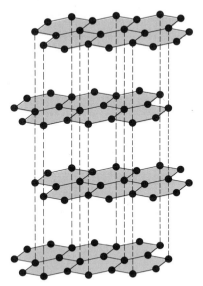

Structure of the graphite lattice

Figure 9.8

The molecular structures of the two allotropes of carbon.

Carbon and silicon both form only covalent compounds. For example, carbon forms liquid carbon tetrachloride, CCl_4, and methane gas, CH_4.

As tin and lead are metals, we would expect their compounds to be ionic. Tin(II) chloride and lead(II) nitrate are typical salts — at room temperature they are white solids that dissolve in water to give solutions containing the metal ion and the appropriate anion. On the other hand, tin(IV) and lead(IV) compounds have properties that are typical of covalent compounds. For example, tin(IV) chloride is a liquid at room temperature, with a boiling point of 114 °C.

Carbon

We use the term **allotrope** to describe different forms of the same element. Allotropes have different physical and chemical properties because the atoms are arranged differently in each form. Carbon exists as two allotropes: *diamond* and *graphite* (Figure 9.8). Pure diamonds are colourless crystals, the hardest naturally occurring substance known. Graphite is a slippery black powder. It is the only naturally occurring nonmetallic substance known to conduct electricity.

Apart from hydrogen, carbon forms more compounds than any other element. This is because carbon atoms have the ability to bond together to form molecules containing long chains and/or rings of carbon atoms. This ability is called **catenation**.

Carbon Dioxide (CO_2). Carbon dioxide is a colourless, odourless, tasteless gas with a density 1.5 times that of air. It does not support combustion, other than of the alkali and alkaline earth metals, and consequently it is used in some types of fire extinguishers. Carbon dioxide is formed when either of the allotropes of carbon is burned in an excess of air. Burning is thus an excellent, if expensive, method of checking whether a diamond is genuine. The equation for the reaction is as follows:

$$C_{(s)} + O_{2\,(g)} \longrightarrow CO_{2\,(g)}$$

Figure 9.9

The world's three largest diamonds (shown left to right):
a) the Star of Sierra Leone
b) the Cullinan (a replica)
c) the Excelsior (a replica)
In their natural state, diamonds are usually quite rough and irregular in shape.

Carbon dioxide is also produced when carbon-containing compounds burn. A typical example is the combustion of natural gas, which consists mainly of methane, CH_4:

$$CH_{4\ (g)}\ +\ 2\ O_{2\ (g)}\ \longrightarrow\ CO_{2\ (g)}\ +\ 2\ H_2O_{(g)}$$

In the laboratory we can prepare carbon dioxide using a double displacement reaction between an acid and a carbonate. We usually use calcium carbonate (in the form of marble chips) and hydrochloric acid. The apparatus is set up as shown in Figure 9.10, with the marble chips in the Erlenmeyer flask. Hydrochloric acid is poured down the thistle funnel and the carbon dioxide gas that is produced flows through the tube and can be collected in jars for study:

$$CaCO_{3\ (s)}\ +\ 2\ HCl_{(aq)}\ \longrightarrow\ CaCl_{2\ (aq)}\ +\ H_2O_{(\ell)}\ +\ CO_{2\ (g)}$$

The standard test for carbon dioxide is to bubble the gas that is being investigated through a solution of calcium hydroxide. Carbon dioxide will react to give a milky-white precipitate of calcium carbonate. No other gas gives a precipitate when tested in this manner.

$$Ca(OH)_{2\ (aq)}\ +\ CO_{2\ (g)}\ \longrightarrow\ CaCO_{3\ (s)}\ +\ H_2O_{(\ell)}$$

In low concentrations, carbon dioxide is harmless. Approximately 4% of our exhaled breath is carbon dioxide. This carbon dioxide has an interesting physiological function. The concentration of carbon dioxide in our blood controls our breathing rate. During heavy exercise, the rate of carbon dioxide formation in the body increases and therefore we breathe more rapidly. Small amounts of carbon dioxide can be used to stimulate breathing, but inhalation of high concentrations of this gas over prolonged periods causes asphyxiation.

Figure 9.10

The laboratory preparation of carbon dioxide from calcium carbonate and hydrochloric acid.

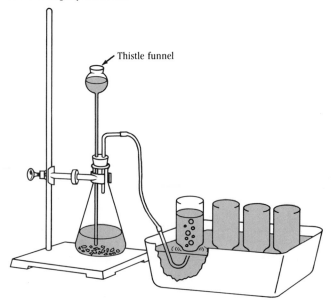

Thistle funnel

Figure 9.11

The hole in these clouds was caused by dry-ice seeding. Carbon dioxide crystals dropped from an aircraft cause cloud droplets to coalesce and form precipitation (rain or snow).

The level of carbon dioxide in our atmosphere has been increasing at a slow but steady rate. It is estimated that the amount of carbon dioxide increased from 0.029% of the atmosphere (by mass) in 1900 to 0.033% in 1950. The level has been rising even faster over the past 20 years and there is concern that this growing amount of carbon dixide could lead to substantial changes in climate at some time in the future.

Solid carbon dioxide sublimes (i.e. turns directly to gas) at $-78\,°C$. For this reason, it is often called *dry ice*. Liquid carbon dioxide can only be obtained by compressing the gas.

Large quantities of dry ice are used as a refrigerant. The carbonated-beverage industry provides a large market for carbon dioxide, which is dissolved under pressure in these beverages. (Gases are more soluble in liquids at higher pressures.) When the pressure is released, bubbles of carbon dioxide are liberated. A little of the dissolved carbon dioxide reacts with the water in the beverage to form carbonic acid, which acts as a preservative:

$$CO_{2\,(g)} \;+\; H_2O_{(\ell)} \;\rightleftharpoons\; H_2CO_{3\,(aq)}$$

Carbon Monoxide (CO). The second common oxide of carbon, carbon monoxide, is a colourless, odourless, poisonous gas. Carbon monoxide is produced during the incomplete burning of carbon-containing materials such as tobacco (in cigarettes) and gasoline (in internal-combustion engines).

When sufficient oxygen is present, carbon monoxide will burn with a blue flame to produce carbon dioxide:

$$2\,CO_{(g)} \;+\; O_{2\,(g)} \;\longrightarrow\; 2\,CO_{2\,(g)}$$

If people or animals are exposed to carbon monoxide from automobile exhausts or from poorly ventilated furnaces, death can result. The hemoglobin in blood cells has a 200 times greater affinity for carbon monoxide than for oxygen. Therefore, a small amount of carbon monoxide in the blood can have a major effect on the ability of the blood to transport oxygen. Early symptoms of carbon monoxide poisoning include headache, dizziness, difficulty in breathing, and muscle weakness. Heavy smokers have a higher than normal concentration of carbon monoxide in their blood. This results in shortness of breath because of the reduced oxygen-carrying capacity of the blood.

Silicon

The chemistry of silicon is rarely studied in introductory chemistry courses and we will only briefly mention the element here. Very pure silicon is used in transistors and in devices for converting light to electrical energy. The element silicon should not be confused with a series of compounds called silicones that contain silicon, oxygen, carbon, and hydrogen. Most waterproofing compounds contain silicones, as does Silly Putty.

The two most abundant elements on the earth are silicon and oxygen. It is therefore not surprising that most rocks on the earth consist of either silicon dioxide (SiO_2) or silicates. Silicates are salts formed by high-temperature reactions between metal compounds and the acidic oxide, silicon dioxide. Most oxides of nonmetals are acidic oxides (Section 8.4) and you may hear geologists refer to rocks rich in silicon dioxide as acid rocks. The sand found on beaches is composed mainly of silicon dioxide.

QUESTIONS

10. Write the formula of the compound formed between carbon and
    a) fluorine   b) sulfur

11. Write a balanced molecular equation for
    a) the combustion of propane, $C_3H_{8\ (g)}$ (often called "bottled gas")
    b) the reaction between sulfuric acid ($H_2SO_{4\ (aq)}$) and a solution of sodium carbonate

12. Draw the electron-dot structure for
    a) methane, CH_4 b) carbon dioxide

Group VA

9.6

As with the Group IVA elements, the elements in Group VA change from nonmetallic to metallic as we go down the group. Again, we find that the nonmetals at the top of the group form covalent compounds and that the metals in the group form ionic compounds.

Figure 9.12
Ammonia being applied directly as a fertilizer. Nitrogen compounds are vital for the growth of plants. To improve crop yields, nitrogen is added to the soil in the form of ammonia or ammonium salts.

TABLE 9.6 *Properties of the Group VA Elements*

Element	Phase at 20 °C	Appearance	Classification
Nitrogen	Gas	Colourless	Nonmetal
Phosphorus	Solid	Red powder	Nonmetal
Arsenic	Solid	Grey	Semimetal
Antimony	Solid	Shiny grey	Metal
Bismuth	Solid	Silvery	Metal

Nitrogen (N₂)

Nitrogen is a colourless, odourless, tasteless gas that condenses to a liquid at $-196\,°C$ and solidifies at $-210\,°C$. It is very unreactive. The only element with which nitrogen reacts at room temperature is lithium. This lack of reactivity is one of the most important properties of nitrogen because it makes air, which consists of 78% nitrogen and 21% oxygen, less reactive than it would otherwise be.

Ammonia (NH₃).   Ammonia is a colourless gas. It has a strong odour, which you may have noticed in ammonia-containing household cleaners. Ammonia is the only common gas that turns red litmus blue, i.e. it is basic. The gas is very soluble in water, with a small fraction of the ammonia actually reacting with water. The equation for this reaction is as follows:

$$NH_{3\,(g)} \;+\; H_2O_{(\ell)} \;\rightleftharpoons\; NH_4^{+}{}_{(aq)} \;+\; OH^-{}_{(aq)}$$

Some bacteria found in the roots of leguminous plants (such as peas, beans, clover, and alfalfa) convert the nitrogen in the air to ammonia. The ammonia is then used by the plants to synthesize salts. Ammonia can also be added to the soil as fertilizer, e.g., ammonium phosphate $(NH_4)_3PO_4$.

Ammonia was first produced industrially in 1913. This was achieved by reacting nitrogen with hydrogen at high temperature and pressure in the presence of a suitable catalyst:

$$N_{2\,(g)} \;+\; 3\,H_{2\,(g)} \;\rightleftharpoons\; 2\,NH_{3\,(g)}$$

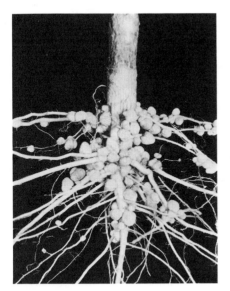

Figure 9.13
Some plants obtain ammonia from bacteria that grow on their roots. Bacteria are in these nodules on the roots of a pea plant.

Nitrogen Dioxide (NO₂).   Nitrogen dioxide is a poisonous, red-brown gas with an irritating odour. Nitrogen dioxide, and the less common nitrogen monoxide (NO) (also called nitric oxide), are produced naturally from oxygen gas and nitrogen gas during flashes of lightning. They are also produced in the cylinders of gasoline engines, especially in high-compression engines. Nitrogen oxides play a major role in generating photochemical smog in large cities such as Los Angeles.

Figure 9.14

The structure of a molecule of yellow phosphorus, P_4.

Nitrogen dioxide is an acidic gas that dissolves in water to produce a mixture of nitric acid and nitrous acid:

$$2\ NO_{2\ (g)}\ +\ H_2O_{(\ell)}\ \longrightarrow\ HNO_{3\ (aq)}\ +\ HNO_{2\ (aq)}$$

Dinitrogen Oxide (N_2O). Dinitrogen oxide is a colourless gas. Also known as nitrous oxide, it was discovered by the English clergyman Joseph Priestley, who isolated and studied more new gases than any person did before or has done since. (He also invented soda water.) Still used as an anesthetic, in low concentrations dinitrogen oxide can cause involuntary giggling in people. For this reason, it is often referred to as *laughing gas*. The gas can be prepared by the unusual decomposition reaction described in Section 8.5. The equation for this reaction is

$$NH_4NO_{3\ (s)}\ \xrightarrow{\ \Delta\ }\ N_2O_{(g)}\ +\ 2\ H_2O_{(\ell)}$$

Phosphorus

Phosphorus is an interesting element in that it has two common allotropes: red phosphorus (a dark red powder) and yellow phosphorus (an off-white waxy substance sometimes called white phosphorus). The molecules of yellow phosphorus each contain four atoms. The structure of a P_4 molecule is shown in Figure 9.14. The molecular structure of red phosphorus is more complex. These two allotropes differ, not only in the way their atoms are arranged, but also in their reactivity. Yellow phosphorus must be stored under water because it catches fire in air to produce tetraphosphorus decaoxide (also called phosphorus pentoxide):

$$P_{4\ (s)}\ +\ 5\ O_{2\ (g)}\ \longrightarrow\ P_4O_{10\ (s)}$$

If either of the allotropes of phosphorus is burned with a shortage of oxygen, tetraphosphorus hexaoxide (phosphorus trioxide) is formed:

$$P_{4\ (s)}\ +\ 3\ O_{2\ (g)}\ \longrightarrow\ P_4O_{6\ (s)}$$

Figure 9.15

The structures of tetraphosphorus hexaoxide P_4O_6 (top) and tetraphosphorus decaoxide P_4O_{10} (bottom).

The structures of these two oxides are interesting because the P_4 unit of yellow phosphorus is the centre of each oxide molecule. In P_4O_6, oxygen atoms link each of the four phosphorus atoms and in P_4O_{10} an additional oxygen atom is bonded to each phosphorus atom (Figure 9.15).

Because of its reactivity, yellow phosphorus is used in napalm bombs. In contrast, red phosphorus is quite stable in air and is used in safety matches.

Phosphorus, like potassium, is necessary for plant growth. Plants usually obtain their phosphorus in the form of phosphate ions. About 25% of our bones and teeth are composed of calcium phosphate. Phosphate units also comprise a vital part of the complex nucleic acid molecules, such as ribonucleic acid (RNA) and deoxyribonucleic acid (DNA) that form the basis of living material.

Figure 9.16
Yellow phosphorus bursts into flame as soon as it is exposed to air.

QUESTIONS

13. Write a balanced molecular equation for the reaction that occurs between each of the following:
    a) ammonia gas and phosphoric acid ($H_3PO_{4\ (aq)}$)—a combination-neutralization reaction
    b) lithium metal and nitrogen gas

14. Draw the electron-dot structure of
    a) N_2 b) NH_3

15. Write chemical formulas for the compounds formed between
    a) phosphorus and chlorine (two compounds)
    b) sodium and phosphorus (one compound)

Group VIA

9.7 By far the most important elements in Group VIA are oxygen and sulfur.

TABLE 9.7 *Properties of the Group VIA Elements*

Element	Phase at 20 °C	Appearance	Classification
Oxygen	Gas	Colourless	Nonmetal
Sulfur	Solid	Yellow	Nonmetal
Selenium	Solid	Shiny grey	Semimetal
Tellurium	Solid	Silvery-white	Semimetal

Oxygen (O_2)

Oxygen is the most prevalent element on the surface of the earth. Oxygen constitutes 21% (by mass) of the atmosphere, nearly 90% (by mass) of water, and more than 50% (by mass) of sand. In the atmosphere, oxygen is present as the element, but in sand it is present as silicon dioxide (SiO_2). Oxygen was first isolated and studied by the great Swedish chemist, Carl Scheele, around 1773. It is a colourless, odourless, tasteless gas that condenses to a liquid at −183 °C and solidifies at −216 °C. As a liquid or solid, it is blue. It is the only common gas that will ignite a glowing splint, and it is therefore said to support combustion. However, oxygen itself does not burn. Like most gases, oxygen dissolves better in cold water than in hot water. This explains why the best fishing areas are in cold currents, such as the Labrador current off the eastern coast of Canada and the Humboldt current off the coast of Chile and Peru.

The easiest way to prepare oxygen gas in the laboratory is to add a catalyst, such as manganese(IV) oxide, to a solution of hydrogen peroxide:

$$2\ H_2O_{2\ (aq)} \xrightarrow{\ MnO_2\ } 2\ H_2O_{(\ell)} + O_{2\ (g)}$$

Oxygen has two _allotropes_, dioxygen (O_2), which is usually just called oxygen, and trioxygen (O_3), which is also called ozone. Dioxygen boils at $-183\,°C$ and ozone boils at $-110\,°C$. Dioxygen is odourless and harmless, but ozone is very poisonous and has a metallic smell. This smell is often noticeable near electrical switchgear. Ozone is also generated in thunderstorms, and in the upper atmosphere where it plays an important role in reducing the amount of ultraviolet light from the sun that reaches the earth. Very low concentrations of ozone are sometimes used as a bactericide in the purification of water.

Very few elements do not react with oxygen. Some elements, such as aluminum, form a "skin" of oxide that protects the metal underneath from further oxidation (Section 9.4). This protective layer makes the metal appear to be less reactive than it really is.

Although we can go for weeks without food and days without water, life ceases within minutes without oxygen. The average active adult inhales at least 10 000 L of air per day (about half the volume of a large gasoline truck). From this amount of air, some 500 L of oxygen are absorbed by the lungs and more than 400 L of carbon dioxide are exhaled. Because the body has no warning system to indicate a lack of oxygen, we can lose consciousness because of a shortage of oxygen without realizing what is happening.

Sulfur

Sulfur, the element below oxygen in Group VIA, is a yellow solid. In its most common allotropic form, it consists of puckered rings of eight atoms (Figure 9.17). Heating sulfur produces a series of interesting changes. On melting at $112\,°C$, the solid sulfur forms a pale yellow liquid. As the temperature is raised further, the colour deepens to a dark red-brown and the viscosity of the liquid increases. At $180\,°C$, the liquid has such a high viscosity that it cannot be poured from its container. Heating the sulfur even more causes the viscosity to decrease and the colour to change to red.

We can account for these changes by assuming that the pale yellow liquid consists of the same S_8 rings as the solid allotrope. At higher temperatures, it is believed that the rings break open and join with each other to form long chains of sulfur atoms. The formation of the long chains causes the increase in viscosity. Finally, at even higher temperatures, the long chains start breaking up and enable the liquid to flow more freely. If we pour liquid sulfur at about $300\,°C$ into cold water, a rubbery brown solid is formed. Rubbery properties are characteristic of some long-chain molecules, such as natural rubber, and provide evidence for the existence of long chains of atoms in sulfur molecules.

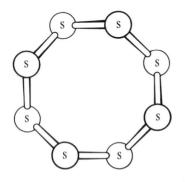

Figure 9.17

The common allotrope of sulfur consists of rings of eight sulfur atoms, S_8.

_Sulfur Dioxide (SO_2)._   Sulfur burns with a blue flame when it is heated strongly in air. The product is sulfur dioxide:

$$S_{(s)} + O_{2\,(g)} \longrightarrow SO_{2\,(g)}$$

Sulfur dioxide is a colourless, poisonous gas with a choking odour. It dissolves in water to produce an acidic solution of sulfurous acid:

$$SO_{2\,(g)} + H_2O_{(\ell)} \rightleftharpoons H_2SO_{3\,(aq)}$$

The reaction of an acid with any sulfite salt produces sulfur dioxide. For example

$$2\,HCl_{(aq)} + Na_2SO_{3\,(aq)} \longrightarrow 2\,NaCl_{(aq)} + H_2O_{(\ell)} + SO_{2\,(g)}$$

Sulfur dioxide is used as a bleaching agent for paper, textiles, and flour, and sometimes, in small amounts, as a food preservative in dried fruits. Its most important use is in the production of sulfur trioxide (SO_3), which, in turn, is used to manufacture sulfuric acid.

Sulfur dioxide is an air pollutant that is produced when sulfur-containing coal or oil is burned. It is also emitted from most pulp mills and is a natural product of volcanic activity. Emissions of sulfur dioxide in combination with coal dust particles can be very irritating to the respiratory system.

Air pollutants are usually dispersed in the upper atmosphere, but a weather condition known as thermal inversion can trap them close to the ground. During a thermal inversion in London, England, in 1952, sulfur dioxide and other air pollutants combined with water droplets to produce the disastrous London smog that contributed to the premature deaths of about 4000 people in a few days.

Sulfur dioxide released into the atmosphere is the major cause of **acid rain**. This rain, in turn, acidifies lakes and rivers and causes widespread damage to the environment. Acid rain is also detrimental to stone. In Italy and Greece, many old statues and other relics are disintegrating because of the effects of acid rain.

Figure 9.18
A London, England, bus in the smog of December 1952. This daytime picture illustrates a smog involving the sulfur dioxide formed by burning sulfur-rich coal and oil.

Hydrogen Sulfide (H_2S). Hydrogen sulfide is a very poisonous, colourless gas with a characteristic smell of rotten eggs. It can be found wherever proteins decompose, and also in some petroleum and natural-gas deposits.

In the laboratory hydrogen sulfide is formed by the reaction of an acid with a sulfide salt:

$$2\,HCl_{(aq)} + Na_2S_{(aq)} \longrightarrow 2\,NaCl_{(aq)} + H_2S_{(g)}$$

Small quantities of hydrogen sulfide are sometimes used in qualitative analysis. The hydrogen sulfide gas is bubbled into a solution of a metal ion. Many ions will react with this gas to form an insoluble sulfide by a double displacement reaction. These sulfides have characteristic colours and properties by which the metal can be identified. For example, a solution containing cadmium ions gives a yellow precipitate that is characteristic of cadmium sulfide:

$$H_2S_{(aq)} + Cd(NO_3)_{2\ (aq)} \longrightarrow CdS_{(s)} + 2\ HNO_{3\ (aq)}$$

QUESTIONS

16. Draw the electron-dot structure for
   a) SO_2 b) SO_3 c) SF_6
   (NOTE: There are more than eight electrons around the central sulfur atom in SF_6).

17. Write a balanced molecular equation for the reaction between each of the following:
   a) sulfur dioxide and oxygen in the presence of heat and a platinum catalyst to give sulfur trioxide
   b) sulfur trioxide and water to give sulfuric acid ($H_2SO_{4\ (aq)}$)
   c) sodium sulfite solution and hydrochloric acid (NOTE: review Section 8.7 if you are unsure of the product.)

18. Classify each of the reactions in Question 17.

Group VIIA (The Halogens)

9.8

This group of nonmetallic elements is referred to as the halogen (salt-forming) elements. The halogens are nonmetals.

will always form 1− anions ? because they are group 7 − need 1 more

TABLE 9.8   *Properties of the Group VIIA Elements*

Element	Phase at 20 °C	Appearance	Classification
Fluorine	Gas	Pale green	Nonmetal
Chlorine	Gas	Pale green	Nonmetal
Bromine	Liquid	Red-brown	Nonmetal
Iodine	Solid	Violet-black	Nonmetal

Both fluorine (F_2) and chlorine (Cl_2) are pale green, poisonous gases. Bromine, a dense red-brown liquid, boils at 58 °C and, even at room temperature, vaporizes readily to produce toxic yellow-brown fumes. Iodine is a violet-black shiny solid that looks almost metallic. A solution of iodine in alcohol is called *tincture of iodine* and is still used as an antiseptic.

The halogens are relatively reactive. Fluorine, in particular, will combine with all known elements except helium, neon, and argon. For example, it combines with metallic zinc to give zinc flouride:

$$Zn_{(s)} + F_{2\ (g)} \longrightarrow ZnF_{2\ (s)}$$

Fluorine is so reactive that even asbestos burns in an atmosphere of fluorine gas, and a stream of fluorine flowing onto the surface of water causes the water to burn:

$$2\ F_{2\ (g)} + 2\ H_2O_{(\ell)} \longrightarrow 4\ HF_{(aq)} + O_{2\ (g)}$$

It is interesting to note that, if we omit the noble gases, the groups at the extreme ends of the Periodic Table (the alkali metals on the left and the halogens on the right) are the two most reactive groups of elements. One difference between them is that the reactivity of the alkali metals increases down the group (i.e., as the elements become more electropositive), whereas the reactivity of the halogens increases up the group (i.e., as the elements become more electronegative).

Chlorine (Cl₂)

Chlorine liquifies at −35 °C and solidifies at −101 °C. It is a very toxic gas and was used as a chemical warfare agent during World War I. Chlorine is used in very low concentrations to kill bacteria in water to make the water safe for drinking. It also has numerous applications in the manufacture of dyes, textiles, pharmaceuticals, insecticides, plastics, bleaching solutions, and organic solvents such as chloroform and carbon tetrachloride.

We can prepare chlorine in the laboratory by reacting hydrochloric acid with manganese(IV) chloride:

$$MnO_{2\ (s)} + 4\ HCl_{(aq)} \longrightarrow MnCl_{2\ (aq)} + Cl_{2\ (g)} + 2\ H_2O_{(\ell)}$$

In this reaction, two chloride ions are oxidized to chlorine gas and the manganese is reduced. The apparatus used in this preparation is shown in Figure 9.19. Some manganese(IV) oxide is placed in the flask. Hydrochloric acid is added through a dropping funnel and the mixture is gently heated. The green chlorine gas can be collected in an open Erlenmeyer flask, as it is about two-and-a-half times as dense as air.

Chlorine reacts with most other elements, including metals and non-metals. For example, chlorine reacts with hydrogen, sodium, and phosphorus as follows:

$$H_{2\ (g)} + Cl_{2\ (g)} \longrightarrow 2\ HCl_{(g)}$$
$$2\ Na_{(s)} + Cl_{2\ (g)} \longrightarrow 2\ NaCl_{(s)}$$
$$P_{4\ (s)} + 10\ Cl_{2\ (g)} \longrightarrow 4\ PCl_{5\ (s)}$$

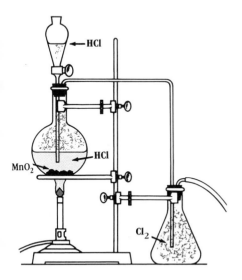

Figure 9.19
The laboratory preparation of chlorine gas from hydrogen chloride and manganese(IV) oxide.

As we have seen previously, chlorine will displace the bromide or iodide ion:

$$Cl_{2\,(g)} + 2\,Br^-_{\,(aq)} \longrightarrow 2\,Cl^-_{\,(aq)} + Br_{2\,(aq)}$$

$$Cl_{2\,(g)} + 2\,I^-_{\,(aq)} \longrightarrow 2\,Cl^-_{\,(aq)} + I_{2\,(aq)}$$

The reaction with the bromide ion is used in the industrial extraction of bromine from seawater. Both of the above reactions are used in the qualitative analysis of anions.

Hydrogen Chloride (HCl). Hydrogen chloride is a colourless gas with a very sharp odour. It is an acidic gas (turns blue litmus paper red) that dissolves in water to form hydrochloric acid:

$$HCl_{(g)} \xrightarrow[\text{in water}]{\text{dissolve}} H^+_{\,(aq)} + Cl^-_{\,(aq)}$$

Hydrogen chloride gas combines with ammonia gas to form a white smoke, ammonium chloride:

$$NH_{3\,(g)} + HCl_{(g)} \rightleftharpoons NH_4Cl_{(s)}$$

Ammonium chloride, produced by the reaction of hydrogen chloride and ammonia that has leaked from bottles, sometimes covers laboratory glassware with a white film.

QUESTIONS

19. Which of the halogens
   a) is most reactive
   b) is a liquid at room temperature
   c) has the highest electronegativity

20. Draw the electron-dot structure for
   a) ClO_4^-　　b) NaCl　　c) PCl_5

21. Write a balanced equation for the reaction between
   a) liquid bromine and a solution of iodide ion
   b) chlorine gas and magnesium metal

Group 0 (Group VIIIA, The Noble Gases)

9.9

Until 1894 the existence of the noble gases was not even suspected. Yet between 1894 and 1898, the English chemist Sir William Ramsay discovered argon, helium, neon, krypton, and xenon. All these elements, except helium, were isolated from air, in which they are found in small concentrations.

Element	Phase at 20 °C	Appearance	Classification	
Helium	Gas	Colourless	Nonmetal	1% of Atmosphere.
Neon	Gas	Colourless	Nonmetal	
Argon	Gas	Colourless	Nonmetal	
Krypton	Gas	Colourless	Nonmetal	
Xenon	Gas	Colourless	Nonmetal	

TABLE 9.9 *Properties of the Group O (Group VIIIA) Elements*

Figure 9.20
Crystals of the noble gas compound, xenon tetrafluoride, XeF₄.

Sandy

D. Alexander

Figure 9.21
A Canadian company is developing a revolutionary new airship. This airship has particular potential in forestry and in oil exploration.

The existence of helium was first suggested by studies of the spectrum of the light emitted by the sun (Section 3.11). As researchers thought helium was a metal, they took the Greek word for the sun, *helios*, and used the ending chosen for metals, *-ium*, when selecting its name. The name helium was retained even after the element was found to be a gaseous nonmetal. Helium is found mixed with methane in most deposits of natural gas.

As each of the noble gases has a completely filled valence shell, chemists virtually ignored them for years, reasoning that nothing could be learned from studying them. Until 1962 the gases were known as the "inert gases" because few people believed that they could undergo chemical reactions. However, the chemical world was startled in 1962 by the work of Neil Bartlett, a chemist at the University of British Columbia.

By a simple chemical reaction, Bartlett prepared a compound containing xenon. Since then a significant number of xenon compounds have been produced, including xenon tetrafluoride (XeF_4), xenon hexafluoride (XeF_6), xenon trioxide (XeO_3), and xenon tetraoxide (XeO_4). Xenon tetrafluoride can be prepared easily by combining xenon and fluorine in the presence of a nickel catalyst:

$$Xe_{(g)} + 2\ F_{2\ (g)} \xrightarrow[400°C]{Ni} XeF_{4\ (s)}$$

Since 1962, some krypton and radon compounds have also been synthesized.

Helium (He)

Of the noble gases, helium has the most uses, partly because it undergoes no known chemical reactions. Helium has the lowest boiling point of any known substance (-268.9 °C) and is therefore used as the cooling agent when extremely low temperatures are necessary. The only gas with a lower density than helium is hydrogen. Hydrogen, however, is very reactive, whereas helium can be regarded as chemically inert. A Canadian, Sir John McLennan, first realized that its low density and lack of chemical reactivity would make helium an ideal gas for use in balloons and other lighter-than-air craft. This is still one of its major uses. Another use is in underwater

Bartlett and the Noble Gas Compounds

Neil Bartlett was born in Newcastle-upon-Tyne, England, in 1932. After completing his Ph.D. in England, he accepted a position at the University of British Columbia (UBC) in Vancouver. He set his first research student to the task of identifying a strange compound that Bartlett had accidentally prepared during his thesis work. The compound proved to be O_2PtF_6, which is composed of O_2^+ and PtF_6^- ions. The interesting thing about this compound was that platinum(VI) fluoride, PtF_6, had an electron affinity high enough to remove an electron from an oxygen molecule.

While preparing to teach a class of second-year university students, Bartlett happened to glance down a list of first ionization energies. He noticed that almost the same amount of energy was required to remove an electron from radon or xenon atoms as was required to remove an electron from oxygen molecules. As the radioactive gas, radon, was unavailable at UBC, Bartlett asked his colleagues if any of them had some xenon gas. He was greeted by laughter when he told them that he proposed to form a chemical compound with xenon, because everyone *knew* that the element was completely inert.

Bartlett, however, managed to obtain some xenon gas, and on 23 March 1962 was ready to try to prepare a xenon compound. He later remarked:

> "It had taken the entire day to get everything set up and I wasn't ready to break the glass capillary separating the xenon and PtF_6 until about 6:45 p.m. My students had left for supper (they never admitted to scepticism) and I was alone when the capillary was broken. Of course, I was overjoyed when there was an immediate interaction of the gases. Everything had gone as predicted."

When the two gases mixed, a yellow-orange crystalline solid rapidly formed. Bartlett concluded that the reaction had occurred according to the equation

$$Xe_{(g)} + PtF_{6(g)} \longrightarrow XePtF_{6(s)}$$

As soon as the result of Bartlett's experiment was published, other research groups rushed into this completely new field of xenon chemistry. Within two months, groups at the Argonne Laboratory in the U.S., and at the University of Münster in West Germany had prepared other new compounds of xenon. Since then, many books have been written on the chemistry of the noble gases.

The key to Bartlett's success was that he, like Dr. Plunkett who discovered Teflon, was interested in finding explanations for unexpected reactions and he was not afraid to challenge existing ideas about chemistry.

Figure 9.22 *Neil Bartlett (1932–   ).*

work, where a mixture of 80% helium and 20% oxygen is used as an artificial atmosphere for divers and others working in deep water under high pressures. One interesting side-effect of breathing helium–oxygen mixtures is that a person's voice begins to resemble that of Donald Duck!

QUESTIONS

22. Draw the electron-dot structure of
   a) XeO_3 b) XeO_4 c) XeF_4

23. Which of the noble gases
   a) has the lowest boiling point of any substance?
   b) is the only one which forms a large number of chemical compounds?
   c) has the lowest ionization energy?
   d) is a major component of the sun?

Hydrogen   9.10

_– has I valence electron so it can lose it to become I+ cation like group 1 A
Here it is resp. for acids._

Hydrogen represents more than 90% of the atoms in the universe and roughly 75% of the mass. Most of the hydrogen gas originally present in the earth's atmosphere escaped into space a long time ago.

    Hydrogen is a colourless, odourless, tasteless gas that liquifies at $-252\,°C$ and solidifies at $-259\,°C$. It occurs mainly in combination with oxygen (in water), with carbon (in petroleum or natural gas), and with both carbon and oxygen (in living matter).

    We can prepare hydrogen in the laboratory by adding an acid to any metal that is above hydrogen in the activity series. For example

$$2\ HCl_{(aq)}\ +\ Zn_{(s)}\ \longrightarrow\ ZnCl_{2\ (aq)}\ +\ H_{2\ (g)}$$

An alternative method is to pass an electric current through water to which an electrolyte such as sodium hydroxide has been added (Figure 9.23):

$$2\ H_2O_{(\ell)}\ \xrightarrow[\text{current}]{\text{electric}}\ 2\ H_{2\ (g)}\ +\ O_{2\ (g)}$$

    When a mixture of hydrogen and oxygen is ignited, there is an explosive reaction. The formula can be represented as

$$2\ H_{2\ (g)}\ +\ O_{2\ (g)}\ \longrightarrow\ 2\ H_2O_{(\ell)}$$

Thus, if a lighted splint is placed at the mouth of a small test tube containing hydrogen gas, a loud "pop" will occur. This is the standard test for the presence of hydrogen gas. The destruction of the Zeppelin _Hindenburg_ in 1937 was a result of the explosive reaction of hydrogen with oxygen. Because of the danger associated with using hydrogen, helium, which is an inert gas, is used in modern airships.

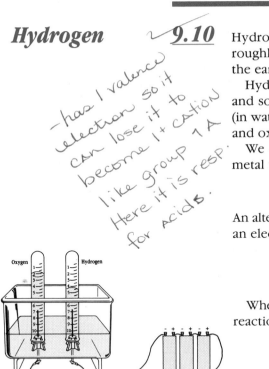

Figure 9.23
An electric current can be used to decompose water into hydrogen and oxygen.

Hydrogen shares some of the properties of the elements in both Group IA and VIIA. Like the alkali metals, hydrogen will combine directly with any halogen:

$$H_{2\,(g)} + Cl_{2\,(g)} \longrightarrow 2\,HCl_{(g)}$$

$$2\,Na_{(s)} + Cl_{2\,(g)} \longrightarrow 2\,NaCl_{(s)}$$

On this basis it could be argued that hydrogen belongs in Group IA; however, the products formed in these reactions are very different:

1. Hydrogen chloride is a colourless choking gas, whereas sodium chloride is a harmless white solid;
2. In hydrogen chloride the bonding is predominantly covalent, but in sodium chloride the bonding is ionic;
3. Hydrogen chloride dissolves in water to give an acidic solution, whereas an aqueous solution of sodium chloride is neutral.

When behaving like a halogen, hydrogen can accept one electron to form an anion (H^-). Thus, sodium hydride is formed by heating sodium metal in hydrogen gas:

$$2\,Na_{(s)} + H_{2\,(g)} \longrightarrow 2\,NaH_{(s)}$$

This reaction is analogous to the reaction between sodium metal and chlorine gas. However, there is an important difference in the properties of the products formed in these reactions. When sodium chloride dissolves in water, a solution containing Na^+ and Cl^- ions is formed; but if water is added to sodium hydride, an exothermic reaction takes place and hydrogen gas is produced:

$$NaH_{(s)} + H_2O_{(\ell)} \longrightarrow NaOH_{(aq)} + H_{2\,(g)}$$

Since hydrogen shares the properties of elements in Group IA and VIIA, it is difficult to assign it to either one. Placing it in a group by itself allows us to recognize its unique properties.

QUESTIONS

24. Write a balanced molecular equation for the reaction between
    a) sulfuric acid ($H_2SO_{4\,(aq)}$) and aluminum metal
    b) hydrogen gas and fluorine gas

25. Write the formula of the compound formed between hydrogen and
    a) nitrogen   b) sulfur   c) calcium

Figure 9.24
The Hindenburg burning at Lakehurst, New Jersey, in 1937. Early airships used hydrogen because it is the gas with the lowest density. Unfortunately, only a spark was needed to cause the spectacular and tragic reaction between the hydrogen gas in the airship and the oxygen gas in the atmosphere.

The Transition Metals

9.11

The transition metals are located in the centre of the Periodic Table (Figure 9.25) and belong to Groups IB through VIIIB. Some of the transition metals we have mentioned include iron, copper, silver, zinc, and mercury. The oxyanions of two others, chromium (chromate, dichromate) and manganese (permanganate), were discussed in Section 6.4. We will only discuss a few of the transition metals here. Many of them have only minor and specialized uses, but a few are very important.

Several of the transition metals play a vital role in modern technology, especially for military purposes. In this category are cobalt (used in magnets and jet aircraft engines), manganese (a component of steel), chromium (used in stainless steel and ball bearings), and titanium (used in submarine and aircraft bodies). A serious concern is that North America relies on imports of these strategic metals from countries that might decide to terminate supplies. Of the total world production of these elements, over 40% of the cobalt comes from Zaïre in Africa, over 40% of the manganese and over 50% of the titanium comes from the Soviet Union, and about one-third of the chromium is produced by South Africa. Exploration for these elements is therefore being conducted in North America, as is research to find more readily available substitutes.

IIIB	IVB	VB	VIB	VIIB	VIIIB			IB	IIB
Sc Scandium	**Ti** Titanium	**V** Vanadium	**Cr** Chromium	**Mn** Manganese	**Fe** Iron	**Co** Cobalt	**Ni** Nickel	**Cu** Copper	**Zn** Zinc
Y Yttrium	**Zr** Zirconium	**Nb** Niobium	**Mo** Molybdenum	**Tc** Technetium	**Ru** Ruthenium	**Rh** Rhodium	**Pd** Palladium	**Ag** Silver	**Cd** Cadmium
La Lanthanum	**Hf** Hafnium	**Ta** Tantalum	**W** Tungsten	**Re** Rhenium	**Os** Osmium	**Ir** Iridium	**Pt** Platinum	**Au** Gold	**Hg** Mercury
Ac Actinium									

SANDY

Figure 9.25
The transition metals.

Iron

Iron plays a vital role in our civilization, despite the fact that its major disadvantage is that it rusts easily. Whereas the oxide coating on aluminum is strong and impermeable, the oxide that forms on iron (known as rust) is powdery and permeable. This means that it allows water and oxygen to pass through and attack the metal underneath.

Iron has assumed its important role for a number of reasons. Iron ore, usually in the form of Fe_2O_3, is abundant and is easily and cheaply converted to the pure metal by a process that uses heat and two inexpensive materials: coke (impure carbon from coal) and limestone.

Another advantage that iron has over many other metals is that it melts at a comparatively low temperature (1540 °C) and can thus be poured into

Figure 9.26

The tungsten filament of an electric light bulb. As we require the filament to become very hot without melting, we need a metal with a very high melting point. Tungsten, with a melting point of 3380 °C, is the most suitable metal for this purpose.

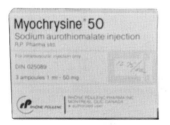

Figure 9.27

Two important pharmaceuticals containing rare transition metals: a) Myochrysine 50, a gold compound used in the treatment of arthritis, b) Platinol, a platinum compound used in cancer chemotherapy.

molds (e.g. for engine castings). It is easily drawn into wires or pressed into sheets. The properties of iron can be altered to make it more suitable for a specific use by adding small amounts of other elements to produce an alloy. Steel, for example, is a mixture of iron and 0.1 to 1.5% carbon and other elements. This gives it qualities superior to those of iron, including increased hardness and toughness.

Some metals might appear to be more useful than iron. For example, tungsten is harder than iron and corrodes less easily. Like many of the transition metals however, ores of tungsten are rare, and tungsten has the disadvantage of melting at a very high temperature (3380 °C).

Gold

Gold has been the most valued and most sought after element in many civilizations. From King Midas to the Yukon miners, people have lusted for gold. Even today, the wealth of a nation is often judged by the amount of gold it has in its vaults. One attraction of gold is its resistance to corrosion. Gold does not react with air, nor with most acids or bases. By referring to the activity series (Section 8.6) you will see that gold is the least reactive of all the metals.

Copper

Copper has a distinctive red colour. It is one of the easiest elements to obtain from its ores and, as with iron, these ores are abundant. Bronze, a copper-containing alloy, was used for making tools long before a process for smelting iron was found.

Copper is usually found in compounds as the copper(II) ion, but the copper(I) ion is also known.

Mercury

The shiny metal globules of liquid mercury held a fascination for medieval alchemists. Today we are concerned with its poisonous vapour and compounds. In compounds, mercury is found as the mercury(I) or mercury(II) ion. The mercury(I) ion is unusual in that it exists as Hg_2^{2+} rather than as Hg^+ (Section 6.2).

QUESTIONS

26. Write the chemical formulas of
    a) the two compounds formed between iron and chlorine
    b) the two compounds formed between mercury and chlorine
    c) the two compounds formed between copper and oxygen

27. Calculate the oxidation number of manganese in the permanganate ion, MnO_4^-.

Mercury — A Hazardous Element

At present there are about 3000 uses for mercury, either as the element or as one of its many compounds. We use mercury in dental fillings (where it has been shown to be quite safe) and in thermometers. Compounds of mercury are used to kill bacteria and fungi in the pulp and paper industry, in agriculture, and in the paint and wallpaper industry.

The metal itself is a health hazard because liquid mercury slowly evaporates. The mercury vapour is absorbed by the lungs and passes into the bloodstream and then into the brain, causing serious damage to the central nervous system. A major problem has been the loss of mercury from broken mercury thermometers. In Canada, up to ten tonnes of mercury is "lost" in this way every year. To reduce this hazard, alcohol-filled thermometers are being increasingly favoured, particularly for school use. Where mercury thermometers have to be used, special mercury sponges are now available to collect the droplets of spilled mercury. It is also possible to obtain mercury thermometers with a Teflon coating. With these, even if the glass is broken, the Teflon shell prevents the mercury from escaping.

Compounds of mercury are also poisonous. Many workers in the felt hat industry, in which mercury salt solutions were used, suffered from mercury poisoning. Symptoms include trembling and mental disorders. The mercury poisoning of hat makers is the source of the "Mad Hatter" in the book *Alice's Adventures in Wonderland*, and of the phrase "mad as a hatter."

Many health hazards are caused by the compounds formed by mercury and carbon, in particular, methyl mercury, CH_3Hg, and dimethylmercury, $(CH_3)_2Hg$. These compounds cause numbness, paralysis, deformity, and death. These symptoms were first seen in communities around Minamata Bay in Japan, where a local chemical company was pumping mercury wastes into the bay. At the time, nobody realized that the wastes were being converted by marine organisms into the deadly methyl mercury. The inhabitants of the area mainly ate seafood, and after a while they started to have severe health problems. After the origin of the illnesses (now called Minamata disease) was diagnosed, warnings were issued about the hazards related to mercury wastes.

In Canada, a study of the mercury content of fish showed that we, too, had a significant mercury pollution problem. Contaminated fish were found in Lake St. Clair and the English-Wabigoon river system in Ontario, in the South Saskatchewan river, and in many other locations. The Canadian native peoples were affected by the subsequent bans on fishing because they relied heavily on fish as a food and as a source of income. Health and Welfare Canada found unacceptable levels of mercury in people from Northwestern Ontario, Northwestern Quebec, and the Northwest Territories.

It is extremely difficult to remove the mercury that has entered the environment. However, the federal and provincial governments have passed legislation that limits the release of mercury into the environment and bans the use of mercury in agriculture or in paints used for children's toys. As a result, Environment Canada estimates that between 1970 and 1977, the release of mercury diminished to 0.5% of its previous level.

Figure 9.28
The poisoning of hat makers provided the idea for the Mad Hatter.

Figure 9.29
Mercury(II) iodide. HgI_2, is used in some soaps sold in Africa. This compound causes a lightening of skin colour. Like most compounds of mercury, it is poisonous, and those who use it are unknowingly facing health hazards.

The Lanthanons

9.12

The lanthanons are sometimes referred to as the rare earths, although they are not particularly rare. They all form +3 ions and occur together in the same ores. The transition elements scandium, yttrium, and lanthanum are also found in the same ores, and as the chemistry of these three elements closely resembles that of the lanthanons, they are often regarded as lanthanons. Minerals of these elements were first found near the small Swedish town of Ytterby, after which the elements yttrium, ytterbium, erbium, and terbium are named.

None of the 14 lanthanons is essential for plant or animal growth and very few people have ever heard of them. They do not have any large-scale uses, but they do play important roles in very specialized materials.

Figure 9.30
The Lanthanons.

Ce	Pr	Nd	Pm	Sm	Eu	Gd	Tb	Dy	Ho	Er	Tm	Yb	Lu
Cerium	Praseodymium	Neodymium	Promethium	Samarium	Europium	Gadolinium	Terbium	Dysprosium	Holmium	Erbium	Thulium	Ytterbium	Lutetium

The Actinons

9.13

As we saw in Section 4.3, the elements beyond bismuth (atomic number 83) in the Periodic table are unstable. Elements 90 through 103 constitute a series known as the actinons (or actinides).

Thorium and uranium, which were discovered early in the 19th century, are the only two actinons found in nature. These were the only known members of the series until 1940, when the alchemists' dream of synthesizing new elements came true. Teams of nuclear physicists and chemists, were responsible for the breakthrough. The greatest contribution to this field was made by Glenn T. Seaborg of the University of California at Berkeley.

Isotopes of uranium are used in nuclear power generation, and plutonium is mainly used in nuclear weapons. Most smoke detectors use small amounts of americium.

Figure 9.31
The Actinons.

Th	Pa	U	Np	Pu	Am	Cm	Bk	Cf	Es	Fm	Md	No	Lr
Thorium	Protractinium	Uranium	Neptunium	Plutonium	Americium	Curium	Berkelium	Californium	Einsteinium	Fermium	Mendelevium	Nobelium	Lawrencium

Summary

- The Group IA metals are highly reactive and their reactivity increases as we move down the group.

- Alkaline earth metals are all harder and denser than the alkali metals and have much higher melting points. They are not as reactive as the alkali metals.

- The most important Group IIIA element is aluminum. It is a reactive metal, but generally has a thin protective oxide layer which prevents attack by air or water.

- Group IVA elements range from nonmetallic (carbon), through semimetallic (silicon and germanium), to metallic (tin and lead). Carbon has two allotropes, diamond and graphite. Because of its ability to form long-chain molecules (catenation), carbon forms more compounds than any other element apart from hydrogen. Two important compounds of carbon are carbon dioxide and carbon monoxide.

- The Group V elements change from nonmetallic at the top of the group to metallic at the bottom of the group. The nonmetals form covalent compounds and the metals form ionic compounds. Nitrogen is the major component of air (78%) and is very unreactive. Important compounds of nitrogen are ammonia, nitrogen dioxide, and dinitrogen oxide. Phosphorus has two common allotropes: red phosphorus, which is stable in air, and yellow phosphorus (white phosphorus) which must be stored under water because it catches fire in air.

- The two important elements in Group VIA (oxygen and sulfur) are both nonmetals. Oxygen is the most common element on the surface of the earth. Oxygen has two allotropes, dioxygen and trioxygen (ozone). Important compounds of sulfur are sulfur dioxide, sulfuric acid, and hydrogen sulfide.

- The halogens are all nonmetals and are very reactive. Their reactivity decreases as we move down the group.

- The noble gases are relatively unreactive and do not form compounds easily.

- Hydrogen is grouped by itself because of its unique properties. It is the most common element in the universe, but not on the earth.

- The transition metals are located in the centre of the Periodic Table and belong to Groups IB through VIIIB. Many of the transition elements are important in the formation of alloys used in the manufacturing industry.

- The lanthanons, consisting of elements 58 to 71, do not have any large-scale uses.

- The actinons are the elements 89 to 103. The nuclei of these elements are all unstable. Only thorium and uranium occur in nature; the others are artificially produced.

KEY WORDS   acid rain
allotrope
catenation

1. a) LiI   b) Li_2O

2. a) $2 K_{(s)} + Br_{2 (g)} \longrightarrow 2 KBr_{(s)}$

b) $2 Rb_{(s)} + 2 H_2O_{(\ell)} \longrightarrow 2 RbOH_{(aq)} + H_{2 (g)}$

3. a) lithium   b) lithium   c) cesium   d) cesium

4. a) $CaCl_2$ b) CaO

5. a) $Ca_{(s)} + 2 H_2O(\ell) \longrightarrow Ca(OH)_{2 (aq)} + H_{2 (g)}$

b) $2 Ba_{(s)} + O_{2 (g)} \longrightarrow 2 BaO_{(s)}$

c) $BaO_{(s)} + H_2O_{(\ell)} \longrightarrow Ba(OH)_{2 (aq)}$

6. a) barium   b) beryllium   c) calcium

7. Al_2S_3

8. a) boron   b) thallium

9. a) $:\ddot{C}l:$ b) $[Al]^{3+} \, 3[:\ddot{C}l:]^{-}$

$\ddot{C}l\!:\! \overset{\textstyle ..}{\underset{\textstyle B}{}} \!:\!\ddot{C}l$

10. a) CF_4 b) CS_2

11. a) $C_3H_{8 (g)} + 5 O_{2 (g)} \longrightarrow 3 CO_{2 (g)} + 4 H_2O_{(g)}$

b) $H_2SO_{4 (aq)} + Na_2CO_{3 (aq)} \longrightarrow Na_2SO_{4 (aq)} + CO_{2 (g)} + H_2O(\ell)$

12. a) $\begin{array}{c} H \\ H\!:\!\ddot{C}\!:\!H \\ H \end{array}$ b) $\ddot{O}\!:\!:\!C\!:\!:\!\ddot{O}$

13. a) $3 NH_{3 (g)} + H_3PO_{4 (aq)} \longrightarrow (NH_4)_3PO_{4 (s)}$

b) $6 Li_{(s)} + N_{2 (g)} \longrightarrow 2 Li_3N_{(s)}$

14. a) $:N\!:\!:\!:N:$ b) $\begin{array}{c} H\!:\!\ddot{N}\!:\!H \\ H \end{array}$

15. a) PCl_3, PCl_5 b) Na_3P

16. a) $\ddot{O}\!:\!:\!\ddot{S}\!:\!\ddot{O}:$ b) $\begin{array}{c}\ddot{O}\!:\!:\!\ddot{S}\!:\!\ddot{O}: \\ :\ddot{O}:\end{array}$ c) $\begin{array}{ccc} & :\ddot{F}: & \\ :\ddot{F}: & & :\ddot{F}: \\ & S & \\ :\ddot{F}: & & :\ddot{F}: \\ & :\ddot{F}: & \end{array}$

17. a) $2 SO_{2 (g)} + O_{2 (g)} \xrightarrow[Pt]{\Delta} 2 SO_{3 (g)}$

b) $SO_{3 (g)} + H_2O_{(\ell)} \longrightarrow H_2SO_{4 (aq)}$

c) $Na_2SO_{3 (aq)} + 2 HCl_{(aq)} \longrightarrow 2 NaCl_{(aq)} + H_2O_{(\ell)} + SO_{2 (g)}$

18. a) combination   b) combination   c) double displacement

19. a) fluorine   b) bromine   c) fluorine

20. a) $\left[\begin{array}{c} :\ddot{O}: \\ :\ddot{O}:\ddot{C}l:\ddot{O}: \\ :\ddot{O}: \end{array} \right]^{-}$ b) $[Na]^{+} [:\ddot{C}l:]^{-}$ c) $\begin{array}{ccc} & :\ddot{C}l: & \\ :\ddot{C}l: & P & :\ddot{C}l: \\ :\ddot{C}l: & & :\ddot{C}l: \end{array}$

21. a) $Br_{2\,(\ell)} + 2\,I^-_{(aq)} \longrightarrow 2\,Br^-_{(aq)} + I_{2\,(aq)}$

b) $Mg_{(s)} + Cl_{2\,(g)} \longrightarrow MgCl_{2\,(s)}$

22. a) $\ddot{O}::\ddot{Xe}::\ddot{O}$
$:\ddot{O}:$

b) $:\ddot{O}:$
$\ddot{O}::\ddot{Xe}::\ddot{O}$
$:\ddot{O}:$

c) $:\ddot{F}::\ddot{F}:$
Xe
$:\ddot{F}::\ddot{F}:$

23. a) helium   b) xenon   c) xenon   d) helium

24. a) $2\,Al_{(s)} + 3\,H_2SO_{4\,(aq)} \longrightarrow Al_2(SO_4)_{3\,(aq)} + 3\,H_{2\,(g)}$

b) $H_{2\,(g)} + F_{2\,(g)} \longrightarrow 2\,HF_{(g)}$

25. a) NH_3 b) H_2S c) CaH_2

26. a) $FeCl_2$, $FeCl_3$ b) Hg_2Cl_2, $HgCl_2$ c) Cu_2O, CuO

27. $+7$

COMPREHENSION QUESTIONS

1. Give the common name used to refer to the elements
   a) in Group IA   e) in Groups IIIB to VIIIB
   b) in Group IIA   f) numbered 58 to 71
   c) in Group VIIA   g) numbered 90 to 103
   d) in Group 0

2. How does the reactivity of the elements change in going down each of the following groups:
   a) the alkali metals   b) the halogens   c) the noble gases

3. What colours do the alkali metals produce when heated in a flame?

4. Identify each of the following elements:
   a) the only metal that is a liquid at 20 °C
   b) the least dense alkali metal
   c) the only semimetal in Group IIIA
   d) the only nonmetal that is a liquid at 20 °C
   e) the element with an allotrope that must be stored under water
   f) the nonmetallic element with an allotrope that conducts electricity

5. What is the charge on the ions formed by
   a) the alkali metals   b) the alkaline earth metals   c) the lanthanons

6. What are the products of the reaction between an alkali metal or an alkaline earth metal and water?

7. Although aluminum is a reactive metal, it is used extensively in manufacturing. Why?

8. What is meant by the term allotrope?

9. Compare the properties of the two common allotropes of carbon. What is the reason for the differences?

10. In what way(s) do the two common allotropes of phosphorus differ?

11. Compare the properties of the two allotropes of oxygen.

12. Which groups in the Periodic Table contain semimetals?

13. What is meant by the term catenation? Which element readily undergoes catenation?

14. What is the standard test for
    a) hydrogen   b) oxygen   c) carbon dioxide

---

15. Why are the elements from Groups IA and VIIA never found in pure form in nature?

16. Magnesium is currently being used in parts of car engines and wheels. Why is this a problem for firefighters involved in putting out car fires?

17. Explain why the reactivity of the alkali metals increases down the group whereas the reactivity of the halogens increases up the group.

18. Give examples of properties of hydrogen that
    a) are similar to those of the Group IA metals
    b) are similar to those of the Group VIIA nonmetals
    c) make hydrogen a unique element

19. Compare the physical and chemical properties of sodium and phosphorus.

20. Compare the physical and chemical properties of mercury and bromine.

21. Elements A, B, C, D, and E all belong to the same period in the Periodic Table. Element B is a nonmetal that combines with A to form a colourless gas, BA_2, which turns limewater milky. Element E is a colourless gas that forms a brown toxic gas, EA_2, which in turn produces an acidic solution when dissolved in water. Element C is a reactive metal that reacts with E to form the compound C_3E. Element D is an unreactive monatomic gas. Identify elements A, B, C, D, and E giving reasons for your choice.

22. Elements M, N, O, P, and Q are all in the same period in the Periodic Table. Element N has the highest ionization energy of the five elements and Q has the lowest. Element P is a pale green gas that reacts with Q to form the ionic solid QP_2. Element M, which is usually stored under water, reacts violently with an excess of P to form a covalent compound MP_5. The ionic compound QO is formed by reacting together the elements Q and O. Identify the elements M, N, O, P, and Q, giving reasons for your choices.

23. Predict the formula for the compound formed by each of the following pairs of elements and indicate whether each compound is predominantly ionic or covalent.
    a) beryllium and oxygen   d) tellurium and iodine
    b) indium and iodine   e) silicon and fluorine
    c) cerium and oxygen

24. Predict the formula of the compound formed between the following pairs of elements and indicate whether the bonding is predominantly ionic or covalent.
    a) boron and fluorine   d) barium and hydrogen
    b) terbium and chlorine   e) thallium and iodine
    c) sodium and astatine

25. Draw the electron-dot structure for each of the following:
    a) SiH_4 b) N_2O (hint: nitrogen is the central atom)   c) NH_2^-

26. Draw the electron-dot structure for each of the following:
    a) NOF (hint: nitrogen is the central atom)   b) CaO   c) XeF_2

27. Write a balanced equation for the reaction that occurs between each of the following:
    a) cesium metal and water   d) carbon and oxygen (two
    b) strontium oxide and water   reactions)
    c) potassium metal and iodine   e) butane, C_4H_{10}, and oxygen

28. Write a balanced equation for the reaction that occurs between
    a) calcium metal and fluorine   c) sulfur and oxygen
    b) magnesium oxide and water   d) calcium metal and oxygen

---

SUGGESTED PROJECTS

1. Prepare a paper on one of the essential trace elements. Indicate how it is used in the body, the major sources of the element in our diet, and what can happen to us if our supply is not sufficient.

2. A mixture of helium and oxygen, rather than nitrogen and oxygen, is used for deep-sea divers. Find out why and report to the class.

3. Dinitrogen oxide is only one of a number of chemicals that can be used as an anesthetic. Use reference books to find out what other compounds are used for this purpose. Prepare a report on these chemicals.

Mole Calculations in Chemical Reactions

In Chapter 7 we discussed the mole concept in depth, and in Chapter 8 we introduced you to the principles of chemical reactions. We will now see how to apply mole calculations so that the quantities of chemicals used and produced in chemical reactions can be determined. This important branch of chemistry is called **stoichiometry** (pronounced stoy-key-om-eh-tree).

The Law of Conservation of Mass

10.1

Suppose we conduct an experiment to see if there is any reaction between aqueous barium chloride and aqueous potassium sulfate. First we measure out approximately equal volumes (say 50.0 mL) of these two solutions into two 100 mL beakers. Next we place both beakers on the pan of a balance and determine the total mass of the beakers and their contents. If we then pour the contents of one beaker into the second beaker and mix the two solutions, a chemical reaction takes place and a precipitate forms:

$$BaCl_{2\,(aq)} + K_2SO_{4\,(aq)} \longrightarrow BaSO_{4\,(s)} + 2\,KCl_{(aq)}$$

If we again place both beakers on the balance pan we find that the total mass of the two beakers (one empty and one containing the reaction mixture) has not changed! This is an illustration of the **Law of Conservation of Mass**, which states that

> **In any chemical reaction there is no detectable difference between the total mass of the reactants and the total mass of the products.**

The Law of Conservation of Mass was discovered in the late 18th century by the French chemist, Antoine Lavoisier.

EXAMPLE 10.1

When mercury(II) oxide is heated, it decomposes into mercury metal and oxygen gas, according to the following equation:

$$2 \, HgO_{(s)} \xrightarrow{\Delta} 2 \, Hg_{(\ell)} + O_{2 \, (g)}$$

In a simple experiment it was found that when 1.000 g of mercury(II) oxide decomposed, 0.926 g of mercury remained. Calculate the mass of oxygen that must have been released.

SOLUTION

According to the Law of Conservation of Mass, the mass of the products must equal the mass of the reactants. Thus

$$
\begin{aligned}
\text{Mass of mercury(II) oxide} &= \text{Mass of mercury} + \text{Mass of oxygen gas} \\
1.000 \, g &= 0.926 \, g + \text{Mass of oxygen gas} \\
\text{Mass of oxygen gas} &= 1.000 \, g - 0.926 \, g \\
&= 0.074 \, g
\end{aligned}
$$

Figure 10.1
An experiment to demonstrate the Law of Conservation of Mass. A candle is burned in a sealed flask of oxygen gas. When combustion stops, the mass of the flask and contents is unchanged.

QUESTIONS

1. Limestone (calcium carbonate) can be decomposed into calcium oxide and carbon dioxide by heating it to a temperature of 800 °C. The reaction is

$$CaCO_{3 \, (s)} \xrightarrow{\Delta} CaO_{(s)} + CO_{2 \, (g)}$$

In an experiment, a 0.500 g sample of calcium carbonate was heated and 0.280 g of calcium oxide was produced. What mass of carbon dioxide would also have been formed?

2. Ethanol burns in oxygen to give carbon dioxide and water vapour. The reaction is

$$C_2H_6O_{(\ell)} + 3\,O_{2\,(g)} \longrightarrow 2\,CO_{2\,(g)} + 3\,H_2O_{(g)}$$

If 96 g of oxygen is sufficient to support the combustion of 46 g of ethanol, and the reaction produces 88 g of carbon dioxide, what mass of water will also be produced?

Lavoisier, The Founder of Modern Chemistry

Antoine-Laurent de Lavoisier was born in Paris, France in 1743. Lavoisier started his chemical studies at a time when it was thought that the process of burning metals involved the loss of a substance called phlogiston. Because metals gain weight when they burn, it was reasoned that phlogiston had to have a negative mass.

After years of careful experimentation, Lavoisier showed that the phlogiston theory was totally wrong. In 1786 he published a devastating attack on the theory. This attack marked the end of alchemy and the beginning of modern chemistry. For this work alone, Lavoisier should be remembered as one of the most important chemists of all time.

Although Lavoisier is often regarded as the perfect chemist, he had one major flaw in his character. He sometimes used measurements and discoveries made by other scientists but did not acknowledge these contributions in his publications. Even today, some of the discoveries that were made by other scientists are still attributed to Lavoisier.

Lavoisier was executed on the guillotine in 1794 by the revolutionary French government. Although some of his former colleagues held influential positions in the new regime, they made no attempt to save him. It may be more than coincidence that Lavoisier had appropriated some of the work of these chemists.

Figure 10.2
Antoine-Laurent de Lavoisier (1743–1794) with his wife and assistant, Marie-Anne Paulze (1758–1836).

What Chemical Equations Tell Us

10.2

Every balanced chemical equation contains a great deal of qualitative and quantitative information. Let us examine the equation for the reaction of carbon with oxygen to give carbon dioxide:

$$C_{(s)} + O_{2\,(g)} \longrightarrow CO_{2\,(g)}$$

From this balanced chemical equation we can obtain the following information:

1. The identity of the reactants and products. Here, solid carbon reacts with oxygen gas to give carbon dioxide gas.

2. The formula of each reactant and product. The formula for solid carbon is $C_{(s)}$, for oxygen gas it is $O_{2\,(g)}$, and for carbon dioxide gas it is $CO_{2\,(g)}$.

3. The relative number of atoms or molecules involved in the reaction. In this case one atom of carbon reacts with one molecule of oxygen to give one molecule of carbon dioxide.

4. The number of moles of each substance involved in the reaction. If we multiply everything in our equation by 6.02×10^{23}, we see that 6.02×10^{23} atoms of carbon will react with 6.02×10^{23} molecules of oxygen to give 6.02×10^{23} molecules of carbon dioxide. You will recall from Section 3.7 that 6.02×10^{23} (Avogadro's number) represents the number of particles in one mole of material. Therefore we can now say that one mole of carbon atoms reacts with one mole of oxygen molecules to give one mole of carbon dioxide molecules.

To summarize these four points, we can list the appropriate information beneath the reactants and products in the chemical equation as follows:

$C_{(s)}$	+	$O_{2\,(g)}$	$\longrightarrow$	$CO_{2\,(g)}$
1 atom		1 molecule		1 molecule
6.02×10^{23} atoms		6.02×10^{23} molecules		6.02×10^{23} molecules
1.00 mol		1.00 mol		1.00 mol

It is the relationships between the numbers of moles that will concern us most in this chapter. Thus, the important point to note is that

A balanced chemical equation indicates the number of moles of each of the chemicals involved in a reaction.

Let us now look at how we can use this information to help us to solve problems that we might encounter in a laboratory situation.

Mass Relationships In Chemical Equations

10.3

As we saw in Section 10.2, the equation

$$C_{(s)} + O_{2\,(g)} \longrightarrow CO_{2\,(g)}$$

tells us that one mole of carbon reacts with one mole of oxygen to produce one mole of carbon dioxide. By referring to the Periodic Table, we find that the mass of one mole of carbon (C) is 12.0 g and the mass of one mole of oxygen (O_2) is 32.0 g. The Law of Conservation of Mass tells us that when 12.0 g of carbon reacts with 32.0 g of oxygen, 44.0 g of carbon dioxide should be produced.

The Law of Conservation of Mass forms the basis from which we develop the mole method. This method can be used, for example, to find the mass of oxygen that would be required to convert a known quantity of carbon to carbon dioxide. The key to using the mole method is to obtain balanced equations from which we can derive a number of equation factors. Before outlining the mole method we will explain how these equation factors are determined.

Equation Factors

10.4

In Chapter 2 we stressed the importance of the conversion-factor method in chemical calculations. We used the conversion-factor approach again in Chapter 3 when we introduced the mole concept. In many respects, an equation factor is similar to a conversion factor, but instead of indicating a relationship between units such as grams and kilograms, an **equation factor** indicates the relationship between the number of moles of different chemicals used or produced in chemical reactions. Let us again consider the following reaction:

$$C_{(s)} + O_{2\,(g)} \longrightarrow CO_{2\,(g)}$$

One mole of carbon reacts with one mole of oxygen to produce one mole of carbon dioxide. The equation factors that relate the number of moles of carbon used to the number of moles of oxygen used are

$$\frac{1 \text{ mol } C_{(s)}}{1 \text{ mol } O_{2\,(g)}} \quad \text{and} \quad \frac{1 \text{ mol } O_{2\,(g)}}{1 \text{ mol } C_{(s)}}$$

Similarly, the equation factors relating the number of moles of carbon and carbon dioxide are

$$\frac{1 \text{ mol } C_{(s)}}{1 \text{ mol } CO_{2\,(g)}} \quad \text{and} \quad \frac{1 \text{ mol } CO_{2\,(g)}}{1 \text{ mol } C_{(s)}}$$

Let us consider a more complicated equation in the following example.

EXAMPLE 10.2 Using the equation below, derive the equation factors for:

$$N_{2\,(g)} + 3\,H_{2\,(g)} \longrightarrow 2\,NH_{3\,(g)}$$

a) the number of moles of nitrogen and hydrogen used
b) the number of moles of nitrogen used and the number of moles of ammonia produced
c) the number of moles of hydrogen used and the number of moles of ammonia produced

SOLUTION The balanced equation tells us that one mole of nitrogen combines with three moles of hydrogen to form two moles of ammonia. The equation factors are therefore

a) $\dfrac{1 \text{ mol } N_{2\,(g)}}{3 \text{ mol } H_{2\,(g)}}$ and $\dfrac{3 \text{ mol } H_{2\,(g)}}{1 \text{ mol } N_{2\,(g)}}$

b) $\dfrac{1 \text{ mol } N_{2\,(g)}}{2 \text{ mol } NH_{3\,(g)}}$ and $\dfrac{2 \text{ mol } NH_{3\,(g)}}{1 \text{ mol } N_{2\,(g)}}$

c) $\dfrac{3 \text{ mol } H_{2\,(g)}}{2 \text{ mol } NH_{3\,(g)}}$ and $\dfrac{2 \text{ mol } NH_{3\,(g)}}{3 \text{ mol } H_{2\,(g)}}$

QUESTIONS

3. Write down all the possible equation factors for the overall reaction that occurs during photosynthesis:

$$6\,H_2O_{(\ell)} + 6\,CO_{2\,(g)} \longrightarrow C_6H_{12}O_{6\,(s)} + 6\,O_{2\,(g)}$$

The Mole Method

10.5 The **mole method** is essentially a three-step process that can be used to solve almost any problem in which we wish to find any of the following:

a) The mass of a particular product formed in a given reaction from a specified mass of one or more reactants
b) The mass of a specified reactant that must be used in order to completely convert a given mass of another reactant into products
c) The mass of each reactant required in order to produce a given mass of product

As an example, let us assume that we wish to calculate the mass of substance B that can be produced from a given mass of substance A. The three steps would involve

1. **Conversion of the given mass of substance A to the number of moles of A, using the molar mass of A as the conversion factor (Mass of A $\longrightarrow$ Moles of A)**

2. **Use of the equation factor to determine the number of moles of substance B that can be produced from the number of moles of substance A determined in Step 1 (Moles of A ⟶ Moles of B)**
3. **Conversion of the number of moles of substance B found in Step 2 to the corresponding mass, using the molar mass of B as the conversion factor (Moles of B ⟶ Mass of B)**

Now let's look at the reaction that occurs between lead and sulfur, and in so doing, demonstrate the use of the mole method. The pertinent equation is

$$Pb_{(s)} + S_{(s)} \longrightarrow PbS_{(s)}$$

The balanced equation indicates that one mole of lead reacts with one mole of sulfur to form one mole of lead(II) sulfide. As we do not have an instrument that measures moles directly, we usually measure mass instead. From the Periodic Table we see that the molar mass of lead is $207.2\,g \cdot mol^{-1}$ and that of sulfur is $32.1\,g \cdot mol^{-1}$. If we heat $207.2\,g$ of lead with $32.1\,g$ of sulfur, the Law of Conservation of Mass tells us that $239.3\,g$ of lead(II) sulfide should be produced (Figure 10.3). A mass of $239.3\,g$ of lead(II) sulfide corresponds to one mole of lead(II) sulfide, which is precisely the amount of lead(II) sulfide that, according to the chemical equation, should be formed. Suppose, however, that we only had $50.0\,g$ of lead with which to carry out this reaction. How much sulfur would we need? What mass of lead(II) sulfide would be formed? In this type of situation we use the mole method to obtain the answers.

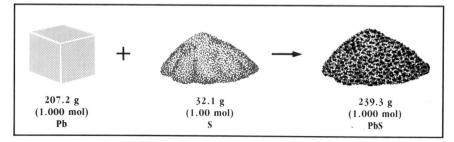

Figure 10.3

The reaction between one mole of lead and one mole of sulfur to produce one mole of lead(II) sulfide.

The first step in the mole method is to determine the number of moles of the substance whose mass is known (in this case lead):

$$\text{Number of moles of Pb} = 50.0\,g\,Pb \times \frac{1\,mol\,Pb}{207.2\,g\,Pb}$$

$$= 0.241\,mol\,Pb$$

To find the number of moles of sulfur required we need to use an equation factor that relates lead and sulfur. The two possible factors are

$$\frac{1\,mol\,S}{1\,mol\,Pb} \quad \text{and} \quad \frac{1\,mol\,Pb}{1\,mol\,S}$$

To select the correct factor, note that we are starting with a known number of moles of lead and wish to determine the number of moles of sulfur that will react with it. In our calculation it is necessary for the unit "mol Pb" to cancel when we multiply the number of moles of lead by the equation factor. For this to happen, the units "mol Pb" must be in the denominator (i.e., on the bottom) of the equation factor. In general, the units that we want to eliminate must be in the denominator of the equation factor. Thus

Number of moles of S required

$$= \text{Number of moles of Pb used} \times \frac{1 \text{ mol S}}{1 \text{ mol Pb}}$$

$$= 0.241 \; \cancel{\text{mol Pb}} \times \frac{1 \text{ mol S}}{1 \; \cancel{\text{mol Pb}}}$$

$$= 0.241 \text{ mol S}$$

In the final step, the number of moles of sulfur is converted to something measurable, namely mass:

$$\text{Mass of S required} = 0.241 \; \cancel{\text{mol S}} \times \frac{32.1 \text{ g S}}{1 \; \cancel{\text{mol S}}}$$

$$= 7.74 \text{ g S}$$

Thus we need 7.74 g of sulfur to ensure the complete consumption of 50.0 g of lead.

We could use the mole method to determine the mass of lead(II) sulfide that would be produced. However, in this instance it is probably simpler to use the Law of Conservation of Mass:

$$\begin{aligned} \text{Mass of PbS} &= \text{Mass of Pb} + \text{Mass of S} \\ &= 50.0 \text{ g} + 7.74 \text{ g} \\ &= 57.7 \text{ g} \end{aligned}$$

EXAMPLE 10.3

Passing a spark through a mixture of hydrogen and oxygen gas causes water to be produced according to the equation

$$2 \, H_{2 \, (g)} + O_{2 \, (g)} \longrightarrow 2 \, H_2O_{(\ell)}$$

Calculate the mass of hydrogen needed to completely convert 4.00 g of oxygen into water.

SOLUTION

STRATEGY

In this problem we start with a known mass of oxygen (Substance A) and must try to find the mass of hydrogen (Substance B) required. Our overall strategy will be

1. Mass of A $\longrightarrow$ Moles of A
2. Moles of A $\longrightarrow$ Moles of B
3. Moles of B $\longrightarrow$ Mass of B

STEP 1:   We begin by converting the mass of oxygen into moles, as follows:

$$\text{Number of moles of O}_2 = 4.00\,\cancel{g\,O_2} \times \frac{1 \text{ mol O}_2}{32.0\,\cancel{g\,O_2}} = 0.125 \text{ mol O}_2$$

STEP 2:   From the balanced equation, we see that the required equation factor relating hydrogen and oxygen is

$$\frac{2 \text{ mol H}_2}{1 \text{ mol O}_2}$$

Thus, the number of moles of hydrogen required is

$$\text{Number of moles of H}_2 = 0.125\,\cancel{\text{mol O}_2} \times \frac{2 \text{ mol H}_2}{1\,\cancel{\text{mol O}_2}}$$
$$= 0.250 \text{ mol H}_2$$

STEP 3:   We can now calculate the mass of hydrogen required

$$\text{Mass of H}_2 \text{ needed} = 0.250\,\cancel{\text{mol H}_2} \times \frac{2.02 \text{ g H}_2}{1\,\cancel{\text{mol H}_2}}$$
$$= 0.505 \text{ g H}_2$$

EXAMPLE   **10.4**   For the reaction described in Example 10.3, calculate the maximum mass of water that could be produced from 4.00 g of oxygen.

SOLUTION   **STRATEGY**

As in Example 10.3, we are starting with a known mass of oxygen (Substance A). This time we must determine the mass of water (Substance B) produced. Our three-step strategy will be:

1. Mass of A ⟶ Moles of A
2. Moles of A ⟶ Moles of B
3. Moles of B ⟶ Mass of B

STEP 1:   First, we need to know the number of moles of oxygen. This quantity was already calculated in Example 10.3 as 0.125 mol O_2.

STEP 2:   Now we use the balanced equation

$$2 \text{ H}_{2\,(g)} + \text{O}_{2\,(g)} \longrightarrow 2 \text{ H}_2\text{O}_{(\ell)}$$

to deduce the required equation factor

$$\frac{2 \text{ mol H}_2\text{O}}{1 \text{ mol O}_2}$$

Using this factor, we can calculate the number of moles of water produced:

$$\text{Number of moles of } H_2O = 0.125 \text{ mol } O_2 \times \frac{2 \text{ mol } H_2O}{1 \text{ mol } O_2}$$

$$= 0.250 \text{ mol } H_2O$$

STEP 3: The mass of water that will be formed is calculated using its molar mass, $18.0 \text{ g} \cdot \text{mol}^{-1}$:

$$\text{Mass of } H_2O = 0.250 \text{ mol } H_2O \times \frac{18.0 \text{ g } H_2O}{1 \text{ mol } H_2O}$$

$$= 4.50 \text{ g } H_2O$$

Alternatively, we could have found the mass of water produced by using the Law of Conservation of Mass. Thus

$$\text{Mass of water produced} = \text{Mass of hydrogen} + \text{Mass of oxygen}$$
$$= 0.505 \text{ g} + 4.00 \text{ g}$$
$$= 4.51 \text{ g}$$

EXAMPLE   **10.5**   The reaction between ammonia and oxygen is one step in the industrial preparation of nitric acid:

$$4 \text{ NH}_{3\,(g)} + 5 \text{ O}_{2\,(g)} \longrightarrow 4 \text{ NO}_{(g)} + 6 \text{ H}_2\text{O}_{(g)}$$

If we use 6.80 g of ammonia in a laboratory-scale experiment to demonstrate this reaction, what mass of oxygen will be required to consume all of the ammonia?

SOLUTION

STRATEGY

Here we are being asked to determine the mass of oxygen (Substance B) that is required to consume a given mass of ammonia (Substance A). We can follow our usual three-step approach:

1. Mass of A $\longrightarrow$ Moles of A
2. Moles of A $\longrightarrow$ Moles of B
3. Moles of B $\longrightarrow$ Mass of B

STEP 1: We must first determine the number of moles of ammonia to be reacted. The molar mass of ammonia, NH_3, is $17.0 \text{ g} \cdot \text{mol}^{-1}$. Hence

$$\text{Number of moles of } NH_3 = 6.80 \text{ g } NH_3 \times \frac{1 \text{ mol } NH_3}{17.0 \text{ g } NH_3}$$

$$= 0.400 \text{ mol } NH_3$$

STEP 2: Looking at the given equation we see that the required equation factor which relates ammonia and oxygen is

$$\frac{5 \text{ mol } O_2}{4 \text{ mol } NH_3}$$

Thus the number of moles of oxygen needed to react with 0.400 mol of ammonia is found as follows:

$$\text{Number of moles of } O_2 = 0.400 \, \text{mol NH}_3 \times \frac{5 \text{ mol } O_2}{4 \text{ mol NH}_3}$$

$$= 0.500 \text{ mol } O_2$$

STEP 3:   The mass of oxygen required to carry out the reaction is then found using the molar mass of oxygen ($32.0 \, \text{g} \cdot \text{mol}^{-1}$):

$$\text{Mass of } O_2 \text{ required} = 0.500 \, \text{mol } O_2 \times \frac{32.0 \text{ g } O_2}{1 \text{ mol } O_2}$$

$$= 16.0 \text{ g } O_2$$

We must emphasize that the coefficients in a balanced equation relate the number of moles of chemicals taking part in the reaction, not the masses. Thus, the equation shown in Example 10.5 tells us that five moles of oxygen react with four moles of ammonia, not that 5 g of oxygen react with 4 g of ammonia.

QUESTIONS

4. As we saw in Example 10.3, hydrogen gas and oxygen gas combine to form water according to the equation

$$2 \, H_{2\,(g)} + O_{2\,(g)} \longrightarrow 2 \, H_2O_{(\ell)}$$

a) Calculate the mass of oxygen needed to completely convert 5.00 g of hydrogen to water.

b) Calculate the mass of water produced when 5.00 g of hydrogen reacts with the appropriate mass of oxygen.

5. Ammonium dichromate, $(NH_4)_2Cr_2O_7$, exists as orange crystals. On strong heating, the crystals decompose to give green chromium(III) oxide, nitrogen gas, and water vapour according to the equation

$$(NH_4)_2Cr_2O_{7\,(s)} \longrightarrow Cr_2O_{3\,(s)} + N_{2\,(g)} + 4 \, H_2O_{(g)}$$

Calculate the mass of (a) chromium(III) oxide, (b) nitrogen, and (c) water that can be formed from 1.00 g of ammonium dichromate.

6. Dinitrogen oxide (nitrous oxide, N_2O) is often called "laughing gas" because of the effect it has on humans when it is inhaled. It can be prepared in the laboratory by heating ammonium nitrate, NH_4NO_3:

$$NH_4NO_{3\,(s)} \xrightarrow{\Delta} N_2O_{(g)} + 2 \, H_2O_{(g)}$$

a) Calculate the mass of ammonium nitrate required to produce 2.00 g of dinitrogen oxide.

b) What mass of water would accompany the formation of 2.00 g of dinitrogen oxide?

The Limiting- 10.6
Reagent Problem

So far we have applied the mole method only to reactions in which the reactants were mixed together in **stoichiometric quantities**. By this we mean that the quantities of the reagents were such that each of them would be completely used up during the course of the reaction. In typical laboratory situations, however, we often find that we have more of one reactant than we really need. For example, in Section 10.5, we described how to produce 239.3 g of lead(II) sulfide, by reacting 207.2 g of lead with 32.1 g of sulfur. When the reaction was complete, no lead or sulfur remained. If we had used the same amount of lead, but twice the amount of sulfur, the reaction would have proceeded in the same way. However, at the end of the reaction half the original sulfur would remain (Figure 10.4). After all the lead has been used up, no further reaction can occur. In this example, lead is the **limiting reagent** and all of it is consumed during the reaction. Sulfur is the **reagent in excess**, as we had more of it than was really necessary and some of it was left over at the end of the reaction.

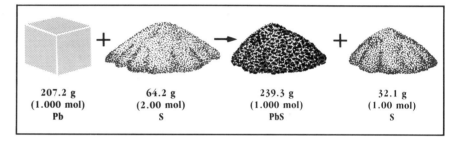

207.2 g	64.2 g	239.3 g	32.1 g
(1.000 mol)	(2.00 mol)	(1.000 mol)	(1.00 mol)
Pb	S	PbS	S

Figure 10.4

The reaction between one mole of lead and two moles of sulfur.

We could reverse the roles of these two reactants in the following manner. If we had taken two moles of lead and one mole of sulfur, we would only have had enough sulfur to react with one mole of lead. Consequently one mole of lead would remain. In this case sulfur would be the limiting reagent and lead the reagent in excess.

In any experimental situation, the limiting reagent determines the amount of product formed. Therefore, in any stoichiometry problem we must first determine if a limiting reagent is involved. If it is, we must base the calculation of the amount of product formed on this reagent, not on the reagent in excess.

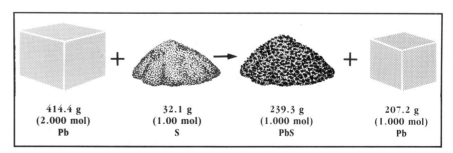

414.4 g	32.1 g	239.3 g	207.2 g
(2.000 mol)	(1.00 mol)	(1.000 mol)	(1.000 mol)
Pb	S	PbS	Pb

Figure 10.5

The reaction between two moles of lead and one mole of sulfur.

EXAMPLE **10.6** Ammonia gas readily combines with hydrogen chloride to produce a white solid, ammonium chloride:

$$NH_{3\,(g)} + HCl_{(g)} \longrightarrow NH_4Cl_{(s)}$$

If 1.00 g of ammonia is mixed with 1.00 g of hydrogen chloride, calculate the mass of ammonium chloride that will be formed.

SOLUTION **STRATEGY**

Our strategy will be to determine the limiting reagent and then use the mole method to find the mass of ammonium chloride (Substance B) produced.

1. **Determine the number of moles of each reactant.**
2. **Use the equation factor to find the limiting reagent.**
3. **Moles of limiting reagent (A) $\longrightarrow$ Moles of product (B)**
4. **Moles of product (B) $\longrightarrow$ Mass of product (B)**

STEP 1: We must begin by determining the number of moles of each of the reagents provided. The molar mass of ammonia (NH_3) is $17.0\,g \cdot mol^{-1}$, and that of hydrogen chloride is $36.5\,g \cdot mol^{-1}$. Thus

$$\text{Number of moles of } NH_3 = 1.00\,g\,NH_3 \times \frac{1\ mol\ NH_3}{17.0\,g\,NH_3}$$

$$= 5.88 \times 10^{-2}\ mol\ NH_3$$

$$\text{Number of moles of } HCl = 1.00\,g\,HCl \times \frac{1\ mol\ HCl}{36.5\,g\,HCl}$$

$$= 2.74 \times 10^{-2}\ mol\ HCl$$

STEP 2: From our equation we see that the equation factor relating ammonia and hydrogen chloride in this reaction is

$$\frac{1\ mol\ HCl}{1\ mol\ NH_3}$$

Thus we find the number of moles of hydrogen chloride needed to completely convert 5.88×10^{-2} mol of ammonia into ammonium chloride as follows:

$$\text{Number of moles of } HCl = 5.88 \times 10^{-2}\,mol\,NH_3 \times \frac{1\ mol\ HCl}{1\ mol\ NH_3}$$

$$= 5.88 \times 10^{-2}\ mol\ HCl$$

In Step 1 we found that we have only 2.74×10^{-2} mol of HCl available for reaction. As this is obviously less than the 5.88×10^{-2} mol needed in order to react all of the ammonia, hydrogen chloride is the limiting reagent.

STEP 3: We must use the limiting reagent (hydrogen chloride) to calculate how many moles of ammonium chloride will be produced:

$$\text{Number of moles of NH}_4\text{Cl} = 2.74 \times 10^{-2} \, \text{mol HCl} \times \frac{1 \text{ mol NH}_4\text{Cl}}{1 \text{ mol HCl}}$$

$$= 2.74 \times 10^{-2} \text{ mol NH}_4\text{Cl}$$

STEP 4: Now we can find the mass of ammonium chloride (molar mass $53.5 \, \text{g} \cdot \text{mol}^{-1}$) produced as follows:

$$\text{Mass of NH}_4\text{Cl produced} = 2.74 \times 10^{-2} \, \text{mol NH}_4\text{Cl} \times \frac{53.5 \text{ g NH}_4\text{Cl}}{1 \text{ mol NH}_4\text{Cl}}$$

$$= 1.47 \text{ g NH}_4\text{Cl}$$

Note what would happen in Example 10.6 if we based our calculation of the mass of ammonium chloride formed on the reagent in excess (NH_3) instead of on the limiting reagent (HCl):

Number of moles of NH_4Cl formed

$$= 5.88 \times 10^{-2} \, \text{mol NH}_3 \times \frac{1 \text{ mol NH}_4\text{Cl}}{1 \text{ mol NH}_3}$$

$$= 5.88 \times 10^{-2} \text{ mol NH}_4\text{Cl}$$

$$\text{Mass of NH}_4\text{Cl formed} = 5.88 \times 10^{-2} \, \text{mol NH}_4\text{Cl} \times \frac{53.5 \text{ g NH}_4\text{Cl}}{1 \text{ mol NH}_4\text{Cl}}$$

$$= 3.15 \text{ g NH}_4\text{Cl}$$

This answer cannot be correct, because the mass of the products (3.15 g) would be greater than the total mass of the reactants (2.00 g) and would violate the Law of Conservation of Mass.

You might have noticed that, in the reaction dealt with in Example 10.6, one mole of ammonia reacts with one mole of hydrogen chloride. We say that ammonia and hydrogen chloride combine in a 1:1 ratio. In such situations it is relatively easy to determine which of the reactants is the limiting reagent. However, in reactions where the reagents react in a different ratio, 2:1 or 3:2 for example, we need to be much more careful when trying to find the limiting reagent. Here the reagent that is present in the greatest number of moles may actually be the limiting reagent.

Perhaps we can make this point clearer through the use of an analogy. When bicycles are assembled we require two wheels for each frame. This is equivalent to two chemicals reacting in a 2:1 ratio. If we have 4 wheels and 3 frames, as shown in Figure 10.6, we can only assemble 2 bicycles. In this instance the wheels determine the number of complete bicycles that can be assembled, despite the fact that we have more wheels than frames. The chemical equivalent of this situation is dealt with in Example 10.7.

Figure 10.6
When determining how many bicycles can be assembled from 4 wheels and 3 frames, the wheels are, in effect, the limiting reagent.

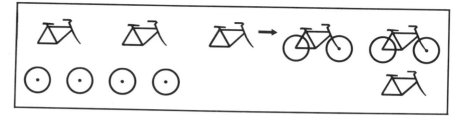

EXAMPLE   **10.**7   Calcium metal burns in oxygen gas to give calcium oxide according to the equation

$$2\ Ca_{(s)}\ +\ O_{2\ (g)} \longrightarrow 2\ CaO_{(g)}$$

Calculate the mass of calcium oxide that will be formed when 0.48 g of calcium is burned in 0.32 g of oxygen.

SOLUTION

STRATEGY

First the limiting reagent will be determined and then the mass of calcium oxide (Substance B) formed can be calculated using the mole method.

1. **Determine the number of moles of each reagent.**
2. **Use the equation factor to determine which is the limiting reagent (A).**
3. **Moles of limiting reagent (A) ⟶ Moles of product (B)**
4. **Moles of product (B) ⟶ Mass of product (B)**

STEP 1:   First we calculate the number of moles of each reactant:

$$\text{Number of moles of calcium}\ =\ 0.48\ g\ Ca \times \frac{1\ mol\ Ca}{40.1\ g\ Ca}$$

$$=\ 1.2\ \times\ 10^{-2}\ mol\ Ca$$

$$\text{Number of moles of oxygen}\ =\ 0.32\ g\ O_2 \times \frac{1\ mol\ O_2}{32.0\ g\ O_2}$$

$$=\ 1.0\ \times\ 10^{-2}\ mol\ O_2$$

STEP 2:   Next, we will find the limiting reagent by determining how much calcium is needed to react with $1.0\ \times\ 10^{-2}$ mol of oxygen. We can do this using the equation factor

$$\frac{2\ mol\ Ca}{1\ mol\ O_2}$$

Thus, the number of moles of calcium needed

$$=\ 1.0\ \times\ 10^{-2}\ mol\ O_2 \times \frac{2\ mol\ Ca}{1\ mol\ O_2}$$

$$=\ 2.0\ \times\ 10^{-2}\ mol\ Ca$$

As we have only 1.2×10^{-2} mol of calcium instead of the required 2.0×10^{-2} mol, calcium must be the limiting reagent.

STEP 3: We can now calculate the number of moles of calcium oxide formed:

$$\text{Number of moles of CaO} = 1.2 \times 10^{-2} \,\text{mol Ca} \times \frac{2 \text{ mol CaO}}{2 \text{ mol Ca}}$$

$$= 1.2 \times 10^{-2} \text{ mol CaO}$$

STEP 4: Finally, the mass of calcium oxide can be found:

$$\text{Mass of CaO} = 1.2 \times 10^{-2} \,\text{mol CaO} \times \frac{56.1 \text{ g CaO}}{1 \text{ mol CaO}}$$

$$= 0.67 \text{ g CaO}$$

QUESTIONS

7. Zinc and bromine react readily together to form zinc bromide.

$$\text{Zn}_{(s)} + \text{Br}_{2\,(\ell)} \longrightarrow \text{ZnBr}_{2\,(s)}$$

Calculate the mass of zinc bromide that can be formed when 1.00 g of zinc is mixed with 1.00 g of bromine.

8. Sodium metal reacts violently with chlorine gas according to the following equation:

$$2 \text{ Na}_{(s)} + \text{Cl}_{2\,(g)} \longrightarrow 2 \text{ NaCl}_{(s)}$$

What mass of sodium chloride would be expected from the reaction of 0.460 g of sodium with 0.426 g of chlorine?

Percentage Yield

10.7 The majority of chemical reactions do not produce the exact amount of product that is predicted by the balanced chemical equation. The amount obtained is usually less than that predicted. That is, the **actual yield** is usually less than the **theoretical yield**. Chemists often speak in terms of the **percentage yield** of a reaction, where

$$\textbf{Percentage yield} = \frac{\textbf{Actual yield}}{\textbf{Theoretical yield}} \times \textbf{100\%}$$

There are a number of reasons why the actual yield is usually less than the theoretical yield. One reason is that some fraction of the reacting molecules may not react to give the desired product. Instead, they may undergo a different reaction to yield **by-products**. For example, in the presence of sulfuric acid, ethanol (C_2H_5OH) reacts to give diethyl ether ($C_2H_5OC_2H_5$):

$$2 \text{ C}_2\text{H}_5\text{OH}_{(\ell)} \xrightarrow[\text{H}_2\text{SO}_4]{\Delta} \text{C}_2\text{H}_5\text{OC}_2\text{H}_{5\,(\ell)} + \text{H}_2\text{O}_{(\ell)}$$

However, the yield of diethyl ether is always much less than 100%, partly because of the formation of ethene (C_2H_4). The ethene is an example of a by-product.

$$C_2H_5OH_{(\ell)} \xrightarrow[H_2SO_4]{\Delta} C_2H_{4\,(g)} + H_2O_{(\ell)}$$

(NOTE: Ethanol, diethyl ether, and ethene are examples of organic compounds. These and other organic compounds will be discussed in Chapters 14 and 15.)

Some reactions, however, do give essentially 100% yields. Such reactions are said to give *quantitative yields* and are used in analytical chemistry.

Many chemists try to find ways of obtaining the maximum possible yield from a given reaction. In industrial processes it is especially important that the highest possible yield is obtained from the minimum amount of raw materials in order to achieve maximum cost efficiency. Industrial chemists therefore spend much time and effort working towards this goal.

EXAMPLE   **10.8** If 189 g of lead(II) sulfide was actually obtained in a reaction for which the theoretical yield was 239 g, calculate the percentage yield.

SOLUTION   Percentage yield $= \dfrac{\text{Actual yield}}{\text{Theoretical yield}} \times 100\%$

$$= \frac{189\,\text{g}}{239\,\text{g}} \times 100\%$$

$$= 79.1\%$$

In Example 10.8 you were given both the actual yield and the theoretical yield and asked to find the percentage yield. In practice, we usually have to determine the theoretical yield ourselves. This often involves calculations of the limiting reagent type. Example 10.9 illustrates the technique used in these situations.

EXAMPLE   **10.9** When heated, sodium metal combines with chlorine gas to form solid sodium chloride:

$$2\,Na_{(s)} + Cl_{2\,(g)} \longrightarrow 2\,NaCl_{(s)}$$

If 8.30 g of sodium and 14.0 g of chlorine are heated together, a total of 19.5 g of sodium chloride is isolated. Determine the percentage yield of sodium chloride.

SOLUTION   *STRATEGY*

After finding the limiting reagent and using the mole method to find the theoretical yield of sodium chloride (Substance B), the percentage yield can be determined.

1. **Determine the number of moles of each reactant.**
2. **Use the equation factor to find the limiting reagent (A).**
3. **Moles of limiting reagent (A) $\longrightarrow$ Moles of product (B)**
4. **Moles of product (B) $\longrightarrow$ Mass of product (Theoretical yield)**
5. **Theoretical yield $\longrightarrow$ Percentage yield**

STEP 1:   We begin by calculating the number of moles of each reactant:

$$\text{Number of moles of Na} = 8.30 \text{ g Na} \times \frac{1 \text{ mol Na}}{23.0 \text{ g Na}}$$

$$= 0.361 \text{ mol Na}$$

$$\text{Number of moles of Cl}_2 = 14.0 \text{ g Cl}_2 \times \frac{1 \text{ mol Cl}_2}{71.0 \text{ g Cl}_2}$$

$$= 0.197 \text{ mol Cl}_2$$

STEP 2:   The balanced equation indicates that 2 mol of sodium are required to react with 1 mol of chlorine. We use the equation factor

$$\frac{1 \text{ mol Cl}_2}{2 \text{ mol Na}}$$

to calculate the number of moles of chlorine required to react with all the sodium present. Thus

$$\text{Number of moles of Cl}_2 \text{ required} = 0.361 \text{ mol Na} \times \frac{1 \text{ mol Cl}_2}{2 \text{ mol Na}}$$

$$= 0.180 \text{ mol Cl}_2$$

It now becomes apparent that chlorine is in excess. We have 0.197 mol of chlorine present, but require only 0.180 mol of chlorine to react with all the sodium. Thus, sodium must be the limiting reagent.

STEP 3:   We now use the limiting reagent to determine the maximum number of moles of sodium chloride that can be formed:

$$\text{Number of moles of NaCl} = 0.361 \text{ mol Na} \times \frac{2 \text{ mol NaCl}}{2 \text{ mol Na}}$$

$$= 0.361 \text{ mol NaCl}$$

STEP 4:   From this, we can find the theoretical yield of sodium chloride:

$$\text{Theoretical yield of NaCl} = 0.361 \text{ mol NaCl} \times \frac{58.5 \text{ g NaCl}}{1 \text{ mol NaCl}}$$

$$= 21.1 \text{ g NaCl}$$

STEP 5:   Finally, we calculate the percentage yield as required:

$$\text{Percentage yield} = \frac{\text{Actual yield}}{\text{Theoretical yield}} \times 100\%$$

$$= \frac{19.5\,g}{21.1\,g} \times 100\%$$

$$= 92.4\%.$$

QUESTIONS

9. Lead(II) nitrate decomposes on heating to give solid lead(II) oxide, nitrogen dioxide gas, and oxygen as illustrated below:

$$2\ Pb(NO_3)_{2\ (s)} \xrightarrow{\Delta} 2\ PbO_{(s)} + 4\ NO_{2\ (g)} + O_{2\ (g)}$$

When 3.31 g of lead(II) nitrate was heated in an experiment, the yield of lead(II) oxide was found to be 1.75 g. Calculate the percentage yield obtained.

10. The pain reliever acetylsalicylic acid can be prepared by reacting salicylic acid, $C_7H_6O_3$, with acetic anhydride, $C_4H_6O_3$, in the presence of sulfuric acid:

$$\underset{\substack{\text{salicylic}\\\text{acid}}}{C_7H_6O_3} + \underset{\substack{\text{acetic}\\\text{anhydride}}}{C_4H_6O_3} \xrightarrow{H_2SO_4} \underset{\substack{\text{acetyl-}\\\text{salicylic}\\\text{acid}}}{C_9H_8O_4} + \underset{\substack{\text{acetic}\\\text{acid}}}{C_2H_4O_2}$$

When this reaction was carried out using 10.0 g of salicylic acid and 15.3 g of acetic anhydride, a yield of 9.20 g of acetylsalicylic acid was obtained. What was the percentage yield?

Impure Reactants

10.8 Another case where the quantity of reactant cannot be used directly to calculate the quantity of product occurs when the reactant is not pure. An example of such a situation is found in the extraction of a metal from its ore. Most ores are impure; this must be taken into account when calculating the amount of reagent needed to extract the metal, and the amount of a given by-product that might be formed.

EXAMPLE   **10.10** What mass of hydrogen is produced when 15.0 t of ore containing 0.100% of zinc reacts with excess sulfuric acid? The equation for the reaction is:

$$Zn_{(s)} + H_2SO_{4\ (aq)} \longrightarrow ZnSO_{4\ (aq)} + H_{2\ (g)}$$

STRATEGY

Before using the three-step mole method to determine the mass of hydrogen (Substance B) produced, we must first determine the mass of zinc (Substance A) present in the given mass of ore.

1. Mass of ore ⟶ Mass of A (zinc)
2. Mass of A ⟶ Moles of A
3. Moles of A ⟶ Moles of B (hydrogen)
4. Moles of B ⟶ Mass of B

STEP 1: First we find the mass of ore, in grams:

$$\text{Mass of ore} = 15.0 \, \cancel{t} \, \text{ore} \times \frac{1000 \, \cancel{kg}}{1 \, \cancel{t}} \times \frac{1000 \, g}{1 \, \cancel{kg}}$$

$$= 1.50 \times 10^7 \, g \, \text{ore}$$

Then we calculate the mass of zinc in the ore:

$$\text{Mass of zinc} = 1.50 \times 10^7 \, \cancel{g \, ore} \times \frac{0.100 \, g \, Zn}{100 \, \cancel{g \, ore}}$$

$$= 1.50 \times 10^4 \, g \, Zn$$

STEP 2: Now we use the mole method to find the number of moles of zinc being reacted:

$$\text{Number of moles of Zn} = 1.50 \times 10^4 \, \cancel{g \, Zn} \times \frac{1 \, mol \, Zn}{65.4 \, \cancel{g \, Zn}}$$

$$= 2.29 \times 10^2 \, mol \, Zn$$

STEP 3: By using the equation factor that relates zinc and hydrogen in this reaction, we can now find the number of moles of hydrogen produced:

$$\text{Number of moles of } H_2 = 2.29 \times 10^2 \, \cancel{mol \, Zn} \times \frac{1 \, mol \, H_2}{1 \, \cancel{mol \, Zn}}$$

$$= 2.29 \times 10^2 \, mol \, H_2$$

STEP 4: Finally, we can calculate the mass of hydrogen formed (molar mass of $H_2 = 2.02 \, g \cdot mol^{-1}$):

$$\text{Mass of } H_2 = 2.29 \times 10^2 \, \cancel{mol \, H_2} \times \frac{2.02 \, g \, H_2}{1 \, \cancel{mol \, H_2}}$$

$$= 4.63 \times 10^2 \, g \, H_2$$

Summary

■ Stoichiometry involves the use of mole calculations to determine the quantities of chemicals used and produced in chemical reactions.

■ The Law of Conservation of Mass states that in any chemical reaction, there is no detectable difference between the total mass of the reactants and the total mass of the products.

- From a balanced equation, the relative number of moles of each substance involved in the reaction can be determined.

- Equation factors indicate the relationship between the numbers of moles of different substances used or produced in chemical reactions.

- The mole method is a three-step process used when solving almost any kind of problem concerning the mass of the reactant used or the mass of the product formed in a chemical reaction. The three steps are as follows:
  1. Conversion of the mass of substance A to the number of moles of substance A
  2. Conversion of the number of moles of substance A to number of moles of substance B, using the appropriate equation factor
  3. Conversion of the number of moles of substance B to mass of substance B

- If the reactants are not present in stoichiometric quantities, then the limiting reagent, i.e. the reactant that is not in excess, determines the amount of product formed.

- Because of the formation of by-products, and because of other factors, the amount of product obtained in a chemical reaction is usually less than predicted. The percentage yield is calculated by dividing the theoretical yield into the actual yield and multiplying by 100%.

- Reactions that give essentially 100% yield are said to be quantitative and are often used in analysis.

KEY WORDS

actual yield	percentage yield
by-product	reagent in excess
equation factor	stoichiometric quantities
Law of Conservation of Mass	stoichiometry
limiting reagent	theoretical yield
mole method	

ANSWERS TO SECTION QUESTIONS

1. 0.220 g carbon dioxide
2. 54 g water
3. $\dfrac{6 \text{ mol } H_2O_{(\ell)}}{6 \text{ mol } CO_{2\,(g)}}$ $\quad$ $\dfrac{6 \text{ mol } CO_{2\,(g)}}{6 \text{ mol } H_2O_{(\ell)}}$ $\quad$ $\dfrac{6 \text{ mol } H_2O_{(\ell)}}{1 \text{ mol } C_6H_{12}O_{6\,(s)}}$ $\quad$ $\dfrac{1 \text{ mol } C_6H_{12}O_{6\,(s)}}{6 \text{ mol } H_2O_{(\ell)}}$

$\dfrac{6 \text{ mol } H_2O_{(\ell)}}{6 \text{ mol } O_{2\,(g)}}$ $\quad$ $\dfrac{6 \text{ mol } O_{2\,(g)}}{6 \text{ mol } H_2O_{(\ell)}}$ $\quad$ $\dfrac{6 \text{ mol } CO_{2\,(g)}}{1 \text{ mol } C_6H_{12}O_{6\,(s)}}$ $\quad$ $\dfrac{1 \text{ mol } C_6H_{12}O_{6\,(s)}}{6 \text{ mol } CO_{2\,(g)}}$

$\dfrac{6 \text{ mol } CO_{2\,(g)}}{6 \text{ mol } O_{2\,(g)}}$ $\quad$ $\dfrac{6 \text{ mol } O_{2\,(g)}}{6 \text{ mol } CO_{2\,(g)}}$ $\quad$ $\dfrac{1 \text{ mol } C_6H_{12}O_{6\,(s)}}{6 \text{ mol } O_{2\,(g)}}$ $\quad$ $\dfrac{6 \text{ mol } O_{2\,(g)}}{1 \text{ mol } C_6H_{12}O_{6\,(s)}}$

4. a) 39.7 g O_2 b) 44.6 g H_2O

5. a) 0.602 g Cr_2O_3 b) 0.111 g N_2 c) 0.285 g H_2O

6. a) 3.64 g NH_4NO_3 b) 1.64 g H_2O

7. 1.41 g $ZnBr_2$

8. 0.702 g NaCl

9. 78.5%

10. 70.6%

COMPREHENSION QUESTIONS

1. State the Law of Conservation of Mass.

2. What four pieces of information can be obtained from a balanced chemical equation?

3. What are equation factors? What are they used for?

4. What do we mean by "the mole method"?

5. Explain the terms "limiting reagent" and "reagent in excess".

6. Explain the following terms:
a) actual yield   b) theoretical yield   c) percentage yield

7. If there is an apparent decrease in total mass during a chemical reaction, what must have happened?

8. If there is an apparent increase in total mass during a chemical reaction, what must have happened?

9. What information is conveyed by the following equation:

$$2 \, C_2H_6 \, {}_{(g)} \; + \; 7 \, O_2 \, {}_{(g)} \longrightarrow 4 \, CO_2 \, {}_{(g)} \; + \; 6 \, H_2O_{(g)}$$

10. What information is conveyed by the following equation:

$$CaCO_3 \, {}_{(s)} \longrightarrow CaO_{(s)} \; + \; CO_2 \, {}_{(g)}$$

PROBLEMS

11. Water can be decomposed by an electric current according to the equation

$$2 \, H_2O_{(\ell)} \longrightarrow 2 \, H_2 \, {}_{(g)} \; + \; O_2 \, {}_{(g)}$$

If 5.00 g of water produces 0.561 g of hydrogen, what mass of oxygen must also be produced?

12. Iron ore, Fe_2O_3, reacts with carbon monoxide to produce iron according to the equation

$$Fe_2O_3 \, {}_{(s)} \; + \; 3 \, CO_{(g)} \longrightarrow 2 \, Fe_{(s)} \; + \; 3 \, CO_2 \, {}_{(g)}$$

If 1.00 t (1000 kg) of iron ore produces 0.699 t of iron and 0.826 t of carbon dioxide, what mass of carbon monoxide must have been used?

13. Write down all the equation factors for the following equation:

$$2 \, KClO_3 \, {}_{(s)} \longrightarrow 2 \, KCl_{(s)} \; + \; 3 \, O_2 \, {}_{(g)}$$

14. Write down all the equation factors for the equation below:

$$CH_{4\,(g)} + 2\,O_{2\,(g)} \longrightarrow CO_{2\,(g)} + 2\,H_2O_{(g)}$$

15. Ammonia burns in oxygen to give nitrogen and water. The equation is

$$4\,NH_{3\,(g)} + 3\,O_{2\,(g)} \longrightarrow 2\,N_{2\,(g)} + 6\,H_2O_{(g)}$$

a) How many moles of oxygen are needed to completely react with 1.0 mol of ammonia?
b) How many moles of nitrogen will be produced from the complete reaction of 2.0 mol of ammonia?
c) How many moles of water will be produced from the complete reaction of 3.0 mol of ammonia?

16. Ammonia burns in oxygen in the presence of a platinum catalyst to give nitrogen monoxide and water:

$$4\,NH_{3\,(g)} + 5\,O_{2\,(g)} \xrightarrow{\text{Pt}} 4\,NO_{(g)} + 6\,H_2O_{(g)}$$

a) How many moles of oxygen are needed to react completely with 3.0 mol of ammonia?
b) How many moles of nitrogen monoxide will be produced from the complete reaction of 2.0 mol of ammonia?
c) How many moles of water will be produced from the complete reaction of 1.0 mol of ammonia?

17. Sulfuric acid is formed when sulfur trioxide combines with water:

$$SO_{3\,(g)} + H_2O_{(\ell)} \longrightarrow H_2SO_{4(\ell)}$$

a) What is the minimum mass of water required to convert 8.00 g of sulfur trioxide to sulfuric acid?
b) What mass of sulfur trioxide is needed in order to produce 10.0 g of sulfuric acid?

18. Magnesium metal combines with chlorine gas to produce magnesium chloride:

$$Mg_{(s)} + Cl_{2\,(g)} \longrightarrow MgCl_{2\,(s)}$$

a) What mass of chlorine gas is needed to completely react with 12.2 g of magnesium?
b) What mass of magnesium is required in order to produce 5.00 g of magnesium chloride?

19. Oxygen gas is commonly prepared on a small scale by heating potassium chlorate with a manganese(IV) oxide catalyst:

$$2\,KClO_{3\,(s)} \xrightarrow[\text{MnO}_2]{\Delta} 2\,KCl_{(s)} + 3\,O_{2\,(g)}$$

Determine the mass of oxygen gas that can be prepared from 5.12 g of potassium chlorate.

20. Chlorine gas may be prepared by adding hydrochloric acid to manganese(IV) oxide:

$$MnO_{2\,(s)} + 4\,HCl_{(aq)} \longrightarrow MnCl_{2\,(aq)} + Cl_{2\,(g)} + 2\,H_2O_{(\ell)}$$

Determine the mass of chlorine gas that can be prepared from 15.6 g of manganese(IV) oxide.

21. Nickel metal will react with silver nitrate solution to give metallic silver and a solution of nickel(II) nitrate:

$$Ni_{(s)} + 2\,AgNO_{3\,(aq)} \longrightarrow 2\,Ag_{(s)} + Ni(NO_3)_{2\,(aq)}$$

If 15.32 g of nickel reacts with excess silver nitrate solution, calculate the mass of silver metal produced.

22. The average amount of energy required by the body every hour can be provided by the metabolism of 34.0 g of sucrose according to the equation

$$C_{12}H_{22}O_{11\,(s)} + 12\,O_{2\,(g)} \longrightarrow 12\,CO_{2\,(g)} + 11\,H_2O_{(\ell)}$$

What mass of oxygen is required to react with this mass of sucrose?

23. Aluminum oxide decomposes according to the equation:

$$2\,Al_2O_{3\,(s)} \longrightarrow 4\,Al_{(s)} + 3\,O_{2\,(g)}$$

What mass of oxygen is produced when 1.50 kg of Al_2O_3 is decomposed in this manner?

24. Sodium carbonate, Na_2CO_3, is used in the manufacture of glass and is made from calcium carbonate and sodium chloride according to the equation:

$$CaCO_{3\,(s)} + 2\,NaCl_{(aq)} \longrightarrow Na_2CO_{3\,(s)} + CaCl_{2\,(aq)}$$

a) What mass of sodium chloride is required to completely react with 1.00 kg of calcium carbonate?
b) What mass of sodium carbonate could be produced from the reaction of 1.00 kg of sodium chloride?

25. Triple superphosphate is a fertilizer with the formula $Ca(H_2PO_4)_2$. In the industrial preparation of this fertilizer, phosphate rock is stripped of sand and clay and treated with phosphoric acid:

$$Ca_3(PO_4)_{2\,(s)} + 4\,H_3PO_{4\,(aq)} \longrightarrow 3\,Ca(H_2PO_4)_{2\,(aq)}$$

What mass (in tonnes) of calcium phosphate is needed to produce 2.50 t of superphosphate?

26. Coke is an impure form of carbon obtained from coal. It is often used as an industrial fuel. When 1.00×10^2 t of coke is burned, what mass of carbon dioxide will be produced?

$$C_{(s)} + O_{2\,(g)} \longrightarrow CO_{2\,(g)}$$

27. If 12.0 g of barium nitrate is dissolved in water and added to a solution containing 16.0 g of potassium sulfate, a double displacement reaction occurs:

$$Ba(NO_3)_{2\ (aq)} + K_2SO_{4\ (aq)} \longrightarrow BaSO_{4\ (s)} + 2\ KNO_{3\ (aq)}$$

a) Which reagent is in excess?
b) What mass of barium sulfate would be produced?

28. If 8.6 g of sodium sulfide is dissolved in water and added to a solution containing 10.7 g of silver nitrate, the following reaction occurs:

$$Na_2S_{(aq)} + 2\ AgNO_{3\ (aq)} \longrightarrow Ag_2S_{(s)} + 2\ NaNO_{3\ (aq)}$$

a) Which reagent is in excess?
b) What mass of silver sulfide would be produced?

29. Sodium and water react according to the equation

$$2\ Na_{(s)} + 2\ H_2O_{(\ell)} \longrightarrow 2\ NaOH_{(aq)} + H_{2\ (g)}$$

If 10.0 g of sodium is placed in 50.0 mL of water, what mass of hydrogen gas will be produced?

30. Propane will burn in oxygen according to the equation

$$C_3H_{8\ (g)} + 5\ O_{2\ (g)} \longrightarrow 3\ CO_{2\ (g)} + 4\ H_2O_{(g)}$$

Suppose 1.00×10^2 g of propane is mixed with an equal mass of oxygen in a closed container and ignited.
a) What mass of carbon dioxide will be produced?
b) What mass of water will be produced?

31. Equal masses of sodium and iodine are allowed to react to produce sodium iodide according to the equation below:

$$2\ Na_{(s)} + I_{2\ (s)} \longrightarrow 2\ NaI_{(s)}$$

Which reagent is in excess and what percentage of this reagent will remain at the end of the reaction?

32. Equal masses of phosphorus and chlorine react according to the following equation:

$$2\ P_{(s)} + 3\ Cl_{2\ (g)} \longrightarrow 2\ PCl_{3\ (\ell)}$$

Which reagent is in excess and what percentage of it will remain at the end of the reaction?

33. A certain reaction is calculated to give a theoretical yield of 4.214 g of product. Calculate
a) the percentage yield if only 3.615 g of product is obtained
b) the actual yield obtained if the percentage yield is only 63.5%

34. A chemist intends to carry out the following hypothetical reaction sequence:

1. A $\longrightarrow$ B
2. B $\longrightarrow$ C
3. C $\longrightarrow$ D

The percentage yield normally obtained in each of these reactions is as follows: Step 1, 82%; Step 2, 55%; and Step 3, 96%. If the chemist starts out with 1.00 mol of substance A, what is the maximum number of moles of D that can be obtained?

35. Dinitrogen oxide can be prepared by the decomposition of ammonium nitrate:

$$NH_4NO_{3\ (s)} \xrightarrow{\Delta} N_2O_{(g)} + 2\ H_2O_{(g)}$$

When 10.0 g of ammonium nitrate was decomposed in this manner, 3.61 g of N_2O was obtained. What was the percentage yield of the reaction?

36. In a reaction to produce xenon tetrafluoride, according to the equation

$$Xe_{(g)} + 2\ F_{2\ (g)} \longrightarrow XeF_{4\ (s)}$$

1.58 g of xenon reacts with excess fluorine. If the yield of xenon tetrafluoride was 0.11 g, what was the percentage yield of the reaction?

37. Pure iron can be produced by the reaction between magnetite (Fe_3O_4) and hydrogen:

$$Fe_3O_{4\ (s)} + 4\ H_{2\ (g)} \longrightarrow 3\ Fe_{(s)} + 4\ H_2O_{(\ell)}$$

If 100.0 g of both magnetite and hydrogen are initially present
a) Which reagent, if any, is in excess?
b) Calculate the percentage yield if 32.0 g of iron was actually isolated.

38. One of the reactions involved in the smelting of copper sulfide ores involves copper(I) oxide and copper(I) sulfide:

$$2\ Cu_2O_{(s)} + Cu_2S_{(s)} \longrightarrow 6\ Cu_{(s)} + SO_{2\ (g)}$$

If 50.0 g of copper(I) oxide is heated with 25.8 g of copper(II) sulfide
a) determine which reagent, if any, is in excess
b) calculate the theoretical yield of copper
c) determine the percentage yield if 58.0 g of copper is actually isolated.

SUGGESTED PROJECTS   1. As with many laws and theories, the Law of Conservation of Mass has had to be revised because of new discoveries. This law is now known as the Law of Conservation of Mass and Energy. Use reference books to find out why the change became necessary.

2. Carrying out a reaction in the laboratory is one thing; turning it into a profitable industrial process is another. Chemical engineers play an important role in the chemical industry. Use books on career guidance, and other reference material, to find out what kind of training a chemical engineer receives, and what his or her job entails.

CHAPTER *11*

Gases

I n Chapter 1 we explained some aspects of the behaviour of gases in terms of the kinetic-molecular theory. In this chapter, we will again use this theory in discussing the properties of gases and the gas laws.

Common Properties of Gases

11.1   Unlike solids and liquids, which have definite volumes, gases expand to fill any space made available to them. They do not have clear boundaries and thus the volume of a gas is defined by the volume of the vessel in which it is contained. As most gases are colourless and many are odourless, detecting them can sometimes be quite difficult.

Gases have very low densities. For example, if half a cup of water evaporates, the resulting water vapour (water in the gas phase) at atmospheric pressure and 100 °C will occupy a volume roughly equal to that of a 200 L oil drum.

Provided that they do not react with one another to form a solid or liquid, any two or more gases can be mixed together to form a solution. This differs from the behaviour we observe when we try to mix either solids or liquids. For example, certain pairs of liquids cannot be mixed together to form a solution. Oil and water are one such pair. If these two liquids are mixed together, two distinct layers are formed, with the oil floating on top of the water. Similarly, when we form a solution from a solid and a liquid, there is a limit to the amount of solid that will dissolve in a given volume of liquid. If we try to exceed this amount, some of the solid will not dissolve. This is quite different from the way gases behave. Gases can be mixed together in *any* proportion to form a homogeneous solution.

Although the volume of a solid or liquid changes as the temperature and pressure increases or decreases, these changes are so small that they are usually considered to be negligible. In contrast, the volume of a gas changes dramatically with a change in pressure or temperature. The volume, pressure, and temperature of a specific mass of gas are interrelated. We will study these relationships in detail later, but first we must learn how gas pressures are measured.

The Practical Measurement of Gas Pressure

11.2 The Barometer   *The Barometer*

Early in the seventeenth century the Italian scientist, Torricelli, designed the first **barometer**, an instrument used for measuring atmospheric pressure. In its simplest form, a barometer consists of a long glass tube that is sealed at one end and filled with liquid. The tube is then inverted, with the open end immersed in a dish containing the same liquid as the tube (Figure 11.1).

Some of the liquid flows from the tube into the dish, creating a vacuum at the sealed end of the tube. However, some of the liquid remains in the tube! The force exerted by the atmosphere on the surface of the liquid in the dish supports a column of liquid in the sealed tube. The height, h, of the column of liquid is a measure of the pressure being exerted by the atmosphere. The height of this column of liquid depends on the liquid used. If water is used the atmosphere will support a column about 10 m high; however, if mercury is used, the height of the column will be about 0.76 m (760 mm). The mercury column is shorter because mercury is about thirteen times denser than water.

The pressure exerted by the atmosphere fluctuates throughout the day. This causes our weather to change as air flows from areas of high pressure to areas of low pressure. Atmospheric pressure also changes with altitude; as the altitude increases, the atmospheric pressure decreases. On very high mountains, such as those in the Himalayas, climbers often experience difficulty in breathing. The low atmospheric pressure at these very high

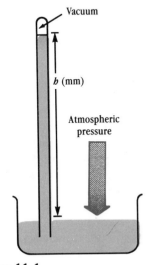

Figure 11.1
A barometer.

altitudes means that the density of the air is very low and there is insufficient oxygen to meet the body's normal oxygen requirements.

Because the pressure exerted by the atmosphere is not constant, scientists have defined a **standard atmospheric pressure** for use in calculations. In terms of the mercury barometer described above, standard atmospheric pressure is the pressure that supports a column of mercury 760 mm high. In other words, standard atmospheric pressure is equal to 760 mm Hg. Other units for expressing pressure are discussed in Section 11.3.

The Manometer

Scientists often have to measure the pressure exerted by a gas in a closed container. If the gas pressure is not extremely high, we can use a simple instrument that compares the pressure of the gas in the container with the atmospheric pressure. This device, called a **manometer** (Figure 11.2), is similar to the barometer in its construction and also in the way it measures gas pressure. One end of a glass U-tube is connected to the vessel containing the gas and the other end is open to the atmosphere. The U-tube contains a known volume of liquid, usually mercury.

In Figure 11.2a, the flask is open to the atmosphere and the pressure of the gas in the flask is therefore equal to atmospheric pressure (in symbols, $P_{gas} = P_{atm}$). Because the pressure inside the flask is equal to the pressure outside the flask, the level of the mercury in the two arms of the U-tube is the same, that is, $h_1 = h_2$.

If we allow some gas (e.g. from a gas cylinder) to enter the flask, the pressure of the gas in the flask will be greater than the atmospheric pressure. The level of the mercury in the left arm of the U-tube will therefore be lower than the level of the mercury in the right arm (Figure 11.2b). If we express the pressure in millimetres of mercury (mm Hg), we can calculate the pressure of the gas in the flask as follows:

$$P_{gas} = P_{atm} + \Delta h$$

Here $\Delta h = h_2 - h_1$, represents the difference (in millimetres) between the two mercury levels.

If we connect the flask containing the gas to a vacuum pump and remove some of the gas from the flask so that the pressure inside the flask is less than that of the surrounding atmosphere, the level of mercury in the right arm of the tube will fall and the level of mercury in the left arm will rise (Figure 11.2c). The difference between the two levels, $\Delta h = h_1 - h_2$, still represents the difference between the pressure inside the flask and the pressure outside the flask. As the atmospheric pressure is now greater than the pressure inside the flask, the latter can be found by subtracting Δh from the atmospheric pressure:

$$P_{gas} = P_{atm} - \Delta h$$

Figure 11.2

A manometer.
a) When the flask is open to the atmosphere, the liquid is at the same level in both arms of the U-tube.
b) The gas in the flask is at greater than atmospheric pressure.
c) The gas in the flask is at less than atmospheric pressure.

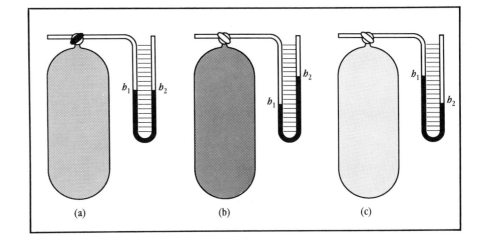

(a)   (b)   (c)

EXAMPLE **11.1** When a container of gas is connected to a manometer of the type shown in Figure 11.2, the mercury in the open-ended arm rises by 61 mm. If the atmospheric pressure is 754 mm Hg, what is the gas pressure in the container?

SOLUTION If the mercury on the open side rises by 61 mm, then that on the container side must fall by 61 mm. The difference in the two levels will therefore be 122 mm. Because the mercury on the open side rises, the pressure in the flask must be greater than atmospheric pressure. Thus

$$\text{Pressure} = 754\,\text{mm Hg} + 122\,\text{mm Hg} = 876\,\text{mm Hg.}$$

QUESTIONS

1. When the gas container described in Example 11.1 is connected to a vacuum pump and partially evacuated, the level of the mercury in the arm attached to the container rises until it is 645 mm above the level of the mercury in the open-ended arm. What is the pressure of the gas in the partially-evacuated flask? Assume that the atmospheric pressure remains at 754 mm Hg.

Pressure = 756 mm Hg + 480 = 1236 mmHg

Units of Pressure

11.3 In his early experiments with the mercury barometer, Torricelli measured gas pressures in millimetres of mercury (mm Hg). These units were used for many years and are still sometimes used today. Because millimetres of mercury is rather cumbersome to write, this unit is often called a **torr** (after Torricelli).

The SI unit of pressure is the **pascal** (symbol Pa), named after Blaise Pascal, a philosopher, mathematician, and physicist. The pascal is a very

The Atmospheres of the Planets

As inhabitants of the earth, we think of our own atmosphere as 'normal', but compared to the atmospheres of other planets our atmosphere is very unusual. The main components of the atmospheres of the planets in our solar system are described below.

Mercury: This planet has no detectable atmosphere.

Venus: The atmospheric pressure at the surface of Venus is about 9.3 MPa (93 atmospheres) and the temperature is about 740 K (470 °C). The major components of the atmosphere of Venus are carbon dioxide (96 %) and nitrogen (4 %). There are also small quantities of sulfur-containing gases such as sulfur dioxide and hydrogen sulfide. Sulfur seems to be an important element on Venus and it is believed that the clouds in the upper atmosphere of the planet may consist of droplets of sulfuric acid.

Earth: The earth's present atmosphere consists mainly of nitrogen (78.1 %) and oxygen (20.9 %). When the age of the earth is taken into consideration, this atmosphere has existed

for a relatively short time. The initial atmosphere of the earth is believed to have consisted of carbon monoxide, methane, and hydrogen. However, these gases escaped into space and were replaced by carbon dioxide and nitrogen which were produced by the earth's interior. The oxygen in our present atmosphere has been produced over the last two billion years by the process of photosynthesis.

Mars: The atmosphere of Mars consists mainly of carbon dioxide (95.3 %), nitrogen (2.7 %), and oxygen (1.6 %). This is quite similar to the composition of the atmosphere of Venus. However, there are some dramatic differences between the two planets. The atmospheric pressure on Mars (about 0.6 kPa or 6×10^{-3} atm) is much lower than that of Venus, as is the surface temperature which ranges between 130 K and 290 K (about −140 °C to 20 °C).

The Outer Planets: The atmospheres of Jupiter, Saturn, Uranus, and Neptune are completely different from those of the inner planets. The major components of these planets' atmospheres are believed to be hydrogen, helium, methane, and ammonia. The colours of the clouds that envelop Jupiter are probably caused by sulfur compounds (yellow) and elemental phosphorus (red). Little is known of the atmosphere of Pluto, except that it contains methane.

By studying the atmospheres of other planets, scientists can formulate theories about the earth's atmosphere in the past, and can speculate on the possible existence of life forms on planets in other solar systems. The study of planetary atmospheres has become an exciting part of cosmochemistry. Chemists are particularly interested in compounds that do not exist on the earth, but that might form at the temperatures and pressures of other planets. The space probes to Jupiter provided much new information about the larger moons of Jupiter, each of which appears to have a unique atmosphere.

Figure 11.3

Jupiter and its moons. The atmospheres of these bodies are quite different in chemical composition, temperature, and pressure from that of the earth.

Figure 11.4
The newer air pressure gauges at gas stations display pressures in kilopascals.

small unit. It has been calculated that a dollar bill lying flat on a table exerts a pressure of about one pascal! For most purposes, the **kilopascal** is a more practical unit, although for very high pressures the megapascal is more appropriate. Normally, at sea level, our atmosphere exerts a pressure of about 100 kPa (Table 11.1). The standard atmospheric pressure of 760 mm Hg, expressed in SI units, is 101.3 kPa. Meteorologists sometimes express pressure in **bars**. One bar is equal to 100 kPa. The smaller unit, the millibar, is often used for the day-to-day measurement of atmospheric pressure. Although metric, neither of these units is part of SI.

TABLE 11.1 *Approximate Pressures in Terms of Kilopascals*	
Human blood pressure	10–20 kPa
Atmospheric pressure at sea-level	88–108 kPa
Automobile tire pressure (gauge reading)	200–240 kPa

Another unit that is not part of SI, the atmosphere (atm), is still used by many scientists when measuring very high pressures. An atmosphere is defined as being equal to standard atmospheric pressure, i.e., 7.60×10^2 mm Hg or 101.3 kPa. We can readily convert a pressure expressed in atmospheres to either millimetres of mercury or kilopascals. For example, a pressure of 15.0 atm is equivalent to

$$15.0 \text{ atm} \times \frac{101.3 \text{ kPa}}{1 \text{ atm}} = 1.52 \times 10^3 \text{ kPa (or 1.52 MPa)}$$

In English-speaking countries, a unit of pressure that is still used frequently is **pounds per square inch** (lb·in^{-2}, or psi). Some automobile tire pressure gauges (especially older ones) show pressures in these units, but newer gauges give readings in kilopascals. Many gases are supplied to laboratories and industry in pressurized cylinders, and the gauges which can be attached to these cylinders are normally calibrated in pounds per square inch. Standard atmospheric pressure can be expressed as 14.7 lb·in^{-2}.

Boyle's Law— 11.4
The Relationship
Between Pressure
and Volume

An Irish physicist, Robert Boyle, was one of the first scientists to study the effect of pressure on a gas. Although the qualitative relationship between the pressure (P) and volume (V) of a gas was probably known to many of his contemporaries, Boyle was first to express the relationship mathematically. We will not give all the details of the experiments carried out by Boyle, but will describe an experiment that gives similar results.

The apparatus consists of a 50 mL syringe and an absolute pressure gauge, Figure 11.5. Suppose the syringe is filled with air to the 20 mL mark and

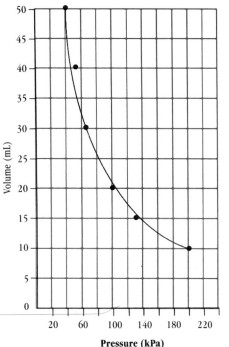

Figure 11.5

An apparatus for demonstrating Boyle's Law.

the initial gauge reading is 100 kPa. If the plunger is pulled out, thereby increasing the volume of air, the gauge reading decreases. Similarly, if the volume of air is decreased, the pressure increases. A set of typical results is shown in Table 11.2.

TABLE 11.2	*The Relationship Between the Pressure and Volume of a Gas at Constant Temperature*					
Volume (mL)	50	40	30	20	15	10
Pressure (kPa)	40	50	67	100	133	200

We can use graphs to illustrate the relationship between the pressure and volume of a gas. If we plot pressure against volume (Figure 11.6) we get a curve. A plot of one over pressure (1/pressure) against volume results in a straight line (Figure 11.7). If we conduct further experiments with other gases, we observe exactly the same kind of behaviour.

The general form for the equation of a straight line that passes through the origin of a graph (Figure 11.7) is $y = mx$, where m, the slope of the line, is a constant. If we substitute $1/P$(1/pressure) for x, V(volume) for y, and replace m with the word "constant" we get the following:

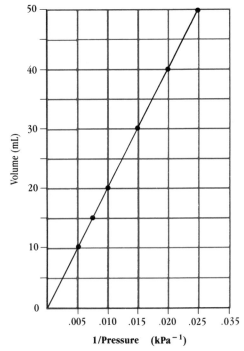

Figure 11.6

A plot of pressure against volume for a gas at constant temperature.

Figure 11.7

A plot of 1/pressure against volume for a gas at constant temperature.

$$y = mx$$

$$y = (\text{constant})\, x$$

$$y = (\text{constant})\, \frac{1}{P}$$

$$V = \frac{\text{constant}}{P}$$

This is one of the mathematical forms for **Boyle's Law**, which can be stated as follows:

At a constant temperature, the volume of a fixed mass of gas is inversely proportional to its pressure.

If we rearrange the last equation by multiplying both sides by P we arrive at the following:

$$PV = \frac{(\text{constant})\, P}{P}$$

$$PV = \text{constant}$$

Thus we can see that when we compress a fixed mass of gas at a given temperature, the product of the initial pressure, P_1, and the initial volume V_1, will be equal to the product of the new pressure, P_2, and the new volume, V_2. That is

$$P_1 V_1 = P_2 V_2 = \text{constant}$$

You might check this using the data shown in Table 11.2. The most common mathematical representation of Boyle's Law is

$$P_1 V_1 = P_2 V_2$$

and it is this form that we shall be using most frequently.

EXAMPLE　　*11.2*　　In Vancouver, a balloon with a volume of 5.0 L is filled with air at 101 kPa pressure. The balloon is then taken to Banff, where the atmospheric pressure is only 91 kPa (Banff is 1386 m above sea level). If the temperature is the same in both places, what will be the new volume of the balloon?

SOLUTION　　From Boyle's Law, the product of the original volume and pressure must equal the product of the new volume and pressure:

$$P_1 V_1 = P_2 V_2$$

$$101 \text{ kPa} \times 5.0 \text{ L} = 91 \text{ kPa} \times V_2$$

Rearranging, we find

$$V_2 = \frac{101 \text{ kPa} \times 5.0 \text{ L}}{91 \text{ kPa}} = 5.5 \text{ L}$$

QUESTIONS

2. A certain mass of gas in a 2.00 L container has a pressure of 164 kPa. What will the new pressure of the gas be if the volume of the container is reduced to 1.00 L?

3. A balloon is filled with a gas at a pressure of 102.4 kPa and its volume is determined to be 1.37 L. What will the volume of the balloon be if the pressure increases to 110.7 kPa?

Charles' Law— 11.5 The Relationship Between Volume and Temperature

We know that when a gas is heated it expands. We can show this by taking an inflated balloon and immersing it in a pan of boiling water. The balloon will increase in size and may even burst.

Measurements of the effect of temperature on the volume of a gas were first made in 1787 by the French scientist, Jacques Charles. An apparatus that can be used to make similar measurements in a high-school laboratory is shown in Figure 11.8.

A thin glass tube is sealed at one end and a plug of oil is inserted at the top of the tube. The mass of air trapped in the tube remains constant as the oil prevents the air from escaping. The top of the tube is open and therefore the pressure on the trapped air is also constant. The tube is then attached to a scale and inserted in a waterbath. The temperature of the waterbath is varied and at each temperature the height of the air in the column is measured. From the area of the cross-section of the tube and the length of the air column, we can calculate the volume of the gas at each temperature. A plot of the data obtained will show us the relationship between temperature and volume. Typical results from such an experiment are shown in Table 11.3 and Figure 11.9. Note that in practice it is not really necessary to calculate the volume of the air column in each case. As noted previously, the volume of the air column is the product of the length of the column and the cross-sectional area of the tube. The latter is a constant; thus the volume of air is directly proportional to the length of the air column, and the relationship between temperature and volume can be obtained by plotting temperature against the length of the column.

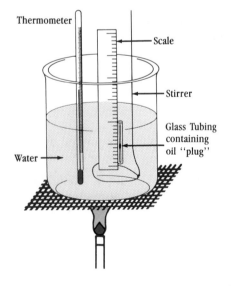

Figure 11.8

An apparatus for investigating the effect of temperature on the volume of a gas.

TABLE 11.3	*The Relationship Between the Temperature and the Volume of a Gas at Constant Pressure*					
Temperature (°C)	0	15	30	50	75	100
Volume (mm³)	32	34	36	38	41	44

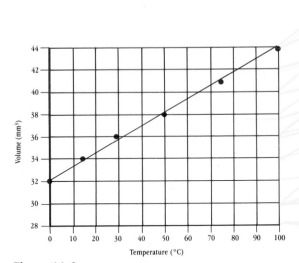

Figure 11.9
A plot of temperature against volume for a sample of gas at constant pressure.

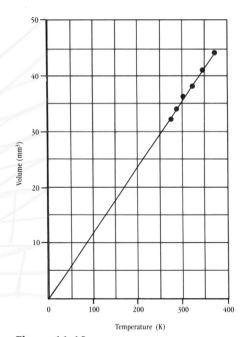

Figure 11.10
A plot of Kelvin temperature against volume for a sample of gas at constant pressure.

The straight line shown in Figure 11.9 does not pass through the origin. If we were to extend the straight line to the point where it crosses the temperature axis we would get a reading in the range of −275 °C. More precise measurements reveal that the temperature at which the line intersects the temperature axis is −273.15 °C.

A temperature scale using −273.15 °C as the zero point was developed by Lord Kelvin in 1848 and is called, not surprisingly, the **Kelvin temperature scale**. Degrees used on the Kelvin scale are called **kelvins** and are the same size as those used on the Celsius scale. The symbol for kelvins is K, not °K.

We can convert the Celsius temperatures in Table 11.3 to kelvins by adding 273.15 to each temperature value, although in practice we usually round this figure off and add 273. If we then plot a graph of Kelvin temperature against volume, a straight line passing through the origin is produced (Figure 11.10). The equation for this line can be written as

$$V = (\text{constant})\, T \quad \text{or} \quad \frac{V}{T} = \text{constant}$$

The relationship between the volume and temperature of a gas is known as **Charles' Law**, and may be expressed as follows:

At constant pressure, the volume of a fixed mass of any gas is directly proportional to its Kelvin temperature.

Since the result of dividing the volume of a fixed mass of gas at constant pressure by its Kelvin temperature is a *constant*, we can write the following relationship:

$$\frac{V_1}{T_1} = \frac{V_2}{T_2}$$

where V_1 represents the volume of the gas at a temperature T_1, and V_2 represents the volume at a second temperature, T_2. It is this form of Charles' Law that we shall use most frequently.

EXAMPLE   **11.3**   Normal body temperature is 37.0 °C. What is it on the Kelvin scale?

SOLUTION   Kelvin temperature $=$ Celsius temperature $\times \dfrac{1\ K}{1\ °C} + 273\ K$

$$= 37.0\ °\!\!\!/C \times \frac{1\ K}{1\ °\!\!\!/C} + 273\ K$$

$$= 310\ K$$

EXAMPLE   **11.4**   A balloon is filled with helium gas to a volume of 1.20 L at a pressure of 105 kPa and a temperature of 15 °C. If the pressure remains constant and the temperature rises to 30 °C, what will be the new volume of the balloon?

SOLUTION   First, the temperature must be changed to the Kelvin scale by adding 273 to the Celsius temperature. The Kelvin temperatures are 288 K and 303 K respectively.

From Charles' Law, $V_1/T_1 = V_2/T_2$, where $V_1 = 1.20\ L$, $T_1 = 288\ K$, and $T_2 = 303\ K$. Hence

$$\frac{1.20\ L}{288\ K} = \frac{V_2}{303\ K}$$

Rearranging, we find

$$V_2 = \frac{1.20\ L \times 303\ \!\!\!/K}{288\ \!\!\!/K} = 1.26\ L$$

QUESTIONS

4. The melting point of table salt is 801 °C. What is its melting point expressed in kelvins?

5. A 50.0 mL sample of gas is cooled from 119 °C to 80.0 °C. If the pressure remains constant, what is the final volume of the gas?
6. A 12 L cylinder of gas is stored at room temperature (20 °C) and a pressure of 2000 psi. If the gas is transferred to a 6.0 L cylinder, at what Celsius temperature would it have to be stored in order for the pressure to remain at 2000 psi?

Gay-Lussac's Law—The Relationship Between Pressure and Temperature

11.6

If a gas is contained in a vessel that cannot expand, such as a steel cylinder or an automobile tire, as the temperature is increased the pressure will increase. If we were to plot a graph of pressure against Kelvin temperature for a fixed mass of gas at constant volume, a straight line would be obtained. In other words, the pressure of the gas is directly proportional to the Kelvin temperature. **Gay-Lussac's Law** expresses this relationship as follows:

At constant volume, the pressure of a fixed mass of any gas is directly proportional to its Kelvin temperature.

We can write Gay-Lussac's Law in mathematical terms as

$$\frac{P}{T} = \text{constant}$$

However, the most frequently used form of this relationship is

$$\frac{P_1}{T_1} = \frac{P_2}{T_2}$$

where P_1 and P_2 represent the pressure of the gas at the temperatures T_1 and T_2. Note that Kelvin temperatures must be used throughout any calculation in which this relationship is used.

EXAMPLE　　**11.5**　A steel cylinder with a volume of 450 mL contains a gas at a pressure of 520 kPa at 25 °C. If the cylinder is heated to 410 °C, what will the new pressure be?

SOLUTION　As in Example 11.4, we must first change the temperatures to kelvins by adding 273 to the Celsius temperatures: 25 °C becomes 298 K and 410 °C becomes 683 K.
From Gay-Lussac's Law,

$$\frac{P_1}{T_1} = \frac{P_2}{T_2}$$

where $P_1 = 520$ kPa, $T_1 = 298$ K, $T_2 = 683$ K, and P_2 is the required pressure. Hence

$$\frac{520 \text{ kPa}}{298 \text{ K}} = \frac{P_2}{683 \text{ K}}$$

When rearranged, this gives

$$P_2 = \frac{520\,\text{kPa} \times 683\,\cancel{K}}{298\,\cancel{K}}$$

$$= 1.2 \times 10^3\,\text{kPa} = 1.2\,\text{MPa}$$

NOTE: In this example we have assumed that 520 kPa is correct to only two significant figures.

QUESTIONS

7. A glass vessel that can only withstand a maximum internal pressure of 225 kPa is filled with gas at 21.0 °C and 100.0 kPa and then heated. At what temperature would the vessel burst?

8. A steel cylinder is filled with gas at a temperature of 23 °C and a pressure of 2.50×10^2 kPa. What will the pressure be if the temperature is doubled to 46 °C?

The Combined Gas Equation

11.7

In each of the three gas laws discussed, one of the variables (pressure, volume, or temperature) was held constant. In practice, we often find that all three variables change. For example, when a weather balloon is released the temperature, volume, and pressure of the gas inside the balloon all change as the balloon ascends into the atmosphere. We can calculate the new value of any one of the three variables, provided that the new values of the other two are known, by using the following relationship:

$$\frac{P_1 V_1}{T_1} = \frac{P_2 V_2}{T_2}$$

This relationship is known as the **combined gas equation** because it is a combination of the equations pertaining to Boyle's, Charles', and Gay-Lussac's laws. Any units of pressure or volume may be used in this equation, but the temperature must be expressed in kelvins.

EXAMPLE   **11.6**   An aerosol can with a volume of 325 mL contains propellant gas at 445 kPa and 12 °C. What volume would the gas occupy if it was allowed to escape at 101 kPa and 21 °C?

SOLUTION   First, it is helpful to organize our data as follows:

$$P_1 = 445\,\text{kPa} \qquad P_2 = 101\,\text{kPa}$$
$$V_1 = 325\,\text{mL} \qquad V_2 = ?$$
$$T_1 = 285\,\text{K} \qquad T_2 = 294\,\text{K}$$

Inserting these values into the combined gas equation gives us

$$\frac{445 \, \text{kPa} \times 325 \, \text{mL}}{285 \, \text{K}} = \frac{101 \, \text{kPa} \times V_2}{294 \, \text{K}}$$

$$V_2 = \frac{445 \, \cancel{\text{kPa}} \times 325 \, \text{mL}}{285 \, \cancel{\text{K}}} \times \frac{294 \, \cancel{\text{K}}}{101 \, \cancel{\text{kPa}}}$$

$$= 1.48 \times 10^3 \, \text{mL}$$

$$= 1.48 \, \text{L}$$

When using the combined gas equation to solve a problem you should always check your answer to see if it seems reasonable. Note that in Example 11.6 the pressure dropped to about one-fourth of its original value. This would cause the volume to increase about four times. The temperature increased slightly, which would lead to a small further increase in volume. The new volume should therefore be over four times its old value. This was found in the calculation.

Figure 11.11

An apparatus for demonstrating Gay-Lussac's Law. The bulb is placed in baths held at different temperatures and the corresponding pressure readings are noted.

Figure 11.12

Mount St. Helen's in eruption. This photograph shows an extreme example of the combined gas law. The gases, which are at high temperature and very high pressure inside the earth, expand with explosive force when they are exposed to atmospheric pressure at the earth's surface.

QUESTIONS

9. A weather balloon with a volume of 55.0 L is filled with hydrogen gas at a pressure of 98.5 kPa and a temperature of 13 °C. When the balloon is released, it rises to the stratosphere where the temperature is −48 °C and the pressure is 19.7 kPa. What is the volume of the balloon under these conditions?

10. At 20 °C, a cylinder of acetylene gas has a pressure of 17.0 atm and a volume of 2.00 L. What volume would the contents of this cylinder occupy at a pressure of 1.0 atm and a temperature of 25.0 °C?

11. A balloon is filled with gas at a pressure of 103.2 kPa and a temperature of 50.0 °C. Its volume under these conditions is 13.6 L. The balloon is taken into a decompression chamber where the volume is measured as 2.75 L. If the temperature is 34 °C, what is the pressure in the chamber?

12. A weather balloon contains 15.0 L of helium at a pressure of 97.6 kPa and a temperature of 11 °C. If this gas was stored in a 1.00 L cylinder at 19 °C, what must the pressure in the cylinder have been?

The Kinetic–   <u>11.8</u>   Molecular Theory Revisited

From the kinetic-molecular theory, we picture a gas as consisting of many particles (atoms or molecules) that move around both randomly and independently within the volume defined by the vessel containing the gas. In developing this theory, a number of assumptions were made about these particles. These are summarized below:

1. The volume of the particles is negligible compared to the volume of the container. In other words, a sample of gas is mainly empty space.
2. The particles are in rapid, straight-line motion. They collide with each other, and with the walls of the container.
3. There is no loss of energy when two particles collide.
4. In the gas phase there are no attractive forces between particles (this is in contrast with the liquid and solid phases).
5. At any given temperature, the average kinetic energy of the particles in all gases is the same.

We will now see how the kinetic-molecular theory helps us to explain Boyle's Law.

Suppose we have a small sample of gas consisting of several million particles moving around in a confined space. According to the kinetic-molecular theory (assumption 2), there will be collisions occurring between the particles, and also between the particles and the surface of the container. The collisions between the particles and the walls of the container are recorded as pressure. The greater the number of collisions per second on a given surface area, the greater the pressure. As the volume of the gas container is decreased, the particles collide more frequently with the container walls (Figure 11.13). This means that the particles exert a greater force over any given area, and an increase in pressure is observed (pressure = force per

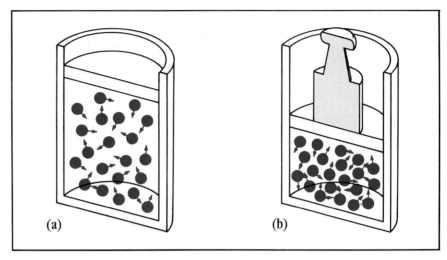

Figure 11.13
When the volume of a gas container is decreased, the gas particles collide with the container walls more frequently and an increase in pressure is observed.

(a)   (b)

unit area). Conversely, if the volume of the container is increased, the particles will have much further to travel between collisions with the container walls, and hence they will collide with the walls less frequently. The number of particles colliding with a given area of the wall at any instant will be lower than before and a decrease in pressure will be observed.

QUESTIONS

13. Use the kinetic-molecular theory to explain why it is much easier to compress gases than solids or liquids.

The Kinetic Energy of Gas Molecules

11.9 According to assumption 5 of the kinetic-molecular theory, at any given temperature, the average kinetic energy of the particles in all gases is the same. **Kinetic energy** is the energy possessed by a moving object. The kinetic energy of an object depends on both its mass and its velocity. The exact relationship is

$$\text{Kinetic energy} = \frac{1}{2} \times \text{Mass} \times \text{Velocity}^2$$

or, expressed in algebraic form

$$KE = \frac{1}{2} mv^2$$

If assumption 5 of the kinetic-molecular theory is valid, then we must conclude that, if we have a sample of hydrogen gas (H_2) and oxygen gas (O_2) at the same temperature, the hydrogen molecules and the oxygen molecules will have the same average kinetic energy. As the mass of an oxygen molecule is sixteen times greater than the mass of a hydrogen molecule, this means that the average velocity of an oxygen molecule must be less than the average velocity of a hydrogen molecule in order for both molecules to have the same average kinetic energy. In general, at any given temperature, the higher the molar mass of a gas, the lower the average velocity of its molecules (Table 11.4).

TABLE 11.4 *Average Velocity of Selected Gas Molecules at 25 °C*

Gas	Molar Mass	Average Velocity	Average Velocity
	$(g \cdot mol^{-1})$	$(m \cdot s^{-1})$	$(km \cdot hr^{-1})$
H_2	2.02	1769	6368
He	4.00	1250	4500
O_2	16.0	442	1590
UF_6	352	133	479

The relatively high velocities of hydrogen molecules and helium atoms explain why the earth's atmosphere contains very little of these two gases. They escaped from the earth's gravitational field many millions of years ago.

The average velocity of gas particles also depends on the temperature of the gas. As the temperature increases, the average velocity of the particles increases. Similarly, if the temperature decreases, the average velocity of the particles decreases. The temperature at which the particles would cease to move and would therefore have zero kinetic energy is called absolute zero. Absolute zero is equivalent to zero on the Kelvin temperature scale (i.e. $-273.15 °C$).

QUESTIONS

14.. How can the increase in kinetic energy of gas molecules that accompanies an increase in temperature be used to explain a) Charles' Law, and b) Gay-Lussac's Law?

Standard Temperature and Pressure (STP) 11.10

To compare the results obtained in experiments involving gases at various temperatures and pressures, scientists have defined a **standard temperature and pressure** (STP). Experimental results can then be converted to give values that would have been obtained under the standard conditions.

The conditions selected were a temperature of 273 K (0 °C) and a pressure of 101.3 kPa (1 atm). It is normally inconvenient to carry out an experiment at STP as the temperature in a laboratory is usually well above 0 °C and the atmospheric pressure is seldom exactly 101.3 kPa. However, if we record the temperature and pressure when we make our measurements, we can use the combined gas equation to convert our data to values that would have been obtained at STP. This is illustrated in the following example.

EXAMPLE **11.7**   A gas occupies a volume of 18.0 L at a pressure of 88.7 kPa and a temperature of 127 °C. What would its volume be at STP?

SOLUTION   We use the combined gas equation

$$\frac{P_1 V_1}{T_1} = \frac{P_2 V_2}{T_2}$$

to find the unknown volume. If we let P_1, V_1, and T_1 represent the given pressure, volume, and temperature, then P_2, V_2, and T_2 will represent these variables at STP. Thus we have

P_1 = 88.7 kPa	P_2 = 101.3 kPa
V_1 = 18.0 L	V_2 = ?
T_1 = 400 K	T_2 = 273 K

Hence

$$\frac{88.7 \text{ kPa} \times 18.0 \text{ L}}{400 \text{ K}} = \frac{101.3 \text{ kPa} \times V_2}{273 \text{ K}}$$

$$V_2 = \frac{88.7 \text{ kPa} \times 18.0 \text{ L} \times 273 \text{ K}}{400 \text{ K} \times 101.3 \text{ kPa}}$$

$$= 10.8 \text{ L}$$

QUESTIONS

15. A gas occupies a volume of 25.0 L at a pressure of 105 kPa and a temperature of −25 °C. What volume would the gas occupy at STP?

Molar Volume

11.11   If we measure the densities of helium and neon gas at STP we obtain values of 0.1786 g·L⁻¹ and 0.901 g·L⁻¹ respectively. Let us now calculate the volume occupied by exactly one mole of each of these noble gases at STP. In each case we can use the inverted form of density as our conversion factor:

$$\text{Volume of 1 mol (4.00 g) of He} = 4.00 \text{ g} \times \frac{1 \text{ L}}{0.1786 \text{ g}}$$

$$= 22.4 \text{ L}$$

$$\text{Volume of 1 mol (20.2 g) of Ne} = 20.2 \cancel{g} \times \frac{1 \text{ L}}{0.901 \cancel{g}}$$

$$= 22.4 \text{ L}$$

You can see that the volume occupied at STP by one mole of both these gases is 22.4 L. This is true not only for helium and neon, but for all the noble gases. In fact, the volume of one mole of any gas at STP is usually quite close to 22.4 L. As a fair approximation, we can say that

At STP, one mole of any gas occupies a volume of 22.4 L.

Thus, $22.4 \text{ L} \cdot \text{mol}^{-1}$ is known as the **molar volume**, and just as molar mass may be considered to be a conversion factor relating moles of substance to mass, molar volume relates moles of gas to volume (measured at STP).

EXAMPLE ***11.8*** Calculate the density of hydrogen gas at STP.

SOLUTION Despite the apparent lack of information given in the question this problem can be readily solved by considering 1.00 mol of $H_{2 \text{ (g)}}$ at STP. We can use the molar mass ($2.02 \text{ g} \cdot \text{mol}^{-1}$) to obtain the mass of $H_{2 \text{ (g)}}$:

$$\text{Mass of 1.00 mol of } H_2 = 1.00 \cancel{\text{mol } H_2} \times \frac{2.02 \text{ g } H_2}{1 \cancel{\text{mol } H_2}}$$

$$= 2.02 \text{ g } H_2$$

The volume of $H_{2 \text{ (g)}}$ can then be obtained from its molar volume ($22.4 \text{ L} \cdot \text{mol}^{-1}$):

$$\text{Volume of 1.00 mol of } H_2 \text{ at STP} = 1.00 \cancel{\text{mol } H_2} \times \frac{22.4 \text{ L } H_2}{1 \cancel{\text{mol } H_2}}$$

$$= 22.4 \text{ L } H_2$$

Thus

$$\text{Density of } H_2 \text{ at STP} = \frac{\text{mass of 1.00 mol } H_2}{\text{volume of 1.00 mol } H_2 \text{ at STP}}$$

$$= \frac{2.02 \text{ g}}{22.4 \text{ L}}$$

$$= 9.02 \times 10^{-2} \text{ g} \cdot \text{L}^{-1}$$

QUESTIONS

16. Calculate the density of sulfur dioxide at STP.

17. The density of a gaseous element at STP is $5.86 \text{ g} \cdot \text{L}^{-1}$. Determine the molar mass of this element and identify it.

The Ideal Gas Equation

An ideal gas is defined as a gas that conforms to the assumptions of the kinetic-molecular theory and follows the gas laws exactly. In reality, no gas conforms completely with these assumptions. Two of the assumptions in the kinetic-molecular theory are that the gas particles have zero volume and that there are no attractive forces acting between them. In practice the particles do have volumes and there are attractive forces between them.

Although ideal gases do not exist, as long as we avoid low temperatures and high pressures most gases behave as if they were ideal. Thus the relationships described in Sections 11.4 through 11.7 are quite valid. An additional relationship, which in general is more useful than those previously described, is the **ideal gas equation**. This equation relates the pressure, volume and temperature of a gas to the number of moles of gas present. Let us see how this equation can be derived, starting from the combined gas equation:

$$\frac{P_1 V_1}{T_1} = \frac{P_2 V_2}{T_2}$$

Suppose that P_2, V_2, and T_2 apply to one mole of a gas at STP. Then $P_2 = 101.3$ kPa, $V_2 = 1$ mol $\times$ (22.4 L/1 mol), and $T_2 = 273$ K. Thus we would write

$$\frac{P_1 V_1}{T_1} = \frac{101.3 \text{ kPa}}{273 \text{ K}} \times \frac{1 \text{ mol} \times 22.4 \text{ L}}{1 \text{ mol}}$$

If, instead of having just one mole of gas we have n moles, the expression becomes

$$\frac{P_1 V_1}{T_1} = \frac{101.3 \text{ kPa}}{273 \text{ K}} \times n \times \frac{22.4 \text{ L}}{1 \text{ mol}}$$

Let us rearrange this expression so that all the symbols are on the left-hand side of the equation:

$$\frac{P_1 V_1}{n T_1} = \frac{101.3 \text{ kPa} \times 22.4 \text{ L}}{273 \text{ K} \times 1 \text{ mol}}$$

If we now drop the subscripts and evaluate the numerical portion of the equation, we obtain

$$\frac{PV}{nT} = 8.31 \text{ kPa} \cdot \text{L} \cdot \text{mol}^{-1} \cdot \text{K}^{-1}$$

Thus for any sample of gas, the product of the pressure and volume divided by the product of the temperature and the number of moles of gas present is equal to a constant, 8.31 kPa$\cdot$L$\cdot$mol$^{-1}\cdot$K^{-1}. This constant is

P = Pressure

known as the **universal gas constant** and is given the symbol R. Substituting this symbol into the previous equation, we obtain

$$PV/nT = R \quad \text{Or} \quad PV = nRT$$

The latter form, which is the form encountered most frequently, is known as the ideal gas equation.

Although R is a constant, it does have other values that correspond to different systems of units. For example, if the pressure is given in atmospheres instead of kilopascals, the constant is $0.0821 \ L \cdot atm \cdot mol^{-1} \cdot K^{-1}$.

EXAMPLE   **11.9**   A 2.50 L container is filled with sulfur dioxide gas at a pressure of 120.0 kPa and a temperature of 27.0 °C. Calculate the mass of sulfur dioxide gas in the container.

SOLUTION   **STRATEGY**

1. Volume of gas $\longrightarrow$ Moles of gas
2. Moles of gas $\longrightarrow$ Mass of gas

STEP 1:   We apply the ideal gas equation to determine the number of moles of $SO_{2\ (g)}$ present:

$$PV = nRT$$

$$120.0 \ kPa \times 2.50 \ L = n \times 8.31 \ kPa \cdot L \cdot mol^{-1} \cdot K^{-1} \times 300 \ K$$

Thus

$$n = \frac{120.0 \ kPa \times 2.50 \ L}{8.31 \ kPa \cdot L \cdot mol^{-1} \cdot K^{-1} \times 300 \ K}$$

$$= 0.120 \ mol$$

STEP 2:   We now use the molar mass of sulfur dioxide ($64.1 \ g \cdot mol^{-1}$) to convert from number of moles to mass.

$$\text{Mass of sulfur dioxide} = 0.120 \ mol \ SO_2 \times \frac{64.1 \ g \ SO_2}{1 \ mol \ SO_2}$$

$$= 7.69 \ g \ SO_2$$

EXAMPLE   **11.10**   Find the volume of 1.00 g of water in the gas phase at its boiling point (100 °C) at standard atmospheric pressure.

SOLUTION   **STRATEGY**

1. Mass of gas $\longrightarrow$ Moles of gas
2. Moles of gas $\longrightarrow$ Volume of gas

Figure 11.14

An apparatus that can be used for measuring the molar mass of a gas. By finding the mass of a known volume of gas at a known temperature and pressure, we can calculate its molar mass.

STEP 1:   We first determine the number of moles of water using the molar mass of water ($18.0 \, \text{g} \cdot \text{mol}^{-1}$) as our conversion factor.

$$\text{Number of moles of water} \; = \; 1.00 \, \text{g H}_2\text{O} \times \frac{1 \, \text{mol H}_2\text{O}}{18.0 \, \text{g H}_2\text{O}}$$

$$= \; 5.56 \times 10^{-2} \, \text{mol H}_2\text{O}$$

STEP 2:   Using the ideal gas equation

$$PV \; = \; nRT$$

$$1.00 \, \text{atm} \times V \; = \; 5.56 \times 10^{-2} \, \text{mol} \times 0.0821 \, \text{L} \cdot \text{atm} \cdot \text{mol}^{-1} \cdot \text{K}^{-1} \times 375 \, \text{K}$$

Thus

$$V \; = \; \frac{5.56 \times 10^{-2} \, \text{mol} \times 0.0821 \, \text{L} \cdot \text{atm} \cdot \text{mol}^{-1} \cdot \text{K}^{-1} \times 373 \, \text{K}}{1.00 \, \text{atm}}$$

$$= \; 1.70 \, \text{L}$$

(This is very different from the 1.00 mL that the 1.00 g of water would occupy as a liquid at room temperature!)

The ideal gas equation is of particular use to us when we wish to determine the molar mass of an unknown gas. The experimental procedure involves pumping the air out of a glass bulb of known volume, measuring the mass of the empty bulb, and then filling it with the gas of unknown molar mass at a known temperature and pressure. The mass of the bulb and its contents is then determined, and by subtracting the mass of the empty bulb we can then determine the mass of the unknown gas. The required molar mass can then be determined by the method shown in Example 11.11.

EXAMPLE   11.11   At 100 °C, a glass bulb with a volume of 248 mL contains 1.24 g of a compound in the gas phase. If the pressure of the gas is 101 kPa, what is the molar mass of the compound?

SOLUTION

> **STRATEGY**
>
> 1. Volume of gas ⟶ Moles of gas
> 2. Moles of gas ⟶ Molar mass of gas

STEP 1:   First, we determine the number of moles of gas in the container using the ideal gas equation, which we rearrange as follows:

$$n \; = \; \frac{PV}{RT}$$

$$= \; \frac{101 \, \text{kPa} \times 0.248 \, \text{L}}{8.31 \, \text{kPa} \cdot \text{L} \cdot \text{mol}^{-1} \cdot \text{K}^{-1} \times 373 \, \text{K}}$$

$$= \; 8.08 \times 10^{-3} \, \text{mol}$$

STEP 2: Since we know that 8.08×10^{-3} mol of the gas has a mass of 1.24 g, we can determine the required molar mass:

$$\text{Molar mass of gas} = \frac{1.24 \text{ g}}{8.08 \times 10^{-3} \text{ mol}}$$

$$= 153 \text{ g} \cdot \text{mol}^{-1}$$

In Section 7.5, we saw how the empirical formula of a compound can be determine from its percentage composition. We also saw that the molar mass of the compound is required in order to find its molecular formula once the empirical formula is known. We have just seen how the molar mass of a compound can be determined experimentally. Example 11.12 shows how we can use the ideal gas equation in combination with percentage composition data in order to determine the molecular formula of an unknown compound.

EXAMPLE   *11.12*   One of the components of gasoline is benzene, a compound that consists of 92.24% carbon and 7.76% hydrogen. When a sample of 15.62 g of benzene was placed in a sealed container with a volume of 3.78 L and heated to 110 °C, the benzene vaporized and the resulting pressure inside the container was 168.4 kPa. Determine the molecular formula of benzene.

SOLUTION   First we will determine the molar mass of benzene using the same strategy that we employed in Example 11.11. The number of moles of benzene can be found using the ideal gas equation:

$$n = \frac{PV}{RT} = \frac{168.4 \text{ kPa} \times 3.78 \text{ L}}{8.31 \text{ kPa} \cdot \text{L} \cdot \text{mol}^{-1} \cdot \text{K}^{-1} \times 383 \text{ K}}$$

$$= 0.200 \text{ mol}$$

Thus, 0.200 mol of benzene has a mass of 15.62 g.

$$\text{Molar mass of benzene} = \frac{15.62 \text{ g}}{0.200 \text{ mol}}$$

$$= 78.1 \text{ g} \cdot \text{mol}^{-1}$$

Let us now determine the empirical formula of benzene from its percentage composition. If we assume that we have 100.0 g of benzene, we will have 92.24 g of carbon and 7.76 g of hydrogen. Converting from mass to moles, we obtain

$$92.24 \text{ g C} \times \frac{1 \text{ mol C}}{12.0 \text{ g C}} = 7.68 \text{ mol C}$$

$$7.76 \, g\cancel{H} \times \frac{1 \, mol \, H}{1.01 \, g\cancel{H}} = 7.68 \, mol \, H$$

As the number of moles of carbon and hydrogen are equal, benzene must contain an equal number of carbon and hydrogen atoms. In other words, in the benzene molecule we have a 1:1 ratio of carbon to hydrogen, and the empirical formula is therefore CH. The empirical-formula mass of benzene is

$$12.0 \, g + 1.01 \, g = 13.0 \, g$$

and, as we have just found, its molar mass is $78.1 \, g \cdot mol^{-1}$. Thus

$$\frac{\text{Mass of one mole}}{\text{Empirical-formula mass}} = \frac{78.1 \, g}{13.0 \, g} = 6.00$$

Therefore

$$\text{Molecular formula} = 6 \times \text{Empirical formula}$$
$$= (CH)_6 = C_6H_6$$

QUESTIONS

18. A gas cylinder with a capacity of 105 L contains helium at a pressure of 6.70 MPa and a temperature of 27 °C. Calculate the mass of helium gas in the cylinder.

19. The ill-fated dirigible, Hindenburg, contained 8.92×10^6 mol of hydrogen gas. Calculate the volume occupied by this amount of hydrogen at a temperature of 27 °C and a pressure of 105 kPa.

20. A chemist isolated an unreactive gas. As it would not give a positive response to any of the tests for the common gases, the molar mass was determined to help with its identification. At 30.0 °C and 98.0 kPa, it was found that 2.00 L of the gas had a mass of 6.52 g. What is the molar mass of the gas?

21. A gas formed by uranium and fluorine is used to assist in the separation of the isotopes U-235 and U-238. At a temperature of 75 °C and a pressure of 98.5 kPa, 1.00 g of this uranium-fluorine compound occupies a volume of 83.3 mL. Determine the molar mass of the gas and deduce its formula.

22. Combustion of 0.100 g of a compound containing only carbon, oxygen, and hydrogen produced 0.238 g of carbon dioxide and 0.122 g of water. In a separate experiment, it was found that 2.418 g of this substance occupied a volume of 1.00 L at a pressure of 101.3 kPa and a temperature of 100 °C. Find the molecular formula of the unknown compound.

Vapour Pressure

11.13

John Dalton, an English schoolteacher, performed many experiments that involved measuring the water content of air. In the course of his experiments, Dalton found that if water is placed in a sealed container, some of the liquid evaporates to form water vapour. He also observed that the water vapour exerted a pressure on the walls of the container. This pressure is known as the **vapour pressure** of water.

At any given temperature and pressure, only a certain proportion of a liquid will evaporate. The air above the liquid is said to be saturated when it can no longer hold any more vapour of that liquid; thus, at any given temperature, there is a maximum value for the vapour pressure of a liquid. The term **relative humidity**, used by weather broadcasters, refers to the actual proportion of water vapour present in the air compared to the maximum that could be present at that temperature. Warm air can contain a larger proportion of water vapour than cold air. This is why some of the water vapour falls to the ground as precipitation when warm moist air cools down.

Boiling Point of a Liquid

Every liquid evaporates until the air above that liquid is saturated. In other words, every liquid exerts a vapour pressure, and this vapour pressure increases with increasing temperature. When the vapour pressure equals atmospheric pressure, the liquid begins to boil. The temperature at which this occurs is called the **boiling point** of the liquid. Thus we may now correctly define the boiling point of a liquid as the temperature at which its vapour pressure equals atmospheric pressure. As atmospheric pressure varies from one location to another, we should say that the *normal* boiling point of a liquid is the temperature at which its vapour pressure is 101.3 kPa. For water, this temperature is 100 °C (373 K). The variation of the vapour pressure of water with temperature is shown in Table 11.5.

The increase in the vapour pressure of a substance with increasing temperature can be explained using the kinetic-molecular theory. At the melting point of a substance, only a very small portion of the molecules will have sufficient kinetic energy to escape to the gas phase. Thus at the melting point, the vapour pressure is very low. As the temperature increases, the average kinetic energy of the molecules increases. More molecules acquire enough energy to escape into the gas phase, and therefore the vapour pressure increases.

Can you suggest why different liquids have different boiling points? As we saw in Chapter 1, substances are held in the liquid state by the attraction between particles (molecules). If this attraction is strong, only a small number of molecules will have enough energy to overcome it and escape into the gas phase. If the attraction is weak, more particles will escape. Thus, at any given temperature, liquids with strong attractive forces between

TABLE 11.5
Vapour Pressure of Water at Various Temperatures

Temperature (°C)	Pressure (kPa)
0	0.61
20	2.34
40	7.37
60	19.9
80	47.3
100	101.3

molecules have a lower vapour pressure than liquids with weak attractive forces between molecules. Vapour pressure and boiling point data for some liquids are listed in Table 11.6. As you can see from the table, the lower the vapour pressure at room temperature, the higher the boiling point.

Liquid	Vapour Pressure at 25 °C (kPa)	Normal Boiling Point (°C)
Diethyl ether	57.9	34
Ethyl alcohol	5.6	78
Water	2.3	100
Mercury	2.4×10^{-2}	357

TABLE 11.6 *The Vapour Pressure (at 25 °C) and Boiling Points of Some Liquids*

Liquids such as diethyl ether, which have a high vapour pressure at room temperature, will evaporate rapidly if left in open containers. These liquids should be stored in sealed containers that once opened, should be refrigerated to lower the vapour pressure and slow the evaporation process. As we discussed in Chapter 9, mercury vapour is extremely poisonous. The vapour pressure of mercury is very low and a small quantity of mercury can emit poisonous vapour for many years. This is why it is very important to ensure that all spilled mercury (for example, from a broken thermometer bulb) is collected and disposed of safely.

Boiling Point and Atmospheric Pressure

The boiling points in Table 11.6 are for liquids at an atmospheric pressure of 101.3 kPa. If the pressure changes, the boiling point will also change. The boiling point of water is less than 100 °C at any place significantly above sea level because atmospheric pressure decreases with increased altitude. Thus it will take longer to cook a hard-boiled egg if you are camping high in the Rocky Mountains than it will if you are holding a cook-out on an Atlantic beach in New Brunswick, which is at sea level. The cooking time is longer at the higher altitude because the vapour pressure of the water reaches atmospheric pressure at a lower temperature and therefore the boiling point of water is lower. Conversely, if we were to increase the air pressure acting on the surface of the water, the boiling point of the water would be above 100 °C. This is the principle used in pressure cookers. A weight placed on top of the lid prevents steam (water vapour at the boiling point of water) from escaping. This allows the pressure of the steam to build up inside the pan to well above normal atmospheric pressure. The increase in pressure raises the boiling point of the water in the pan, resulting in a higher water temperature and a shorter cooking time.

Dalton's Law 11.14 of Partial Pressures

In Chapter 8, we saw that gases are produced in many chemical reactions. For example, we studied the decomposition reaction

$$2 \, H_2O_{2 \, (aq)} \xrightarrow{MnO_2} 2 \, H_2O_{(\ell)} + O_{2 \, (g)}$$

the single displacement reaction

$$Zn_{(s)} + 2 \, HCl_{(aq)} \longrightarrow ZnCl_{2 \, (aq)} + H_{2 \, (g)}$$

and the double displacement reaction

$$CaCO_{3 \, (s)} + 2 \, HCl_{(aq)} \longrightarrow CaCl_{2 \, (aq)} + H_2O_{(\ell)} + CO_{2 \, (g)}$$

In the laboratory preparation of gases such as oxygen and hydrogen, the gas is usually collected by the displacement of water (Figure 11.15).

When all the water is displaced, the pressure of the gas in the jar is equal to the atmospheric pressure. The jar is now full of the gas that we are preparing... or is it? As we discussed in the last section, some of the water molecules in the gas jar will have sufficient energy to change to the vapour phase. Thus our jar really contains a mixture of gases, i.e. water vapour plus the gas we are preparing (for example, oxygen or hydrogen). Each of these gases contributes to the total pressure in the jar. The contribution made by each gas is called its **partial pressure**.

John Dalton combined many observations on gases to formulate his **Law of Partial Pressures**. This law states that

> **The total pressure of a mixture of gases is equal to the sum of the partial pressures of the component gases.**

Thus if we have a mixture of water vapour and oxygen at standard atmospheric pressure and 25 °C, where the vapour pressure of water is 2.3 kPa, the partial pressure of the oxygen present is 99.0 kPa (101.3 kPa − 2.3 kPa).

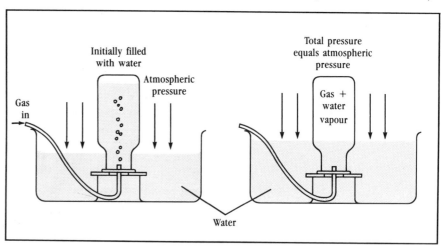

Figure 11.15

Collecting a gas by the displacement of water. The gas-filled jar also contains water vapour.

Dalton and Modern Chemistry

John Dalton was born in Cumberland, England in 1766. He was a self-educated professional scientist at a time when science was mainly the preserve of the rich and university-educated sector of society. Dalton's first (and lifelong) scientific study was in the field of meteorology. For 57 years he kept records of the weather, looking for patterns in rainfall and temperature. We now know this is a fruitless exercise as a basis for weather prediction. However, Dalton's interest in the atmosphere resulted in the development of the Law of Partial Pressures, one of his first major achievements.

Dalton is remembered most for his atomic theory, although at the time it was formulated it was strongly criticized. We still do not have a good understanding of how Dalton developed his ideas on atomic theory. Biographers of Dalton (and of many other scientists) have mixed myth, ideology, and reality, which has resulted in a simplistic and erroneous image of the man. For example, it is often said that Dalton had a contempt for books, but this is contradicted by the fact that his personal collection is known to have totalled over 700 volumes!

Dalton was colour-blind, and was the first person to examine this phenomenon on a scientific basis. He proposed an explanation for colour blindness and instructed that, on his death, his eyes should be dissected in an attempt to confirm his hypothesis. His wishes were carried out, but ironically the results of the dissection contradicted his hypothesis.

Figure 11.16
John Dalton (1766–1844), the founder of modern atomic theory.

EXAMPLE   *11.13*   When nitrogen is introduced into a 1.0 L flask that already contains oxygen, the pressure in the flask increases from 35 kPa to 77 kPa. Calculate the partial pressure of each gas in the final mixture.

SOLUTION   The original pressure of O_2 (35 kPa) becomes the partial pressure of O_2 when the gases are mixed. As we know the total pressure of the mixture (77 kPa), we can use Dalton's Law of Partial Pressures to determine the partial pressure of N_2 in the mixture:

$$P_{tot} = P_{O_2} + P_{N_2}$$
$$77 \text{ kPa} = 35 \text{ kPa} + P_{N_2}$$
$$P_{N_2} = 77 \text{ kPa} - 35 \text{ kPa} = 42 \text{ kPa}$$

Therefore, partial pressures in the final mixture are

$$P_{N_2} = 42 \text{ kPa} \text{ and } P_{O_2} = 35 \text{ kPa}$$

If we collect a gas in the laboratory using the apparatus shown in Figure 11.5, and we wish to carry out a calculation that involves using the pressure of the gas, we must first correct for the water vapour present. We do this by subtracting the vapour pressure of water at the appropriate temperature from the pressure of the gas plus the water vapour (i.e. from the total atmospheric pressure). The difference is the partial pressure of the gas that has been collected. The following example illustrates a typical application of such a calculation.

EXAMPLE   *11.14*   A student performs an experiment in which hydrogen gas is prepared by the action of hydrochloric acid on zinc metal. After collecting 250 mL of the gas by the method illustrated in Figure 11.15, the student records the atmospheric pressure as 99.2 kPa and the temperature in the laboratory as 24 °C. Given that the vapour pressure of water is 2.98 kPa at 24 °C, what mass of hydrogen has been collected?

SOLUTION   *STRATEGY*

1. **Total pressure of mixture** ⟶ **Partial pressure of hydrogen**
2. **Partial pressure of hydrogen** ⟶ **Moles of hydrogen**
3. **Moles of hydrogen** ⟶ **Mass of hydrogen**

STEP 1:   The jar contains a mixture of hydrogen gas and water vapour. The total pressure of this mixture is equal to the partial pressure of the hydrogen gas plus the partial pressure of the water vapour. The latter is equal to the vapour pressure of water under the experimental conditions. In addition, the total pressure of the hydrogen–water vapour mixture is equal to the atmospheric pressure. Thus, using the Law of Partial Pressures, we can find the partial pressure of hydrogen gas as follows:

$$P_{tot} = P_{H_2} + P_{H_2O}$$
$$99.2 \text{ kPa} = P_{H_2} + 2.98 \text{ kPa}$$
$$P_{H_2} = 99.2 \text{ kPa} - 2.98 \text{ kPa}$$
$$= 96.2 \text{ kPa}.$$

STEP 2:   The partial pressure of the hydrogen gas is the pressure that the gas would exert in the jar if no other gases were present. We can use this partial pressure in the ideal gas equation $PV = nRT$ to find the number of moles of hydrogen gas present.

Where

$$n = \text{number of moles of hydrogen gas}$$

$$P = 96.2 \text{ kPA} \qquad V = 250 \text{ mL} = 0.25 \text{ L}$$

$$R = 8.31 \text{ kPa} \cdot \text{L} \cdot \text{mol}^{-1} \cdot \text{K}^{-1} \qquad T = 297 \text{ K}$$

Rearranging the ideal gas equation, we obtain

$$n = \frac{PV}{RT} = \frac{96.2 \text{ kPa} \times 0.25 \text{ L}}{8.31 \text{ kPa} \cdot \text{L} \cdot \text{mol}^{-1} \cdot \text{K}^{-1} \times 297 \text{ K}}$$

$$= 9.7 \times 10^{-3} \text{ mol}$$

NOTE: We are now using only two significant figures, as the volume, i.e. 250 mL, is assumed to have only two significant figures.

STEP 3: The mass of hydrogen gas can now be determined using the molar mass of hydrogen ($2.02 \text{ g} \cdot \text{mol}^{-1}$) as the conversion factor

$$\text{Mass of H}_{2 \, (g)} \text{ formed} = 9.7 \times 10^{-3} \text{ mol H}_2 \times \frac{2.02 \text{ g H}_2}{1 \text{ mol H}_2}$$

$$= 2.0 \times 10^{-2} \text{ g H}_2$$

We can derive a general formula that will allow us to calculate the partial pressure of each component in a mixture of gases if the total pressure and the composition of the mixture are known. Suppose the total pressure of the gas mixture is P_{tot} with a volume V at temperature T, and the total number of moles of gas is n_{tot}. We can use the ideal gas equation to write

$$P_{tot}V = n_{tot}RT$$

If one of the components, A, of this mixture consists of n_A moles of gas exerting a partial pressure of P_A, we can write

$$P_A V = n_A RT$$

By dividing one expression into the other we obtain

$$\frac{P_A V}{P_{tot} V} = \frac{n_A RT}{n_{tot} RT}$$

and cancelling V, R, and T, we obtain

$$\frac{P_A}{P_{tot}} = \frac{n_A}{n_{tot}}$$

which we can rearrange to give a new expression for the partial pressure of A

$$P_A = P_{tot} \times \frac{n_A}{n_{tot}}$$

The fraction n_A/n_{tot} (i.e. the number of moles of gas A divided by the total number of moles of gas) is called the **mole fraction** of A. We shall use this term again in Chapter 12.

A similar expression may be written for the partial pressure of component B of our gas mixture, i.e.

$$P_B = P_{tot} \times \frac{n_B}{n_{tot}}$$

EXAMPLE **11.15** A mixture of 1.0 g of hydrogen and 8.0 g of oxygen has a total pressure of 66 kPa. Calculate the partial pressure exerted by each gas.

SOLUTION We first calculate the number of moles of each gas present as follows:

$$\text{Number of moles of hydrogen} = n_{H_2} = 1.0\,\text{g}\,\cancel{H_2} \times \frac{1\;\text{mol}\;H_2}{2.02\,\text{g}\,\cancel{H_2}}$$

$$= 0.50\;\text{mol}\;H_2$$

$$\text{Number of moles of oxygen} = n_{O_2} = 8.0\,\text{g}\,\cancel{O_2} \times \frac{1\;\text{mol}\;O_2}{32.0\,\text{g}\,\cancel{O_2}}$$

$$= 0.25\;\text{mol}\;O_2$$

We have just seen that the partial pressure of any component in a mixture of gases is equal to the mole fraction of that component multiplied by the total pressure of the mixture. Hence

$$P_{H_2} = P_{tot} \times \frac{n_{O_2}}{n_{H_2} + n_{O_2}} = 66\;\text{kPa} \times \frac{0.50\;\text{mol}}{0.50\;\text{mol} + 0.25\;\text{mol}}$$

$$= 66\;\text{kPa} \times \frac{0.50\;\cancel{\text{mol}}}{0.75\;\cancel{\text{mol}}} = 44\;\text{kPa}$$

and

$$P_{O_2} = P_{tot} \times \frac{n_{O_2}}{n_{H_2} + n_{O_2}} = 66\;\text{kPa} \times \frac{0.25\;\text{mol}}{0.50\;\text{mol} + 0.25\;\text{mol}}$$

$$= 66\;\text{kPa} \times \frac{0.25\;\cancel{\text{mol}}}{0.75\;\cancel{\text{mol}}} = 22\;\text{kPa}$$

QUESTIONS

23. Clean, dry air is a mixture of nitrogen and oxygen, with small quantities of other gases. If the partial pressure of nitrogen and the minor components is 80.1 kPa, what is the partial pressure of oxygen in our atmosphere?

24. In an experiment in which oxygen is produced by decomposing hydrogen peroxide and the gas formed is collected by the method shown in Figure 11.15, a student succeeds in collecting 375 mL of gas at 19 °C and 100.2 kPa. What mass of oxygen gas has been collected? (The vapour pressure of water at 19 °C is 2.2 kPa.)

25. A flask contains 0.50 mol nitrogen gas and 2.50 mol carbon dioxide gas. The total pressure in the flask is 150 kPA. What is the partial pressure of each gas?

Summary

- As all gases expand to fill the available space, the volume of a gas is determined by the volume of its container. All gases have low densities, and can be mixed in any proportion to form a solution.

- Atmospheric pressure is measured with a barometer. The pressure of a gas in a closed container is measured with a manometer which compares the pressure in the container with the atmospheric pressure.

- Standard atmospheric pressure is equal to 760 mm Hg (760 torr), 101.3 kPa, 1.00 atmospheres, or 14.7 psi (pounds per square inch).

- The relationship between the pressure and volume of a gas is known as Boyle's Law.

- The relationship between the volume and temperature of a gas is known as Charles' Law.

- Kelvin temperature is found by adding 273.15 to the Celsius temperature. A kelvin and a Celsius degree are of the same magnitude.

- The relationship between the pressure and temperature of a gas is known as Gay-Lussac's Law.

- The combined gas equation shows the relationship between the three variables i.e. pressure, volume, and temperature, for a fixed mass of gas. Any units of pressure or volume may be used in this equation, but the temperature must be in kelvins.

- The kinetic-molecular theory makes the following assumptions about a gas:
  a) The volume of the particles themselves is negligible compared to the volume of the container.
  b) The particles are in rapid, straight-line motion. They collide with each other, and with the walls of the container.
  c) There is no loss of energy when two particles collide.
  d) There are no attractive forces between particles.
  e) At any given temperature, the average kinetic energy of the particles in all gases is the same.

- The higher the molar mass of a gas, the lower will be the average velocity of its particles at any given temperature.

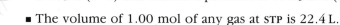

- Standard temperature and pressure (STP) is a standard set of conditions at which experimental results can be compared. Standard temperature is 273 K (0 °C) and standard pressure is 101.3 kPa (1 atm).

- The volume of 1.00 mol of any gas at STP is 22.4 L.

- The ideal gas equation relates four variables: pressure, temperature, volume, and the number of moles of gas.

- The molar mass of a gas can be determined experimentally by measuring the mass of a known volume of a gas at a known temperature and pressure.

- When a liquid is placed in a closed container, some of the molecules escape from the surface of the liquid into the space above it. These molecules exert a pressure on the walls of the container; this pressure is called the vapour pressure of the liquid.

- The vapour pressure of a liquid increases with increasing temperature.

- The boiling point of a liquid is the temperature at which its vapour pressure equals atmospheric pressure. The normal boiling point of a liquid is the temperature at which its vapour pressure is 101.3 kPa.

- The pressure exerted by a gas in a mixture of gases is called its partial pressure. Dalton's Law of Partial Pressures states that the total pressure of a mixture of gases is equal to the sum of the partial pressures of the component gases.

KEY WORDS

bar
barometer
boiling point
Boyle's Law
Charles' Law
combined gas equation
Gay-Lussac's Law
ideal gas equation
kelvin
Kelvin temperature scale
kilopascal
kinetic energy
Law of Partial Pressures
manometer
molar volume
mole fraction
partial pressure

pascal
pounds per square inch
relative humidity
standard atmospheric pressure
standard temperature and pressure
torr
universal gas constant
vapour pressure

1. 109 mm Hg
2. 328 kPa
3. 1.27 L
4. 1074 K
5. 45.0 mL
6. −130 °C

7. 662 K, 389 °C
8. 269 kPa
9. 216 L
10. 35 L
11. 485 kPa
12. 1.51×10^3 kPa

13. As the volume of the particles of a gas is negligible compared to the volume of the gas itself, a gas can be compressed by moving the particles closer together. In a liquid and a solid, most of the space is taken up by the particles themselves; thus liquids and solids cannot be compressed significantly.

14. a) As the temperature increases, the average kinetic energy of the particles increases, causing them to strike the walls of the container with more force. In order to keep the pressure constant, the volume must increase so that the collisions with the walls are less frequent.

b) Increasing the temperature increases the average kinetic energy of the particles, causing the particles to strike the walls of the container with more force, thereby increasing the pressure.

15. 28.5 L
16. $2.86 \text{ g} \cdot \text{L}^{-1}$
17. $131 \text{ g} \cdot \text{mol}^{-1}$, xenon
18. 1.12×10^3 g
19. 2.12×10^8 L
20. $83.8 \text{ g} \cdot \text{mol}^{-1}$

21. $352 \text{ g} \cdot \text{mol}^{-1}$, UF_6
22. $C_4H_{10}O$
23. 21.2 kPa
24. 0.485 g
25. $P_{N_2} = 25$ kPa
   $P_{CO_2} = 125$ kPa

---

1. List four ways in which gases differ from liquids.

2. What is the difference between a barometer and a manometer?

3. a) What is meant by the term "standard temperature and pressure"?
   b) What is standard temperature
      i) on the Celsius scale
      ii) on the Kelvin scale
   c) What is standard pressure
      i) in millimetres of mercury (torr)   iii) in pascals
      ii) in atmospheres   iv) in psi

4. State
   a) Boyle's Law   b) Charles' Law   c) Gay-Lussac's Law

5. In the kinetic-molecular theory, what is the significance of absolute zero?

6. What is meant by the term "molar volume"?

7. What is meant by the term "ideal gas"?

8. When can the ideal gas equation not be used?

9. Explain the difference between vapour pressure and partial pressure.

10. What is Dalton's Law of Partial Pressures?

11. When you are walking into a wind, what can you say about the air pressure in front of you compared to the air pressure behind you?

PROBLEMS

12. Although the SI unit for pressure is the pascal, many gauges still use pounds per square inch. Express each of the following pressures in pascals:
    a) a car tire pressure of 28 psi
    b) a bicycle tire pressure of 45.0 psi
    c) a pressure of 2.00×10^2 psi in a gas cylinder

13. Express the following temperatures in kelvins:
    a) 25 °C　　b) 150 °C　　c) −169 °C　　d) 770 °C

14. Express the following temperatures in degrees Celsius:
    a) 4 K　　b) 100 K　　c) 323 K　　d) 1355 K

15. Explain the following observations in terms of the kinetic-molecular theory:
    a) The total pressure of a mixture of gases is the sum of the pressures of the component gases.
    b) When two containers of different gases are placed together and a barrier between them removed, the result is a solution of the two gases.
    c) At the same temperature, molecules of carbon dioxide move more slowly than molecules of oxygen.

16. Describe the following changes in terms of the kinetic-molecular theory:
    a) When a balloon is placed in a freezer, it contracts.
    b) As a weather balloon rises, it expands.
    c) When a balloon is cooled below the boiling points of oxygen and nitrogen, its volume decreases to a small fraction of its former value.

17. Using the kinetic-molecular theory, explain the effect of increasing the number of particles on the
    a) volume if the pressure and temperature are held constant;
    b) pressure if the volume and temperature are held constant.

18. A mercury-filled manometer was connected to a container of gas. The level of the mercury on the side connected to the container was 24.0 cm higher than that on the side open to the atmosphere. The

atmospheric pressure was measured at 756 mm Hg. What is the pressure of the gas in the container expressed in
a) mm Hg   b) kPa

19. When a mercury-filled manometer was connected to a gas-filled container, the level of the mercury on the side connected to the container fell by 22.1 mm. If the atmospheric pressure is 98.8 kPa, what is the pressure of the gas in the container expressed in
a) kPa   b) mm Hg

20. A balloon contains 5.0 L of air at a pressure of 149 kPa. If the temperature remains constant, what will be the pressure in the balloon if its volume is decreased to 4.0 L?

21. A cylinder of volume $1.50 \, m^3$ contains compressed air at a pressure of 10.0 MPa. What volume would the air occupy at the same temperature and a pressure of 101 kPa?

22. A balloon contains 5.0 L of air at 25 °C. At what temperature would the balloon shrink to half that volume? Assume that the pressure is held constant.

23. A balloon contains 125 L of air at 35 °C. What will be the new volume of the balloon if the temperature drops to −35 °C while the pressure is kept constant?

24. Temperatures in a burning building can reach 1.50×10^3 °C. Calculate the pressure inside an airtight building at this temperature, assuming that the initial temperature and pressure are 20.2 °C and 102 kPa respectively.

25. A gas in a rigid container with a volume of 2.50×10^2 mL has a pressure of 99.7 kPa at 25 °C. What will the pressure inside the container be if
a) the Celsius temperature is doubled;
b) the Kelvin temperature is doubled?

26. An observation balloon with a volume of 8.60×10^4 L is filled with helium at a temperature of 18 °C and a pressure of 104 kPa. The balloon rises into the stratosphere until the volume of the balloon is 8.18×10^4 L and the pressure is 82.3 kPa. Determine the air temperature at this altitude.

27. A balloon is filled with 2.2 L of gas at a pressure of 108 kPa and a temperature of 21 °C. It is then taken down to the bottom of the ocean where the pressure is 11.8 MPa and the temperature is 6 °C. Find the new volume of the balloon.

28. The gas in a cylinder of a diesel engine occupies 1.00 L at 24 °C and 101.3 kPa. What is the pressure in the cylinder when the gas is compressed to 0.0714 L at 480 °C?

29. A certain mass of gas has a volume of 4.50 L at 95.6 kPa and 28 °C. Calculate the missing value for each set of conditions given in the table below:

	Pressure	Volume	Temperature
a)	74.4 kPa	2.80 L	? K
b)	? kPa	8.75 L	259 °C
c)	715 kPa	? L	58 K

30. A certain gas has a volume of 7.6 mL at a temperature of 55 °C and a pressure of 1.00×10^3 kPa. Calculate its volume at STP.

31. The self-contained breathing apparatus (SCBA) worn by firefighters has a volume of 7.85 L, and at 22 °C contains air at a pressure of 1.55×10^4 kPa.
    a) What volume of air will be supplied to the lungs at a pressure of 101 kPa and a temperature of 36 °C?
    b) The SCBA is designed to supply air for 30.0 minutes. If the firefighter takes 15 breaths per minute, use your answer from a) to determine the volume of air taken into the lungs during each breath.

32. A piece of dry ice (solid CO_2) of mass 30.0 g is allowed to sublime and warm up to STP. What volume will the gaseous carbon dioxide occupy?

33. What mass of nitrogen gas will be required to fill a 25.0 L container at STP?

34. What volume will 1.00 mol of an ideal gas occupy
    a) on the surface of Venus where the temperature is about 470 °C and the pressure is 9.3 MPa;
    b) on the surface of Mars where the temperature is about −10 °C and the pressure is 0.6 kPa?

35. Fill in the spaces in the following table:

	Gas	Mass	Pressure	Volume	Temperature
a)	NH_3	?	158 kPa	0.500 L	27 °C
b)	H_2	2.00 g	124 kPa	20.0 L	?
c)	CO	4.00 g	?	0.500 L	21 °C

36. A cylinder of acetylene gas has a pressure of 1.72×10^3 kPa at a temperature of 70.0 °C. If the volume of the cylinder is 87.0 L, calculate the mass of acetylene present (molar mass of acetylene is 26.0 g·mol¹).

37. A Goodyear blimp holds 5.74×10^6 L of helium at 17 °C and 101.3 kPa. What is the mass of helium in the blimp?

38. Calculate the density of the least dense gas, hydrogen, at 25 °C and 101.3 kPa.

39. Calculate the density of the densest gas, uranium(VI) fluoride (UF_6) at 70.0 °C and 25.0 kPa.

40. An unknown monatomic gas X has a density of $5.37\ g \cdot L^{-1}$ at 25 °C and 101.3 kPa. Calculate the molar mass of the gas and determine its identity.

41. An unknown monatomic gas Y has a density of $3.43\ g \cdot L^{-1}$ at 25 °C and 101.3 kPa pressure. Calculate the molar mass of the gas and thereby determine its identity.

42. Freon-23 (fluoroform), a refrigerant, is sold in cylinders with a volume of 10.9 L in which the pressure of the gas is 4.38×10^3 kPa at 24 °C. If the cylinder contains 1.35 kg of Freon-23, calculate the molar mass of this compound.

43. The major ingredient in solid air fresheners is a compound known as paradichlorobenzene. If a 9.87 g block of air freshener is vaporized in a 1.50 L container at 125 °C, the resulting pressure is 148.2 kPa. Determine the molar mass of paradichlorobenzene.

44. A certain liquid compound contains 92.3% carbon and 7.7% hydrogen.
   a) Calculate the empirical formula of the compound.
   b) When 0.573 g of this liquid was evaporated in a 226 mL container, the vapour produced exerted a pressure of 101.0 kPa at 100.0 °C. What is the molar mass of the compound?
   c) Use the results of your calculations in parts a) and b) to determine the molecular formula of the compound.

45. One of the compounds responsible for the aroma of bananas is a liquid known as isoamyl acetate. It contains 64.56% carbon, 10.86% hydrogen, and 24.58% oxygen.
   a) Calculate the empirical formula of this compound.
   b) If 10.29 g of this compound is evaporated in a 1.88 L container, the pressure of the vapour produced at 175 °C is 156.5 kPa. Determine the molar mass of isoamyl acetate.
   c) Use your answers from parts a) and b) to find the molecular formula of isoamyl acetate.

46. A 5.20 g sample of X_2H_6 (g) occupies a volume of 1.26 L at 196.4 kPa and 83.3 °C.
   a) Determine the molecular mass of X_2H_6.
   b) Identify the element X.

47. A 2.68 g sample of XH_3 (g) occupies a volume of 775 mL at 115 kPa and 38.7 °C.
   a) Determine the molar mass of XH_3.
   b) Identify element X.

48. If we place 2.0 g of oxygen and 4.0 g of methane ($CH_{4\ (g)}$) in a 1.00 L container at 50.0 °C, what would the total pressure be?

49. If we place 2.36 g of carbon dioxide and 8.98 g of argon in a 2.50 L container at 75 °C, what would the total pressure be?

50. A gas mixture used as an atmosphere for growing anaerobic bacteria contains 3.0% by mass of hydrogen and 97.0% by mass of carbon dioxide. If the total pressure of the mixture is 102 kPa, what is the partial pressure of each gas?

51. A common gas mixture used in lasers contains 12.5% by mass of neon, with the remainder being helium. If the total pressure of the gas mixture in the laser is 105 kPa, what is the partial pressure of each of the component gases?

52. In an experiment, 28.6 mL of hydrogen gas was collected over water at a pressure of 762 mm Hg and a temperature of 15 °C. If the vapour pressure of water at 15 °C is 13 mm Hg, what mass of hydrogen was obtained?

53. In an experiment, 43.2 mL of oxygen was collected over water at 20.0 °C. If the total pressure was 104 kPa and the vapour pressure of water at 20.0 °C is 2.3 kPa, what mass of oxygen was collected?

54. A gas mixture is prepared at 298 K and 101.3 kPa using 74 mL of sulfur dioxide and 52 mL of oxygen. The mixture is then heated with a catalyst and a reaction occurs. Upon cooling back to 298 K a liquid product appears, but 15 mL of gas at a pressure of 101.3 kPa is also present. When tested, this gas relights a glowing splint. Determine the empirical formula of the liquid that is produced in this reaction.

55. In an experiment, 25 mL of xenon was added to 150 mL of fluorine at 298 K and 101.3 kPa. The mixture was heated with a catalyst until no more reaction occurred. Upon cooling to 298 K, a solid product was formed, but 75 mL of a very reactive gas with a pressure of 101.3 kPa remained. What is the empirical formula of the solid product?

SUGGESTED PROJECTS

1. Recent space probes have provided scientists with much information about the moons of Jupiter and Saturn. Look up reports of these probes in news magazines and popular science journals to find out as much as you can about the atmospheres of the four largest moons of Jupiter — Ganymede, Callisto, Io, and Europa — and of the largest moon of Saturn — Titan. Prepare a report for presentation to the class.

2. Use reference books to find out more about the three scientists (Boyle, Charles, and Gay-Lussac) whose names are associated with the three gas laws studied in this chapter. Write an essay in which you discuss when and where each one lived, and what other major contributions they made to science.

3. Chemicals that react to produce gases are useful as rocket fuels because the tremendous volume expansion produces enough pressure to push the rocket forward. Write a report on some of the chemical reactions that have been used to propel rockets.

4. The principle on which explosives work is that gases have a much greater molar volume than solids or liquids. One of the developers of explosives was Alfred Nobel, after whom the Nobel prizes are named. Write a report on the contributions of Nobel to science and his connection with the Nobel prizes.

C H A P T E R 12

Solutions

In Chapter 1, we defined a solution as a mixture of pure substances with uniform properties throughout. In this chapter we will study various types of solutions in more detail, examine some of their properties, and see how chemists prepare and use solutions in the laboratory. We will also look at some of the environmental problems caused by one particular solution — acid rain.

Components of a Solution

12.1 A **solution** is composed of two or more pure substances, one of which is a solvent and the others, solutes. When instant coffee is dissolved in hot water, a solution is formed. The instant coffee is the substance being dissolved and is called the **solute**. The hot water is known as the **solvent**. If sugar is added to the coffee solution, the sugar will also dissolve and give us a solution composed of one solvent and two solutes. Water is the most common solvent encountered in a high-school chemistry laboratory. Solutions in which water is the solvent are called **aqueous solutions**.

The solute and the solvent can be in any of the three states of matter: solid, liquid, or gas. Therefore there are nine possible solute–solvent combinations. These are shown in Table 12:1. In this text our discussion will focus mainly on the solution types which are marked with an X, as these are the most common. Important features of some of the nine solution types are described below.

TABLE 12.1	*The Nine Solution Types*		
Solute		**Solvent**	
	Solid	Liquid	Gas
Solid	☐	X	☐
Liquid	☐	X	☐
Gas	☐	X	☐

Solids Dissolved in Liquids. The majority of the solutions encountered in an introductory chemistry laboratory course are of this type. In these solutions the solid is the solute and the liquid is the solvent.

A solid that dissolves in a given liquid is said to be **soluble** in that liquid. A solid that does not dissolve in a given liquid is said to be **insoluble**.

Liquids Dissolved in Liquids. Two liquids that will dissolve in each other are said to be **miscible**. Usually the liquid present in the smaller quantity is regarded as the solute. **Immiscible** liquids will not dissolve in each other when they are mixed together. Water and ethyl alcohol are miscible in any proportions, but water and gasoline are immiscible. If these last two liquids are mixed, the gasoline will form a layer on top of the water.

Gases Dissolved in Liquids. Solutions formed by dissolving gases in liquids are the basis of the soft-drink industry. Carbonated drinks consist of a flavoured liquid containing dissolved carbon dioxide gas. In these solutions the amount of solute (i.e. gas) that can be dissolved in a given volume of solvent is dependent upon both pressure and temperature. The solubility of a gas in a given liquid increases as the pressure of the gas increases, but decreases with an increase in temperature.

Gases Dissolved in Gases. The air we breathe is an example of a solution. Nitrogen, the main component of air, can be considered as the solvent and oxygen as the solute. A number of other gases, such as carbon dioxide and argon, are also present as very minor components of this solution.

Liquids Dissolved in Solids.   A solution of a liquid in a solid is referred to as an amalgam. Dental amalgams, which are used as tooth fillings, are prepared by mixing liquid mercury with one or more solid metallic elements, such as silver, tin, or copper.

Solids Dissolved in Solids.   Solutions formed by dissolving one solid in another are usually referred to as alloys. Steels are alloys formed from iron and small quantities of one or more other elements that have been added to improve the durability or other qualities of the metal.

Water as a Solvent

12.2

One of the most important properties of water is its ability to dissolve a wide range of substances. Although most covalent liquids are only able to dissolve other covalent compounds, water can dissolve both ionic and covalent compounds.

The large variety of ions in seawater is a result of the soluble components of rocks being dissolved by the water. This process, known as leaching, has taken place over billions of years. Although we usually think of seawater as containing only common salt (i.e. sodium, Na^+, and chloride, Cl^-, ions), seawater also contains significant quantities of six other important ions: magnesium, Mg^{2+}, calcium, Ca^{2+}, potassium, K^+, hydrogen carbonate, HCO_3^-, bromide, Br^-, and sulfate, SO_4^{2-}.

Most of the world's supply of bromine and magnesium is obtained from seawater (Sections 8.6 and 8.7). Small quantities of many other ions, including gold, silver, and uranium, are also present, but they are not economical to extract because of the enormous volumes of seawater that would have to be processed.

Why do some substances dissolve in a given liquid while others do not? Many factors are involved in the solution process, including the type of bonding in both solvent and solute. In this text we will focus on some of the important features of water that make it such a good solvent for many ionic compounds.

In Section 5.10, we noted that the bonding electrons involved in the covalent bonds formed between atoms with different electronegativities are not shared equally by the atoms, but are, on average, closer to the more electronegative atom. This results in one atom having a slightly positive charge (δ^+) and the other atom having a slightly negative charge (δ^-). We discussed this phenomenon with reference to hydrogen chloride. A similar situation exists with water molecules, as shown below and in Figure 12.1:

$$^{\delta-}:\overset{..}{\underset{..}{O}}:H^{\delta+}$$
$$\overset{..}{H}^{\delta+}$$

Figure 12.1

A representation of a water molecule. The two hydrogen atoms have a slightly positive charge (δ^+) and the oxygen atom has a slightly negative charge (δ^-).

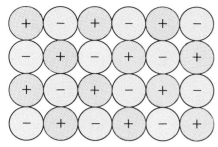

Figure 12.2

A representation of part of a crystal of sodium chloride. Each sodium ion has a positive charge and each chloride ion a negative charge.

The polar nature of the water molecule enables it to dissolve many ionic compounds. Let us consider what happens when a crystal of sodium chloride dissolves in water. In the sodium chloride crystal, the sodium ions and chloride ions are packed in a regular array (Section 5.4). A representation of part of such a crystal is shown in Figure 12.2.

When a crystal of sodium chloride is placed in water, the water molecules immediately surround the ions on the surface of the crystal. The slightly positive hydrogen atoms of some of the water molecules are attracted by the negative chloride ions, and the slightly negative oxygen atoms of other water molecules are attracted by the positive sodium ions. The water molecules remove these ions into solution (Figure 12.3), thereby exposing more ions to "attack".

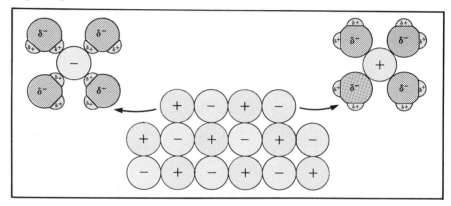

Figure 12.3

A representation of the process by which sodium chloride dissolves in water.

From this description, we might expect all ionic compounds to be water-soluble. However, some ionic compounds are insoluble in water. Why is this? What determines whether an ionic compound will dissolve in water? The solubility of a compound in water is dependent on the strength of the ionic bonds within the crystal and on the strength of the attraction between the ions and the water molecules. A compound with strong ionic bonds, and therefore with ions that are weakly attracted by water molecules, will be insoluble. Conversely, in a compound with weak ionic bonds, the ions are strongly attracted by water molecules and the compound will be very soluble.

Quantitative Solubility

12.3

There is no sharp dividing line separating soluble compounds from insoluble ones. Even the compounds that we have described as being insoluble in water dissolve in water to a very small, but measurable, extent. The mass of a substance that will dissolve in a given volume or mass of a solvent is referred to as its **solubility**. If more of a substance dissolves in one solvent than in a second solvent, the substance is said to be more soluble in the first solvent. When the maximum amount of solid has been dissolved in a given volume of solvent, a **saturated solution** is obtained.

Figure 12.4
Commercial harvesting of salt crystals from a salt water evaporation pond in California. As the water evaporates, a saturated solution of sodium chloride is formed. Further evaporation results in the formation of salt crystals.

It is possible to dissolve 2.22 kg of silver nitrate in 1 L of water at room temperature. We describe silver nitrate as being very soluble in water because 2.22 kg is quite a large mass of solid to dissolve in 1 L of liquid. On the other hand, only 0.002 g of silver chloride will dissolve in 1 L of water. The mass of silver chloride that dissolves is so small that we generally describe this compound as being insoluble in water. "Very soluble" and "insoluble" are qualitative terms used to describe solubility. Although these terms do not describe exact amounts, they are used to indicate ranges. The ranges of solubility for which these and other terms are used are listed in Table 12.2.

TABLE 12.2	*Terms Used When Discussing Solubility*			
Solubility (per litre of water)	Greater than 100 g	Between 10 g and 100 g	Between 1 g and 10 g	Less than 1 g
Term Used	Very soluble	Soluble	Slightly soluble	Insoluble

In general, as the temperature of the solvent increases, the solubility of a solid solute also increases. However, as shown in Table 12.3, there are exceptions. Although the solubility of silver nitrate increases rapidly with increasing temperature, that of sodium chloride remains approximately the same. Notice that lithium carbonate is actually less soluble in hot water than it is in cold water.

TABLE 12.3	*Solubility of Selected Compounds at 20 °C, 50 °C, and 100 °C*		
Compound	Solubility (g per litre H_2O)		
	20 °C	50 °C	100 °C
NaCl	360	370	391
$NaNO_3$	880	1140	1800
$AgNO_3$	2220	4550	9520
Ag_2SO_4	8	11	14
Li_2CO_3	14	11	7

QUESTIONS

1. Classify the compounds listed in Table 12.3 as being very soluble, soluble, slightly soluble, or insoluble at 20 °C.

Concentration in Moles per Litre

12.4

In the previous section, we expressed the solubilities of various substances using units of grams per litre of water. These figures represent the maximum possible **concentrations** that can be obtained when these substances are dissolved in water. A number of other units are used for concentrations; the SI unit that we will be using is **moles per litre** ($mol \cdot L^{-1}$).

To determine the concentration of a solution in moles per litre we must know the number of moles of solute present in a given volume of the solution. The relationship we use to calculate the concentration of a solution is

$$\text{Concentration} = \frac{\text{Moles of solute}}{\text{Volume of solution}}$$

The following examples show how any of the three variables (moles of solute, volume of solution, and concentration) can be calculated if the other two are known.

EXAMPLE

12.1

A solution contains 5.85 g of sodium chloride dissolved in 5.00×10^3 mL of water. What is the concentration of the sodium chloride in $mol \cdot L^{-1}$?

SOLUTION

STRATEGY

1. Mass of solute ⟶ Moles of solute
2. Moles of solute ⟶ Concentration of solution

Before starting the problem, we must convert the volume of the solution to litres, as follows:

$$\text{Volume} = 5.00 \times 10^3 \, \text{mL} \times \frac{1 \, L}{10^3 \, \text{mL}}$$

$$= 5.00 \, L$$

STEP 1: We use the molar mass of sodium chloride ($58.5 \, g \cdot mol^{-1}$) to find the number of moles of solute (NaCl):

$$\text{Number of moles of NaCl} = 5.85 \, \text{g NaCl} \times \frac{1 \, \text{mol NaCl}}{58.5 \, \text{g NaCl}}$$

$$= 0.100 \, \text{mol NaCl}$$

STEP 2: Now we can calculate the concentration using the relationship

$$\text{Concentration of solution} = \frac{\text{moles of solute}}{\text{volume of solution}}$$

Thus

$$\text{Concentration} = \frac{0.100 \text{ mol}}{5.00 \text{ L}}$$

$$= 2.00 \times 10^{-2} \text{ mol} \cdot \text{L}^{-1}$$

EXAMPLE   **12.2** What mass of potassium hydroxide is required to prepare 6.00×10^2 mL of a solution with a concentration of $0.225 \text{ mol} \cdot \text{L}^{-1}$?

SOLUTION

STRATEGY

1. Volume of solution $\longrightarrow$ Moles of solute
2. Moles of solute $\longrightarrow$ Mass of solute

STEP 1: First we find the number of moles of potassium hydroxide (KOH) required:

$$\text{Concentration of KOH} = \frac{\text{Moles of KOH}}{\text{Volume}}$$

$$\text{Number of moles of KOH} = \text{Concentration} \times \text{Volume}$$

$$= \frac{0.225 \text{ mol KOH}}{1 \text{ L}} \times 0.600 \text{ L}$$

$$= 0.135 \text{ mol KOH}$$

STEP 2: To find the mass of potassium hydroxide required, we multiply the number of moles by the molar mass ($56.1 \text{ g} \cdot \text{mol}^{-1}$):

$$\text{Mass of KOH} = 0.135 \text{ mol KOH} \times \frac{56.1 \text{ g KOH}}{1 \text{ mol KOH}} = 7.57 \text{ g KOH}$$

EXAMPLE   **12.3** A solution containing $1.25 \times 10^{-1} \text{ mol} \cdot \text{L}^{-1}$ of magnesium chloride is required for an experiment. What is the maximum volume of solution that can be prepared if only 87.8 g of solid magnesium chloride are available?

SOLUTION

STRATEGY

1. Mass of solute $\longrightarrow$ Moles of solute
2. Moles of solute $\longrightarrow$ Volume of solution

STEP 1: The number of moles of magnesium chloride available is determined using the reciprocal of the compound's molar mass:

$$\text{Number of moles of MgCl}_2 = 87.8 \text{ g MgCl}_2 \times \frac{1 \text{ mol MgCl}_2}{95.3 \text{ g MgCl}_2}$$

$$= 0.921 \text{ mol MgCl}_2$$

STEP 2:   We can now determine the volume of solution with the required concentration that can be prepared:

$$\text{Volume of solution} = \frac{\text{Mol of MgCl}_2}{\text{Concentration}}$$

$$= \frac{0.921 \text{ mol MgCl}_2}{0.125 \text{ mol} \cdot \text{L}^{-1}}$$

$$= 7.37 \text{ L}$$

A non-SI term that you will often see and hear used instead of moles per litre is **molarity** (symbol *M*). If you encounter this term, remember that molarity and moles per litre are numerically equivalent.

Two other ways of expressing concentrations in strict SI units are moles per cubic decimetre $(\text{mol} \cdot \text{dm}^{-3})$ and kilomoles per cubic metre $(\text{kmol} \cdot \text{m}^{-3})$. The former expression is identical in value to moles per litre, as a litre and a cubic decimetre have the same capacity. Similarly, kilomoles per cubic metre is numerically equal to moles per cubic decimetre, and thus also to moles per litre. For example, sulfuric acid is supplied commercially with a concentration of $18.4 \text{ mol} \cdot \text{dm}^{-3}$. We can convert this concentration to kilomoles per cubic metre as follows:

$$\frac{18.4 \text{ mol}}{1 \text{ dm}^3} \times \frac{1 \text{ kmol}}{1000 \text{ mol}} \times \frac{10 \text{ dm}}{1 \text{ m}} \times \frac{10 \text{ dm}}{1 \text{ m}} \times \frac{10 \text{ dm}}{1 \text{ m}}$$

$$= 18.4 \text{ kmol} \cdot \text{m}^{-3}$$

Other terms used to express concentrations and the types of solutions for which they are usually employed are given below.

Mass Percent.   The composition of an alloy is usually expressed as mass percent. Mass percent refers to the percentage of solute (by mass) in a given solution.

Thus

$$\% \text{ solute (by mass)} = \frac{\text{Mass of solute}}{\text{Mass of solute} + \text{Mass of solvent}} \times 100\%$$

Volume Percent.   When two liquids are mixed to form a solution, it is often convenient to express the composition of the solution in terms of volume percent. You will find that the alcohol content of beers, wines, and spirits is usually given in this way. The volume percentage of the solute is calculated as follows:

$$\% \text{ solute (by volume)} = \frac{\text{Volume of solute}}{\text{Volume of solution}} \times 100\%$$

Alloys

Alloys consist of two or more metals that have been melted together and then cooled to the solid state. They are thus solid solutions. An alloy can also be obtained by forming a solid solution from a metal (or metals) and a small porportion of a nonmetal such as carbon, silicon, or phosphorus. The properties of an alloy can be very different from those of the metals from which it is formed. Silver and gold are both soft metals and therefore items made from them often have small amounts of copper added to improve their durability. In effect, such items are made from a silver-copper or gold-copper alloy. The composition of an alloy is usually expressed as mass percent.

Figure 12.5
A 10th century B.C. Chinese bronze ritual wine vessel. The earliest useful alloy was bronze (about 80% copper, 20% tin by mass). Even 3000 years ago beautiful objects were cast from this versatile alloy.

TABLE 12.4	Composition of Some Common Alloys
Alloy	Composition (mass %)
Brass	Cu(85), Zn(15)
Stainless steel	Fe(74), Cr(18), Ni(8)
Nickel coinage	Cu(75), Ni(25)
Sterling silver	Ag(92.5), Cu(7.5)
18-carat gold	Au(75), Ag(10–20), Cu(5–15)
Pewter	Sn(85), Cu(7), Bi(6), Sb(2)
Plumber's solder	Pb(67), Sn(33)

Mole Fraction. Mole fractions were used to express the compositions of gas mixtures in our discussion of Dalton's Law of Partial Pressures (Section 11.14). However, mole fractions may also be used to express the composition of other types of solutions. The mole fraction of a solute may be calculated as follows:

$$\text{Mole fraction of solute} = \frac{\text{Moles of solute}}{\text{Moles of solute} + \text{Moles of solvent}}$$

Parts per million and parts per billion. When reading an account of an environmental problem in a newspaper or magazine, you may have encountered the terms parts per million (ppm) or parts per billion (ppb).

These terms are used to express very low concentrations. They are calculated according to the following formulas:

$$ppm = \frac{\text{Mass of solute}}{\text{Mass of solution}} \times 10^6$$

$$ppb = \frac{\text{Mass of solute}}{\text{Mass of solution}} \times 10^9$$

QUESTIONS

2. Calculate the concentration, in moles per litre, of each of the following aqueous solutions:
   a) 1.06 g of sodium carbonate dissolved in 100.0 mL of solution
   b) 111.1 g of calcium chloride dissolved in 20.0 L of solution
   c) 1.70×10^2 g of silver nitrate dissolved in 5.00 L of solution

3. What mass of copper sulfate pentahydrate ($CuSO_4 \cdot 5H_2O$) is required to prepare 1.50 L of aqueous copper sulfate solution with a concentration of 0.500 mol·L^{-1}?

4. A laboratory technician wishes to prepare a large volume of sodium hydroxide solution with a concentration of 3.00 mol·L^{-1}. In the stockroom, there is one unopened bottle containing 5.00 kg of sodium hydroxide pellets. What volume of solution can be prepared?

Ionic Concentrations

12.5   When certain substances are dissolved in water the resulting solutions conduct electricity. This conductivity results from the presence of ions in the solution. Ions are formed when an ionic substance dissolves in water, and also when some covalent substances (such as hydrogen chloride) form aqueous solutions. In ionic solutions, the concentration of the cations and anions can be determined if we know the formula for the compound and the concentration of the solution.

EXAMPLE   **12.4**   In a solution containing 15.6 g of magnesium chloride in 1.25 L of solution, what are the concentrations of the magnesium and chloride ions?

SOLUTION

> **STRATEGY**
>
> 1. Mass of solute $\longrightarrow$ Moles of solute
> 2. Moles of solute $\longrightarrow$ Concentration of solution
> 3. Concentration of solution $\longrightarrow$ Concentration of ions

STEP 1: We determine the number of moles of magnesium chloride in the solution using the reciprocal of molar mass as a conversion factor. Thus

$$\text{Number of moles of MgCl}_2 = 15.6\,g\,\text{MgCl}_2 \times \frac{1\;\text{mol MgCl}_2}{95.3\;g\,\text{MgCl}_2}$$

$$= 0.164\;\text{mol MgCl}_2$$

STEP 2: The concentration of magnesium chloride is found as follows:

$$\text{Concentration} = \frac{0.164\;\text{mol}}{1.25\;\text{L}} = 0.131\;\text{mol}\cdot\text{L}^{-1}$$

Generally we enclose chemical symbols in square brackets when we wish to represent the concentration of a substance. Therefore, to indicate "concentration of magnesium chloride", we write

$$[\text{MgCl}_2] = 0.131\;\text{mol}\cdot\text{L}^{-1}$$

STEP 3: As each formula unit of magnesium chloride consists of one magnesium ion (Mg^{2+}) and two chloride ions (Cl^-), it follows that one mole of magnesium chloride consists of one mole of magnesium ions and two moles of chloride ions. When we dissolve magnesium chloride in water, the process may be represented as

$$\text{MgCl}_{2\,(s)} \xrightarrow[\text{in water}]{\text{dissolve}} \text{Mg}^{2+}{}_{(aq)} + 2\;\text{Cl}^-{}_{(aq)}$$

The concentration of magnesium ions is therefore equal to the concentration of magnesium chloride, while the concentration of chloride ions is twice the concentration of the magnesium chloride. Thus

$$[\text{Mg}^{2+}] = \frac{0.131\;\text{mol MgCl}_2}{1\;\text{L}} \times \frac{1\;\text{mol Mg}^{2+}}{1\;\text{mol MgCl}_2} = 0.131\;\text{mol}\cdot\text{L}^{-1}$$

$$[\text{Cl}^-] = \frac{0.131\;\text{mol MgCl}_2}{1\;\text{L}} \times \frac{2\;\text{mol Cl}^-}{1\;\text{mol MgCl}_2} = 0.262\;\text{mol}\cdot\text{L}^{-1}$$

EXAMPLE *12.5* If 525 mL of a solution containing 6.78 g of calcium bromide ($CaBr_2$) is mixed with 325 mL of a solution containing 11.4 g of potassium bromide (KBr), what is the bromide ion concentration in the resulting solution? Assume that the volumes are additive (i.e. the final volume is the sum of the two initial volumes).

SOLUTION First we will determine the number of moles of Br^- in each solution:

Number of moles of Br^- from $CaBr_2$

$$= 6.78\,g\,\text{CaBr}_2 \times \frac{1\;\text{mol CaBr}_2}{199.9\;g\,\text{CaBr}_2} \times \frac{2\;\text{mol Br}^-}{1\;\text{mol CaBr}_2}$$

$$= 6.78 \times 10^{-2}\;\text{mol Br}^-$$

Number of moles of Br^- from KBr

$$= 11.4\,\text{g KBr} \times \frac{1\,\text{mol KBr}}{119.0\,\text{g KBr}} \times \frac{1\,\text{mol Br}^-}{1\,\text{mol KBr}}$$

$$= 9.58 \times 10^{-2}\,\text{mol Br}^-$$

Thus, the total number of moles of Br^- in the solution is

$6.78 \times 10^{-2}\,\text{mol Br}^- + 9.58 \times 10^{-2}\,\text{mol Br}^-$

$$= 16.36 \times 10^{-2}\,\text{mol Br}^-$$
$$= 0.1636\,\text{mol Br}^-$$

The final volume of the solution is therefore

$$525\,\text{mL} + 325\,\text{mL} = 850\,\text{mL} = 850\,\text{mL} \times \frac{1\,\text{L}}{10^3\,\text{mL}} = 0.850\,\text{L}$$

Thus the bromide ion concentration is

$$[\text{Br}^-] = \frac{0.1636\,\text{mol}}{0.850\,\text{L}} = 0.192\,\text{mol}\cdot\text{L}^{-1}$$

QUESTIONS

5. What is the concentration of each of the ions present in the following solutions:
   a) $1.50\,\text{mol}\cdot\text{L}^{-1}$ NaCl
   b) $0.225\,\text{mol}\cdot\text{L}^{-1}$ $(NH_4)_2CO_3$
   c) $1.1\,\text{mol}\cdot\text{L}^{-1}$ $Al_2(SO_4)_3$

6. Calculate the concentration of the nitrate ions when each of the following solutions is prepared:
   a) $1.00\,\text{g}$ of KNO_3 is dissolved to give $250.0\,\text{mL}$ of solution
   b) $35.4\,\text{g}$ of $Pb(NO_3)_2$ is dissolved to give $2.50\,\text{L}$ of solution

7. If $25.0\,\text{mL}$ of sodium nitrate $(NaNO_3)$ solution $(0.100\,\text{mol}\cdot\text{L}^{-1})$ is added to $10.0\,\text{mL}$ of sodium carbonate (Na_2CO_3) solution $(0.150\,\text{mol}\cdot\text{L}^{-1})$, what is the concentration of sodium ions in the resulting mixture? Assume that the volumes are additive.

Standard Solutions

12.6 In the laboratory we often need to prepare a solution of known concentration for use in an experiment. Solutions prepared by dissolving a precise mass of solute in a precise volume of solution are called **standard solutions**. Special containers, called **volumetric flasks**, are used for preparing standard solutions. Volumetric flasks are available in sizes ranging from $1.00\,\text{mL}$ to $2.00\,\text{L}$. The sizes which you are most likely to use in your school laboratory are $100.0\,\text{mL}$ and $250.0\,\text{mL}$. These volumes are usually written as whole numbers; that is, as $100\,\text{mL}$ and $250\,\text{mL}$. However, the line (graduation mark) on the neck of a flask indicates a volume that is more

Figure 12.6
Volumetric flasks are available in sizes ranging from 1.00 mL to 2.00 L.

Figure 12.7

Preparation of a standard solution of copper(II) sulfate.

a) A known mass of copper(II) sulfate is placed in the volumetric flask;

b) Distilled water is added until the flask is about half full;

c) The flask is shaken until the solid has completely dissolved;

d) Distilled water is again added until the flask is full to the mark.

precise than this. When a 100.0 mL flask is filled to the graduation mark, it contains a volume of 100.0 ± 0.1 mL (i.e. the volume is known to four significant figures).

Standard solutions can be prepared using many different solvents, but we will consider only aqueous solutions, i.e. those in which the solvent is water.

Suppose that we require a 0.500 mol·L^{-1} solution of sodium chloride. How would we prepare it using a 250.0 mL volumetric flask? The first step is to determine the mass of sodium chloride required:

$$\text{Concentration of NaCl} = 0.500 \text{ mol·L}^{-1} = \frac{\text{Moles of NaCl}}{\text{Volume of solution}}$$

As the volume of the solution is 250.0 mL or 0.2500 L, we can write

$$\text{Number of moles of NaCl} = \frac{0.500 \text{ mol NaCl}}{1 \text{ L}} \times 0.2500 \text{ L}$$

$$= 0.125 \text{ mol NaCl}$$

$$\text{Mass of NaCl required} = 0.125 \text{ mol NaCl} \times \frac{58.5 \text{ g NaCl}}{1 \text{ mol NaCl}}$$

$$= 7.31 \text{ g NaCl}$$

To prepare the solution, 7.31 g of sodium chloride is placed in the volumetric flask. Distilled water is added until the flask is about half full. The flask is then stoppered and shaken until the sodium chloride has all dissolved. Distilled water is then carefully added until the level of the solution reaches the graduation mark on the flask, and the flask is again shaken. The flask now contains 250.0 mL of 0.500 mol·L^{-1} sodium chloride solution.

This procedure cannot always be followed exactly because heat is sometimes required to accelerate the solution process. As volumetric flasks are expensive, carefully calibrated pieces of glassware, they should never be heated. Instead, if heat is required, the solution is first prepared in a beaker and then transferred to the volumetric flask. The beaker is then rinsed

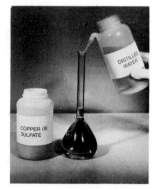

several times with distilled water to ensure that all the solution is removed from it, and these rinsings are added to the solution in the flask. After shaking, the level of the solution in the flask is brought up to the mark with more distilled water, the stopper is inserted, and the flask is shaken.

QUESTIONS

8. What effect would each of the following have on the final concentration of a standard solution?
   a) During preparation, some solute is spilled on a laboratory bench.
   b) When the distilled water is added, the solution level rises above the graduation mark on the flask.

Dilution

12.7

You may occasionally find that your laboratory work calls for the use of a solution with a lower concentration than that of the available standard solution. In this situation, we add water to the standard solution according to a procedure that we call **dilution**. When we have two solutions of the same compound at different concentrations, the solution with the higher concentration is referred to as a **concentrated solution**, and the solution with the lower concentration is said to be a **dilute solution**. Note that the terms "concentrated" and "dilute" are relative. A dilute solution does not necessarily indicate that the solution is weak, and therefore as much care should be taken when working with a dilute solution as when working with one that is concentrated.

To prepare a dilute solution of known concentration from a concentrated solution whose concentration is also known, we will need, in addition to a volumetric flask, a **volumetric pipette**. Volumetric pipettes are available in sizes ranging from 0.50 mL to 100.0 mL. The volumetric pipettes that you are most likely to use in your school laboratory are the 10.0 mL and 25.0 mL sizes. The number of significant figures used when citing these volumes indicates the precision we can obtain with these pipettes.

Suppose you are given a solution of nitric acid (HNO_3) that has a concentration of $1.00 \ mol \cdot L^{-1}$. From this you are asked to prepare 250 mL of the acid having a concentration of $0.200 \ mol \cdot L^{-1}$.

The first step is to determine how many moles of nitric acid are required for the solution being prepared. Since this solution should have a volume of 250 mL and a concentration of $0.200 \ mol \cdot L^{-1}$, the number of moles can be found as follows:

$$\text{Number of moles of } HNO_3 = 0.250 \, \cancel{L} \times \frac{0.200 \ mol \ HNO_3}{1 \, \cancel{L}}$$

$$= 5.00 \times 10^{-2} \, mol \ HNO_3.$$

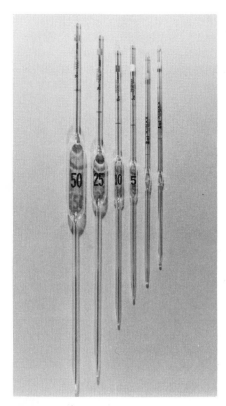

Figure 12.8

Pipettes are available in sizes ranging from 0.50 mL to 100.0 mL. The 10.0 mL and the 25.0 mL pipettes are used most.

This number of moles must be obtained from the more concentrated ($1.00 \text{ mol} \cdot \text{L}^{-1}$) solution of nitric acid that was supplied. What volume of this solution will be required in order to provide 5.00×10^{-2} mol HNO_3?

$$\text{Volume} = 5.00 \times 10^{-2} \text{ mol } HNO_3 \times \frac{1 \text{ L}}{1.00 \text{ mol } HNO_3}$$

$$= 5.00 \times 10^{-2} \text{ L} = 5.00 \times 10^{-2} \text{ L} \times \frac{10^3 \text{ mL}}{1 \text{ L}}$$

$$= 50.0 \text{ mL}$$

A $0.200 \text{ mol} \cdot \text{L}^{-1}$ solution is thus obtained by adding water to 50.0 mL of the $1.00 \text{ mol} \cdot \text{L}^{-1}$ solution until the total volume is 250.0 mL. The dilution is carried out in a volumetric flask as follows:

More than 50 mL of the nitric acid solution ($1.00 \text{ mol} \cdot \text{L}^{-1}$) is placed in a clean dry beaker. A small amount of this solution is drawn into 50.0 mL pipette by means of a rubber bulb (Figure 12.9a). (NOTE: Never use your mouth to suck a solution into a pipette, as this can be an extremely dangerous practice.) The pipette is then rotated to rinse the walls with the solution, and the solution is discarded. Next the pipette is filled up to the graduation mark. The solution is then allowed to run from the pipette into a clean 250.0 mL volumetric flask (Figure 12.9b). (NOTE: When the pipette is being emptied, the solution is allowed to run out under the force of gravity. The small amount of solution that remains in the tip of the pipette should never be blown out as this would make the volume of solution delivered greater than that for which the pipette is designed.) Finally, distilled water is added until the level of the solution in the flask reaches the graduation mark on the neck of the flask (Figure 12.9c) and the flask is shaken to ensure thorough mixing (Figure 12.9d). The flask now contains 250.0 mL of $0.200 \text{ mol} \cdot \text{L}^{-1}$ nitric acid.

Figure 12.9

Dilution of a standard solution:
a) the concentrated solution is drawn into a pipette;
b) the precisely measured volume is transferred to a volumetric flask;
c) water is added up to the graduation mark;
d) the flask is capped and then shaken to mix the contents.

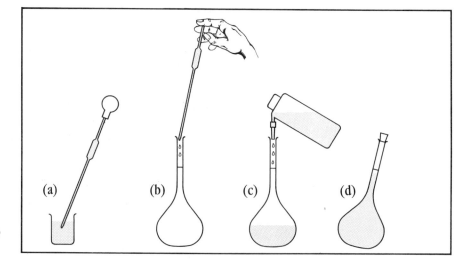

| EXAMPLE | **12.6** | What volume of $0.500 \text{ mol} \cdot L^{-1}$ sodium hydroxide solution can be prepared from 10.0 mL of a $6.00 \text{ mol} \cdot L^{-1}$ solution? |

SOLUTION We must first determine the number of moles of NaOH in the 10.0 mL of $6.00 \text{ mol} \cdot L^{-1}$ solution:

Number of moles of NaOH

$$= \frac{6.00 \text{ mol NaOH}}{1 \text{ L}} \times 10.0 \text{ mL} \times \frac{1 \text{ L}}{1000 \text{ mL}}$$

$$= 6.00 \times 10^{-2} \text{ mol NaOH}.$$

The volume of $0.500 \text{ mol} \cdot L^{-1}$ that can be prepared is

$$\text{Volume} = 6.00 \times 10^{-2} \text{ mol NaOH} \times \frac{1 \text{ L}}{0.500 \text{ mol NaOH}}$$

$$= 0.120 \text{ L}$$

QUESTIONS

9. What would be the concentration of a hydrochloric acid solution prepared by diluting 25.0 mL of concentrated hydrochloric acid ($12 \text{ mol} \cdot L^{-1}$) to a volume of 2.00 L?

10. A laboratory director requires 1.00 L of dilute ammonia solution with a concentration of $0.150 \text{ mol} \cdot L^{-1}$. The only ammonia solution in stock has a concentration of $15.0 \text{ mol} \cdot L^{-1}$. What instructions should be given to the assistant for preparing the required dilute solution?

Acids and Bases: An Introduction

12.8 Solutions of acids and bases are among the first solutions we encounter when we begin to work in a chemical laboratory. In 1884 the Swedish chemist, Svante Arrhenius, defined acids and bases as follows:

An acid is a substance that, when dissolved in water, produces $H^+_{(aq)}$ ions. A base is a substance that, when dissolved in water, produces $OH^-_{(aq)}$ ions.

Let us consider the compound hydrogen chloride. We mentioned in Section 5.10 that this compound has partial ionic character because of the difference in electronegativity between the hydrogen and chlorine atoms. When an aqueous solution of hydrogen chloride is tested in the conductivity apparatus described in Section 5.1, the light bulb glows very brightly indicating the presence of ions in the solution. Thus we must conclude that the partial ionic character of the bond in hydrogen chloride is large enough to allow the hydrogen chloride molecule to **dissociate** into hydrogen cations and chloride anions when it dissolves in water:

$$HCl_{(g)} \xrightarrow[\text{in water}]{\text{dissolve}} H^+_{(aq)} + Cl^-_{(aq)}$$

Because hydrogen cations are produced when hydrogen chloride dissolves in water, hydrogen chloride is an acid by the Arrhenius definition.

A similar result is obtained if we test a solution of sodium hydroxide in the conductivity apparatus. The light bulb glows very brightly because of the presence of sodium ions and hydroxide ions. The equation for this reaction can be written as follows:

$$NaOH_{(s)} \xrightarrow[\text{in water}]{\text{dissolve}} Na^+_{(aq)} + OH^-_{(aq)}$$

The Names and Formulas of Acids

12.9

If you look among the reagent bottles in your school laboratory, you are unlikely to find one with a label reading "hydrogen chloride solution." The bottle containing the hydrogen chloride solution will have a label reading "hydrochloric acid." In general, chemists use different names for solutions of acids than for the acids used to prepare the solutions. Thus, $HCl_{(g)}$ is called hydrogen chloride, $HCl_{(aq)}$ is called hydrochloric acid. Let us look at how the names of some other acids are derived.

Binary Acids

A **binary acid** is composed of two elements: hydrogen and a nonmetallic element, usually a halogen.

TABLE 12.5 *The Common Binary Acids*

Formula	Name
$HF_{(aq)}$	Hydrofluoric acid
$HCl_{(aq)}$	Hydrochloric acid
$HBr_{(aq)}$	Hydrobromic acid
$HI_{(aq)}$	Hydroiodic acid

An acid with a similar name to the binary acids, which actually contains three elements, is hydrocyanic acid, $HCN_{(aq)}$.

Oxyacids

An **oxyacid** contains three elements, two of which are hydrogen and oxygen. The formula of an oxyacid can be obtained by considering the charge on the corresponding oxyanion (Section 6.4). For example, the sulfate ion, SO_4^{2-}, can combine with two hydrogen ions, H^+, to give $H_2SO_{4\ (aq)}$ (sulfuric acid). Some common oxyacids are listed in Table 12.6. Note that some elements form more than one oxyacid, for example nitrogen forms $HNO_{3\ (aq)}$ and $HNO_{2\ (aq)}$. The acid with more oxygen atoms has the ending *-ic*, and the one with fewer oxygen atoms has the ending *-ous*.

Chlorine also forms two other acids, one with even more oxygen ($HClO_{4\ (aq)}$ –perchloric acid) and one with even less oxygen ($HClO_{(aq)}$ – hypochlorous acid).

TABLE 12.6 *Some Common Oxyacids*

Formula	Name	Formula	Name
$H_2CO_{3\ (aq)}$	Carbonic acid		
$HNO_{3\ (aq)}$	Nitric acid	$HNO_{2\ (aq)}$	Nitrous acid
$H_3PO_{4\ (aq)}$	Phosphoric acid	$H_3PO_{3\ (aq)}$	Phosphorous acid
$H_2SO_{4\ (aq)}$	Sulfuric acid	$H_2SO_{3\ (aq)}$	Sulfurous acid
$HClO_{3\ (aq)}$	Chloric acid	$HClO_{2\ (aq)}$	Chlorous acid

Acids and Bases: Strong or Weak?

omit first / to end of chapter / to end of chapter

Figure 12.10
Testing the conductivity of a solution of acetic acid. As the bulb only glows dimly, acetic acid must be a weak acid.

12.10 *Acetic Acid — A Weak Acid*

Acetic acid differs in a number of ways from some of the other acids we will discuss. First, the name used for pure acetic acid, $CH_3CO_2H_{(\ell)}$, is the same as that used for its aqueous solution, $CH_3CO_2H_{(aq)}$. Acetic acid is an example of a weak acid, whereas acids such as hydrochloric acid and nitric acid are examples of strong acids.

There are a number of differences between weak and strong acids. When an aqueous solution of hydrogen chloride (hydrochloric acid) was tested in the conductivity apparatus (Section 5.1), the light bulb shone very brightly, just as it did when an aqueous solution of sodium chloride was tested. However, if we test an aqueous solution of acetic acid with a concentration similar to that of the hydrochloric acid, the light from the bulb will be very dim. What causes this difference?

First, the brighter light given by the hydrochloric acid indicates that hydrochloric acid conducts electricity better than acetic acid. As solutions that do not contain ions do not conduct electricity, it seems reasonable to suggest that if more ions are present the solution will be a better conductor of electricity. If this is true, then we must conclude that a solution of hydrochloric acid contains more ions than a solution of acetic acid. More sophisticated experiments support this theory and show that when hydrogen chloride is dissolved in water, all the molecules dissociate into hydrogen ions and chloride ions. However, when acetic acid is dissolved in water, only a small number of the molecules dissociate into hydrogen ions and acetate ions. Acids that behave like hydrogen chloride are called **strong acids**, and those that behave like acetic acid are called **weak acids**.

Let us look at the structure of acetic acid and see what happens when this substance dissolves in water. The hydrogen atom attached to oxygen forms the hydrogen ion and the negatively charged acetate ion remains.

Acetic acid   Acetate ion

Notice that the bonds between carbon and hydrogen are not broken. This is one reason why we prefer to write the formula of acetic acid as CH_3CO_2H rather than as $C_2H_4O_2$. The former helps us to visualize the structure of acetic acid and to remember what happens when it dissolves in water.

Acetic acid has the characteristic odour of vinegar. In fact, vinegar is a 5% solution of acetic acid in water with flavourings added. Vinegar is produced by the action of bacteria (*Acetobacter*) on ethanol (grain alcohol) in the presence of oxygen. The same reaction takes place when a bottle of beer or wine is left open too long, and is the reason why the beer or wine eventually acquires a vinegary taste.

Pure (100%) acetic acid is often called glacial acetic acid. Solid acetic acid has an ice-like crystalline appearance — hence the word "glacial". Its melting point is $17\,°C$.

Ammonia: A Weak Base

When sodium hydroxide dissolves in water it dissociates completely into sodium ions and hydroxide ions:

$$NaOH_{(s)} \xrightarrow[\text{in water}]{\text{dissolve}} Na^+{}_{(aq)} + OH^+{}_{(aq)}$$

Thus, when a solution of sodium hydroxide is tested in the conductivity apparatus, the light bulb shines brightly. Sodium hydroxide is an example of a **strong base**.

If we test an aqueous solution of ammonia with red litmus paper, we observe that the litmus paper turns blue and we conclude that the solution is basic. If the same solution is tested in the conductivity apparatus, we find that the light bulb glows, but not very brightly — a result very similar to the one we obtained with acetic acid. Hydroxide ions are produced when ammonia, NH_3, is dissolved in water because a small portion of the ammonia molecules react with water according to the equation:

$$NH_{3(g)} + H_2O_{(\ell)} \rightleftharpoons NH_4{}^+{}_{(aq)} + OH^-{}_{(aq)}$$

Because only a fraction of the ammonia molecules reacts in this way, only a few hydroxide ions are produced, and the solution is not a very good conductor of electricity. Ammonia is therefore classified as a **weak base**.

Note that a solution of ammonia in water may be referred to as either ammonia solution or as ammonium hydroxide. Ammonium hydroxide (NH_4OH) does not exist as a solid.

Properties of Some Acids and Bases

12.11

Although all acids have certain properties in common, each acid has its own unique properties and uses. In this section, we will discuss the properties of three common acids: hydrochloric acid, sulfuric acid, and nitric acid; and one common base, sodium hydroxide.

Hydrochloric Acid ($HCl_{(aq)}$)

Hydrogen chloride is a colourless gas that dissolves readily in water to form hydrochloric acid. The ''concentrated hydrochloric acid'' bottles in your school laboratory contain solutions with a concentration of 12 $mol \cdot L^{-1}$ HCl. These solutions are potentially very hazardous and you should be very careful when using them.

Hydrochloric acid is produced in the stomach to assist in the breakdown of some types of food. Normally the lining of the stomach is not affected by the acid but sometimes, if we have eaten too much food, excess hydrochloric acid is produced and we start to experience discomfort. To alleviate the discomfort, many people take one of the commercially available antacids in which the active ingredient is a compound that will react with, and neutralize, the hydrochloric acid. Thus, Milk of Magnesia contains magnesium hydroxide $Mg(OH)_2$; Rolaids contain dihydroxyaluminum sodium carbonate, $NaAl(OH)_2CO_3$; and Tums contain calcium carbonate. You should be aware of the fact, however, that some antacids can have undesirable side-effects. For example, magnesium ions can act as a laxative, and therefore large doses of Milk of Magnesia should be avoided.

Figure 12.11
Hydrochloric acid is available commercially under the ancient name of muriatic acid.

Sulfuric Acid ($H_2SO_{4\,(aq)}$)

Hydrogen sulfate is a dense oily liquid which, when mixed with a little water (to give sulfuric acid), can produce enough heat to boil the water. Extreme caution should be used if you are ever required to mix sulfuric acid with water. Remember, always add acid to water and *never* water to acid. Adding water to an acid can cause the acid to spurt out of the container and splash your hands, face, or eyes.

The concentrated sulfuric acid that is supplied to school laboratories contains 18 $mol \cdot L^{-1}$ H_2SO_4 and has a density of 1.84 $g \cdot mL^{-1}$. Solutions with lower concentrations have lower densities. The sulfuric acid used in automobile batteries has a density of 1.28 $g \cdot mL^{-1}$. As the battery discharges, sulfuric acid is used up. This causes the density of the ''battery acid'' to decrease and approach the density of pure water (1.00 $g \cdot mL^{-1}$). Hence checking the density (or specific gravity) of the acid in a car battery indicates if the battery needs to be charged.

Several million tonnes of sulfuric acid are produced every year. The acid is used in the manufacture of fertilizers, in the production of steel, and in the petroleum industry.

The H_2SO_4 molecule has two hydrogen atoms that could form hydrogen ions when the acid dissolves in water. In practice, one hydrogen is "lost" much more readily than the other. Therefore, in addition to hydrogen ions, a solution of sulfuric acid contains bisulfate (HSO_4^-) and sulfate (SO_4^{2-}) ions:

$$H_2SO_{4\,(aq)} \longrightarrow H^+_{(aq)} + HSO_4^-{}_{(aq)}$$

$$HSO_4^-{}_{(aq)} \rightleftharpoons H^+_{(aq)} + SO_4^{2-}{}_{(aq)}$$

Nitric Acid (HNO₃ (aq))

In your laboratory, most of the reagent bottles that contain acids and bases are made of colourless glass. However, you will see a few that are made of brown glass. It's likely that one of these contains nitric acid. Nitric acid decomposes slightly in light to give brown fumes of nitrogen dioxide, $NO_{2\,(g)}$. This decomposition can be minimized by storing the nitric acid in a brown bottle, out of direct light.

Acids produce a burning sensation if they come into contact with the skin. Nitric acid also causes the skin to turn brown.

Nitric acid has many industrial uses. Two of the most important of these are in the manufacture of fertilizers and explosives.

Sodium Hydroxide (NaOH)

Sodium hydroxide (also known as caustic soda) is the base you will use most in the laboratory. It also has many industrial uses and is an important reagent in the manufacture of soap, rayon, cellophane, paper, and dyes. Drain cleaners and oven cleaners contain sodium hydroxide and these products should be used with care.

Sodium hydroxide feels soapy to the skin because it reacts with the fats in the skin to form a soap. This reaction, called **saponification**, is used in the commercial production of soaps:

Fat + NaOH $\longrightarrow$ Soap + Glycerol

Sodium hydroxide also reacts with the proteins in the skin and can completely destroy living tissue. Whenever you use oven or drain cleaners containing sodium hydroxide, you should wear gloves and ensure that none of the product comes into contact with your skin. Eye protection is also essential when using sodium hydroxide. Bases react with the cornea of the eye to form an opaque coating! When using a drain cleaner, be patient. Resorting to mechanical means because you feel that the chemical product is not working can have disastrous consequences. When the base starts to react with the fat that is clogging up the drain, heat is released because the reaction is exothermic. Using a suction device to help speed the cleaning could result in the hot material being sprayed over your hands or face.

Your school probably receives sodium hydroxide as white pellets. These pellets are **deliquescent**. They absorb moisture from the atmosphere very quickly and eventually dissolve in the absorbed water. (A related term, **hygroscopic**, is used for substances that absorb water but remain in the solid state.)

A concentrated solution of sodium hydroxide will etch glass. It is therefore advisable to use rubber or plastic stoppers in containers of sodium hydroxide solution, as glass stoppers can seize up. A sodium hydroxide solution should not be left open to the air because it will react with the carbon dioxide in the air to form sodium carbonate:

QUESTIONS

11. Name one location (other than a chemical laboratory) where you would find each of the following:
a) hydrochloric acid   d) sulfuric acid
b) acetic acid   e) sodium hydroxide
c) aqueous ammonia

The pH Scale   *12.12*

If a substance produces hydrogen ions when it is dissolved in water it is called an acid and the resulting solution is said to be acidic. The greater the concentration of hydrogen ions, the more acidic the solution is considered to be. In practice, all aqueous solutions contain a small concentration of hydrogen ions produced by the self-ionization of water:

$$H_2O_{(\ell)} \longrightarrow H^+_{(aq)} + OH^-_{(aq)}$$

However, in pure water, the extent of this self-ionization is very low. This explains why water did not appear to conduct electricity in the conductivity experiment described earlier. In pure water the concentration of both the hydrogen ions and the hydroxide ions is 1×10^{-7} mol·L^{-1}. A solution in which [H$^+$] is 1×10^{-7} mol·L^{-1} is said to be neutral. If the concentration of [H$^+$] is greater than 1×10^{-7} mol·L^{-1}, which happens when hydrogen chloride gas is dissolved in water, the solution is said to be acidic. If the concentration of [H$^+$] falls below 1×10^{-7} mol·L^{-1}, as it does when

Figure 12.12
The relationship between [H$^+$] and [OH$^-$] in an aqueous solution.

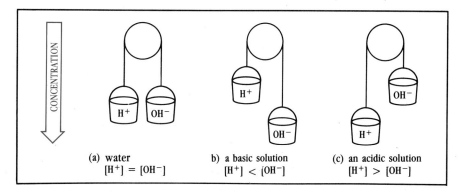

(a) water
[H$^+$] = [OH$^-$]

b) a basic solution
[H$^+$] < [OH$^-$]

(c) an acidic solution
[H$^+$] > [OH$^-$]

sodium hydroxide is dissolved in water, the solution is described as being basic. When sodium hydroxide is added to pure water, the $[H^+]$ drops below 1×10^{-7} mol·L^{-1} because the product of the concentration of hydrogen ions and the concentration of hydroxide ions is a constant, 1×10^{-14} mol²·L^{-2}. We can show this by the equation:

$$[H^+][OH^-] = 1 \times 10^{-14} \text{ mol}^2 \cdot \text{L}^{-2}$$

Thus, when hydroxide ions are added to pure water, the concentration of hydrogen ions must decrease for $[H^+][OH^-]$ to be equal to 1×10^{-14} mol·L^{-2}. This concept is illustrated in Figure 12.12.

Expressing the hydrogen-ion concentration of water as 1×10^{-7} mol·L^{-1} is not particularly convenient. Thus, in 1909, S.P. Sorenson established the **pH scale** so that hydrogen-ion concentrations could be expressed in a more convenient manner. The definition of pH is

$$pH = -\log_{10}[H^+]$$

For most practical purposes the pH scale runs from 0 to 14. For example, in pure water, where the $[H^+]$ is 1×10^{-7} mol·L^{-1}

$$
\begin{aligned}
pH &= -\log_{10}[1 \times 10^{-7}] \\
&= -(-7.0) \\
&= 7.0
\end{aligned}
$$

As the hydrogen-ion concentration in any neutral solution is 1×10^{-7} mol·L^{-1}, it follows that, the pH of a neutral solution is 7.0.

A similar calculation for a solution of 0.01 mol·L^{-1} hydrochloric acid, in which $[H^+]$ is 0.01 mol·L^{-1}, gives us

$$
\begin{aligned}
pH &= -\log_{10}[0.01] \\
&= -(-2.0) \\
&= 2.0
\end{aligned}
$$

Similarly, for 0.01 mol·L^{-1} sodium hydroxide

$$[H^+][OH^-] = 1 \times 10^{-14} \text{ mol}^2 \cdot \text{L}^{-2}$$

$$[H^+] = \frac{1 \times 10^{-14} \text{ mol}^2 \cdot \text{L}^{-2}}{1 \times 10^{-2} \text{ mol} \cdot \text{L}^{-1}}$$

$$= 1 \times 10^{-12} \text{ mol} \cdot \text{L}^{-1}$$

Hence

$$
\begin{aligned}
pH &= -\log_{10}[1 \times 10^{-12}] \\
&= -(-12.0) \\
&= 12.0
\end{aligned}
$$

In general, a pH of less than 7.0 indicates that a solution is acidic The acidity increases as the pH decreases. Likewise, a pH greater than 7.0 indicates that a solution is basic. Basicity increases as the pH increases (Figure 12.13).

To find pH values on a calculator, enter the following or equivalent keys:

1 EXP 7 +/- log +/-

0.01 log +/-

1 EXP 12 +/- log +/-

Figure 12.13
The pH scale and its relationship to [H⁺].

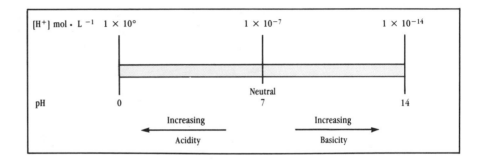

EXAMPLE   **12.7**   What would be the pH of a 2.5×10^{-4} mol·L⁻¹ solution of hydrochloric acid?

SOLUTION   As hydrochloric acid is a strong acid, all the hydrogen chloride molecules will be dissociated in the solution, as shown in the equation

$$HCl_{(aq)} \xrightarrow[\text{dissociation}]{100\%} H^+_{(aq)} + Cl^-_{(aq)}$$

Thus

$$[H^+] = 2.5 \times 10^{-4} \text{ mol·L}^{-1}$$

$\boxed{2.5}$ $\boxed{EXP}$ $\boxed{4}$ $\boxed{+/-}$ $\boxed{\log}$ $\boxed{+/-}$

$$pH = -\log_{10}[H^+] = -\log_{10}[2.5 \times 10^{-4}]$$
$$= -(-3.60)$$
$$= 3.60$$

EXAMPLE   **12.8**   Calculate the pH of a solution containing 5×10^{-5} mol·L⁻¹ sodium hydroxide.

SOLUTION   Sodium hydroxide totally dissociates in water according to the equation

$$NaOH_{(aq)} \xrightarrow[\text{dissociation}]{100\%} Na^+_{(aq)} + OH^-_{(aq)}$$

Therefore the [OH⁻] in this solution will be 5×10^{-5} mol·L⁻¹. To find [H⁺] we must remember that

$$[H^+][OH^-] = 1 \times 10^{-14} \text{ mol}^2\cdot\text{L}^{-2}$$

Thus

$$[H^+] = \frac{1 \times 10^{-14} \text{ mol}^2\cdot\text{L}^{-2}}{[OH^-]}$$

$$= \frac{1 \times 10^{-14} \text{ mol}^2\cdot\text{L}^{-2}}{5 \times 10^{-5} \text{ mol·L}^{-1}}$$

$$= 2 \times 10^{-10} \text{ mol·L}^{-1}$$

Therefore

$$pH = -\log_{10} [H^+]$$
$$= -\log_{10} [2 \times 10^{-10}]$$
$$= -(-9.7)$$
$$= 9.7$$

TABLE 12.7   *The pH Values of Some Common Solutions*

	Solution	pH
Acidic	Stomach acid (0.1 mol·L⁻¹ HCl)	1.0
	Vinegar	2.5
	Urine (depending on diet)	5.0–7.0
Basic	Blood	7.3–7.5
	Milk of Magnesia (saturated $Mg(OH)_2$)	10.3

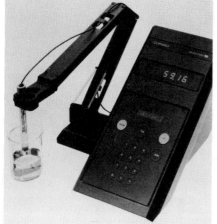

Figure 12.14
We can measure the pH of a solution by using a pH meter. The digital model shown measures pH by means of an electrode dipped in the solution.

When comparing the pH values of two solutions, it is important to remember that a difference of 1 pH unit represents a tenfold difference in hydrogen-ion concentration. Thus, in a solution with a pH of 4.0, the concentration of hydrogen ions is ten times greater than in a solution with a pH of 5.0. The Richter scale for measuring the strength of earthquakes is somewhat similar: an earthquake that registers 6 on the Richter scale is ten times stronger than one that registers 5 on the same scale.

QUESTIONS

12. Calculate the pH of
    a) a 2.0×10^{-3} mol·L⁻¹ nitric acid solution
    b) a 2×10^{-5} mol·L⁻¹ sodium hydroxide solution

13. Arrange the following substances in order of increasing acidity:
    Lemon juice, pH 2.1   Egg white, pH 7.8
    Cow's milk, pH 6.5   Shampoo, pH 6.7

Acid Rain   *12.13*

Acid rain was mentioned in Section 9.7 in the discussion of sulfur dioxide. In recent years, the problem of acid rain has become a very controversial issue.

So called "pure" rainwater is slightly acidic because it contains dissolved carbon dioxide. Thus, "pure" rainwater is really a very dilute solution of carbonic acid:

$$\mathbf{CO_{2\,(g)} + H_2O_{(\ell)} \rightleftharpoons H_2CO_{3\,(aq)}}$$

Carbonic acid is a weak acid and dissociates slightly to give hydrogen ions and bicarbonate ions:

$$H_2CO_{3\,(aq)} \rightleftharpoons H^+_{(aq)} + HCO_3^-_{(aq)}$$

The pH of "pure" rainwater is about 5.6.

Any rainwater with a pH of less than 5.6 can be classed as acid rain. Rain with a pH of 3.6 has been recorded in Toronto. Even more acidic rain with a pH of 2.3 has fallen on Kana, Pennsylvania; and to illustrate the international nature of this problem, rain with a pH of 2.4 was once recorded during a storm in Scotland. Rainwater of this pH contains about the same concentration of hydrogen ions as vinegar!

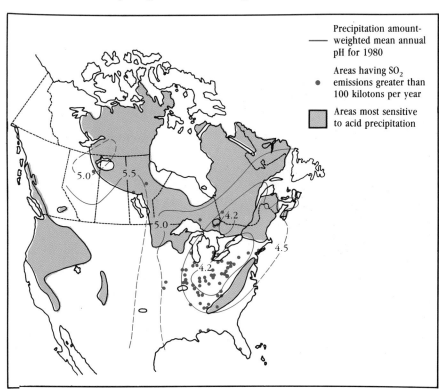

Figure 12.15
Average pH of precipitation in North America.

How does our rainwater become so acidic? To obtain the answer we must find out which of the substances that are released into the atmosphere will combine with the water to form acids. The trail leads us back to the following three activities:

1. the burning of sulfur-containing coal and oil in thermal power plants
2. the smelting operations of industrial plants in which nonferrous metal ores containing sulfur are refined
3. the burning of gasoline in automobiles

Of these activities, the first two produce large amounts of sulfur dioxide from the reaction of sulfur with oxygen:

$$S_{(s)} + O_{2\,(g)} \longrightarrow SO_{2\,(g)}$$

Automobile emissions, the result of the third activity, are the largest single source of the oxides of nitrogen, which we will represent by the formula $NO_{x\,(g)}$.

After these pollutant gases enter the atmosphere they are either deposited close to their source (sometimes referred to as dry deposition) or the sulfur and nitrogen oxides may undergo further oxidation in the atmosphere and combine with the moisture present in the air to form dilute sulfuric and nitric acids. Clouds containing the oxides or acids can be transported thousands of kilometres over a period of several days. Eventually the acids are deposited as acid rain:

$$SO_{2\,(g)} \xrightarrow{\text{oxidation}} SO_{3\,(g)} \xrightarrow{H_2O} H_2SO_{4\,(aq)}$$

$$NO_{x\,(g)} \xrightarrow{\text{oxidation}} \xrightarrow{H_2O} HNO_{3\,(aq)}$$

The term "acid rain" is a little too specific. In Canada, much of our precipitation is in the form of snow. The term "acid precipitation" is sometimes used to include rain, snow, and smog. Environmentalists use the term "acid deposition" to include both acid precipitation and the deposition of dry oxides.

As the gaseous, acidic oxides are often carried thousands of kilometres before being deposited as acid precipitation, it is difficult to solve the problem of acid rain. The main sources of sulfur dioxide in North America are

Figure 12.16

The origin of acid rain.

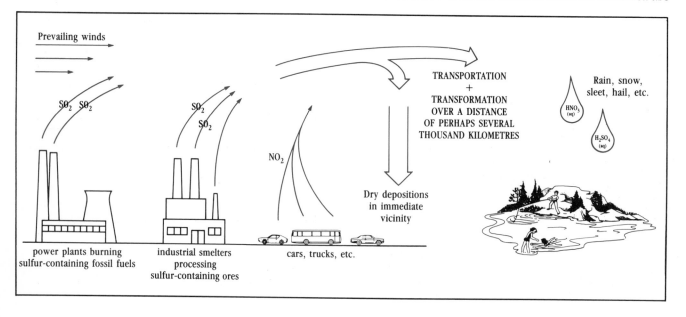

the industrial areas in Ontario (for example, the Sudbury area) and the Ohio River Valley area. Because of the prevailing westerly winds, the sulfur dioxide generated in these regions is eventually deposited as acid precipitation in eastern Canada and the northeastern United States. A major problem facing politicians in areas that receive acid precipitation is how to persuade their counterparts in the sulfur dioxide-producing regions to introduce legislation that would require industry to limit its sulfur dioxide emissions. You may have read articles on this issue in your daily newspaper.

Acid precipitation causes extensive damage to our environment. As with many environmental issues, there is a good deal of controversy about the kinds of damage caused by acid precipitation. Among the alleged effects are the following:

1. An increase in the acidity of freshwater lakes and streams. The ability of a freshwater system to counter an increase in hydrogen ion concentration depends to a large extent on the underlying bedrock. Areas in which the bedrock has a limestone base are not affected to the same extent as those with highly siliceous bedrock (granite, quartz, etc.). The Kawartha Lakes area in Ontario is in the former category. Most of Atlantic Canada and large areas of Northern Ontario and Quebec fall into the latter category. The pH of many lakes and rivers in these regions has dropped so much in recent years that fish can no longer survive.

2. The erosion of buildings, statues, and monuments. Any building stone that contains calcium carbonate erodes as a result of the reaction between the acids in the acidic precipitation and the carbonates in the rock to produce soluble sulfates and nitrates:

$$CaCO_{3\,(s)} + H_2SO_{4\,(aq)} \longrightarrow CaSO_{4\,(aq)} + H_2O_{(l)} + CO_{2\,(g)}$$

3. Damage to forests, soil, and crops. Less is known about the effects of acid precipitation on forests, soil, and crops than on freshwater systems and architecture. However, European studies suggest that species such as beech, white spruce, and fir are being adversely affected. The soils supporting these forests appear to be becoming more acidic, and toxic metals, such as aluminum, are accumulating in these soils. North American studies also suggest that the rate of forest growth declined from 1950 to 1970. Acid precipitation is not known to be the sole cause of this decline, but it appears to be a major factor. Experiments carried out in the U.S. have shown that the foliage of crops such as spinach, lettuce, and radishes can be damaged by acid rain.

The problem of acid rain will be with us for many years. Expensive modifications to industrial plants are required in order to reduce the level of sulfur dioxide emissions. Although most of the technology is available, it is very expensive to install the equipment necessary to reduce these emissions. It is often cheaper to close an older plant and build a new one in a different location. This latter approach is of particular concern to one-industry towns.

Figure 12.17
The acidity of small lakes can be reduced by neutralizing the acid with powdered limestone (calcium carbonate).

Rainwater may be contaminated not only with acids, but with many toxic substances that threaten our environment. The problem of *toxic rain*, like that of acid rain, will be very difficult to solve.

Colloids

12.14

In a solution, one substance (the solute) is dispersed as separate molecules or ions in another substance (the solvent). These solutions are clear. For example, when sodium chloride (salt) is dissolved in water no solid particles are visible. We occasionally encounter a "solution" that is not clear, but appears to be cloudy. An excellent example of this is milk. Even after standing for long periods, the matter responsible for the cloudiness does not settle out; nor is it possible to remove it from the solvent by filtration. Solutions that display these properties are referred to as colloidal solutions or **colloids**.

Although colloidal solutions usually appear to be cloudy, the individual particles, which consist of either extremely large single molecules or clusters of a number of small molecules, are not visible to the naked eye. These particles have diameters ranging from 1 to 10 nm. If we can see the particles, or if the particles settle or can be separated by filtration, the mixture is called a **suspension**.

Colloids may result from eight of the nine possible particle/medium combinations formed by the three states of matter. These combinations, and some examples of colloids produced by each combination, are given in Table 12.8.

TABLE 12.8 *Types of Colloids*

Particle	Medium	Common name	Examples
Gas	Liquid	Foam	Whipped cream
Gas	Solid	Solid foam	Floating soap, meringues, pumice
Liquid	Gas	Liquid aerosol	Fog, cloud
Liquid	Liquid	Liquid emulsion	Milk, mayonnaise
Liquid	Solid	Solid emulsion	Butter, opals
Solid	Gas	Solid aerosol	Smoke
Solid	Liquid	Sol	Starch solutions, paints, Milk of magnesia
Solid	Solid	Solid sol	Pearls

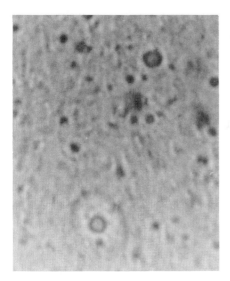

Figure 12.18
Milk is a colloid (a liquid emulsion). The spheres that you see in this photograph are fat globules suspended in an aqueous solution.

A colloid that we sometimes observe in the laboratory is formed when ammonia gas reacts with hydrogen chloride gas to produce ammonium chloride. The latter appears as a white smoke:

$$NH_{3\,(g)} + HCl_{(g)} \longrightarrow NH_4Cl_{(s)}$$

This reaction occurs in laboratories where ammonia and hydrogen chloride are used frequently; the white smoke eventually settles out to give a white film of ammonium chloride on bottles and fumehood windows.

If we pass a beam of light through a "true" solution we will find that it will absorb some of the light and transmit the rest. However, in a colloid, the particles are large enough to scatter some of the light. Thus, when a beam of light is passed through a colloid, the beam becomes visible from the side. This phenomenon is known as the **Tyndall effect** and can be observed when a beam of light from car headlights passes through smoke or fog.

If we look at a colloid through an ultramicroscope, we observe that the colloidal particles are in constant motion. This motion, called **Brownian motion**, is caused by the collisions between the colloidal particles and the molecules of the supporting medium. Brownian motion lends support to the assumption made in the kinetic–molecular theory that the particles present in liquids and gases are in constant random motion.

TABLE 12.9 *Comparison of the Properties of True Solutions, Colloids, and Suspensions*

Property	True Solution	Colloid	Suspension
Does it settle out?	No	No	Yes
Can it be separated by filtration?	No	No	Yes
Size of particles	< 1 nm	> 1 nm but < 100 nm	> 100 nm
Is the Tyndall effect observed?	No	Yes	Yes

Summary

- A solution is composed of a solvent and one or more solutes.

- Water is the most important solvent because of its ability to dissolve a wide range of compounds.

- The solubility of a substance is the mass of a substance that will dissolve in a given volume or mass of a particular solvent.

- The concentration of a solution is determined by dividing the number of moles of solute by the volume of the solution in litres. Concentration can also be expressed in terms of mass percent, volume percent, mole fraction, or parts per million (billion).

- The concentration of cations and ions can be determined from the concentration of the solution and the formula of the compound.

- Solutions that contain a precisely known mass of solute in a precisely known volume of solution are called standard solutions.

- According to the Arrhenius definitions an acid is a substance that dissolves in water to produce H^+ ions, and a base is a substance that dissolves in water to produce OH^- ions.

- Strong acids and strong bases dissociate completely when they are dissolved in water. Weak acids and weak bases dissociate only to a limited extent.

- Pure water dissociates very slightly to give a hydrogen-ion concentration of 1×10^{-7} mol·L^{-1}. This process is called the self-ionization of water.

- In any aqueous solution, the product of the hydrogen-ion concentration and the hydroxide-ion concentration is 1×10^{-14} mol^2·L^{-2}, i.e. $[H^+][OH^-] = 1 \times 10^{-14}$ mol^2·L^{-2}.

- A convenient way of expressing the hydrogen-ion concentration of a solution is through the use of pH. The pH of a solution is defined as the negative logarithm (to the base 10) of the hydrogen-ion concentration, that is, $pH = \log_{10}[H^+]$.

- A solution with a pH of less than 7 is acidic. If the pH of solution is greater than 7, the solution is basic. A neutral solution has a pH equal to 7.

- Pure rainwater is slightly acidic (pH approximately 5.6) because of the presence of dissolved carbon dioxide. Rainwater with a pH of less than 5.6 is called acid rain. Acid rain results from the reaction of the oxides of nitrogen and sulfur with the water in the atmosphere. Acid rain causes damage to the environment.

- Colloids consist of clusters of molecules, invisible to the naked eye, suspended in a medium. The clusters cannot be filtered out and will not settle out on standing.

KEY WORDS

aqueous solution	deliquescent	insoluble
binary acid	dilute solution	mass percent
Brownian motion	dilution	miscible
colloid	dissociate	molarity
concentration	hygroscopic	moles per litre
concentrated solution	immiscible	oxyacid

parts per million	solution	volume percent
pH scale	solvent	volumetric flask
saponification	standard solution	volumetric pipette
saturated solution	strong acid	weak acid
solubility	strong base	weak base
soluble	suspension	
solute	Tyndall effect	

ANSWERS TO
SECTION QUESTIONS

1. NaCl, very soluble; NaNO$_3$, very soluble; AgNO$_3$, very soluble; Ag$_2$SO$_4$, slightly soluble; Li$_2$CO$_3$, soluble

2. a) 0.100 mol·L^{-1} b) 0.0500 mol·L^{-1} c) 0.200 mol·L^{-1}

3. 187 g

4. 41.7 L

5. a) [Na$^+$] = [Cl$^-$] = 1.50 mol·L^{-1}

   b) [NH$_4{}^+$] = 0.450 mol·L^{-1} ; [CO$_3{}^{2-}$] = 0.225 mol·L^{-1}

   c) [Al^{3+}] = 2.2 mol·L^{-1} ; [SO$_4{}^{2-}$] = 3.3 mol·L^{-1}

6. a) 0.0396 mol·L^{-1} b) 0.0856 mol·L^{-1}

7. 0.157 mol·L^{-1}

8. a) a lower concentration   b) a lower concentration

9. 0.15 mol·L^{-1}

10. add 10.0 mL of 15.0 mol·L^{-1} NH$_3$ to water and make up to 1.00 L

11. a) stomach   c) household cleaner   e) drain cleaner
    b) vinegar   d) car battery

12. a) 2.70   b) 9.3

13. egg white, shampoo, cow's milk, lemon juice

COMPREHENSION QUESTIONS

1. What is the difference in meaning between the terms soluble and miscible?

2. What is the difference between an amalgam and an alloy? Give an example of each.

3. Describe the effect of increasing temperature on
   a) the solubility of a solid in a liquid
   b) the solubility of a gas in a liquid

4. What two factors affect the solubility of an ionic compound in water?

5. What is the difference in meaning between the terms saturated and concentrated?

6. What is the difference between mass percent and volume percent?

7. What is the Arrhenius definition of a) an acid and b) a base?

8. Explain the difference in meaning between the terms deliquescent and hygroscopic.

9. What is the pH of
   a) a neutral solution   c) an acidic solution   b) a basic solution

10. Name three activities that are believed to be responsible for the production of acid rain? Which of these activities produce sulfur dioxide? Which produce oxides of nitrogen?

11. List three of the effects of acid rain on our environment.

12. Describe the differences between a solution, a suspension, and a colloid.

13. What is the Tyndall effect?

14. What is Brownian motion? What causes it?

15. What is the essential feature of the water molecule that makes it such a good solvent for ionic compounds?

16. Explain in your own words what happens as an ionic compound dissolves in water.

17. Why should a container of sodium hydroxide solution not be left open to the air?

18. Explain why nitric acid is usually stored in brown bottles.

PROBLEMS

19. Calcium carbonate is usually described as being insoluble in water. About how much calcium carbonate would you expect to dissolve in a litre of water?

20. Lead(II) chloride has a solubility of $6.7 \text{ g} \cdot \text{L}^{-1}$ of water at 0 °C and $33.4 \text{ g} \cdot \text{L}^{-1}$ of water at 100 °C. How would you describe the solubility of lead(II) chloride at these two temperatures?

21. The solubility of each of the compounds listed below is given as the mass of substance (in grams) that will dissolve in one litre of water at 298 K. Classify each compound as very soluble, slightly soluble, or insoluble:

Compound	Solubility ($g \cdot L^{-1}$)
a) sodium chloride	359
b) calcium carbonate	1.30×10^{-2}
c) potassium chlorate	52.2
d) lithium fluoride	1.32
e) silver iodide	2.61×10^{-5}

22. The solubility of each of the compounds below is given as the number of moles of substance that will dissolve in a litre of water. Calculate the solubility of each compound in grams per litre, and state whether each compound is very soluble, soluble, slightly soluble, or insoluble:

Compound	Solubility (mol$\cdot$L^{-1})
a) CuS	2.6×10^{-15}
b) Li$_2$CO$_3$	0.175
c) BaBr$_2 \cdot$ 2H$_2$O	3.56

23. Calculate the mass percent of solute in each of the following solutions:
    a) 8.60 g of sodium chloride dissolved in 95.0 g of water
    b) 3.85 g of calcium chloride in 78.50 g of solution
    c) 3.5 g of sulfuric acid in 20.0 g of solution

24. Silver nitrate has a solubility in water of 222.0 g of silver nitrate per 100.0 g of water at 298 K. What is the mass percent of silver nitrate in a saturated solution of silver nitrate at this temperature? What mass of silver nitrate will be needed to prepare 185 g of a saturated solution?

25. An alloy of gold and copper is used for making jewelry. The composition of the alloy is normally expressed in karats, where 24 karats represents 100% gold. Calculate the composition (mass percent) of 14 karat gold.

26. In Canada, people who consume fish that have been caught in polluted waters are particularly susceptible to mercury poisoning. Health and Welfare Canada recommended in 1977 that fish containing more than 500 ppb of mercury should not be sold or consumed. What mass of mercury would be present in a trout weighing 1.00 kg that has a mercury concentration of 500 ppb?

27. Water is added to 21.0 mL of alcohol until the total volume of the mixture is 100.0 mL. Find the volume percent of alcohol in the mixture.

28. A dilute solution of hydrogen peroxide (used as an antiseptic and for lightening the colour of hair) contains 3.0 g of hydrogen peroxide in 100.0 mL of solution. If the density of hydrogen peroxide is 1.40 g$\cdot$mL^{-1}, what is the volume percent of hydrogen peroxide in the solution?

29. Brass is an alloy that contains 80.0% copper and 20.0% zinc by mass. Calculate the mole fraction of copper in this alloy.

30. Most gold coins contain about 90% gold by mass, the remainder being copper. What is the mole fraction of gold in such coins?

31. Determine the concentration (mol$\cdot$L^{-1}) of a solution containing
    a) 10.0 g of calcium chloride in 645.0 mL of solution
    b) 20.0 g of sodium chloride in 0.850 L of solution
    c) 7.4 g of sugar (C$_{12}$H$_{22}$O$_{11}$) in 84.0 mL of solution

32. Calculate the concentration ($mol \cdot L^{-1}$) of a solution containing
   a) 5.0 g of lithium bromide in 2.50 L of solution
   b) 0.882 g of ammonium chloride in 10.0 mL of solution
   c) 40.0 g of sodium sulfate in 500.0 mL of solution

33. What mass of solute is needed to prepare 1.00 L of each of the following solutions:
   a) sodium hydroxide with a concentration of 0.100 $mol \cdot L^{-1}$
   b) calcium nitrate with a concentration of 0.40 $mol \cdot L^{-1}$

34. Calculate the mass of solute required to prepare the following aqueous solutions:
   a) 25 mL of potassium chloride solution (2.5 $mol \cdot L^{-1}$)
   b) 4.20 L of hydrochloric acid (0.100 $mol \cdot L^{-1}$)

35. Explain how you would prepare 500.0 mL of a 0.100 $mol \cdot L^{-1}$ solution of magnesium sulfate from the solid compound.

36. Ethanol (C_2H_5OH) is a liquid with a density of 0.790 $g \cdot mL^{-1}$. Describe how you would prepare 1.00 L of an aqueous solution of ethanol with a concentration of 1.25 $mol \cdot L^{-1}$.

37. Find the concentration of sodium phosphate, sodium ions, and phosphate ions when 6.00 g of sodium phosphate (Na_3PO_4) is dissolved in water to give 250.0 mL of solution.

38. Calculate the concentration of ammonium ions when 10.0 g of ammonium sulfate is dissolved in sufficient water to give 125 mL of solution.

39. Calculate the concentration of chloride ions when 1.5 g of sodium chloride and 1.5 g of calcium chloride are dissolved together in water to give 2.5×10^2 mL of solution.

 40. When 10.0 mL of sodium chloride solution (0.250 $mol \cdot L^{-1}$) is mixed with 40.0 mL of sodium sulfate solution (0.100 $mol \cdot L^{-1}$), what is the total concentration of sodium ions in the resulting solution?

41. How would you prepare
   a) 2.50×10^2 mL of hydrochloric acid (0.10 $mol \cdot L^{-1}$) from 12.0 $mol \cdot L^{-1}$ hydrochloric acid
   b) 1.50 L of calcium chloride solution (0.200 $mol \cdot L^{-1}$) from a calcium chloride solution of 1.00 $mol \cdot L^{-1}$ concentration

 42. Given an ammonia solution with a concentration of 15.0 $mol \cdot L^{-1}$, how would you prepare
   a) 1.00 L of dilute ammonia with a concentration of 0.100 $mol \cdot L^{-1}$
   b) 250.0 mL of ammonia solution with a concentration of 3.00 $mol \cdot L^{-1}$

 43. If 10.0 mL of a 0.560 $mol \cdot L^{-1}$ solution of aluminum nitrate is diluted to 250.0 mL, what is
   a) the concentration of aluminum nitrate in the new solution
   b) the concentration of nitrate ions in the new solution

44. Calculate the concentration of the solution formed if a 25.0 mL sample of nitric acid ($10.0 \ mol \cdot L^{-1}$) is placed in a 500.0 mL volumetric flask and the flask is filled up to the mark with distilled water.

45. What is the total volume of $3.0 \ mol \cdot L^{-1}$ sulfuric acid that can be prepared from 5.0 L of concentrated sulfuric acid ($18 \ mol \cdot L^{-1}$)?

46. What volume of $0.10 \ mol \cdot L^{-1}$ hydrochloric acid can be prepared from 5.0 L of concentrated hydrochloric acid ($12 \ mol \cdot L^{-1}$)?

47. Predict whether the pH of an aqueous solution of each of the following will be above 7, below 7, or equal to 7:
   a) acetic acid   b) sugar   c) ammonia

48. Predict the approximate pH of each of the following:
   a) rainwater   c) the acid from a car battery
   b) household ammonia

49. Calculate the pH of an aqueous solution containing
   a) $2.5 \times 10^{-5} \ mol \cdot L^{-1}$ HCl
   b) $1.0 \times 10^{-3} \ mol \cdot L^{-1}$ NaOH

50. Calculate the pH of each of the following aqueous solutions:
   a) $4.2 \times 10^{-6} \ mol \cdot L^{-1}$ HNO_3
   b) $5.5 \times 10^{-5} \ mol \cdot L^{-1}$ $Ba(OH)_2$

SUGGESTED PROJECTS

1. Certain additives, called emulsifiers, are added to foods such as mayonnaise and salad dressings in order to stabilize the water–oil emulsion (colloid) present. Prepare a report on the use of such emulsifiers.

2. Fats are potentially difficult to digest because they are immiscible with aqueous body fluids. In order to facilitate the digestion of fats, the human body produces bile to act as an emulsifier. Use reference books to find out as much as you can about bile. Find out which organ produces it, where it is stored, what its chemical composition is, and how its role as an emulsifier allows fats to be digested.

3. The photographer's darkroom contains numerous chemicals, many of them in the form of aqueous solutions. Find out which chemicals are used in producing an image on a negative, developing the negative, producing an image on a print, and developing the print.

4. Find out about the history of the air pollution problems at
   a) Trail, British Columbia   c) Long Harbour, Newfoundland
   b) Sudbury, Ontario   d) one of your local industries

13

Further Applications of the Mole Method

In Chapter 10, we showed how to use the mole concept and chemical equations to relate the masses of solid substances involved in chemical reactions. In this chapter we will see how the mole method can be used to solve problems pertaining to reactions which involve solutions and/or gases.

A Review of the Mole Method   *13.1*

The mole method is a way of relating the quantities of the reagents used in a reaction to the quantities of the products formed in that reaction. As we saw in Section 10.5, the mole method consists of three basic steps. Thus, if we have a reaction in which substance A is converted to substance B, we can determine the mass of B obtained from a given mass of A using the following procedure:

1. Convert the mass of A to the number of moles of A using the molar mass of A as the conversion factor.

2. Use the balanced chemical equation to obtain an equation factor. This can be used to determine the number of moles of B that can be produced from the number of moles of A found in Step 1.

3. Convert the number of moles of B to mass of B using the molar mass of B as the conversion factor.

Reactions Involving Solutions 13.2

As you may recall from Chapter 8, many chemical reactions take place only in solution. It is important to be able to apply the mole method in such situations. From our discussion of the various ways in which the concentration of a solution can be expressed (Section 12.4), you should be familiar with the method used to determine the number of moles of solute present in a given volume of solution of known concentration. The formula is

Number of moles of solute
= Concentration of solution (mol·L⁻¹) × Volume of solution (L)

We shall use some form of this relationship in all mole-method calculations that pertain to reactions occurring in solution.

EXAMPLE **13.1** Calculate the volume of $2.00 \text{ mol} \cdot \text{L}^{-1}$ silver nitrate solution that is needed for 12.0 g of copper metal to react according to the following equation:

$$Cu_{(s)} + 2\,AgNO_{3\,(aq)} \longrightarrow Cu(NO_3)_{2\,(aq)} + 2\,Ag_{(s)}$$

SOLUTION
STRATEGY

Here we are told the mass of copper (Substance A) that is involved. Our goal is to find the volume of $2.00 \text{ mol} \cdot \text{L}^{-1}$ silver nitrate solution (Substance B) that is required in order to consume the given mass of copper. Our strategy will be

1. Mass of A ⟶ Moles of A, using the molar mass of A as a conversion factor
2. Moles of A ⟶ Moles of B, using the appropriate equation factor
3. Moles of B ⟶ Volume of solution B, using the concentration of solution B as the conversion factor

STEP 1: The molar mass of copper is $63.5 \text{ g} \cdot \text{mol}^{-1}$. Hence

$$\text{Number of moles of Cu} = 12.0 \text{ g Cu} \times \frac{1 \text{ mol Cu}}{63.5 \text{ g Cu}} = 0.189 \text{ mol Cu}$$

STEP 2: From the balanced chemical equation we see that two moles of silver nitrate are required for each mole of copper. The equation factor that we must use is

$$\frac{2 \text{ mol AgNO}_3}{1 \text{ mol Cu}}$$

Number of moles of AgNO$_3$

$$= 0.189 \; \text{mol Cu} \times \frac{2 \text{ mol AgNO}_3}{1 \text{ mol Cu}}$$

$$= 0.378 \text{ mol AgNO}_3$$

STEP 3:   The required volume of the 2.00 mol·L^{-1} solution of silver nitrate can be calculated by using the concentration as a conversion factor, as it relates volume of solution and number of moles of solute. Thus

$$\text{Volume required} = 0.378 \; \text{mol AgNO}_3 \times \frac{1 \text{ L}}{2.00 \text{ mol AgNO}_3}$$

$$= 0.189 \text{ L or } 189 \text{ mL}$$

Double displacement reactions, in which two solutions are mixed together in order to produce a precipitate, are often carried out in the laboratory (Section 8.10). Our next example shows how the mole method can be used to solve problems involving this type of reaction.

EXAMPLE   **13.2**   When a solution of silver nitrate is added to a solution of calcium chloride the following reaction takes place:

$$2 \text{ AgNO}_{3 \text{ (aq)}} + \text{CaCl}_{2 \text{ (aq)}} \longrightarrow 2 \text{ AgCl}_{(s)} + \text{Ca(NO}_3)_{2 \text{ (aq)}}$$

Calculate the volume of 0.105 mol·L^{-1} silver nitrate solution that must be added to 25.0 mL of 0.255 mol·L^{-1} calcium chloride solution in order to produce the maximum mass of silver chloride.

SOLUTION   *STRATEGY*

This problem is a little different from those we have solved previously. Instead of being given a certain mass of one of the reactants or products, we are given a volume and a concentration. However, the problem can still be solved using our three-step mole method. The first step will involve finding the number of moles of calcium chloride.

1. Volume of solution A $\longrightarrow$ Moles of A, using the concentration of the solution as a conversion factor

2. Moles of A $\longrightarrow$ Moles of B, using the appropriate equation factor

3. Moles of B $\longrightarrow$ Volume of solution B, using the concentration of solution B as a conversion factor

STEP 1:

Number of moles of $CaCl_2$

$$= \text{Volume } CaCl_{2\,(aq)} \times \text{Concentration } CaCl_{2\,(aq)}$$

$$= 0.0250\,\cancel{L} \times \frac{0.255 \text{ mol } CaCl_2}{1\,\cancel{L}}$$

$$= 6.38 \times 10^{-3} \text{ mol } CaCl_2$$

STEP 2: From our balanced equation we see that, for complete reaction to occur, one mole of calcium chloride requires two moles of silver nitrate. Therefore, the equation factor is

$$\frac{2 \text{ mol } AgNO_3}{1 \text{ mol } CaCl_2}$$

Number of moles $AgNO_3$ required

$$= 6.38 \times 10^{-3} \cancel{\text{mol } CaCl_2} \times \frac{2 \text{ mol } AgNO_3}{1 \cancel{\text{mol } CaCl_2}}$$

$$= 1.28 \times 10^{-2} \text{ mol } AgNO_3$$

STEP 3: Now the necessary volume of $0.105 \text{ mol} \cdot L^{-1}$ of silver nitrate solution can be calculated:

$$\text{Volume required} = 1.28 \times 10^{-2} \cancel{\text{mol } AgNO_3} \times \frac{1 \text{ L}}{0.105 \cancel{\text{mol } AgNO_3}}$$

$$= 0.122 \text{ L or } 122 \text{ mL}$$

QUESTIONS

1. Aluminum reacts with hydrochloric acid according to the equation

$$2 \text{ Al}_{(s)} + 6 \text{ HCl}_{(aq)} \longrightarrow 2 \text{ AlCl}_{3\,(aq)} + 3 \text{ H}_{2\,(g)}$$

Calculate the volume of $1.50 \text{ mol} \cdot L^{-1}$ hydrochloric acid that is required for $5.40\,g$ of aluminum to react completely.

2. Zinc metal reacts with hydrochloric acid according to the equation

$$\text{Zn}_{(s)} + 2 \text{ HCl}_{(aq)} \longrightarrow \text{H}_{2\,(g)} + \text{ZnCl}_{2\,(aq)}$$

A piece of zinc metal is found to require 75.0 mL of $3.00 \text{ mol} \cdot L^{-1}$ hydrochloric acid for complete reaction. Determine the mass of the piece of zinc metal used.

3. Calculate the volume of $0.110 \text{ mol} \cdot L^{-1}$ sodium sulfate required to precipitate the maximum mass of barium sulfate from 60.0 mL of $0.145 \text{ mol} \cdot L^{-1}$ barium chloride solution. The balanced equation is:

$$\text{BaCl}_{2\,(aq)} + \text{Na}_2\text{SO}_{4\,(aq)} \longrightarrow \text{BaSO}_{4\,(s)} + 2 \text{ NaCl}_{(aq)}$$

Volumetric Analysis

<u>**13.3**</u>

In the laboratory, we often have to determine, accurately and precisely, the concentration of a given solution. This is often done by an experimental procedure called **titration**. A titration allows us to analyze a solution by measuring volumes; thus it is an example of **volumetric analysis**.

The most common type of volumetric analysis conducted in high-school laboratories is the **acid–base titration**. This involves the neutralization reaction (Section 8.7) between a solution of acid and a solution of base. Using this technique we are able to determine the volume of acid (or base) of known concentration that will neutralize a given volume of base (or acid) of unknown concentration. Neutralization has occurred when we have equal numbers of moles of hydrogen ions and hydroxide ions in the solution. In other words, it is the point at which neither the acid nor the base is in excess in the reaction mixture.

To carry out a titration, we need three pieces of glassware: a volumetric pipette (Section 12.7), a burette, and an Erlenmeyer flask. A pipette is used to measure, both accurately and precisely, a predetermined volume of solution. A burette is used when we are not sure of the exact volume of solution that will have to be used. The burette consists of a long glass tube with a tap at one end. The tube has graduated marks on it, with the zero mark near the top (i.e. the end farthest from the tap). Burettes are available in both 50.00 mL and 25.00 mL sizes. As with a pipette, the volume delivered by a burette can be measured to a high degree of accuracy and precision. A typical procedure for determining the concentration of a solution of acid or base by titration is described below.

A known volume of the acid is measured out into an Erlenmeyer flask by means of a pipette, and a small amount of a dye solution, called an

Figure 13.1

Determining the concentration of an acid or base by titration:

a) Using a pipette, a measured volume of the acid is placed into an Erlenmeyer flask.

b) Several drops of indicator are added.

c) The solution of base is added from the burette until the indicator changes colour.

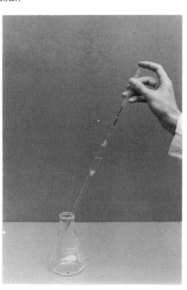

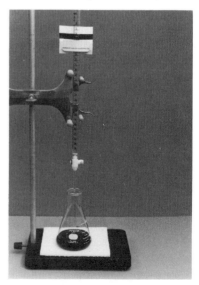

indicator, is added. Indicators have different colours in acidic and basic solutions. Most indicators are extremely sensitive and produce a sharp change in colour when the solution changes from acidic to basic. You are already familiar with the use of litmus to identify acids and bases. However, in a titration we require an indicator that gives a much more dramatic colour change than litmus. Phenolphthalein is often used as an indicator in acid–base titrations. This indicator is colourless in the presence of excess acid and pink in the presence of excess base.

The initial volume of the solution of base in the burette is recorded. Small amounts of base are then allowed to run out of the burette into the Erlenmeyer flask containing the acid. Addition of base is continued until the indicator changes colour. This happens when enough base has been added to react with (i.e., neutralize) all the acid originally present. The volume of base remaining in the burette can be read and the volume of base that has been added is then found by subtraction.

If we know the volumes of acid and base used in the reaction, and the concentration of either the acid or the base, the concentration of the other can be calculated. The following example shows how such a calculation is carried out.

EXAMPLE   **13.3**   In a titration, 31.24 mL of sodium hydroxide solution (0.1004 mol·L^{-1}) was required to neutralize 25.0 mL of hydrochloric acid. Calculate the concentration of the hydrochloric acid.

SOLUTION

STRATEGY

First we write the balanced equation:

$$NaOH_{(aq)} + HCl_{(aq)} \longrightarrow NaCl_{(aq)} + H_2O_{(\ell)}$$

As we know both the volume and the concentration of the sodium hydroxide solution (A), our first step will be to determine the number of moles of sodium hydroxide involved in the reaction. Thus the three steps of our mole-method approach will be as follows:

1. Volume of solution A $\longrightarrow$ Moles of A, using the concentration of solution A as a conversion factor
2. Moles of A $\longrightarrow$ Moles of B, using the appropriate equation factor
3. Moles of B $\longrightarrow$ Concentration of solution B

STEP 1:
Number of moles of NaOH

$$= \text{Volume NaOH}_{(aq)} \times \text{Concentration NaOH}_{(aq)}$$

$$= 0.031\ 24\ \cancel{L} \times \frac{0.1004 \text{ mol NaOH}}{1\cancel{L}}$$

$$= 3.136 \times 10^{-3} \text{ mol NaOH}$$

STEP 2: From the balanced equation we see that the equation factor relating the number of moles of hydrochloric acid to the number of moles of sodium hydroxide is

$$\frac{1 \text{ mol HCl}}{1 \text{ mol NaOH}}$$

Thus, the number of moles of NCl

$$= 3.136 \times 10^{-3} \text{ mol NaOH} \times \frac{1 \text{ mol HCl}}{1 \text{ mol NaOH}}$$

$$= 3.136 \times 10^{-3} \text{ mol HCl.}$$

STEP 3: As we now know both the volume of hydrochloric acid used (25.0 mL) and the number of moles of hydrochloric acid involved in the reaction (3.136×10^{-3} mol HCl), we can calculate the concentration of the solution. Thus

$$\text{Concentration of HCl} = \frac{\text{Number of moles HCl}}{\text{Volume of HCl}_{(aq)}}$$

$$= \frac{3.136 \times 10^{-3} \text{ mol}}{0.0250 \text{ L}} = 0.125 \text{ mol} \cdot \text{L}^{-1}$$

In Example 13.3 the acid and base reacted in a 1:1 ratio. This does not always happen, and you should remember this fact when performing calculations based on the results of a titration. A balanced chemical equation should always be written before starting a mole-method calculation.

EXAMPLE   **13.4**   In a titration, a total of 25.0 mL of sodium hydroxide solution was neutralized by 16.36 mL of sulfuric acid (0.1286 mol $\cdot \text{L}^{-1}$). Determine the concentration of the sodium hydroxide solution. The balanced chemical equation for the reaction is

$$2 \text{ NaOH}_{(aq)} + \text{H}_2\text{SO}_{4 \text{ (aq)}} \longrightarrow \text{Na}_2\text{SO}_{4 \text{ (aq)}} + 2 \text{ H}_2\text{O}_{(\ell)}$$

SOLUTION   *STRATEGY*

We shall begin be determining the number of moles of sulfuric acid (A) consumed in the reaction. From this number and the balanced equation we can determine how many moles of sodium hydroxide (B) were present in the 25.0 mL of solution that was used. The concentration of the sodium hydroxide solution can then be obtained. Thus the three-step, mole-method approach to be used can be summarized as follows:

1. Volume of solution A $\longrightarrow$ Moles of A, using the concentration of solution A as a conversion factor
2. Moles of A $\longrightarrow$ Moles of B, using the appropriate equation factor
3. Moles of B $\longrightarrow$ Concentration of solution B

STEP 1:   Number of moles of H_2SO_4

$$= 0.016\ 36\ \text{L } H_2SO_4 \times \frac{0.1286\ \text{mol } H_2SO_4}{1\ \text{L } H_2SO_4}$$

$$= 2.104 \times 10^{-3}\ \text{mol } H_2SO_4$$

STEP 2:   The equation factor relating the number of moles of sulfuric acid to the number of moles of sodium hydroxide is

$$\frac{2\ \text{mol NaOH}}{1\ \text{mol } H_2SO_4}$$

Thus, the number of moles of sodium hydroxide that has been neutralized

$$= 2.104 \times 10^{-3}\ \text{mol } H_2SO_4 \times \frac{2\ \text{mol NaOH}}{1\ \text{mol } H_2SO_4}$$

$$= 4.208 \times 10^{-3}\ \text{mol NaOH}$$

STEP 3:   Finally, we calculate the concentration of the sodium hydroxide:

$$\text{Concentration of NaOH} = \frac{4.208 \times 10^{-3}\ \text{mol NaOH}}{25.0\ \text{mL}} \times \frac{1000\ \text{mL}}{1\ \text{L}}$$

$$= 0.168\ \text{mol} \cdot \text{L}^{-1}$$

QUESTIONS

4. In an experiment involving a titration, a student found that 18.72 mL of 0.09975 mol·L^{-1} nitric acid was required to neutralize 25.0 mL of potassium hydroxide solution. Calculate the concentration of the potassium hydroxide solution.

5. A 25.0 mL sample of phosphoric acid, H_3PO_4 (aq), was titrated against a solution of 0.1074 mol·L^{-1} ammonium hydroxide. It was found that 33.24 mL of the ammonium hydroxide solution was required to bring about neutralization. What was the concentration of the phosphoric acid?

Gravimetric Analysis <u>13.4</u>

Gravimetric analysis is a method of determining the amount of a specific cation or anion in a solution by precipitating an insoluble compound which contains that ion. The technique can also be used to determine how much of a given element is present in a substance or to establish the purity of a substance. Gravimetric analysis can also assist in determining the identity of an unknown compound. The reactions involved in gravimetric analysis invariably take place in solution. The mole method is used to calculate the results of the analysis.

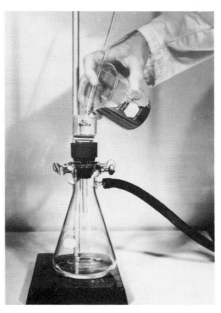

Figure 13.2
The filtration of a precipitate through a sintered glass crucible:
a) The mixture is poured down the glass rod into the crucible.
b) The last of the precipitate is scraped into the crucible with a spatula.

As an example of gravimetric analysis, let us consider how we might determine the concentration of a calcium chloride solution. We can use the reaction of calcium chloride with sodium carbonate to give a precipitate of calcium carbonate:

$$CaCl_{2\ (aq)}\ +\ Na_2CO_{3\ (aq)}\ \longrightarrow\ CaCO_{3\ (aq)}\ +\ 2\ NaCl_{(aq)}$$

A measured volume of the calcium chloride solution is placed in a beaker and sodium carbonate solution is added until no more precipitate forms (that is, until the sodium carbonate is in excess). The calcium carbonate is then filtered off using a sintered glass crucible of known mass. The crucible and contents are dried in an oven and then weighed. The difference in mass gives the mass of calcium carbonate. We can then apply the mole method to determine the concentration of the calcium chloride solution. Typical results from such an analysis are given in Example 13.5, together with the relevant calculations.

EXAMPLE   **13.5**   In an experiment to determine the concentration of a calcium chloride solution, an excess of sodium carbonate solution was added to 25.0 mL of the calcium chloride solution. The mass of calcium carbonate precipitated was 2.50 g. Calculate the concentration of the calcium chloride solution.

SOLUTION   The equation for this double replacement reaction is:

$$CaCl_{2\ (aq)}\ +\ Na_2CO_{3\ (aq)}\ \longrightarrow\ CaCO_{3\ (s)}\ +\ 2\ NaCl_{(aq)}$$

From the number of moles of calcium carbonate (A) produced we can use the balanced equation to determine the number of moles of calcium chloride (B) present in the original 25.0 mL of solution. The concentration of the original solution may then be calculated. All this can be achieved using our usual three-step mole method.

1. Mass of A $\longrightarrow$ Moles of A, using the molar mass of A as the conversion factor
2. Moles of A $\longrightarrow$ Moles of B, using the appropriate equation factor
3. Moles of B $\longrightarrow$ Concentration of solution B

STEP 1:
Number of moles of $CaCO_3$ produced

$$= 2.50 \text{ g } CaCO_3 \times \frac{1 \text{ mol } CaCO_3}{100.1 \text{ g } CaCO_3}$$

$$= 2.50 \times 10^{-2} \text{ mol } CaCO_3$$

STEP 2: The equation factor that relates the number of moles of calcium carbonate produced to the number of moles of calcium chloride used is

$$\frac{1 \text{ mol } CaCl_2}{1 \text{ mol } CaCO_3}$$

Thus the number of moles of calcium chloride present in the original 25.0 mL of solution is given by

$$\text{Moles of } CaCl_2 = 2.50 \times 10^{-2} \text{ mol } CaCO_3 \times \frac{1 \text{ mol } CaCl_2}{1 \text{ mol } CaCO_3}$$

$$= 2.50 \times 10^{-2} \text{ mol } CaCl_2$$

STEP 3: Now that we know the number of moles of calcium chloride present in a given volume of solution, the concentration of the solution can be determined as follows:

$$\text{Concentration} = \frac{2.50 \times 10^{-2} \text{ mol } CaCl_2}{0.0250 \text{ L}}$$

$$= 1.00 \text{ mol} \cdot \text{L}^{-1}$$

We can use gravimetric analysis to find the molar mass of a compound and, under certain circumstances, can determine the identity of the cation present in a given compound. This application of gravimetric analysis is illustrated in Example 13.6.

EXAMPLE **13.6** A student is provided with a sample of an alkali metal sulfate, M_2SO_4, in which the identity of the alkali metal, M, is unknown. A mass of 0.087 15 g of the compound is dissolved in water and an excess of barium chloride solution is added. This produces a precipitate of barium sulfate, which is filtered off and dried. If the mass of the precipitate is 0.1167 g, calculate the molar mass of the alkali metal sulfate and hence identify the alkali metal.

The balanced equation for the observed reaction is

$$BaCl_{2\,(aq)} + M_2SO_{4\,(aq)} \longrightarrow BaSO_{4\,(aq)} + 2\,MCl_{(aq)}$$

STEP 1:
Number of moles of $BaSO_4$ produced

$$= 0.1167\,\text{g BaSO}_4 \times \frac{1\,\text{mol BaSO}_4}{233.4\,\text{g BaSO}_4}$$

$$= 5.000 \times 10^{-4}\,\text{mol BaSO}_4$$

STEP 2: From the balanced equation we can see that the equation factor which relates the unknown metal sulfate to barium sulfate is

$$\frac{1\,\text{mol M}_2SO_4}{1\,\text{mol BaSO}_4}$$

Number of moles of M_2SO_4 reacted

$$= 5.000 \times 10^{-4}\,\text{mol BaSO}_4 \times \frac{1\,\text{mol M}_2SO_4}{1\,\text{mol BaSO}_4}$$

$$= 5.000 \times 10^{-4}\,\text{mol M}_2SO_4$$

STEP 3: Since the mass of M_2SO_4 used, 0.087 15 g, must correspond to 5.000×10^{-4} mol the molar mass can be calculated as

$$\text{Molar mass M}_2SO_4 = \frac{0.087\ 15\,\text{g}}{5.000 \times 10^{-4}\,\text{mol}} = 174.3\,\text{g·mol}^{-1}$$

Klaproth — The Careful Chemist

Martin Klaproth was born in Germany in 1743. He trained as a pharmacist, but when he was in his thirties, his interests turned to chemistry. He rose rapidly in this profession and by the beginning of the 19th century he had become the leading analytical chemist in Europe.

Klaproth and his co-workers analyzed minerals obtained from many parts of the world and discovered the elements zirconium, uranium, titanium, strontium, chromium, and cerium. However, Klaproth will be remembered most for his contributions to the field of quantitative analytical chemistry.

Until the beginning of the 19th century, methods used in analytical chemistry were not very precise, and discrepancies in measurements were usually ignored. Klaproth, however, used discrepancies in measurements to detect faulty and incomplete analyses, and to develop new and more precise analytical methods. He emphasized that chemists should ensure that substances they were working with would not become contaminated by other chemicals. (Contamination can result from dirty apparatus or from impure reagents.) Many of the analytical techniques used today are based on those developed by Klaproth.

Figure 13.3
Martin Klaproth (1743–1817).

The mass of one mole of M_2SO_4 is therefore 174.3 g. Of this, the one mole of sulfate ions accounts for 96.1 g and the remainder (174.3 g − 96.1 g = 78.2 g) is due to the alkali metal, M. As each mole of M_2SO_4 contains two moles of M^+ ions, the molar mass of M is

$$\frac{78.2\,g}{2\,mol} \;=\; 39.1\,g \cdot mol^{-1}$$

By referring to the Periodic Table, we see that the alkali metal with a molar mass closest to 39.1 g mol^{-1} is potassium.

The success of a gravimetric analysis depends not only on the manipulative skills of the person performing the experiment, but also on the quantitative nature of the reaction used. The reaction must give a 100% (or quantitative) yield. We must also ensure that the reagent added to bring about precipitation (barium chloride in the above example) is present in excess, so that there is complete reaction of the substance being analyzed.

QUESTIONS

6. An excess of calcium nitrate solution was added to 50.0 mL of a sodium fluoride solution. The white precipitate of calcium fluoride that was obtained was filtered off and dried. The mass of this calcium fluoride precipitate was 2.93 g. Given that the equation for the reaction is

$$Ca(NO_3)_{2\,(aq)} + 2\,NaF_{(aq)} \longrightarrow CaF_{2\,(s)} + 2\,NaNO_{3\,(aq)}$$

determine the concentration of the sodium fluoride solution.

7. When 0.1155 g of an unknown alkali metal carbonate, X_2CO_3 was dissolved in water and 30.0 mL of 0.500 M calcium chloride solution was added to it, a precipitate of calcium carbonate was obtained:

$$X_2CO_{3\,(aq)} + CaCl_{2\,(aq)} \longrightarrow CaCO_{3\,(s)} + 2\,XCl_{(aq)}$$

After filtering and drying to constant mass, the calcium carbonate precipitate was found to have a mass of 0.0501 g. Determine the molar mass of the alkali metal, X, and hence determine its identity.

Reactions Involving Gases

13.5 The three-step mole method can also be used to solve problems pertaining to reactions in which a gas is either consumed or produced. The major difference that we shall see when we apply the mole method to such reactions is that the first and/or third step(s) will require the use of the ideal gas equation introduced in Section 11.12. You may recall that this equation relates four variables — pressure, volume, temperature, and number of moles of gas:

$$PV = nRT$$

Where: P is the pressure (kPa)
V is the volume (L)
n is the number of moles (mol)
R is the gas constant ($8.31\ \text{kPa·L·mol}^{-1}\cdot\text{K}^{-1}$)
T is the temperature (K)

EXAMPLE

13.7 A common (but hazardous) method of preparing small quantities of oxygen is to heat solid potassium chlorate with a manganese(IV) oxide catalyst:

$$2\,KClO_{3\,(s)} \xrightarrow[MnO_2]{\Delta} 2\,KCl_{(s)} + 3\,O_{2\,(g)}$$

What volume of oxygen, measured at 22 °C and 99.5 kPa, should be produced from 1.00 g of potassium chlorate?

SOLUTION

STRATEGY

We shall use our usual mole-method approach to find the number of moles of oxygen (B) that can be produced from the given mass of potassium chlorate (A). In the third and final step of the mole method we shall use the ideal gas equation to determine the volume of oxygen formed under the given conditions.

1. Mass of A $\longrightarrow$ Moles of A, using the molar mass of A as the conversion factor
2. Moles of A $\longrightarrow$ Moles of B, using the appropriate equation factor
3. Moles of B $\longrightarrow$ Volume of B, using the ideal gas equation

STEP 1:

$$\text{Number of moles of } KClO_3 \text{ used} = 1.00 \, g \, \cancel{KClO_3} \times \frac{1 \text{ mol } KClO_3}{122.6 \, g \, \cancel{KClO_3}}$$

$$= 8.16 \times 10^{-3} \text{ mol } KClO_3$$

STEP 2: From the balanced chemical equation we find that the equation factor relating potassium chlorate and oxygen is

$$\frac{3 \text{ mol } O_2}{2 \text{ mol } KClO_3}$$

Number of moles of O_2 formed

$$= 8.16 \times 10^{-3} \, \cancel{\text{mol } KClO_3} \times \frac{3 \text{ mol } O_2}{2 \, \cancel{\text{mol } KClO_3}}$$

$$= 1.22 \times 10^{-2} \text{ mol } O_2$$

$PV = nRT$

$V = \dfrac{nRT}{P}$

$P = \dfrac{nRT}{V}$

STEP 3:
Volume O_2 formed at 22 °C and 99.5 kPa $= \dfrac{nRT}{P}$

$$= \frac{1.22 \times 10^{-2} \, \cancel{mol} \times 8.31 \, \cancel{kPa} \cdot L \cdot \cancel{mol^{-1}} \cdot \cancel{K^{-1}} \times 295 \, \cancel{K}}{99.5 \, \cancel{kPa}}$$

$$= 0.301 \text{ L or } 301 \text{ mL}$$

When a gas such as oxygen or hydrogen is prepared in the laboratory, it is usually collected by the displacement of water (Figure 11.15). In such cases we must take into account the vapour pressure exerted by the water in any calculation involving the pressure of the gas. Example 13.8 shows how the procedure used in Example 13.7 would have to be modified under such circumstances.

EXAMPLE	13.8	Suppose that the oxygen produced in the experiment described in Example 13.7 was collected by the displacement of water. Calculate the volume of "wet oxygen" (i.e. oxygen and water vapour) that would be collected. The vapour pressure of water at 22 °C is 2.6 kPa.

SOLUTION   We need only modify Step 3 of our previous answer to take this new variation into account. The pressure that we use in the ideal gas equation must be the partial pressure of oxygen, rather than the total pressure. The former can be obtained by subtracting the partial pressure due to the water vapour (i.e. the vapour pressure of water at 22 °C) from the total pressure:

$$P_{O_2} = P_{TOT} - P_{H_2O}$$
$$= 99.5 \text{ kPa} - 2.6 \text{ kPa} = 96.9 \text{ kPa}$$

This partial pressure of oxygen may now be used in a calculation to determine the volume of "wet oxygen" obtained:

Volume of "wet oxygen"

$$= \frac{1.22 \times 10^{-2} \text{ mol} \times 8.31 \text{ kPa} \cdot \text{L} \cdot \text{mol}^{-1} \cdot \text{K}^{-1} \times 295 \text{ K}}{96.9 \text{ kPa}} = 0.309 \text{ L}$$

NOTE: In practice, it is much more likely that we would know the volume of "wet oxygen" and would want to determine the mass of "dry gas" that had been produced.

QUESTIONS

8. On being heated slowly, iron(III) sulfate decomposes according to the following equation:

$$Fe_2(SO_4)_{3 \text{ (s)}} \longrightarrow Fe_2O_{3 \text{ (s)}} + 3 \text{ SO}_{3 \text{ (g)}}$$

What is the maximum volume of sulfur trioxide, measured at 25 °C and 102 kPa, that can be expected from the decomposition of 6.00 g of iron(III) sulfate?

9. Zinc metal reacts with hydrochloric acid to give zinc chloride and hydrogen gas:

$$Zn_{(s)} + 2 \text{ HCl}_{(aq)} \longrightarrow ZnCl_{2 \text{ (aq)}} + H_{2 \text{ (g)}}$$

If the hydrogen gas is collected by the displacement of water, what volume of "wet hydrogen" will be collected at 19 °C and 102.3 kPa from the reaction of 0.218 g of zinc with an excess of hydrochloric acid? (At 19 °C the vapour pressure of water is 2.2 kPa.)

10. One of the reactions used during the extraction of zinc metal from the ore–zinc blend ZnS, is

$$2 \, ZnS_{(s)} + 3 \, O_{2 \, (g)} \longrightarrow 2 \, ZnO_{(s)} + 2 \, SO_{2 \, (g)}$$

Determine the mass of zinc sulfide that can be converted into zinc oxide using 2.64 L of oxygen gas measured at 21 °C and 101 kPa.

The Law of Combining Volumes   13.6

In Section 11.6, we saw that Gay-Lussac derived a relationship between the pressure and the temperature of a gas. Gay-Lussac also conducted studies on the volumes of gases involved in chemical reactions. He found that when hydrogen gas and oxygen gas combine to form water, two volumes of hydrogen gas are required for every one volume of oxygen gas (if both gases are at the same temperature and pressure). From this he concluded that hydrogen and oxygen react in a 2:1 volume ratio.

Gay-Lussac performed experiments with other pairs of gases and found that the gases always combined in simple ratios. Thus he concluded that

In any chemical reaction involving gases, the volumes of the reactants are always in small, whole-number ratios.

This statement is now known as **Gay-Lussac's Law of Combining Volumes**.

Additional experiments showed that the volume of any gaseous product of a reaction between gases is related to the volumes of the reacting gases. For example, when hydrogen gas reacts with an equal volume of chlorine gas, the volume of hydrogen chloride gas produced is equal to the total volume of hydrogen and chlorine used. This is illustrated in Figure 13.4. We see that one volume of hydrogen gas reacts with one volume of chlorine gas to produce two volumes of hydrogen chloride. Thus, the ratio of hydrogen to chlorine to hydrogen chloride is 1:1:2, and the ratio of reactants to products is 1:1.

Figure 13.4
The volume relationship for the reaction of hydrogen gas with chlorine gas to give hydrogen chloride gas.

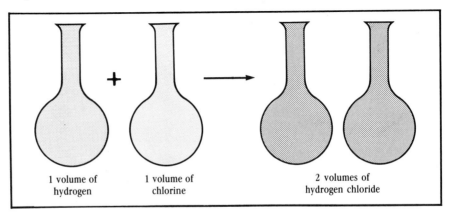

| 1 volume of hydrogen | 1 volume of chlorine | 2 volumes of hydrogen chloride |

The law of combining volumes is a statement of fact based on observation, although Gay-Lussac could not offer an explanation for these observations. However, we can use Avogadro's hypothesis to help us to understand this law and to provide us with a link to the modern mole method. Avogadro's hypothesis states that at the same temperature and pressure, equal volumes of gases contain an equal number of particles (Section 7.7). In view of this, let us once more consider the reaction between hydrogen and chlorine. We have already seen that

One volume hydrogen + One volume chlorine $\longrightarrow$
$$\text{Two volumes hydrogen chloride}$$

From Avogadro's hypothesis we can say that

n molecules hydrogen + n molecules chlorine $\longrightarrow$
$$2n \text{ molecules hydrogen chloride}$$

Now, dividing through by n, we obtain

1 molecule hydrogen + 1 molecule chlorine $\longrightarrow$
$$2 \text{ molecules hydrogen chloride}$$

Multiplying by Avogadro's number, 6.02×10^{23}, we obtain

6.02×10^{23} molecules hydrogen + 6.02×10^{23} molecules chlorine
$$\longrightarrow 2 \times 6.02 \times 10^{23} \text{ molecules hydrogen chloride}$$
Or

1 mol hydrogen + 1 mol chlorine $\longrightarrow$ 2 mol hydrogen chloride

As we now know that hydrogen gas and chlorine gas both contain diatomic molecules, we can write this statement as the balanced equation

$$\mathbf{H_{2\,(g)}} + \mathbf{Cl_{2\,(g)}} \longrightarrow \mathbf{2\,HCl_{(g)}}$$

Thus, by using Avogadro's hypothesis and our modern concept of the mole, we can explain why chemical reactions involving gases follow Gay-Lussac's Law of Combining Volumes. Example 13.9 shows how this law can be used to solve a problem involving a reaction in which the products and reactants are all in the gas phase.

EXAMPLE   *13.9*   On heating, a certain gas containing only chlorine and oxygen decomposes into its constituent elements. When 48 mL of the gas at 1 atm pressure and 298 K is decomposed and the resulting mixture is returned to 298 K and 1 atm pressure, the new volume is 73 mL. After shaking the gas with sodium hydroxide solution to remove the chlorine, the remaining oxygen is found to occupy a volume of 24 mL (at 298 K and 1 atm pressure). What is the formula of the unknown gas?

SOLUTION   STEP 1:   If 24 mL of the final volume (73 mL) is oxygen gas, then the volume of the chlorine gas must be

$$73\,\text{mL} - 24\,\text{mL} = 49\,\text{mL}$$

We can then say

$$48 \text{ mL unknown gas} \longrightarrow 49 \text{ mL chlorine } + \text{ } 24 \text{ mL oxygen}$$

STEP 2: Dividing by the smallest number (24 mL) gives:

2.0 volumes unknown gas $\longrightarrow$
$$2.0 \text{ volumes chlorine } + \text{ } 1.0 \text{ volume oxygen}$$

STEP 3: From Avogadro's hypothesis we can then say

2 molecules unknown gas $\longrightarrow$
$$2 \text{ molecules chlorine } + \text{ } 1 \text{ molecule oxygen}$$

Thus

$$2 \text{ molecules unknown gas} \longrightarrow 2 \text{ Cl}_2 \text{ } + \text{ } O_2$$

If two molecules of the unknown gas supply a total of four atoms of chlorine and two atoms of oxygen, one molecule of the unknown gas must contain two atoms of chlorine and one atom of oxygen. Its formula must be Cl_2O (dichlorine oxide). Problems such as this can also be solved using the ideal gas equation in the three-step mole method.

QUESTIONS

11. Nitrogen gas and oxygen gas can be made to combine at a high temperature to form dinitrogen oxide:

$$2 \text{ N}_{2 \text{ (g)}} \text{ } + \text{ } O_{2 \text{ (g)}} \longrightarrow 2 \text{ N}_2O_{\text{(g)}}$$

What volume of (a) nitrogen and (b) oxygen, would be required to form 1.25 L of dinitrogen oxide? Assume that all gas volumes are measured at the same temperature and pressure.

12. The reaction for photosynthesis is

$$6 \text{ CO}_{2 \text{ (g)}} \text{ } + \text{ } 6 \text{ H}_2O_{(\ell)} \longrightarrow \text{C}_6\text{H}_{12}\text{O}_{6 \text{ (s)}} \text{ } + \text{ } 6 \text{ O}_{2 \text{ (g)}}$$

What volume of oxygen is released from plants during the consumption of 5.00×10^2 L of carbon dioxide? (Assume that the gases are at the same temperature and pressure.)

Reactions Involving Gases and Solutions

13.7

Certain reactions involve both a gas and a solution (or both gases and solutions). The methods used for solving problems related to such reactions do not differ greatly from those which were discussed earlier in this chapter. In general, the three-step mole method is applied in order to find the mass or volume of one reactant or product, B, from the information provided about another reactant or product, A. The three steps can be summarized as follows:

1. Supplied information about A ⟶ Moles of A
2. Moles of A ⟶ Moles of B
3. Moles of B ⟶ Required information about B

The exact problem-solving strategy used depends on the information supplied and required. The various possibilities are summarized in Figure 13.5.

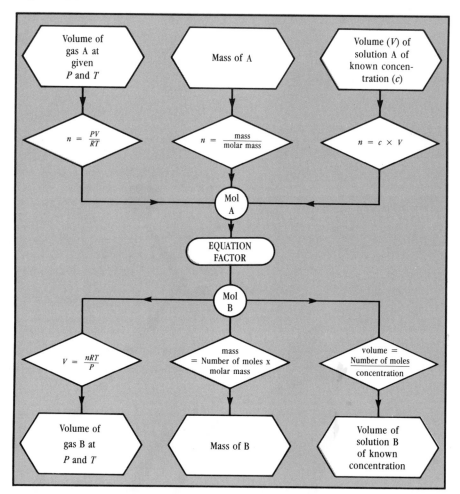

Figure 13.5
A summary of the mole method approach to solving problems.

EXAMPLE   *13.10*   In the presence of a manganese(IV) oxide catalyst, hydrogen peroxide decomposes to form water and oxygen:

$$2\ H_2O_{2\ (aq)} \xrightarrow{\ MnO_2\ } 2\ H_2O_{(\ell)} + O_{2\ (g)}$$

What volume of oxygen gas will be produced at 21 °C and 103 kPa from 125 mL of 6.00 mol·L^{-1} hydrogen peroxide solution?

SOLUTION

STRATEGY

From the information provided about the hydrogen peroxide solution (A) and the balanced chemical equation, we can predict the number of moles of oxygen (B) that will be formed. We can then use the ideal gas equation to determine the volume of oxygen produced under the given conditions of temperature and pressure.

1. Volume of solution A $\longrightarrow$ Moles of A, using the concentration of solution A as a conversion factor
2. Moles of A $\longrightarrow$ Moles of B, using the appropriate equation factor
3. Moles of B $\longrightarrow$ Volume of gas B, using the ideal gas equation

NOTE: If you refer to Figure 13.5, you will see that this strategy corresponds to a route from the top right (Solution A) to the bottom left (Gas B).

STEP 1:

$$\text{Number of moles of } H_2O_2 \text{ used } = 0.125\,\cancel{L} \times \frac{6.00 \text{ mol}}{1\,\cancel{L}}$$

$$= 0.750 \text{ mol}$$

STEP 2: From the balanced equation, we obtain the equation factor

$$\frac{1 \text{ mol } O_2}{2 \text{ mol } H_2O_2}$$

Thus

$$\text{Number of moles of } O_2 \text{ produced } = 0.750 \cancel{\text{ mol } H_2O_2} \times \frac{1 \text{ mol } O_2}{2 \cancel{\text{ mol } H_2O_2}}$$

$$= 0.375 \text{ mol } O_2$$

STEP 3: We can rearrange the ideal gas equation $PV = nRT$ in order to find the volume of oxygen produced at 21 °C and 103 kPa:

Volume of O_2 produced

$$= \frac{nRT}{P}$$

$$= \frac{0.375 \cancel{\text{ mol}} \times 8.31 \text{ kPa} \cdot L \cdot \cancel{\text{mol}}^{-1} \cdot \cancel{K}^{-1} \times 294\,\cancel{K}}{103\,\cancel{\text{kPa}}}$$

$$= 8.89 \text{ L}$$

EXAMPLE **13.11** Copper will not react with dilute acids, but will react with concentrated nitric acid according to the equation

$$3 \text{ Cu}_{(s)} + 8 \text{ HNO}_{3\,(aq)} \longrightarrow 3 \text{ Cu(NO}_3)_{2\,(aq)} + 2 \text{ NO}_{(g)} + 4 \text{ H}_2O_{(\ell)}$$

If 25.0 g of copper metal is used, what volume of nitric acid (16.0 mol·L^{-1}) will be required for a complete reaction?

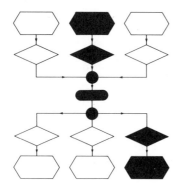

SOLUTION

STRATEGY

After finding the number of moles of copper (A) we shall use an equation factor to find the number of moles of nitric acid (B) required. The volume of 16.0 mol·L^{-1} nitric acid which must be used can then be calculated. By referring to Figure 13.5 it should be apparent that this strategy corresponds to a route from the top centre (Solid A) to the bottom right (Solution B). The three steps are thus

1. Mass of A $\longrightarrow$ Moles of A, using the molar mass of A as a conversion factor
2. Moles of A $\longrightarrow$ Moles of B, using the appropriate equation factor
3. Moles of B $\longrightarrow$ Volume of solution B, using the concentration of solution B as a conversion factor

STEP 1:

$$\text{Number of moles of Cu} = 25.0 \, \text{g Cu} \times \frac{1 \, \text{mol Cu}}{63.5 \, \text{g Cu}}$$

$$= 0.394 \, 5 \, \text{mol Cu}$$

STEP 2: From the balanced equation we see that the equation factor that we require here is

$$\frac{8 \, \text{mol HNO}_3}{3 \, \text{mol Cu}}$$

Thus

$$\text{Number of moles of HNO}_3 \text{ required} = 0.394 \, \text{mol Cu} \times \frac{8 \, \text{mol HNO}_3}{3 \, \text{mol Cu}}$$

$$= 1.05 \, \text{mol HNO}_3$$

STEP 3: Finally we need to find the volume of nitric acid with a concentration of 16.0 mol·L^{-1} that would provide us with 1.05 mol HNO$_3$:

$$\text{Volume of HNO}_{3 \, (aq)} = 1.05 \, \text{mol HNO}_3 \times \frac{1 \, \text{L}}{16.0 \, \text{mol HNO}_3}$$

$$= 0.0656 \, \text{L} \times \frac{1000 \, \text{mL}}{1 \, \text{L}}$$

$$= 65.6 \, \text{mL}$$

NOTE: 65.6 mL represents the minimum volume of nitric acid (16.0 mol·L^{-1}) required. In practice, an excess of acid would be used.

EXAMPLE **13.12** Suppose that we carry out the reaction described in Example 13.11 using 2.50 g of copper and 65.6 mL of 16.0 mol·L^{-1} nitric acid. What would be the volume of nitrogen monoxide (NO) gas produced at 105 kPa and 22 °C?

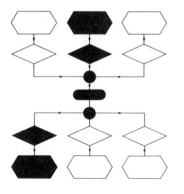

SOLUTION

STRATEGY

In Example 13.11 we established that 65.6 mL of 16.0 mol·L⁻¹ nitric acid was the stoichiometric amount needed to react with 25.0 g of copper. Thus, neither of these substances is in excess, and either one may be considered to be the limiting reagent. In other words, either copper metal or nitric acid can be considered to correspond to substance A. Thus, if we choose to regard the copper metal as substance A, our three-step mole method will consist of the following operations:

1. Mass of A $\longrightarrow$ Moles of A, using the molar mass of A as a conversion factor
2. Moles of A $\longrightarrow$ Moles of B, using the appropriate equation factor
3. Moles of B $\longrightarrow$ Volume of gas B, using the ideal gas equation

STEP 1:

$$\text{Number of moles of Cu consumed} = 25.0 \, \text{g Cu} \times \frac{1 \, \text{mol Cu}}{63.5 \, \text{g Cu}}$$

$$= 0.394 \, \text{mol Cu}$$

STEP 2: The equation factor that relates the number of moles of nitrogen monoxide produced to the number of moles of copper used is

$$\frac{2 \, \text{mol NO}}{3 \, \text{mol Cu}}$$

Thus

$$\text{Number of moles of NO formed} = 0.394 \, \text{mol Cu} \times \frac{2 \, \text{mol NO}}{3 \, \text{mol Cu}}$$

$$= 0.263 \, \text{mol NO}$$

STEP 3: Finally, we rearrange the ideal gas law ($PV = nRT$) in order to calculate the volume of nitrogen monoxide gas produced at 295 K and 105 kPa.

Volume of $NO_{(g)}$ formed

$$= \frac{nRT}{P}$$

$$= \frac{0.263 \, \text{mol} \times 8.31 \, \text{kPa·L·mol}^{-1} \cdot \text{K}^{-1} \times 295 \, \text{K}}{105 \, \text{kPa}}$$

$$= 6.14 \, \text{L}$$

You might like to check to see that the same answer is obtained if the calculation is based on using 65.6 mL of 16.0 mol·L⁻¹ nitric acid instead of 25.0 g of copper.

QUESTIONS

13. Sodium hydrogen carbonate reacts with sulfuric acid to produce carbon dioxide according to the equation:

$$2\ NaHCO_{3\ (aq)} + H_2SO_{4\ (aq)} \longrightarrow Na_2SO_{4\ (aq)} + 2\ H_2O_{(\ell)} + 2\ CO_{2\ (g)}$$

What volume of dry carbon dioxide (measured at STP) can be produced from the complete reaction of 0.250 L of 1.37 mol·L^{-1} sodium hydrogen carbonate?

14. The reaction of ammonium chloride solution with sodium hydroxide solution produces ammonia gas according to the equation:

$$NH_4Cl_{(aq)} + NaOH_{(aq)} \longrightarrow NaCl_{(aq)} + H_2O_{(\ell)} + NH_{3\ (g)}$$

a) What volume of a 2.50 mol·L^{-1} ammonium chloride solution will be required to produce 2.00 L of dry ammonia collected at 25 °C and 101 kPa?

b) What volume of 6.00 mol·L^{-1} sodium hydroxide will be required to completely react with the volume of 2.50 mol·L^{-1} ammonium chloride determined in (a) above?

15. Aluminum metal reacts with hydrochloric acid according to the following equation:

$$2\ Al_{(s)} + 6\ HCl_{(aq)} \longrightarrow 2\ AlCl_{3\ (aq)} + 3\ H_{2\ (g)}$$

a) What is the minimum volume of hydrochloric acid (6.00 mol·L^{-1}) required for the complete reaction of 1.08 g of aluminum?

b) Calculate the volume of hydrogen gas, measured at 25 °C and 104.3 kPa, that should be produced from the reaction of 1.89 g of aluminum with excess hydrochloric acid.

c) If the resulting solution from (b) is evaporated to dryness, what mass of AlCl$_3$·6H$_2$O crystals will be produced?

Summary

■ The mole method can be used to solve problems related to reactions in which solutions and/or gases are involved. In such cases we use the concentration relation and/or the ideal gas law. The common step in these calculations is the use of the equation factor.

■ The concentration of a solution can often be determined by a titration. The most common type of titration is the acid–base titration.

■ In an acid–base titration, neutralization has occurred when equal numbers of moles of hydrogen ions and hydroxide ions are present. An indicator is used to determine when neutralization has occurred.

■ Gravimetric analysis is a method for determining how much of a certain cation or anion is present in a solution. The analysis is done by precipitating an insoluble compound containing the ion in question. In order for a gravimetric analysis to be successful, the precipitation reaction must give a 100% yield and the reagent used to bring about the precipitation must be present in excess. Gravimetric analysis can also be used to determine how much of a given element is present in a compound, to establish the purity of a substance, and to assist in the determination of the identity of an unknown compound.

■ Gay-Lussac's Law of Combining Volumes states that in a chemical reaction involving gases, the reacting volumes and the volumes of any gaseous products are always in a small, whole-number ratio.

KEY WORDS

acid–base titration
Gay-Lussac's Law of Combining Volumes
gravimetric analysis
titration
volumetric analysis

---

*ANSWERS TO
SECTION QUESTIONS*

1. 0.400 L
2. 7.36 g
3. 0.0791 L
4. 0.0747 mol·L^{-1}
5. 0.0476 mol·L^{-1}
6. 1.50 mol·L^{-1}
7. 85.5 g·mol^{-1}, Rb
8. 1.09 L
9. 0.0807 L or 80.7 mL
10. 7.09 g
11. a) 1.25 L N_2 b) 0.625 L O_2
12. 5.00 × 10^2 L
13. 7.67 L
14. a) 0.0326 L or 32.6 mL   b) 0.0136 L or 13.6 mL
15. a) 0.0200 L or 20.0 mL   b) 2.49 L   c) 16.9 g

COMPREHENSION QUESTIONS

1. What step is common to all mole-method calculations?
2. Explain the similarities and differences between a volumetric and a gravimetric analysis.
3. Identify two factors that are essential in order for a gravimetric analysis to be successful.
4. Explain why Avogadro's hypothesis is fully consistent with Gay-Lussac's Law of Combining Volumes.

5. When 0.279 g of metallic iron is added to 100.0 mL of a solution of copper(II) sulfate ($0.0500 \; mol \cdot L^{-1}$), the following reaction takes place:

$$Fe_{(s)} + CuSO_{4\,(aq)} \longrightarrow Cu_{(s)} + FeSO_{4\,(aq)}$$

Calculate the mass of copper produced.

6. What mass of silver will be produced when 0.2394 g of tin is added to 250.0 mL of silver nitrate solution ($0.0300 \; mol \cdot L^{-1}$)? The balanced equation for the reaction is

$$Sn_{(s)} + 2 \; AgNO_{3\,(aq)} \longrightarrow 2 \; Ag_{(s)} + Sn(NO_3)_{2\,(aq)}$$

7. The active ingredient in Rolaids is $NaAl(OH)_2CO_3$, which reacts with excess hydrochloric acid in the stomach according to the equation

$$NaAl(OH)_2CO_{3\,(s)} + 4 \; HCl_{(aq)} \longrightarrow$$
$$NaCl_{(aq)} + AlCl_{3\,(aq)} + 3 \; H_2O_{(\ell)} + CO_{2\,(g)}$$

What mass of $NaAl(OH)_2CO_3$ is required to react with 0.150 L of hydrochloric acid ($0.100 \; mol \cdot L^{-1}$)?

8. Using the equation in problem 7, determine the volume of hydrochloric acid ($0.1058 \; mol \cdot L^{-1}$) that is necessary to react with 24.5 g of $NaAl(OH)_2CO_3$.

9. If 2.00 g of calcium hydroxide is to be reacted with hydrochloric acid ($0.100 \; mol \cdot L^{-1}$) according to the equation

$$Ca(OH)_{2\,(s)} + 2 \; HCl_{(aq)} \longrightarrow CaCl_{2\,(aq)} + 2 \; H_2O_{(\ell)}$$

what volume of acid would be required for complete reaction?

10. If 5.25 g of barium hydroxide is to be reacted with phosphoric acid ($0.200 \; mol \cdot L^{-1}$) according to the equation

$$3 \; Ba(OH)_{2\,(aq)} + 2 \; H_3PO_{4\,(aq)} \longrightarrow Ba_3(PO_4)_{2\,(aq)} + 6 \; H_2O_{(\ell)}$$

what volume of acid would be required for complete reaction?

11. When 25.00 mL of a sodium hydroxide solution of unknown concentration was titrated with a standard hydrochloric acid solution ($0.098 \; 30 \; mol \cdot L^{-1}$), 14.73 mL of the acid was required in order to exactly neutralize the base. Calculate the concentration of the sodium hydroxide solution.

12. The equation for the neutralization of sulfuric acid with ammonium hydroxide is

$$H_2SO_{4\,(aq)} + 2 \; NH_4OH_{(aq)} \longrightarrow (NH_4)_2SO_{4\,(aq)} + 2 \; H_2O_{(\ell)}$$

If 25.00 mL of an ammonium hydroxide solution requires 47.25 mL of sulfuric acid ($0.583 \; mol \cdot L^{-1}$) to neutralize it, determine the concentration of the ammonium hydroxide.

13. Zinc metal reacts with nitric acid, HNO_3, to produce hydrogen gas and a solution of zinc nitrate.
    a) Write a balanced equation for the reaction.
    b) What mass of zinc must be reacted in order to produce 0.250 L of hydrogen gas at 25 °C and 101.3 kPa?

14. The reaction between hydrochloric acid and sodium carbonate produces carbon dioxide gas, a solution of sodium chloride, and water according to the following formula:

$$2 \, HCl_{(aq)} + Na_2CO_{3 \, (aq)} \longrightarrow 2 \, NaCl_{(aq)} + CO_{2 \, (g)} + H_2O_{(\ell)}$$

What mass of sodium carbonate must be used to produce 7.86 L of carbon dioxide gas at 19 °C and 98.7 kPa?

15. White phosphorus ($P_{4 \, (s)}$) is obtained from the reaction at high temperature of calcium phosphate, silicon dioxide, and carbon. The reaction can be represented as follows:

$$2 \, Ca_3(PO_4)_{2 \, (s)} + 6 \, SiO_{2 \, (s)} + 5 \, C_{(s)} \longrightarrow$$
$$P_{4 \, (s)} + 6 \, CaSiO_{3 \, (s)} + 5 \, CO_{2 \, (g)}$$

    a) When 1.00 kg of white phosphorus is formed, what volume of carbon dioxide at a temperature of 400 °C and a pressure of 105 kPa is also produced?
    b) What mass of silicon dioxide (sand) and carbon (coke) will be required in order to form 1.00 kg of white phosphorus?

16. Zinc metal reacts with dilute hydrochloric acid, HCl, to give zinc chloride solution and hydrogen gas. When 4.21 g of an impure sample of zinc was treated with an excess of hydrochloric acid, 1.24 L of hydrogen gas was collected over water at a temperature of 20 °C and a total pressure of 104.7 kPa. (The vapour pressure of water at 20 °C is 2.3 kPa.)
    a) Write a balanced equation for the reaction.
    b) Calculate the mass of zinc present in the sample.
    c) Find the percent purity of the zinc.

17. To determine the purity of a sample of calcium chloride, 2.86 g of the sample was dissolved in water and reacted with an excess of aqueous silver nitrate:

$$CaCl_{2 \, (aq)} + 2 \, AgNO_{3 \, (aq)} \longrightarrow 2 \, AgCl_{(s)} + Ca(NO_3)_{2 \, (aq)}$$

Calculate the percentage purity of the sample if 4.41 g of silver chloride is obtained.

18. A 25.0 g sample of impure silver was treated with excess nitric acid to produce a solution of silver nitrate. Upon the addition of an excess of sodium iodide solution to the silver nitrate solution, 25.0 g of silver iodide was precipitated. Determine the purity of the original sample of silver.

19. Ammonia reacts with oxygen to produce nitrogen monoxide and water according to the equation:

$$4\ NH_{3\ (g)}\ +\ 5\ O_{2\ (g)}\ \longrightarrow\ 4\ NO_{(g)}\ +\ 6\ H_2O_{(g)}$$

Assuming that all gases are at the same temperature and pressure, answer the following:
a) What volume of ammonia and oxygen would be required in order to prepare 15.0 L of nitrogen monoxide?
b) What volume of water would be produced during the formation of 15.0 L of nitrogen monoxide?

20. Propane burns in oxygen according to the equation

$$C_3H_{8\ (g)}\ +\ 5\ O_{2\ (g)}\ \longrightarrow\ 3\ CO_{2\ (g)}\ +\ 4\ H_2O_{(g)}$$

If all gases are at the same temperature and pressure, answer the following questions:
a) What volume of oxygen would be required to burn 225 L of propane?
b) What volumes of carbon dioxide and water would be produced when 225 L of propane burns in this manner?

21. When 0.1382 g of an unknown alkali metal carbonate (i.e. M_2CO_3, where M is the symbol for the unknown metal) is dissolved in water and excess calcium chloride is added to it, 0.1001 g of calcium carbonate precipitates. Find
a) the molar mass of the unknown metal carbonate
b) the molar mass of the unknown alkali metal, M
c) the identity of the unknown alkali metal, M

22. When 0.087 115 g of an unknown alkali metal sulfate (M_2SO_4, where M is the symbol for the unknown metal) is dissolved in water and excess barium chloride is added to it, 0.1167 g of barium sulfate is precipitated. Find
a) the molar mass of the unknown alkali metal sulfate
b) the molar mass of the unknown alkali metal, M
c) the identity of the unknown alkali metal, M

23. Carbon dioxide is commonly prepared by reacting calcium carbonate (marble chips) with dilute hydrochloric acid (3.00 $mol \cdot L^{-1}$) according to the reaction

$$CaCO_{3\ (s)}\ +\ 2\ HCl_{(aq)}\ \longrightarrow\ CaCl_{2\ (aq)}\ +\ CO_{2\ (g)}\ +\ H_2O_{(\ell)}$$

a) What is the maximum mass of calcium carbonate that will react with 0.200 L of hydrochloric acid?
b) What volume of carbon dioxide will be produced at 18 °C and 104 kPa from the quantities used in (a) above?

24. Hydrogen sulfide may be prepared by reacting dilute sulfuric acid ($3.00 \text{ mol} \cdot \text{L}^{-1}$) with sodium sulfide according to the following formula:

$$Na_2S_{(s)} + H_2SO_{4 \, (aq)} \longrightarrow H_2S_{(g)} + Na_2SO_{4 \, (aq)}$$

a) What volume of sulfuric acid will be required to react with 15.0 g of sodium sulfide?

b) What volume of hydrogen sulfide will be produced at 26 °C and 97.8 kPa from the quantities given above?

25. Sodium metal reacts violently with water to produce hydrogen gas and a solution of sodium hydroxide:

$$2 \, Na_{(s)} + 2 \, H_2O_{(\ell)} \longrightarrow H_{2 \, (g)} + 2 \, NaOH_{(aq)}$$

Supposing that 4.60 g of sodium is added to exactly one litre of water, answer the following:

a) What volume of hydrogen gas is produced at 30.0 °C and 100.4 kPa?

b) What volume of hydrochloric acid ($0.100 \text{ mol} \cdot \text{L}^{-1}$) would be required to neutralize the sodium hydroxide solution produced? (Assume that the volume of water remains constant throughout the reaction with sodium.)

26. Barium metal reacts violently with water to produce hydrogen gas and solid barium hydroxide:

$$Ba_{(s)} + 2 \, H_2O_{(\ell)} \longrightarrow H_{2 \, (g)} + Ba(OH)_{2 \, (s)}$$

a) If 8.74 g of barium is added to water, what volume of hydrogen gas is produced at 18 °C and 96.5 kPa?

b) If a total of 15.86 mL of hydrochloric acid is needed to neutralize the barium hydroxide produced in part a), what would be the concentration of the hydrochloric acid?

27. In acid solution, lead(II) nitrate will react quantitatively with potassium chromate to produce a precipitate of lead(II) chromate:

$$Pb(NO_3)_{2 \, (aq)} + K_2CrO_{4 \, (aq)} \longrightarrow PbCrO_{4 \, (s)} + 2 \, KNO_{3 \, (aq)}$$

Supposing that 5.00 mL of potassium chromate ($0.300 \text{ mol} \cdot \text{L}^{-1}$) is added to 30.0 mL of lead(II) nitrate ($0.0105 \text{ mol} \cdot \text{L}^{-1}$), answer the following:

a) Which reagent is present in excess?

b) What mass of lead(II) chromate is produced?

28. A solution of copper(II) sulfate is prepared by placing 5.80 g of copper(II) sulfate in a flask and adding enough water to prepare 125 mL of solution. A 25.0 mL sample of this solution is added to 125 mL of sodium hydroxide ($0.125 \text{ mol} \cdot \text{L}^{-1}$) and the following reaction occurs:

$$CuSO_{4 \, (aq)} + 2 \, NaOH_{(aq)} \longrightarrow Cu(OH)_{2 \, (s)} + Na_2SO_{4 \, (aq)}$$

a) Determine which is the limiting reagent.

b) Determine the mass of copper(II) hydroxide produced.

29. If 12.0 g of barium nitrate is dissolved in water and added to a solution of 16.0 g of potassium sulfate, a double displacement reaction occurs:

$$Ba(NO_3)_{2\ (aq)} + K_2SO_{4\ (aq)} \longrightarrow BaSO_{4\ (s)} + 2\ KNO_{3\ (aq)}$$

a) Which reagent is in excess?

b) What mass of barium sulfate is produced?

30. If 6.94 g of sodium sulfide is dissolved in water and added to a solution containing 8.58 g of silver nitrate, the following reaction occurs:

$$Na_2S_{(aq)} + 2\ AgNO_{3\ (aq)} \longrightarrow Ag_2S_{(s)} + 2\ NaNO_{3\ (aq)}$$

a) Which reagent is in excess?

b) What mass of silver sulfide is produced?

31. Suppose that you are given a solution of sulfuric acid and a solution of sodium hydroxide, but that the concentration of each of these solutions is unknown. By titration you find that 25.0 mL of the sulfuric acid is neutralized by 34.2 mL of the sodium hydroxide solution. The product of this reaction is a solution of sodium sulfate. When you evaporate all the water from this solution, the mass of sodium sulfate obtained, after drying to constant mass, is 0.489 g. Determine the concentration of the sulfuric acid solution and the sodium hydroxide solution.

32. A 2.083 g sample of a mixture containing sodium carbonate and sodium bromide was placed in a 250.0 mL volumetric flask and enough water added to fill to the mark. A 25.00 mL portion of this solution required 17.56 mL of hydrochloric acid ($0.1396\ mol \cdot L^{-1}$) for complete neutralization. Calculate the percentage of sodium carbonate in the mixture.

33. The formula of a hydrate of an alkali metal carbonate may be determined by titration with standard hydrochloric acid. If 2.316 g of a hydrate of sodium carbonate ($Na_2CO_3 \cdot xH_2O$) required 38.49 mL of hydrochloric acid ($0.4198\ mol \cdot L^{-1}$) for complete neutralization, determine the formula of the hydrate (i.e. find the value of x).

34. If 0.2340 g of a hydrate of sodium carbonate ($Na_2CO_3 \cdot xH_2O$) required 12.45 mL of hydrochloric acid ($0.3031\ mol \cdot L^{-1}$) for complete neutralization, determine the formula of the hydrate.

35. Hydrides of the alkaline earth metals react with water to produce hydrogen gas according to the equation

$$XH_{2\,(s)} + 2\,H_2O_{(\ell)} \longrightarrow X(OH)_{2\,(s)} + 2\,H_{2\,(g)}$$

In a certain experiment, a 0.347 g sample of an alkaline earth metal hydride was reacted with an excess of water, and 125 mL of hydrogen gas was collected by the displacement of water at 25 °C and 101.87 kPa. If the vapour pressure of water at 25 °C is 3.17 kPa, determine the following:

a) the number of moles of $H_{2\,(g)}$ produced
b) the molar mass of the alkaline earth metal hydride, XH_2
c) the identity to the alkaline earth metal, **X**

36. An unknown metal carbonate is reacted with excess hydrochloric acid according to the equation

$$X_2CO_{3\,(s)} + 2\,HCl_{(aq)} \longrightarrow 2\,XCl_{(aq)} + H_2O_{(\ell)} + CO_{2\,(aq)}$$

When a 1.185 g sample of an unknown metal carbonate, X_2CO_3, was reacted in this manner, the volume of carbon dioxide gas collected by the displacement of water was 225 mL at 25 °C and 97.57 kPa. If the vapour pressure of water at this temperature is 3.17 kPa, determine the following:

a) the number of moles of carbon dioxide produced
b) the molar mass of X_2CO_3
c) the identity of element **X**

SUGGESTED PROJECTS

1. Volumetric and gravimetric analysis form an important part of a field of chemistry called analytical chemistry. Use career reference material, university or college calendars, or reference material from a library to find out what an analytical chemist does and what training he or she receives.

2. In industrial, government, and university laboratories, automatic titrators are now used instead of simple burettes. Find out how an automatic titrator works, what it costs, and which companies, government agencies, and/or educational institutions in your locality possess such instruments.

C H A P T E R *14*

Organic Chemistry I

The compounds we have discussed in the previous chapters have been mainly inorganic. In this and the following chapter, we will introduce you to the large and very important world of organic chemistry.

After explaining the differences between the properties of inorganic and organic compounds, this chapter will focus on the organic compounds that contain only carbon and hydrogen. We will discuss the classification and structure of these compounds, their properties, and the rules for naming them.

As many of the simple organic compounds introduced in this Chapter are found in crude petroleum, we will also discuss how petroleum is separated into components such as gasoline and diesel oil.

Historical Background

14.1 Before 1828, any substance that was isolated from animal or plant material was thought to contain some kind of "vital force". This *theory of vitalism* suggested that compounds found in living organisms could not be pre-

Figure 14.1
Friedrich Wöhler (1800–1882). His synthesis of urea was a major factor in the decline of the vitalism theory of organic chemistry.

pared in a laboratory. The study of these compounds came to be called *organic chemistry*. Textbooks of the day discussed "animal chemistry" and "vegetable chemistry", and compounds were described from the standpoint of their biological sources and medicinal uses rather than their chemical structures.

In 1828, through the work of Friedrich Wöhler, the vitalism theory was shown to be incorrect. Wöhler was trying to prepare ammonium cyanate (the cyanate ion is OCN^-) by the double displacement reaction of silver cyanate with ammonium chloride:

$$AgOCN_{(aq)} \ + \ NH_4Cl_{(aq)} \ \longrightarrow \ AgCl_{(s)} \ + \ NH_4OCN_{(aq)}$$

After the insoluble silver chloride was filtered off, Wöhler evaporated the water from the remaining solution and obtained some white crystals. He found that the crystals possessed none of the properties of a typical inorganic compound. Instead, the crystals were shown to be identical to crystals of urea, an organic compound that had previously been isolated from urine. Wöhler had achieved the "impossible" and had prepared an organic compound from inorganic sources!

Wöhler did not isolate ammonium cyanate as he had hoped, because during evaporation of the filtrate, the atoms in the ammonium cyanate had rearranged to form urea:

$$NH_4OCN \ \xrightarrow{60\,°C} \ (NH_2)_2CO$$

Although the results of Wöhler's experiment marked the beginning of the end of the vitalism theory, the theory was not renounced immediately by the scientific community. Over the next ten years the synthesis of additional organic compounds from inorganic sources gradually convinced chemists that the vitalism theory was incorrect.

The Differences 14.2 Between Organic and Inorganic Compounds

Organic chemistry can be defined as the chemistry of the compounds of carbon. However, some carbon-containing compounds (such as carbon monoxide, carbon dioxide, and hydrogen cyanide) and carbon-containing salts (such as carbonates and cyanides) are not considered to be organic, but are usually regarded as being inorganic. The properties of a number of these compounds have already been discussed in previous chapters.

Many of the differences between organic and inorganic compounds arise because of the nature of the bonding present in these compounds. Most organic compounds are covalent, whereas a large percentage of all known inorganic compounds are ionic. Thus, the differences between these two classes of compounds are similar to those described in our general comparison of covalent and ionic substances (Section 5.8). For example, organic compounds tend to melt and boil at lower temperatures than inorganic compounds. Obviously, there are exceptions. Water, which

The Manufacture of Urea — Vitalism Revisited?

For soil to be productive, it requires three main nutrients: nitrogen, phosphorus, and potassium. Nitrogen promotes plant growth, increases protein content, and gives plants their healthy green colour. Phosphorus aids seed germination and promotes root development. Potassium helps plants to develop strong roots.

When selecting a fertilizer, a farmer or gardener takes into account the specific needs of each crop: some crops require a fertilizer that is high in nitrogen, whereas others require one with a higher phosphorus or potassium content. Each fertilizer is graded according to its nitrogen (N), phosphorus (P), and potassium (K) content, and is given an NPK rating. An NPK of 20-10-10 means that the fertilizer contains 20% nitrogen, 10% phosphorus, and 10% potassium (by mass).

Urea, $(NH_2)_2CO$, is an important fertilizer with an NPK value of 46-0-0. Millions of tonnes are used annually as a fertilizer. How is urea produced on an industrial scale? Does the modern fertilizer manufacturer use the same reaction that Wöhler used in his classic experiment? Although the answer to the second question is ''no'', urea is still synthesized from inorganic materials.

The Esso Agricultural Chemicals Complex at Redwater, Alberta, has the capacity to produce 1500 t of urea per day by means of the following reaction of ammonia with carbon dioxide:

$$2\ NH_3\ +\ CO_2\ \longrightarrow\ (NH_2)_2CO\ +\ H_2O$$

Both of the starting materials are produced on site. Ammonia is made by the reaction of nitrogen and hydrogen, the latter having been made from natural gas (CH_4) and steam. Carbon dioxide is a by-product of the hydrogen-forming process. The production of urea is not quite as simple as suggested by the above equation. In practice, the reaction is carried out at high pressure and involves the formation of a compound called ammonium carbamate ($NH_2CO_2NH_4$). Some 34% of the ammonion carbamate decomposes into urea, while the remainder decomposes back to ammonia and carbon dioxide.

Urea is not the only fertilizer produced at the Esso Redwater Plant. Some of the ammonia is converted into nitric acid which is used to produce ammonium nitrate, another important fertilizer (34-0-0). Ammonia is also marketed as a fertilizer (82-0-0). Phosphoric acid and sulfuric acid are produced in another part of the plant and are then combined with ammonia to give fertilizers containing a high percentage of both nitrogen and phosphorus (e.g. 18-46-0, 11-51-0, and 16-20-0).

Figure 14.2

The Esso Agricultural Chemical Complex, Redwater, Alberta. About 1500 t of urea per day can be produced at this plant.

Figure 14.3

The numbers on a fertilizer package represent the nitrogen, phosphorus, and potassium content of the fertilizer. Different types of plants require different ratios of these three elements.

is one of the most common inorganic compounds, is one such exception (melting point 0 °C, boiling point 100 °C).

Similarly, most organic compounds do not conduct electricity, either in their pure form or in aqueous solution. Inorganic compounds, such as sodium chloride and sodium hydroxide, do conduct electricity, both in their molten state and in aqueous solution (Sections 5.1, 5.8, and 12.8). Again, we must be careful in our generalizations. Acetic acid (CH_3CO_2H) is an organic compound; yet, in the experiment described in Section 12.10 we saw that an aqueous solution of this compound does conduct electricity, although not very well.

One chemical difference between inorganic and organic compounds is the ease with which the latter burn in oxygen. The products of such **combustion reactions** are usually carbon dioxide gas and water vapour. This point is illustrated below by the equations for the combustion of methane (CH_4) and ethanol (C_2H_5OH):

$$CH_{4\,(g)} + 2\,O_{2\,(g)} \longrightarrow CO_{2\,(g)} + 2\,H_2O_{(g)}$$
$$C_2H_5OH_{(\ell)} + 3\,O_{2\,(g)} \longrightarrow 2\,CO_{2\,(g)} + 3\,H_2O_{(g)}$$

By way of contrast, most inorganic compounds do not readily burn in oxygen.

The millions of organic compounds that exist result from various combinations of some half-dozen or so elements (H, O, N, S, P, and the halogens) with carbon. In inorganic chemistry, the diversity of compounds results from combinations of all the elements. It is unusual to find more than three or four inorganic compounds formed from the same two or three elements. Thus, only four inorganic compounds contain hydrogen, chlorine, and oxygen (HClO, $HClO_2$, $HClO_3$, $HClO_4$). By way of contrast, hundreds of thousands of organic compounds contain only carbon, hydrogen and oxygen.

In general, the formulas of organic compounds tend to be more complex than those of inorganic compounds. Inorganic compounds can usually be represented by very simple formulas consisting of less than a dozen atoms. Examples include NaCl, H_2SO_4, and Na_3PO_4. Some organic compounds, such as urea (CH_4N_2O) and ethanol (C_2H_6O), have simple molecular formulas; but many, such as sucrose ($C_{12}H_{22}O_{11}$), and cholesterol ($C_{27}H_{46}O$), are very complex molecules containing large numbers of atoms.

Although there are exceptions, most empirical formulas in inorganic chemistry represent only one compound. For example, the only compound with the empirical formula $CaSO_4$ is calcium sulfate. However, very few organic empirical or molecular formulas represent only one compound. One of the few that does is CH_4, which represents only methane. Even a simple formula such as C_2H_6O represents two compounds, i.e. ethanol and dimethyl ether. In general, the more atoms present in an organic empirical or molecular formula, the more compounds it can represent. Thus, C_5H_{12} represents three different compounds, $C_{10}H_{22}$

represents 75 compounds, and $C_{20}H_{42}$ represents 366 319 compounds. Different compounds with the same molecular formula are called **isomers**. Isomers result from the variety of ways in which the atoms in organic molecules can be arranged. This in turn is related to the ability of carbon atoms to undergo catenation (Section 9.5), the linking together of atoms to form long chains.

The Shapes of Organic Molecules   *14.3*

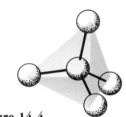

Figure 14.4
A regular tetrahedron.

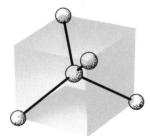

Figure 14.5
The most favourable arrangement of four atoms around a central atom, and its relation to a cube.

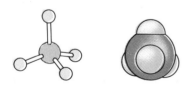

Figure 14.6
The shape of the methane molecule, CH_4
a) as a ball-and-stick model
b) as a space-filling model

Molecules in which the central atom is surrounded by four pairs of bonding electrons have a **tetrahedral** shape. The four bonds are directed towards the four corners of a regular tetrahedron with the central atom at the centre of the tetrahedron (Figure 14.4). To visualize the shape of a tetrahedral molecule, try to imagine the central atom as being at the centre of a cube with the surrounding atoms situated in the corners of the cube in such a way that no two adjacent corners contain atoms. This is illustrated in Figure 14.5.

Chemists often use *molecular models* to help them to visualize molecules. Several types of molecular models are available, but some are intended mainly for research purposes. The two types that you will probably encounter are **ball-and-stick models** and **space-filling models**.

In ball-and-stick models, small plastic balls with holes drilled in them at specific angles are used to represent atoms. A different coloured ball is usually used for each element. These "atoms" can be joined together by inserting plastic or metal rods into the holes to represent bonds. These rods are sometimes proportional in length to known bond lengths. Although this type of model gives us a good indication of the angles between the bonds, it can be misleading because molecules do not really look like this.

Space-filling models, on the other hand, are exact-scale models and do show the relative sizes of the atoms. Also constructed of plastic, each ball represents a specific atom, with the size of the ball proportional to the size of the atom. In the model, the "atoms" are held together by small connectors. The disadvantage of space-filling models is that they give us little idea of bond angles and bond lengths. Sketches of both the ball-and-stick and the space-filling model of methane, CH_4, are shown in Figure 14.6. All the bond angles in molecules of this shape are about 109.5°. This basic tetrahedral shape is very common in organic compounds.

Let us consider the electron-dot formula for methane. If we remove a hydrogen atom from the methane molecule, the fragment that remains is called a **methyl group**:

$$\mathbf{H\!:\!\overset{\displaystyle H}{\underset{\displaystyle H}{C}}\!:\!H} \xrightarrow{-H\cdot} \mathbf{H\!:\!\overset{\displaystyle H}{\underset{\displaystyle H}{C}}\cdot}$$

Figure 14.7

The shape of the ethane molecule, C_2H_6
a) as a ball-and-stick model
b) as a space-filling model

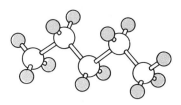

Figure 14.8

The shape of the pentane molecule, C_5H_{12}
a) as a ball-and-stick model
b) as a space-filling model

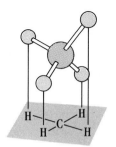

Figure 14.9

The projection of the ball-and-stick model of methane onto a flat (two-dimensional) surface.

To restore the octet around the carbon atom, two methyl groups can be joined together:

$$\begin{array}{ccc} & H & H \\ & | & | \\ H - & C - C & - H \\ & | & | \\ & H & H \end{array}$$

We now have a two-carbon molecule, C_2H_6, called ethane. What will ethane look like? The arrangement around each carbon atom will still be based on the tetrahedral shape, but each of the carbon atoms will be surrounded by three hydrogen atoms and one carbon atom. Models of the ethane molecule are shown in Figure 14.7.

Similarly, we can remove a hydrogen atom from ethane and replace it with another methyl group to form C_3H_8. This procedure can be repeated again and again to give us C_4H_{10}, C_5H_{12}, C_6H_{14}, etc. What shapes will these molecules have? Because the angle between three carbon atoms that are bonded together is still the tetrahedral angle of 109.5°, the chain of carbons will not be in a straight line but will be arranged in a zigzag manner. This is illustrated by the model of pentane (C_5H_{12}) shown in Figure 14.8.

The more carbon atoms in a molecule, the more difficult it becomes to draw its shape. It is much easier to represent a molecule in two dimensions. We do this by projecting the ball-and-stick model onto a two-dimensional surface. Figure 14.9 shows how this is done for methane. Note that the two-dimensional representation makes the H—C—H angles appear to be 90°. Remember that in their real three-dimensional state, these angles are tetrahedral angles of 109.5°.

We can represent pentane (C_5H_{12}) by a similar two-dimensional **structural formula**. This structure can be represented in an even more compact form by using a **condensed formula**:

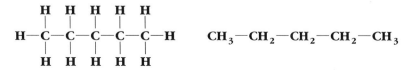

structural formula   condensed formula

This formula can be condensed even further to $CH_3(CH_2)_3CH_3$ and still convey all the essential information.

QUESTIONS

1. Draw the two-dimensional structural formula for each of the following compounds:
   a) C_2H_6 b) C_3H_8 c) C_4H_{10}
   Note that in each case the carbon atoms form a chain.

2. Write the condensed formula for each of the compounds listed in Question 1.

Structural Isomers

14.4

Figure 14.10

The three condensed formulas that correspond to the molecular formula C_5H_{12}:

a)

$$CH_3-CH_2-CH_2-CH_2-CH_3$$

b)

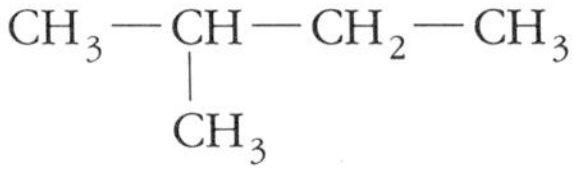

$$CH_3-CH-CH_2-CH_3$$
$$\qquad |$$
$$\qquad CH_3$$

c)

$$\qquad CH_3$$
$$\qquad |$$
$$CH_3-C-CH_3$$
$$\qquad |$$
$$\qquad CH_3$$

Writing structural or condensed formulas allows us to distinguish between different compounds with the same molecular formula. Such compounds have different physical properties and often have very different chemical properties.

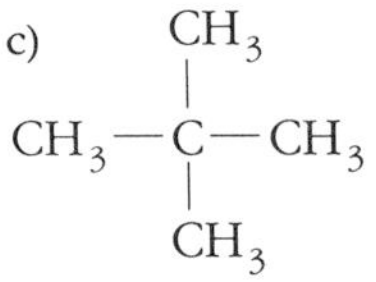

Let us see how many different structural formulas can be drawn for a compound with a molecular formula of C_5H_{12}. We find that there are three, as shown in Figure 14.10. The three structures shown represent the three **structural isomers** of C_5H_{12}. As you can see, they differ from each other in the way that the seventeen atoms (five carbon and twelve hydrogen) are arranged. Compound a) has the five carbons joined in a "straight" chain (remember that the chain is really zigzag rather than straight); compound b) has four carbons in the main chain with a one-carbon **side chain** attached to the second carbon of the main chain; and compound c) has a chain of three carbon atoms with two side chains of one carbon atom each.

You should note that the compound in Figure 14.10b could also have been drawn as

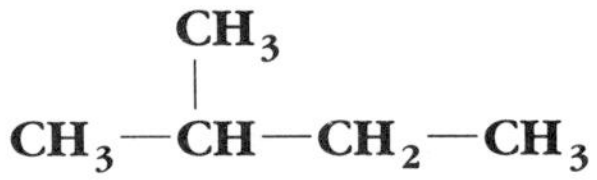

$$CH_3$$
$$|$$
$$CH_3-CH-CH_2-CH_3$$

and that this structure does not represent another isomer. In both formulas, the longest chain is made up of four carbon atoms with a side chain containing one carbon atom attached to the second carbon atom in the main chain. You can use molecular models to convince yourself that the two representations are identical. As you work through this chapter you should quickly come to realize that two structures, which at first glance appear to be quite different, can actually represent the same compound.

EXAMPLE　　*14.1*　　How many different isomers of C_6H_{14} are shown below:

a) 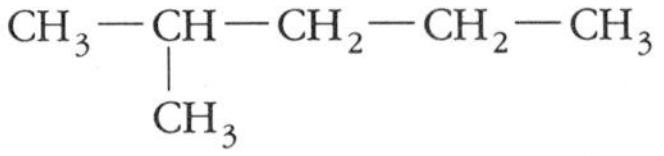　$CH_3-CH-CH_2-CH_2-CH_3$
$$\qquad\quad |$$
$$\qquad\quad CH_3$$

b) 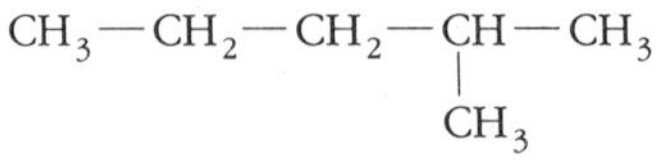　$CH_3-CH_2-CH_2-CH-CH_3$
$$\qquad\qquad\qquad\quad |$$
$$\qquad\qquad\qquad\quad CH_3$$

c) 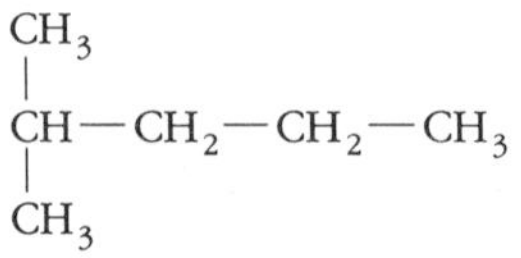　
$$CH_3$$
$$|$$
$$CH-CH_2-CH_2-CH_3$$
$$|$$
$$CH_3$$

d) 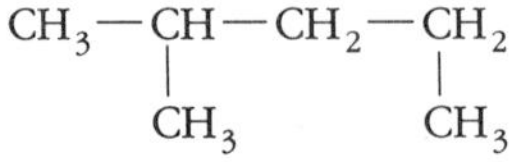　$CH_3-CH-CH_2-CH_2$
$$\qquad\quad |\qquad\qquad |$$
$$\qquad\quad CH_3\qquad\quad CH_3$$

SOLUTION Only one isomer is shown! All the structures represent the same isomer. If you look carefully, you will see that each structure has a main chain of five carbons with a one-carbon side chain attached to the second carbon of the main chain.

QUESTIONS

3. Write the condensed formula for each of the following:

a)

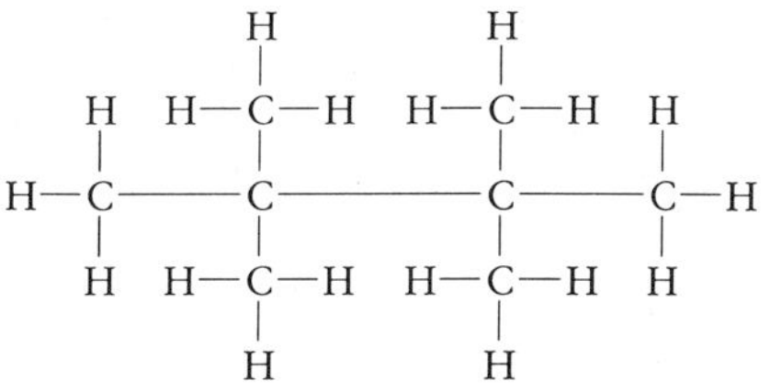

b)

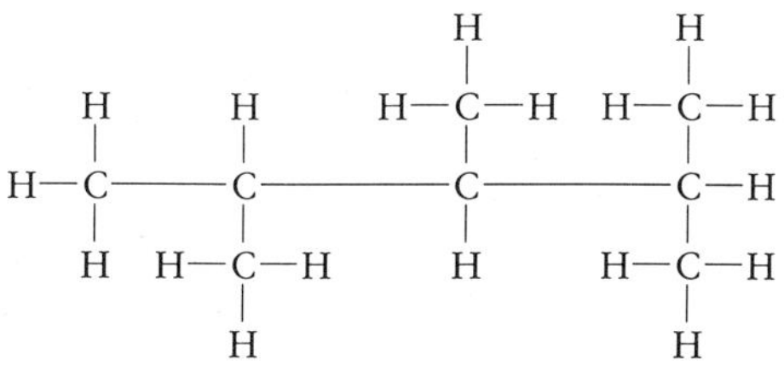

4. Draw the structural formulas for each of the isomers of C_5H_{12} shown in Figure 14.10.

5. Which, if any, of the structures shown below represents a compound that is different from the others:

a)

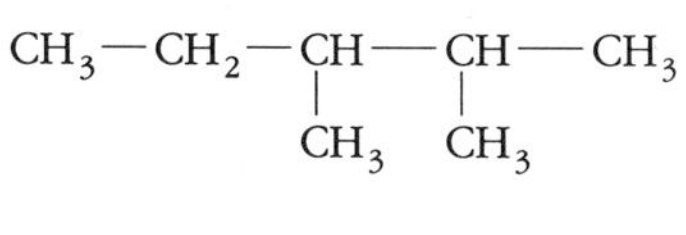

c)

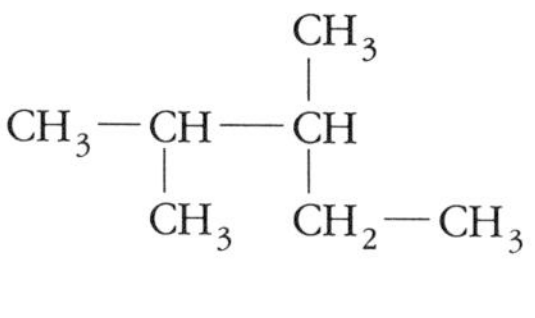

b)

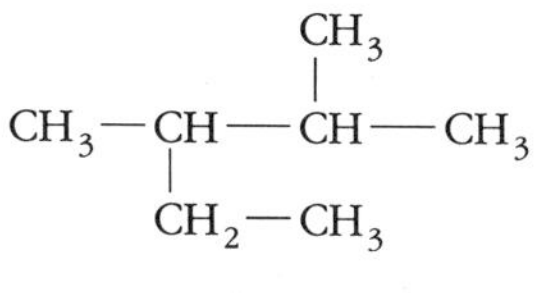

d)

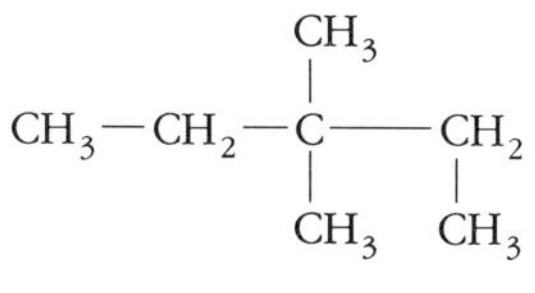

6. Draw the structural formula for each of the five isomers of C_6H_{14}.

The Classification and Naming of Organic Compounds

14.5

Although each of the millions of organic compounds is unique, certain trends and similarities do exist. Organic compounds are subdivided into classes of compounds with similar chemical properties. Each compound that belongs to a given class (or family) contains a specific combination of atoms, called a **functional group**, which is mainly responsible for the properties of that compound. The remainder of the molecule, which usually consists of only carbon and hydrogen atoms, is relatively unimportant in determining the properties of the compound.

Let us look more closely at the classification of organic compounds according to functional groups by considering an example. The functional group common to all the members of the class of organic compounds known as alcohols is the —OH, or hydroxyl, group. Thus, methanol, ethanol, and propanol are all members of the **alcohol** family. These three compounds have a number of properties in common although they each contain a different number of carbon atoms. For example, all three will react with sodium metal to produce hydrogen gas and a base.

As compounds in the alcohol family contain oxygen as well as carbon and hydrogen, we will delay a detailed discussion of them until Chapter 15. In this chapter we are mainly concerned with compounds containing only carbon and hydrogen. The functional groups present in these compounds will be discussed in detail in the next section.

As we saw in Chapter 5, the two main naming systems for inorganic compounds are the classical system and the Stock system. The latter usually tells us something about the structure of the compound. In organic chemistry there are also two naming systems. Most compounds have **common** (or **trivial**) **names** that indicate little or nothing about the structure of the compound. As in inorganic chemistry, however, a systematic method of naming compounds has been established by the International Union of Pure and Applied Chemistry (IUPAC). The **IUPAC system** is based on a series of rules that enables us to deduce the structure of a compound from its name. The IUPAC (or **systematic**) name indicates both the number and arrangement of the carbon atoms, and the type of functional group present in the compound. Prefixes (derived from Greek words) are used to indicate the number of carbon atoms in a compound. The prefixes for the numbers one to ten are listed in Table 14.1.

As you continue your studies in chemistry, you will find that many organic chemicals are known by their common names rather than by their IUPAC names. One reason for this is that some compounds were known long before their structures were determined, and their common names have been used in chemical literature for years. Another reason is that some of the more complex compounds also have very complex systematic names, and it is often much easier to use the common name.

The importance of having one logical system for naming organic molecules is illustrated by the story of the discovery of aniline (C_6H_7N), a

$$CH_3—OH$$
methanol

$$CH_3—CH_2—OH$$
ethanol

$$CH_3—CH_2—CH_2—OH$$
1-propanol

Number of Atoms	Prefix	Number of Atoms	Prefix
1	*meth-*	6	*hex-*
2	*eth-*	7	*hept-*
3	*prop-*	8	*oct-*
4	*but-*	9	*non-*
5	*pent-*	10	*dec-*

TABLE 14.1 *Prefixes Used to Indicate Number of Carbon Atoms*

compound we will learn more about in Chapter 15. August Wilhelm von Hofmann isolated aniline from coal tar in 1845. He showed that it was identical to four compounds that had previously been reported by chemists between 1826 and 1841. These earlier chemists had named the compound *krystallin, anilin, benzidam,* and *kyanol.* The IUPAC system ensures that all chemists assign the same name to a compound and that all chemists can be sure of the exact structure of a particular compound when they are given its IUPAC name.

The Classification of Hydrocarbons

14.6 The simplest organic compounds contain only carbon and hydrogen and are called **hydrocarbons**. As Figure 14.11 shows, hydrocarbons can be subdivided into two main categories, **aromatic** and **aliphatic**. The term aliphatic (from the Greek *aleiphatos,* meaning fat) was used by early chemists for compounds containing long hydrocarbon chains. Like fats, aliphatic compounds are insoluble in water and less dense than water. Aliphatic compounds are further subdivided into **alkanes**, **alkenes**, and **alkynes**. The term aromatic was originally used for hydrocarbons with fragrant aromas. In Section 14.12, we will modify this definition in light of present knowledge.

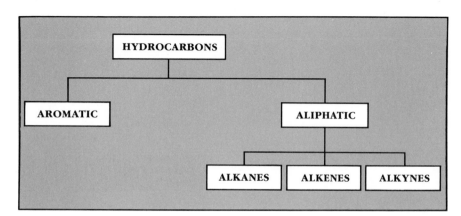

Figure 14.11
Classification scheme for hydrocarbons.

As we mentioned in Section 14.5, each class of compound contains a functional group that distinguishes it from other classes. The functional groups associated with the four classes of hydrocarbons that we shall be considering are shown in Table 14.2

TABLE 14.2 *Functional Groups Present in the Hydrocarbons*

Class	Functional Group
Alkanes	None. (These compounds contain only single-bonded carbon and hydrogen.)
Alkenes	$C=C$
Alkynes	$C\equiv C$
Aromatics	In this text we will only consider aromatic compounds that contain a benzene ring (Section 14.12).

QUESTIONS

7. Classify each of the following compounds as an alkane, an alkene, or an alkyne:

   a) 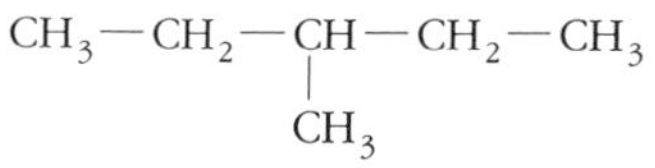 $CH_3-CH_2-\underset{\underset{\displaystyle CH_3}{|}}{CH}-CH_2-CH_3$

   b) 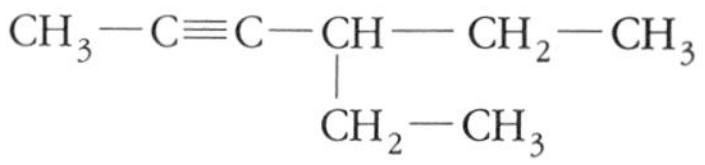 $CH_3-C\equiv C-\underset{\underset{\displaystyle CH_2-CH_3}{|}}{CH}-CH_2-CH_3$

   c) $CH_3-\overset{\overset{\displaystyle CH_3}{|}}{\underset{\underset{\displaystyle CH_3}{|}}{C}}-CH_2-\overset{\overset{\displaystyle CH_2-CH_3}{|}}{\underset{\underset{\displaystyle CH_3}{|}}{C}}-CH_2-CH_2-CH_3$

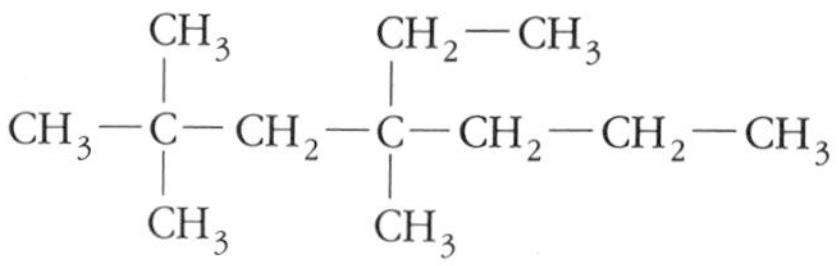

   d) 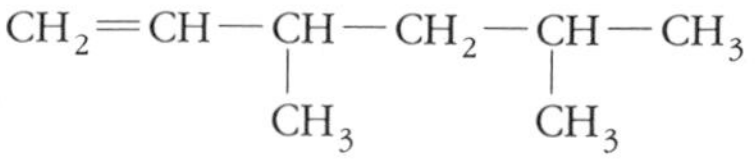 $CH_2=CH-\underset{\underset{\displaystyle CH_3}{|}}{CH}-CH_2-\underset{\underset{\displaystyle CH_3}{|}}{CH}-CH_3$

   e) 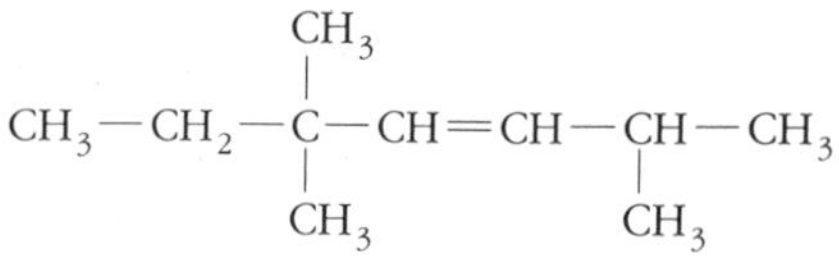 $CH_3-CH_2-\overset{\overset{\displaystyle CH_3}{|}}{\underset{\underset{\displaystyle CH_3}{|}}{C}}-CH=CH-\underset{\underset{\displaystyle CH_3}{|}}{CH}-CH_3$

   f) 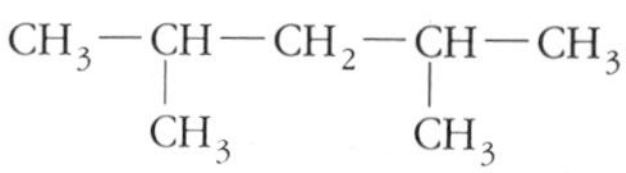 $CH_3-\underset{\underset{\displaystyle CH_3}{|}}{CH}-CH_2-\underset{\underset{\displaystyle CH_3}{|}}{CH}-CH_3$

The Naming of Alkanes

14.7

An organic compound that does not contain any double or triple bonds is said to be a **saturated compound**. As we can see from Table 14.2, alkanes clearly fall into this category. Alkanes can be divided into two groups: those in which all the carbons are joined together in a "straight" chain (Fig. 14.12a), and those in which the carbon chain has one or more branches (Fig. 14.12b). The former is called a **straight-chain** alkane and the latter a **branched-chain** alkane.

As mentioned previously, prefixes are used to indicate the number of carbon atoms in a chain. When naming alkanes, the ending *-ane* is added to the appropriate prefix.

Figure 14.12

The two possible alkanes with the formula C_4H_{10}:
a) A straight-chain molecule
b) A branched-chain molecule

a) $CH_3-CH_2-CH_2-CH_3$

b) $CH_3-CH-CH_3$
         |
       CH_3

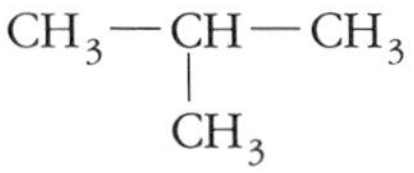

TABLE 14.3	*The Ten Simplest Straight-Chain Alkanes*	
Number of Carbon Atoms	**Formula**	**Name**
1	CH_4	Methane
2	CH_3CH_3	Ethane
3	$CH_3CH_2CH_3$	Propane
4	$CH_3(CH_2)_2CH_3$	Butane
5	$CH_3(CH_2)_3CH_3$	Pentane
6	$CH_3(CH_2)_4CH_3$	Hexane
7	$CH_3(CH_2)_5CH_3$	Heptane
8	$CH_3(CH_2)_6CH_3$	Octane
9	$CH_3(CH_2)_7CH_3$	Nonane
10	$CH_3(CH_2)_8CH_3$	Decane

Branched-Chain Alkanes

Let us now consider how to name branched-chain alkanes. We shall begin with a simple example, one of the isomers of C_5H_{12}:

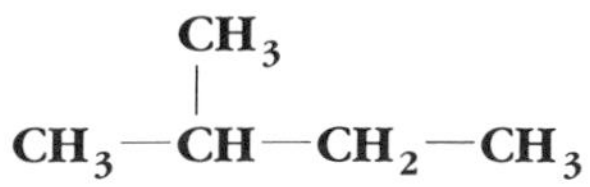

$$CH_3$$
$$|$$
$$CH_3-CH-CH_2-CH_3$$

From this structure, we see that there is a total of five carbon atoms, but only four are in a continuous chain. The fifth carbon atom attached to the main chain is known as a side chain or **substituent**. The term "substituent" is used because we can consider this carbon atom (together with the three hydrogens attached to it) to have replaced, or substituted for, one of the hydrogens in the four-carbon straight-chain alkane (butane).

In this case, the substituent, —CH_3, is a **methyl group**.

In general, the replacement of a hydrogen atom from any alkane will produce an **alkyl group**, which can appear as a side chain in any organic molecule. Alkyl groups are named by adding *-yl* to the prefix indicating the number of carbon atoms.

TABLE 14.4   *Formation of Alkyl Groups from Alkanes*

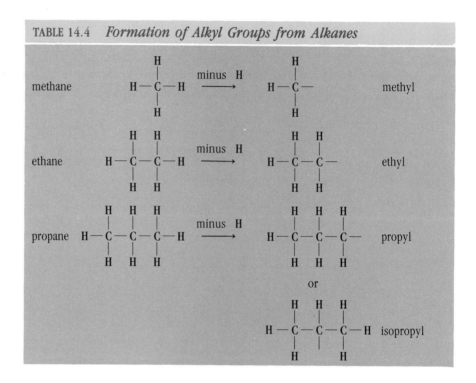

As you can see from Table 14.4, propane can give rise to two alkyl groups, propyl and isopropyl, depending on which hydrogen atom is removed. In general, the more carbon atoms in the alkane, the greater the number of different alkyl groups that can be formed.

If we look again at the compound C_5H_{12}, we see that the longest continuous straight chain contains four carbon atoms. This chain provides the base name for the compound:

$$CH_3-CH-CH_2-CH_3$$

with CH_3 above the CH.

From Table 14.3 we see that the straight-chain alkane containing four carbons is called **butane**. In our compound one of the hydrogens of butane has been replaced by a methyl group. We combine the name of the substituent group with that of the straight-chain base to obtain the name **methyl-**

butane for the compound. Finally, we must identify the carbon atom in the main chain to which the methyl substituent is attached. To do this, we count in from the end of the compound that is *closest* to the carbon atom carrying the substituent. In this fashion, we obtain the lowest possible number for the carbon atom carrying the substituent. We see that, counting from the left, the methyl group is attached to the second carbon atom in the chain. We indicate this by placing a "2", followed by a hyphen, in front of the word "methyl". Thus we obtain a final name of **2-methylbutane** for our compound.

EXAMPLE   ***14.2***   Use the IUPAC system to name the following compound:

$$CH_3-CH_2-CH_2-\underset{\underset{CH_2-CH_3}{|}}{CH}-CH_2-CH_3$$

SOLUTION   a) The longest continuous carbon chain contains six carbon atoms; therefore the base name is **hexane**.

b) An ethyl substituent is present. We combine this with the base name to obtain the name **ethylhexane**.

c) Counting in from the end of the compound that is closest to the carbon atom carrying the substituent, we find that the substituent is on the third carbon atom. Hence the name of the compound is **3-ethylhexane**.

Alkanes with Multiple Side Chains

We still need to extend our naming system for alkanes a little bit further. Suppose we have an alkane such as

$$CH_3-\underset{\underset{\textbf{CH}_3}{|}}{\overset{\overset{\textbf{CH}_3}{|}}{\textbf{C}}}-CH_2-CH_3$$

This alkane has two methyl substituents attached to a four-carbon main chain. When naming such a compound we must indicate the presence of these two identical substituents. We do this by using the appropriate prefix. In addition, we must identify all the carbon atoms in the main chain to which the substituents are attached. This is done through the use of numbers, using the same method that we used when only one substituent was present.

TABLE 14.5	*Prefixes used for identical substituents*		
Number of Substituents	Prefix	Number of Substituents	Prefix
2	*di-*	5	*penta-*
3	*tri-*	6	*hexa-*
4	*tetra-*	7	*hepta-*

Thus, the compound shown above has two methyl groups attached to a butane chain and has the basic name **dimethylbutane**. As both methyl groups are attached to the second carbon in the chain, the full name is **2,2-dimethylbutane**. Notice that a number is required for each substituent and that the two numbers are separated by a comma. Observe that in the isomeric compound

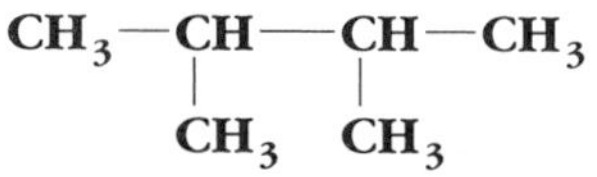

$$CH_3-CH-CH-CH_3$$
$$\qquad\ \ |\qquad\ |$$
$$\qquad\ \ CH_3\ \ \ CH_3$$

the two methyl groups are on different carbon atoms and that this is reflected by the slightly different name, **2,3-dimethylbutane**.

EXAMPLE   **14.3**   Use the IUPAC system to name the following compound:

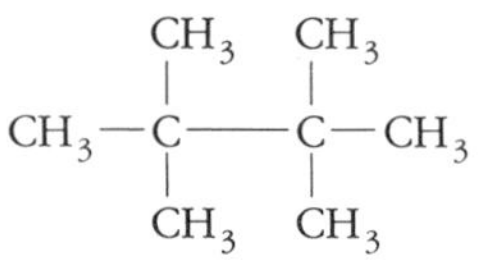

$$\qquad\qquad CH_3\ \ \ CH_3$$
$$\qquad\qquad\ |\qquad\ |$$
$$CH_3-C-----C-CH_3$$
$$\qquad\qquad\ |\qquad\ |$$
$$\qquad\qquad CH_3\ \ \ CH_3$$

SOLUTION   a) The longest continuous carbon chain contains four carbon atoms, therefore the base name is **butane**.

b) There are four methyl substituents. We use the prefix *tetra-* to indicate four identical substituents and obtain the name **tetramethylbutane**.

c) Two methyl groups are on carbon atom two. The other two are on carbon atom three. Therefore **2,2,3,3-tetramethylbutane** is the complete name.

In addition to deriving the correct name for a given structure, we must also be able to draw the structure for a compound for which we have been given the IUPAC name.

EXAMPLE   **14.4**   Draw the condensed formula for 3-ethylheptane.

SOLUTION   As the name of the compound ends with the suffix *heptane*, we know that
the longest carbon chain contains seven carbon atoms:

$$C-C-C-C-C-C-C$$

The name also tells us that we have an ethyl substituent attached at the
third carbon in the chain as shown in the following equation:

$$\begin{array}{c} CH_2-CH_3 \\ | \\ C-C-C-C-C-C-C \end{array}$$

Thus the complete (condensed) formula is

$$\begin{array}{c} CH_2-CH_3 \\ | \\ CH_3-CH_2-CH-CH_2-CH_2-CH_2-CH_3 \end{array}$$

NOTE: Before we leave the subject of branched-chain alkanes, please
be aware of the fact that there are many alkanes that have two or more different alkyl groups attached to the main carbon chain. The naming of these
alkanes is a matter for more advanced study.

Cyclic Hydrocarbons

In addition to forming chains, carbon atoms can also join together to form
rings. When hydrogen is the only other element involved, we call such ring
compounds **cyclic hydrocarbons**. We name these compounds in much
the same way that we name other hydrocarbons, but we now include the
prefix *cyclo-* to indicate the presence of the ring.

$$CH_3-CH_2-CH_2-CH_2-CH_2-CH_3 \qquad\qquad H_2C\begin{array}{c} CH_2-CH_2 \\ \diagdown \\ CH_2-CH_2 \end{array}\begin{array}{c} \diagdown \\ CH_2 \\ \diagup \end{array}$$

hexane   cyclohexane

An important point to note is that the formula of cyclohexane is C_6H_{12}
whereas that for hexane is C_6H_{14}. To create the ring, two hydrogen atoms
have to be removed from the straight-chain molecule. A shorthand way of
depicting cyclic structures is simply to show the bonds connecting the
carbon atoms. Thus, cyclohexane and cyclopentane can be represented
respectively by:

⬡ and ⬠

It is important to remember that, unless another atom or group is indicated, each of the angles formed by the lines in these shorthand representations represents a CH_2 group.

EXAMPLE   **14.5**   Use the IUPAC system to name the following compound:

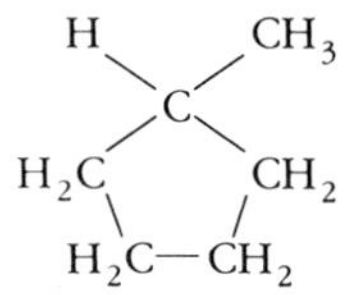

SOLUTION   a) The longest carbon chain contains five carbon atoms in a ring. Hence the base name is **cyclopentane**.

b) A methyl substituent is present, which gives us the name **methylcyclopentane**.

c) When we have a compound with a ring structure, we start numbering carbon atoms from the atom to which the substituent is attached. This gives us the name **1-methylcyclopentane**. However, in this case the number can be omitted, as the name methylcyclopentane is unambiguous.

EXAMPLE   **14.6**   Name the following compound according to the IUPAC system:

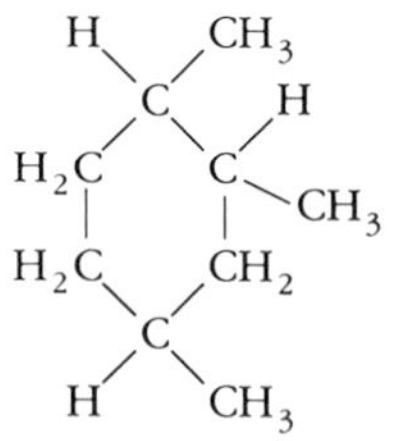

SOLUTION   a) The longest continuous carbon chain contains 6 carbon atoms in a ring. Hence the base name is **cyclohexane**.

b) There are three methyl substituents present. Thus, we modify the name to **trimethylcyclohexane**.

c) The problem now is how to indicate the position of each of the three methyl groups. If we start with the carbon atom at the top of the ring and number in a counter-clockwise direction we obtain 1, 4, and 6. Starting with the same carbon atom and going clockwise we get 1, 2, and 4. This looks bettter, since our objective is to use the lowest possible numbers. However, we could also start numbering with either of the other carbon atoms to which substituents are attached. Doing this we obtain the numbers 1, 3, 6 and 1, 2, 5 starting from the carbon atom at the 2 o'clock position; and 1, 3, 4 and 1, 4, 5 from the carbon atom at the bottom. After considering all these possibilities, we would decide upon a name of **1,2,4-trimethylcyclohexane** for this compound, as this name allows us to use the *lowest possible numbers*.

QUESTIONS

8. Give the IUPAC name of each of the following compounds:

a)

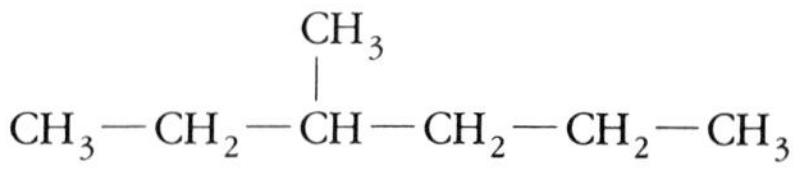

$$CH_3-CH_2-\underset{\underset{CH_3}{|}}{CH}-CH_2-CH_2-CH_3$$

b)

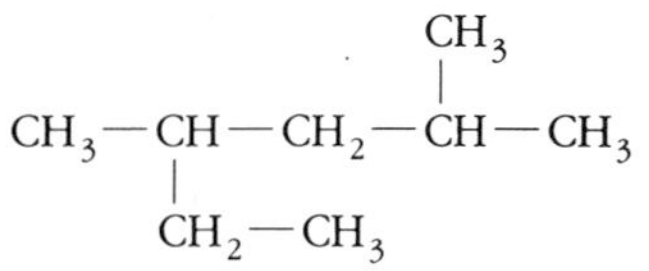

$$CH_3-\underset{\underset{CH_2-CH_3}{|}}{CH}-CH_2-\underset{\underset{CH_3}{|}}{CH}-CH_3$$

c)

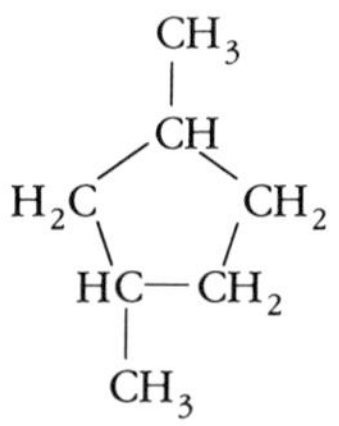

d)

$$CH_3-\underset{\underset{CH_3}{|}}{\overset{\overset{CH_3}{|}}{C}}-\overset{\overset{CH_3}{|}}{CH}-\underset{\underset{CH_3}{|}}{\overset{\overset{CH_3}{|}}{C}}-CH_3$$

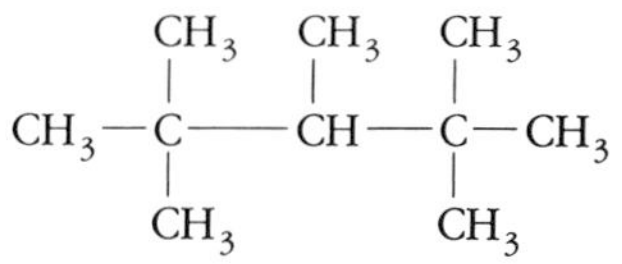

Remember that the carbon atoms which form the longest chain are not necessarily shown in a straight chain.

9. Draw the condensed formula for each of the following:
   a) 5-isopropylnonane
   b) 3,4-diethylhexane
   c) 2,2,3-trimethylpentane
   d) 1,4-diethylcyclohexane

Some Properties of Alkanes

14.8

From Table 14.3 we can see that each member of the alkane series differs from the one above or below it in the table by one CH_2 unit. A series of compounds of this type is known as a **homologous** series. In general, as we ascend a homologous series (that is, as the molar mass of the compounds increases), we find an increase in boiling points. Figure 14.13 illustrates this trend for the alkanes. As we shall soon see, this trend is used to advantage in the petrochemical industry.

Compounds that are isomeric, i.e., that have the same molecular formula but different structures, naturally have identical molar masses. However, their boiling points can be quite different. In the alkane series, branched-chain compounds generally have lower boiling points than their straight-chained isomers. Unfortunately this phenomenon cannot be explained within the scope of this text.

Instead, let us now look at some of the properties of three of the first four members of the alkane series: methane, propane, and butane. You may already be familiar with some of the commercial uses of these compounds.

Methane is the simplest member of the alkane family. It is a gas at room temperature, condenses to a liquid at $-164\,°C$, and solidifies at $-182\,°C$. One of the major components of natural gas, methane is also produced in marshy areas by decaying vegetation. This explains why methane is sometimes called *marsh gas*. The flickering lights occasionally seen over swamps are a result of the combustion of methane and may account for a number of reported UFO sightings. The combustion of methane is an exothermic process, which accounts for its use as a source of energy for home heating:

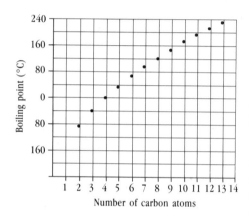

Figure 14.13

A graph of boiling point versus number of carbon atoms for the straight-chain alkanes.

Figure 14.14

Propane is a less expensive fuel than gasoline for motor vehicles. Maintenance costs are also lower.

$$CH_{4 (g)} + 2 O_{2 (g)} \longrightarrow CO_{2 (g)} + 2 H_2O_{(g)} \qquad \Delta H = -890\,kJ$$

In industry, methane is used in the production of the four chlorinated methanes, CH_3Cl, CH_2Cl_2, $CHCl_3$, and CCl_4. These compounds will be discussed in Chapter 15.

Propane is another gaseous alkane; it condenses to a liquid at $-44\,°C$ and solidifies at $-190\,°C$. Propane is often used as the fuel for Bunsen burners in the laboratory, in "gas" barbecues, and in a variety of home-heating devices. Of increasing importance is the use of propane as an inexpensive fuel for modified gasoline engines in commercial fleets of motor vehicles such as taxis.

Butane is used extensively as a fuel for cigarette lighters. Like propane, it is a gas at room temperature and normal atmospheric pressure. Its boiling point is $-0.5\,°C$.

Petroleum 14.9

The processes involved in the formation of crude petroleum began billions of years ago. They started with the decomposition of marine organisms to form a layer of organic material on the bottom of the oceans. Earth movements resulted in the application of pressure and heat over millions of years to this layer and produced the complex mixture of hydrocarbons that we call crude oil or petroleum. Coal results from a similar process involving plant material.

Figure 14.15

A modern oil refinery. The three tall towers in the centre are distillation towers in which the crude oil is separated into components with different boiling ranges.

Crude petroleum is perhaps the world's most important source of organic chemicals. It is also an important source of energy. The world's major oil-producing areas include the Middle East, Mexico, Texas, Venezuela, Alberta, Nigeria and the North Sea.

In general, petroleum is a homogeneous mixture of hydrocarbons. The exact composition depends on the source. As petroleum is derived from living material, small quantities of sulfur and inorganic salts may also be present. The hydrocarbons present include alkanes and cycloalkanes (also called paraffins and naphthenes) and aromatics (benzene and its homologues, also known as the asphalts). Many different compounds of each class may be present in a deposit of crude petroleum. Crude petroleum is often classified by its main components: oil from Iran tends to be paraffinic and that from California is mainly asphaltic. Mexican crude contains about equal amounts of paraffins and asphalts and has a high sulfur content. To effect a partial separation of the components of crude petroleum, a process known as **fractionation** is used (Figure 14.16).

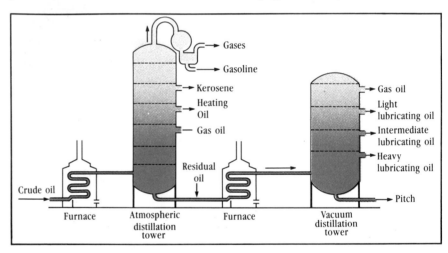

Figure 14.16
The fractionation of crude petroleum.

The crude petroleum is pumped through pipes into a furnace where it is heated to about 350 °C. The resulting mixture of gases and liquids is passed to a distillation tower. The gases are cooled as they rise and condense on trays at different levels in the tower. The layers or fractions of liquid on the trays are then drawn off. The separate fractions contain a variety of different compounds with boiling points in the same range as the temperature of the distillation tower at that particular level.

Any material that does not vaporize in the first tower is passed to a second tower, which is operated at a reduced pressure and is called a vacuum distillation tower. Here, because of the reduced pressure, the material boils at a lower temperature (Section 11.13). Thus, many of the compounds that remained as liquids in the first tower are vaporized and separated into additional fractions. Any material that does not vaporize in the second tower is used in asphalt.

The fractions obtained from the distillation process consist of mixtures of compounds rather than pure compounds. Isolation of the individual compounds is not necessary for most commercial uses.

TABLE 14.6 *Some Common Petroleum Products*

Product	Main alkane component	Boiling range (°C)	Phase at room temperature
Natural gas	CH_4	Below 0°	gas
Propane	C_3H_8	Below 0°	gas
Butane	C_4H_{10}	Below 0°	gas
Gasoline	C_5H_{12} to $C_{10}H_{22}$	35° to 175°	liquid
Kerosene, jet fuel	$C_{10}H_{22}$ to $C_{18}H_{38}$	175° to 275°	liquid
Diesel fuel	$C_{12}H_{26}$ to $C_{20}H_{42}$	190° to 330°	liquid
Fuel oil	$C_{14}H_{30}$ to $C_{22}H_{46}$	230° to 360°	liquid
Lubricating oil	$C_{20}H_{42}$ to $C_{30}H_{62}$	Above 350°	liquid
Petroleum jelly	$C_{22}H_{46}$ to $C_{40}H_{82}$	mp 40° to 60°	semisolid
Paraffin wax	$C_{25}H_{52}$ to $C_{50}H_{102}$	mp 50° to 65°	solid

Gasoline

The internal-combustion engine is one of the best-known devices used to release chemical energy from petroleum. Fuel shortages and the demand by consumers for good performance from smaller engines have encouraged automobile designers to produce engines with increased engine compression ratios and thus better power output.

The compression ratio of an engine is the ratio of the volume of gas in the cylinder at the bottom of the piston downstroke to the volume of the gas in the cylinder at the end of the upstroke. To deliver maximum power, the fuel mixture must not ignite prematurely in the middle of a stroke. Premature ignition (known as engine knock) often results from using a poor grade of gasoline in an engine with a high compression ratio.

Gasoline is graded according to a system, known as the **octane rating**, that was developed in 1928. Isooctane (IUPAC name, 2,2,4-trimethylpentane) was found to be the best alkane for use in internal-combustion engines of that time, and was given an octane rating of 100. Heptane, on the other hand, was given a rating of 0. Mixtures of these two compounds were tested and given an efficiency rating equal to the percentage (by volume) of isooctane present in the mixture. Various gasoline samples were then tested, and each was given a rating equal to that of the isooctane–heptane mixture with a comparable performance. It was found that gasoline samples containing a high proportion of branched-chain alkanes gave the highest octane ratings and therefore the best engine performance.

The gasoline fraction of refined petroleum contains a high percentage of straight-chain alkanes and therefore has a low octane rating. Scientists have developed several methods for increasing the octane rating of this fraction and improving its performance as a fuel for the internal-combustion engine. The first of these methods was the use of additives, the most effective of which was tetraethyl lead, $Pb(CH_2CH_3)_4$. Addition of small amounts of tetraethyl lead could raise the octane rating of gasoline by 10 to 40%. Concern about the health problems related to lead poisoning has resulted in a decrease in the use of leaded gasoline in recent years.

Cracking is the name given to the process in which long-chain alkane molecules, which are unsuitable for use in internal-combustion engines, are broken down into alkanes and alkenes with lower molecular masses. Cracking was originally developed to provide additional (but not necessarily better) gasoline from each barrel of crude petroleum.

Reforming is a process in which gasoline fractions containing large proportions of straight-chain alkanes are passed through beds of inorganic catalysts such as aluminum chloride ($AlCl_3$) and antimony(III) chloride ($SbCl_3$). The straight-chain molecules undergo rearrangement to yield branched molecules with higher octane ratings. For example, hexane (octane number 26) can be reformed to a mixture of branched-chain hydrocarbons with an octane rating of about 80. Most of the high-octane fuels sold today are prepared by this method. It is possible, therefore, to obtain a high-performance fuel without resorting to the addition of tetraethyl lead. It is interesting to note that most of today's cars would not run on the best gasoline that was available 30 years ago.

Alkenes   *14.10*

Figure 14.17
a) Electron-dot formula of ethene
b) Structural formula of ethene

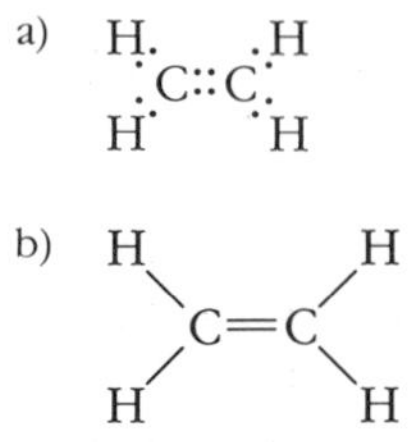

a)   H. .H
   .C::C.
    H. .H

b)   H   H
      \   /
       C=C
      /   \
     H   H

Unsaturated hydrocarbons contain double or triple bonds. Alkenes, which have carbon–carbon double bonds consisting of four electrons shared between two carbon atoms, are unsaturated hydrocarbons. In a molecule of ethene, all the bond angles are 120° (Figure 14.18) and all the atoms are in the same plane. In other words, ethene is an example of a **planar molecule**.

To name an alkene using the IUPAC system, we start by counting the number of carbon atoms in the longest continuous carbon chain *containing the double bond*. The first part of the name is the same as that of the equivalent alkane, but the ending changes from *-ane* to *-ene*. We indicate the position of the double bond by placing the number of the first carbon atom in the double bond before the name, and separating the number from the name with a hyphen. Thus the name of the compound CH_3—CH=CH—CH_3 is 2-butene.

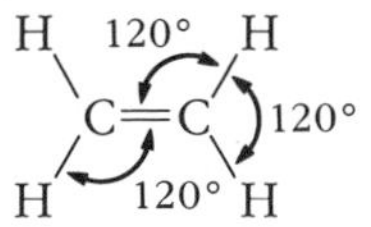

Figure 14.18
The geometry of the ethene molecule.

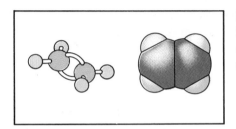

Figure 14.19
The shape of the ethene molecule
a) as a ball-and-stick model
b) as a space-filling model

EXAMPLE   14.7   Name each of the following according to the IUPAC system.

a)

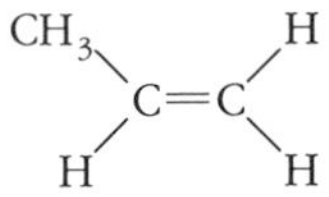

$$CH_3 \diagdown \quad \diagup H$$
$$C=C$$
$$H \diagup \quad \diagdown H$$

b)

$$CH_3 \diagdown \quad \diagup CH_2-CH_3$$
$$C=C$$
$$H \diagup \quad \diagdown H$$

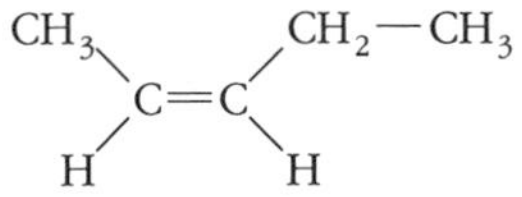

SOLUTION   a) There are three carbon atoms in the chain containing the double bond; therefore the name is **propene**. No number is necessary in this case because even if the double bond appeared to be in the other possible position we would still have the same compound.

b) The chain containing the double bond has five carbons; hence the base name is **pentene**. The double bond is between carbon atoms two and three if we count from the left, and between carbon atoms three and four if we count from the right. As we must use the lowest possible number, the correct name for this compound is **2-pentene**.

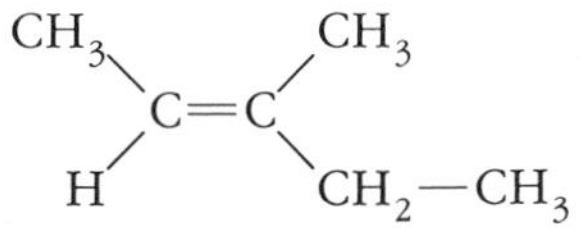

If there is a substituent present in an alkene, we deal with it in much the same way that we deal with a substituent in an alkane. However, we must remember that numbering the atoms in the carbon chains so that we can identify the position of the double bond takes top priority. Thus the chain is numbered so that the double bond gets the lowest possible number. This in turn determines the number of the carbon atom to which the substituent is attached. When writing the name of the compound, the name of the substituent precedes the number indicating the position of the double bond. The name of the substituent is separated from the number with a hyphen.

In the compound 3-methyl-2-pentene, the longest continuous carbon chain containing the double bond is five carbon atoms long. The base name is therefore **pentene**. The double bond is between carbon atoms two and three (counting from the left); hence we obtain the name **2-pentene**. Finally, there is a methyl substituent on carbon atom number three. Thus, the complete name is **3-methyl-2-pentene**.

The geometry of the double bond is such that the two carbon atoms forming the bond and the four atoms attached to those two carbons are all in the same plane. This gives rise to another type of isomerism called **geometric**, or **cis–trans isomerism**. Figure 14.20 shows the geometric

$$CH_3 \diagdown \quad \diagup CH_3$$
$$C=C$$
$$H \diagup \quad \diagdown CH_2-CH_3$$

3-methyl-2-pentene

Figure 14.20
Two isomers of 2-butene:
a) Cis-2-butene
b) Trans-2-butene

a)

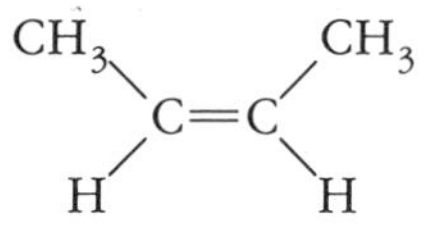

$$CH_3 \diagdown \quad \diagup CH_3$$
$$C=C$$
$$H \diagup \quad \diagdown H$$

b)

$$CH_3 \diagdown \quad \diagup H$$
$$C=C$$
$$H \diagup \quad \diagdown CH_3$$

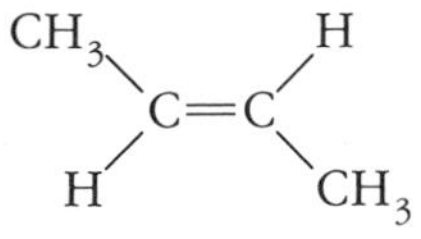

isomers of 2-butene. In the *cis–* isomer, the two methyl groups are on the same side of the line defined by the double bond, whereas in the *trans–* isomer, they are on opposite sides. Note that *cis–trans* isomerism *cannot* occur when one of the carbon atoms making up the double bond has two identical atoms or groups attached to it.

EXAMPLE **14.8** Does geometrical isomerism occur in either 1-butene or 2-pentene?

SOLUTION a) 1-butene has the structure

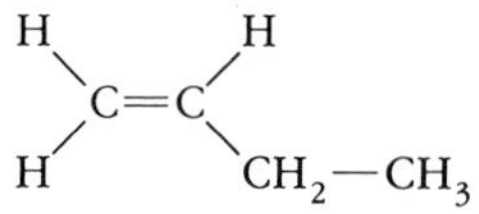

As one of the carbon atoms making up the double bond has two identical hydrogen atoms attached to it, geometrical isomerism does not occur.

b) The structure of 2-pentene is

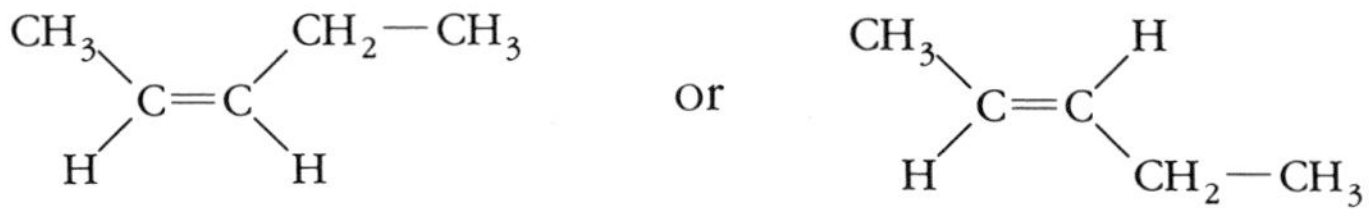

cis- isomer   *trans-* isomer

Here we see that geometrical isomerism does occur; each of the carbon atoms making up the double bond is attached to two different atoms or groups.

Alkenes are much more reactive than alkanes and undergo chemical reactions with a large variety of reagents. Many of these reactions are **addition reactions** that involve addition of a reagent to the carbon atoms joined by the double bond. Examples of two addition reactions are shown below:

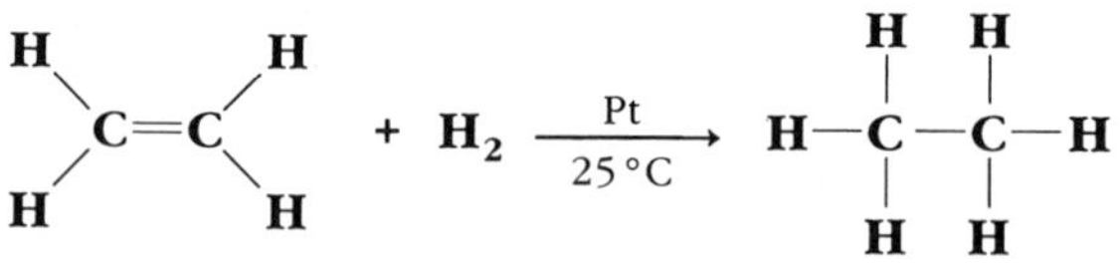

ethene   ethane

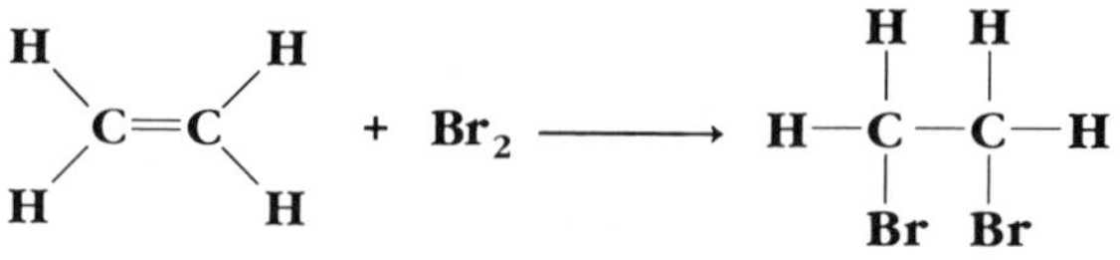

ethene   (dissolved   1,2-dibromoethane
                in CCl_4)

In these reactions, one mole of the reagent reacts with one mole of the alkene. These are typical reactions of alkenes; any alkene will react with hydrogen to give an alkane and, similarly, any alkene will react with bromine in carbon tetrachloride.

One of the major industrial uses of alkenes is in the production of **addition polymers**. A polymer is a large organic molecule made up of many small, identical units. Each unit is called a **monomer**. Many of the plastics that we use are addition polymers formed by the polymerization of alkenes. The **polymerization** reaction requires an **initiator**. This is a molecule that starts the reaction in which monomer units are added one by one to the original monomer. The formation of polythene (formerly called polyethylene) from ethene (formerly called ethylene) is an example:

$$n \ CH_2{=}CH_2 \xrightarrow[\substack{\text{high pressure} \\ \text{+ initiator}}]{\text{high temperature}} (-CH_2{-}CH_2{-})_n$$

$$\text{ethene} \qquad\qquad\qquad\qquad\qquad \text{polythene}$$

The formula of polythene is represented as $(-CH_2{-}CH_2{-})_n$, where n is a large number. Polythene is used to make items such as bottles and vapour barrier sheets.

QUESTIONS

10. Draw the condensed formula of each of the following alkenes:
   a) 2,4-dimethyl-3-heptene   b) 2,3-dimethyl-2-pentene

11. Does geometrical isomerism occur in 2,4-dimethyl-3-heptene and 2,3-dimethyl-2-pentene?

12. Write the equation for
   a) the reaction of propene with hydrogen at 25 °C in the presence of a platinum catalyst
   b) the reaction of propene with bromine in carbon tetrachloride

13. Write an equation to represent the polymerization of propene.

Alkynes

14.11

The alkyne family consists of compounds containing a carbon-carbon triple bond. Like alkenes, these compounds are unsaturated. The simplest member of this series, ethyne (common name, acetylene) is used to fuel oxy-acetylene welding torches. The ethyne molecule is an example of a **linear molecule**. All four atoms lie in a straight line. In general, in any alkyne the two carbon atoms and the two atoms to which they are attached will lie along a straight line. The bond angle in ethyne is 180°.

Figure 14.21
a) Electron-dot formula for ethyne
b) Structural formula for ethyne

a) H:C:::C:H

b) H—C≡C—H

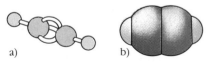

a)   b)

Figure 14.22
The shape of the ethyne molecule
a) as a ball-and-stick model
b) as a space-filling model

Large quantities of ethyne gas are produced annually by a process that uses two abundant and inexpensive raw materials: limestone and coal. The limestone ($CaCO_3$) is converted to calcium oxide (CaO) and the coal is converted to coke (C); these two substances then react to form calcium carbide (CaC_2):

$$CaO_{(s)} + 3\ C_{(s)} \longrightarrow CaC_{2\ (s)} + CO_{(g)}$$

The calcium carbide is then treated with water to give ethyne gas:

$$CaC_{2\ (s)} + 2\ H_2O_{(\ell)} \longrightarrow Ca(OH)_{2\ (s)} + C_2H_{2\ (g)}$$

The rules for naming alkynes are the same as those for alkenes except that the ending *-yne* is used. Note that alkynes cannot exhibit *cis–trans* isomerism because the carbon–carbon triple bond is linear, as shown below:

180°
H—C≡C—H
180°

EXAMPLE   14.9

In an examination, students were asked to name three compounds. One student provided the following *incorrect* IUPAC names:

a)
CH₃
|
CH₃—CH—C≡C—CH₃   2-methyl-3-pentyne

b)
CH₂—CH₃
|
CH₃—CH—C≡C—CH₃   4-ethyl-2-pentyne

c)
CH₃
|
CH₃—C≡C—CH₃   2-methyl-2-butyne

Provide the correct IUPAC names and explain.

SOLUTION

a) Here the correct name would be 4-methyl-2-pentyne. The position of the triple bond must be indicated by the lowest possible number. We must number the carbon atoms from the right.

b) The correct name is 4-methyl-2-hexyne. The longest continuous carbon chain containing the triple bond had not been selected.

c) This structure is incorrect because carbon can form a maximum of only four bonds (i.e. have eight electrons around it). Here there are five bonds shown for one carbon atom. The student failed to check the validity of the structure shown. (Obviously a trick question.)

Ethyne is used in oxyacetylene torches because it burns in oxygen with a very hot flame. The products of the reaction, carbon dioxide and water, are also products of any reaction in which a hydrocarbon is burned in sufficient oxygen (carbon monoxide will be produced if insufficient oxygen is used):

$$2 C_2H_{2\ (g)} + 5 O_{2\ (g)} \longrightarrow 4 CO_{2\ (g)} + 2 H_2O_{(g)}$$

Like alkenes, alkynes undergo addition reactions; however two moles of reagent can be added to one mole of alkyne, whereas only one mole of reagent can be added to one mole of alkene (Section 14.10). Two examples of additions to ethyne are given below:

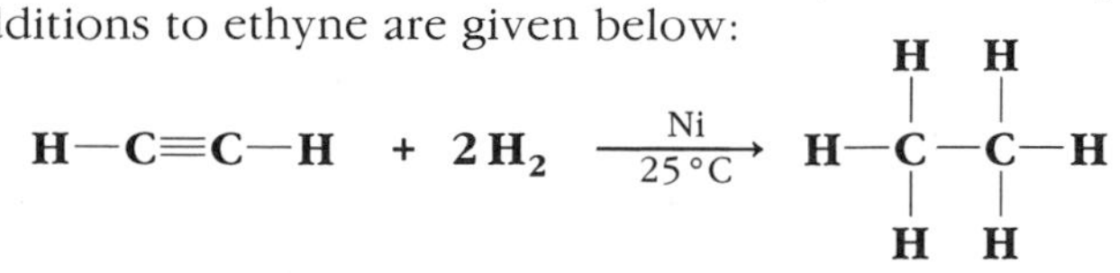

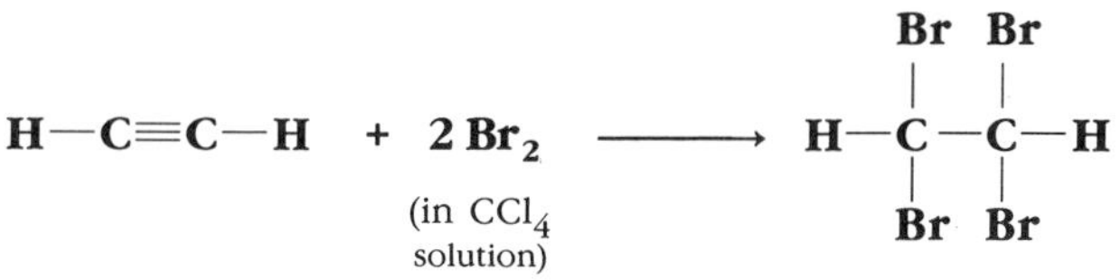

$$H-C\equiv C-H + 2 H_2 \xrightarrow[25\,°C]{Ni} H-\underset{\underset{H}{|}}{\overset{\overset{H}{|}}{C}}-\underset{\underset{H}{|}}{\overset{\overset{H}{|}}{C}}-H$$

$$H-C\equiv C-H + 2 Br_2 \longrightarrow H-\underset{\underset{Br}{|}}{\overset{\overset{Br}{|}}{C}}-\underset{\underset{Br}{|}}{\overset{\overset{Br}{|}}{C}}-H$$

(in CCl$_4$ solution)

QUESTIONS

14. Name the following alkynes according to the IUPAC system:

a) $CH_3-CH_2-C\equiv C-CH_3$

b) 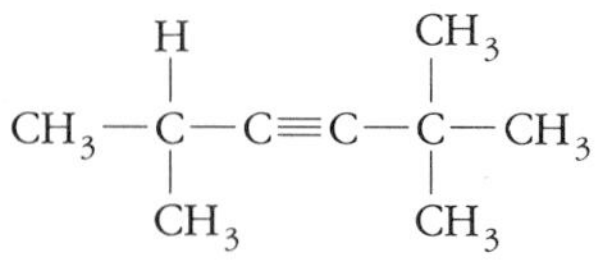 $CH_3-\underset{\underset{CH_3}{|}}{\overset{\overset{H}{|}}{C}}-C\equiv C-\underset{\underset{CH_3}{|}}{\overset{\overset{CH_3}{|}}{C}}-CH_3$

15. Draw the structure of each of the following compounds:
   a) 2-butyne   b) 3,3-dimethyl-1-pentyne

16. Write the equation for the reaction of 1-butyne with
   a) excess hydrogen in the presence of a nickel catalyst
   b) excess bromine in carbon tetrachloride

Aromatic Hydrocarbons

14.12

We mentioned in Section 14.6 that the word "aromatic" was originally used for hydrocarbon compounds with fragrant aromas. Johann Joseph Loschmidt, in 1861, was the first to point out that many of the compounds in this class could be considered as derivatives of the compound benzene. Since then, compounds with the same characteristic chemical properties as benzene have been called aromatic compounds.

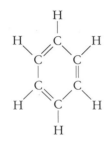

Figure 14.23
A proposal for the structure of benzene.

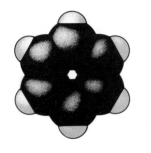

Figure 14.24
The shape of the benzene molecule
a) as a ball-and-stick model
b) as a space-filling molecule

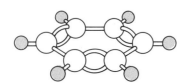

toluene

Let us look at the structure of benzene, which has the formula C_6H_6. Under fairly extreme conditions, one mole of benzene will react with three moles of hydrogen to produce cyclohexane. This suggests that benzene consists of six carbons in a ring and that it may contain three double bonds, or a double bond and a triple bond. Molecular models suggest that the strain resulting from having a double and a triple bond in a six-membered ring would be very great. Thus, the structure shown in Figure 14.23 might be proposed.

This structure, which was first proposed by Friedrich August Kekulé in 1865, is often referred to as the Kekulé structure of benzene. However, it does not account for all the properties of benzene. For example, benzene does not readily undergo the addition reactions that would be expected of this type of molecule. Also, recent experiments have shown that the carbon–carbon bond lengths in benzene are all the same: longer than normal carbon–carbon double bonds but shorter than normal carbon–carbon single bonds.

In light of these facts, rather than draw benzene as shown in Figure 14.23, we normally use one of the representations shown below. The regular hexagon represents six carbon atoms joined in a ring and the circle inside the ring conveys the aromatic nature of the molecule (i.e. unsaturated but not containing normal double or triple bonds). This ring structure is known as the **benzene ring**. We shall therefore define aromatic compounds as compounds containing a benzene ring.

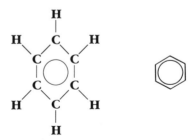

The ball-and-stick model of benzene has to show alternating double and single bonds (we cannot make half bonds). Thus the space-filling model gives a much more realistic image of the benzene molecule. Notice that the benzene molecule is completely planar.

Some other aromatic hydrocarbons are toluene, which is used as a solvent, and naphthalene, which is used as a moth repellant. The compound 3,4-benzopyrene is a carcinogen (cancer-causing compound) present in cigarette smoke and charcoal-broiled meat. The names of these compounds end in *-ene*. Do not confuse the names of aromatic compounds ending in *-ene* with alkenes.

The chemistry of aromatic compounds is dictated by their ability to undergo **substitution** (rather than addition) **reactions**. For example, ben-

naphthalene

3,4-benzopyrene

zene reacts with bromine in the presence of a suitable catalyst to produce the compound bromobenzene, in which one of the hydrogen atoms originally present in the benzene is replaced by a bromine atom:

$$\text{benzene} + Br_2 \xrightarrow{Fe} \text{bromobenzene} + HBr$$

This substitution reaction is strong evidence for the stability of the benzene ring. If you refer to the reaction of an alkene with bromine (Section 14.10), you will note that a normal carbon–carbon double bond undergoes an addition reaction rather than a substitution reaction.

QUESTIONS

17. Draw the structures of the four isomeric aromatic compounds with the formula C_8H_{10}.

Review of the IUPAC Naming System for Hydrocarbons

14.13

To conclude this chapter, we will summarize the rules for naming hydrocarbons. A key feature in the naming system is the use of Greek prefixes to indicate the number of carbon atoms in the longest continuous carbon chain in the compound (Table 14.1).

Alkanes

STRAIGHT-CHAIN ALKANES

The prefix indicating the number of carbon atoms is followed by the ending *-ane*. For example, CH_4 is methane and $CH_3—CH_2—CH_2—CH_2—CH_3$ is pentane.

BRANCHED-CHAIN ALKANES

a) The chain with the highest number of carbon atoms is used to derive the base name. As with straight-chain compounds, the Greek prefix and the ending *-ane* are used.

b) The name of the substituent is obtained by adding *-yl* to the Greek prefix for the number of carbon atoms in the side chain.

c) The number of the carbon atom to which the substituent is attached is indicated by a numerical prefix.

d) The atoms in the main chain are numbered so that the lowest possible number for the position of the substituent is obtained.

For example, the compound

$$CH_3—CH_2—CH_2—CH—CH_3$$
$$\underset{\displaystyle CH_3}{|}$$

is called 2-methylpentane rather than 4-methylpentane. If the compound contains more than one identical substituent the number of substituents is indicated by the prefixes *di-*, *tri-*, *tetra-*, *penta-*, *hexa-*, etc., (Table 14.4):

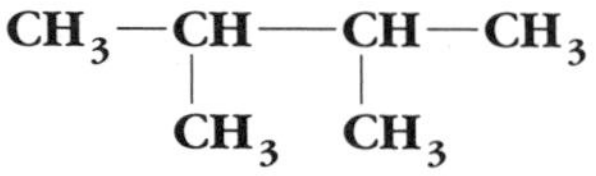

$$CH_3-CH-CH-CH_3$$
$$\quad\;\; CH_3 \;\; CH_3$$

2,3-dimethylbutane

$$\qquad\quad CH_3$$
$$CH_3-C-CH_2-CH_3$$
$$\qquad\quad CH_3$$

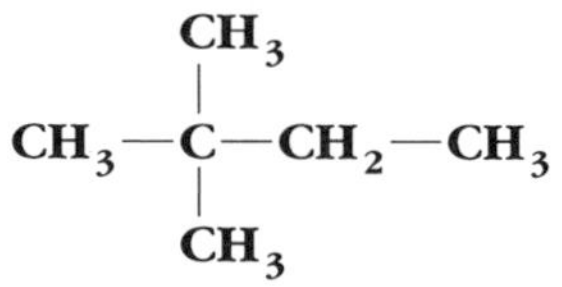

2,2-dimethylbutane

Alkenes

The rules for naming alkenes are the same as those for alkanes with the following modifications:

a) The longest chain containing the double bond is used as the base name.

b) The ending *-ene* is used instead of *-ane*. This indicates that a double bond is present. For example, $CH_2=CH_2$ is ethene.

c) The carbon atoms in the longest chain containing the double bond are numbered, starting at whichever end of the molecule results in the first carbon in the double bond having the lowest number. This number forms part of the compound's name and is used to indicate the position of the double bond. Thus, $CH_2=CH-CH_2-CH_3$ is 1-butene (not 3-butene), while $CH_3-CH=CH-CH_3$ is 2-butene.

d) Substituents are identified using the same names that are used when naming alkanes. The position of the substituent is again identified using the number of the carbon atom to which it is attached, this number having been determined by the numbering process detailed in Step c. Thus

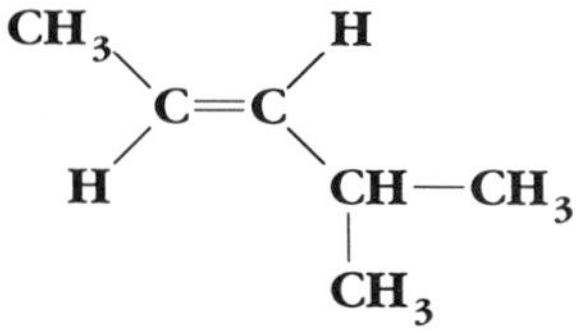

$$CH_3 \qquad\qquad H$$
$$\quad\;\; C=C$$
$$H \qquad\qquad CH-CH_3$$
$$\qquad\qquad\quad CH_3$$

is called 4-methyl-2-pentene (not 2-methyl-3-pentene).

Alkynes

The rules for naming alkynes are the same as those for alkenes, except that the ending *-yne* is used instead of *-ene*:

$$HC\equiv C-CH_2-CH_3$$

1-butyne

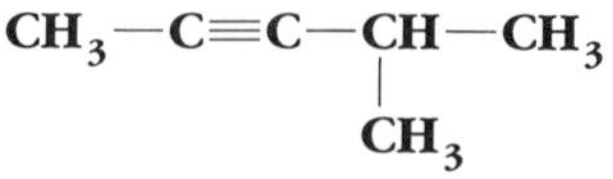

$$CH_3-C\equiv C-CH-CH_3$$
$$\qquad\qquad\qquad CH_3$$

4-methyl-2-pentyne

Summary

- Organic chemistry is the study of the compounds of carbon.

- Organic compounds are generally covalent and have lower melting and boiling points than most inorganic compounds. In pure form or in aqueous solution most organic compounds do not conduct electricity.

- The large number of known organic compounds is due to the ability of carbon to undergo catenation.

- Structural isomers have the same molecular formula but different structural formulas.

- Organic compounds are classified according to the functional group which is present. The functional group largely determines the properties of a compound.

- Hydrocarbons contain only carbon and hydrogen. They can be classified as aliphatic or aromatic. Aliphatic hydrocarbons can be further subdivided into alkanes, alkenes, and alkynes.

- The IUPAC system is used for naming organic compounds. In this system a compound's name is based on the length of the longest carbon chain. Numbers are used to indicate the positions of substituents and functional groups.

- Within any class of organic compounds, the boiling point increases with increasing molar mass.

- Crude oil is an important source of hydrocarbons. Hydrocarbon fuels are obtained from oil by fractionation and reforming.

- Geometric (*cis–trans*) isomerism can occur in certain alkenes, but not in alkanes or alkynes.

- Alkenes and alkynes are unsaturated and are more reactive than alkanes. They undergo addition reactions across the double or triple bond.

- An important industrial use of alkenes is in the production of polymers (plastics).

- Aromatic hydrocarbons contain a benzene ring. They undergo substitution reactions rather than addition reactions.

KEY WORDS

addition polymer	initiator
addition reaction	isomers
alcohol	IUPAC system
aliphatic	linear molecule
alkane	methyl group

alkene

alkyl group

alkyne

aromatic

ball-and-stick model

benzene ring

branched-chain compound

combustion reaction

common name

condensed formula

cracking

cyclic hydrocarbon

fractionation

functional group

geometric (*cis–trans*) isomerism

homologous series

hydrocarbon

monomer

octane rating

planar molecule

polymerization

reforming

saturated compound

side chain

space-filling model

straight-chain compound

structural formula

structural isomer

substituent

substitution reaction

systematic name

tetrahedral

trivial name

unsaturated hydrocarbon

ANSWERS TO SECTION QUESTIONS

1.

a)
$$H-\underset{\underset{H}{|}}{\overset{\overset{H}{|}}{C}}-\underset{\underset{H}{|}}{\overset{\overset{H}{|}}{C}}-H$$

b)
$$H-\underset{\underset{H}{|}}{\overset{\overset{H}{|}}{C}}-\underset{\underset{H}{|}}{\overset{\overset{H}{|}}{C}}-\underset{\underset{H}{|}}{\overset{\overset{H}{|}}{C}}-H$$

c)
$$H-\underset{\underset{H}{|}}{\overset{\overset{H}{|}}{C}}-\underset{\underset{H}{|}}{\overset{\overset{H}{|}}{C}}-\underset{\underset{H}{|}}{\overset{\overset{H}{|}}{C}}-\underset{\underset{H}{|}}{\overset{\overset{H}{|}}{C}}-H$$

2. a) CH_3-CH_3 b) $CH_3-CH_2-CH_3$ c) $CH_3-CH_2-CH_2-CH_3$

3. a)
$$CH_3-\underset{\underset{CH_3}{|}}{\overset{\overset{CH_3}{|}}{C}}-\underset{\underset{CH_3}{|}}{\overset{\overset{CH_3}{|}}{C}}-CH_3$$

b)
$$CH_3-\underset{\underset{CH_3}{|}}{\overset{}{CH}}-\underset{\underset{}{}}{\overset{\overset{CH_3}{|}}{CH}}-\underset{\underset{CH_3}{|}}{\overset{\overset{CH_3}{|}}{CH}}$$
or
$$CH_3-\underset{\underset{CH_3}{|}}{\overset{}{CH}}-\underset{\underset{}{}}{\overset{\overset{CH_3}{|}}{CH}}-\underset{\underset{}{}}{\overset{\overset{CH_3}{|}}{CH}}-CH_3$$

4. a)
$$H-\underset{\underset{H}{|}}{\overset{\overset{H}{|}}{C}}-\underset{\underset{H}{|}}{\overset{\overset{H}{|}}{C}}-\underset{\underset{H}{|}}{\overset{\overset{H}{|}}{C}}-\underset{\underset{H}{|}}{\overset{\overset{H}{|}}{C}}-\underset{\underset{H}{|}}{\overset{\overset{H}{|}}{C}}-H$$

b)

```
        H         H        H   H
        |         |        |   |
  H —  C   ——   C   ——   C — C — H
        |         |        |   |
        H       H—C—H      H   H
                  |
                  H
```

c)

```
                    H
                    |
        H       H—C—H   H
        |         |     |
  H —  C   ——    C   —— C — H
        |         |     |
        H       H—C—H   H
                  |
                  H
```

5. d

6.

```
        H   H   H   H   H   H
        |   |   |   |   |   |
  H —  C — C — C — C — C — C — H
        |   |   |   |   |   |
        H   H   H   H   H   H
```

```
        H         H        H   H   H
        |         |        |   |   |
  H —  C   ——   C   ——   C — C — C — H
        |         |        |   |   |
        H       H—C—H      H   H   H
                  |
                  H
```

```
        H   H         H        H   H
        |   |         |        |   |
  H —  C — C   ——    C   ——   C — C — H
        |   |         |        |   |
        H   H       H—C—H      H   H
                      |
                      H
```

```
                            H
                            |
        H         H       H—C—H   H
        |         |         |     |
  H —  C   ——    C   ——    C   —— C — H
        |         |         |     |
        H       H—C—H             H
                  |
                  H
```

```
                  H
                  |
        H       H—C—H   H   H
        |         |     |   |
  H —  C   ——    C   —— C — C — H
        |         |     |   |
        H       H—C—H   H   H
                  |
                  H
```

7. a) alkane   d) alkene
   b) alkyne   e) alkene
   c) alkane   f) alkane

8. a) 3-methylhexane
   b) 2,4-dimethylhexane
   c) 1,3-dimethylcyclopentane
   d) 2,2,3,4,4-pentamethylpentane

9. a) 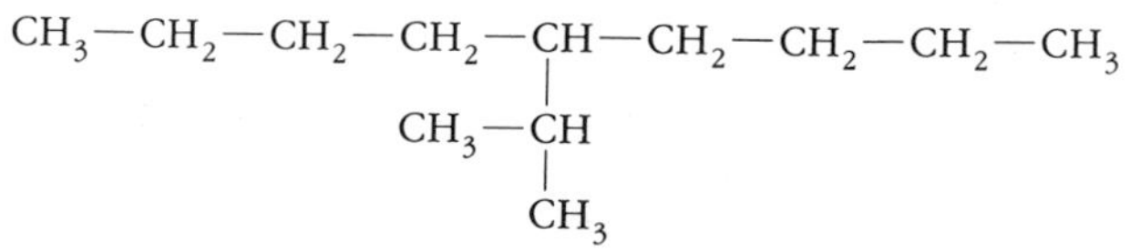 $CH_3-CH_2-CH_2-CH_2-CH-CH_2-CH_2-CH_2-CH_3$
$\qquad\qquad\qquad\qquad\quad\; CH_3-CH$
$\qquad\qquad\qquad\qquad\qquad\qquad\; CH_3$

b) 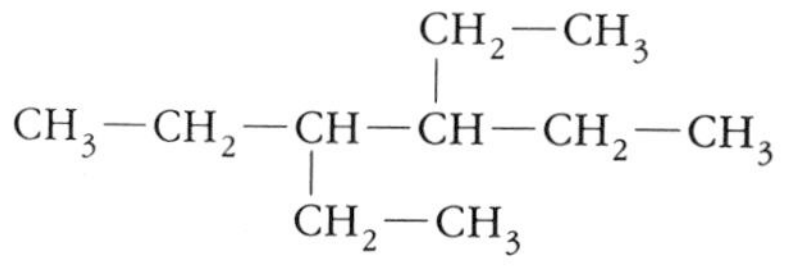 $CH_3-CH_2-CH-CH-CH_2-CH_3$
$\qquad\qquad\qquad\quad |\qquad\; CH_2-CH_3$
$\qquad\qquad\qquad\; CH_2-CH_3$

with CH_2-CH_3 above the CH.

c) 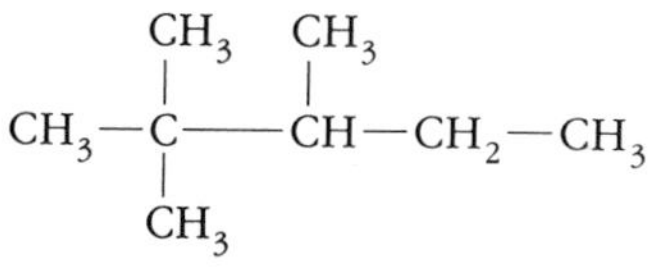
$\qquad\quad CH_3\quad CH_3$
$CH_3-C\;\;\;\;\;-CH-CH_2-CH_3$
$\qquad\quad CH_3$

d) 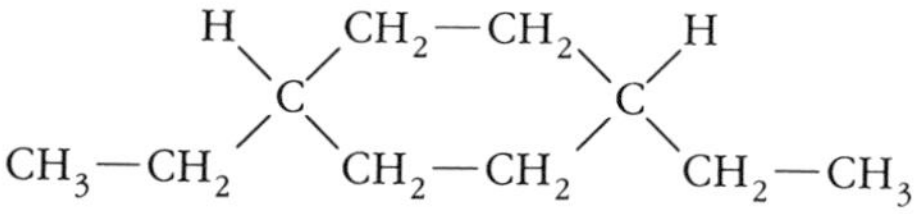 CH_3-CH_2 ... H, CH_2-CH_2, H ... CH_2-CH_3

10. a) 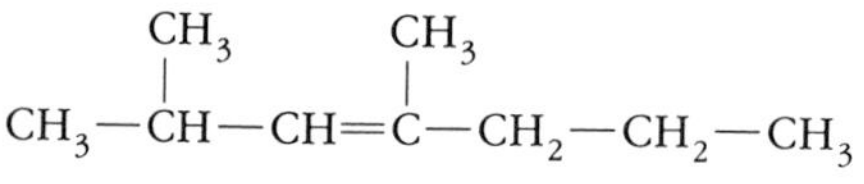
$\qquad\qquad CH_3\qquad\quad CH_3$
$CH_3-CH-CH=C-CH_2-CH_2-CH_3$

b) 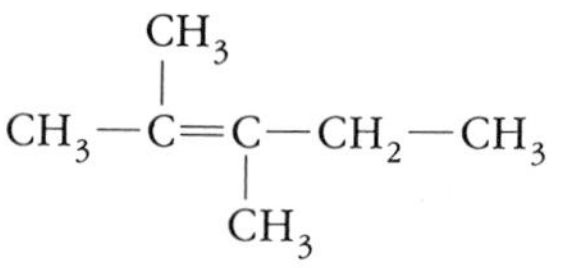
$\qquad\qquad CH_3$
$CH_3-C=C-CH_2-CH_3$
$\qquad\qquad CH_3$

11. Geometrical isomerism occurs in 2,4-dimethyl-3-heptane, but not in 2,3-dimethyl-2-pentene.

12. a) 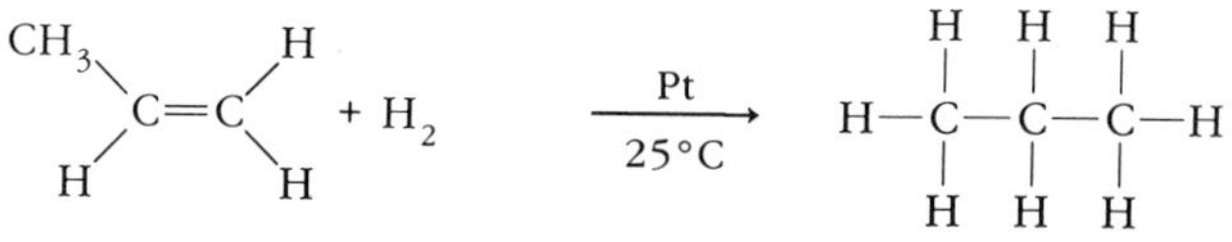 CH_3, H : $C=C$: H, H $+ H_2 \xrightarrow[25°C]{Pt}$ $H-C-C-C-H$ (with H H H above and H H H below)

b)  CH_3, H : $C=C$: H, H $+ Br_2 \longrightarrow$ $H-C-C-C-H$ (with H H H above and H Br Br below)

13. 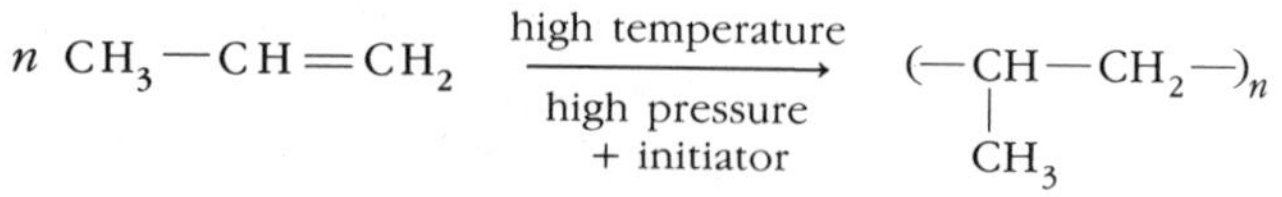 $n\; CH_3-CH=CH_2 \xrightarrow[\substack{\text{high pressure} \\ + \text{ initiator}}]{\text{high temperature}} (-CH-CH_2-)_n$ with CH_3 below the CH.

14. a) 2-pentyne   b) 2,2,5-trimethyl-3-hexyne

15. a) $CH_3-C{\equiv}C-CH_3$ b) $HC{\equiv}C-\overset{\overset{\displaystyle CH_3}{|}}{\underset{\underset{\displaystyle CH_3}{|}}{C}}-CH_2-CH_3$

16. a) $H-C{\equiv}C-\overset{\overset{\displaystyle H}{|}}{\underset{\underset{\displaystyle H}{|}}{C}}-\overset{\overset{\displaystyle H}{|}}{\underset{\underset{\displaystyle H}{|}}{C}}-H \; + \; 2\,H_2 \quad \xrightarrow[25\,°C]{Ni} \quad H-\overset{\overset{\displaystyle H}{|}}{\underset{\underset{\displaystyle H}{|}}{C}}-\overset{\overset{\displaystyle H}{|}}{\underset{\underset{\displaystyle H}{|}}{C}}--\overset{\overset{\displaystyle H}{|}}{\underset{\underset{\displaystyle H}{|}}{C}}-\overset{\overset{\displaystyle H}{|}}{\underset{\underset{\displaystyle H}{|}}{C}}-H$

b) $H-C{\equiv}C-\overset{\overset{\displaystyle H}{|}}{\underset{\underset{\displaystyle H}{|}}{C}}-\overset{\overset{\displaystyle H}{|}}{\underset{\underset{\displaystyle H}{|}}{C}}-H \; + \; 2\,Br_2 \quad \longrightarrow \quad H-\overset{\overset{\displaystyle Br}{|}}{\underset{\underset{\displaystyle Br}{|}}{C}}-\overset{\overset{\displaystyle Br}{|}}{\underset{\underset{\displaystyle Br}{|}}{C}}-\overset{\overset{\displaystyle H}{|}}{\underset{\underset{\displaystyle H}{|}}{C}}-\overset{\overset{\displaystyle H}{|}}{\underset{\underset{\displaystyle H}{|}}{C}}-H$

17.

COMPREHENSION QUESTIONS

1. What carbon-containing compounds are not generally considered to be organic compounds?
2. How do the properties of organic compounds differ from those of inorganic compounds?
3. Explain briefly what is meant by each of the following terms:
   a) hydrocarbon   d) functional group
   b) catenation   e) aliphatic
   c) aromatic
4. Explain the difference between each of the following:
   a) structural isomers and geometrical isomers
   b) saturated compounds and unsaturated compounds
   c) structural formulas and condensed formulas
   d) addition reactions and substitution reactions
   e) straight-chain hydrocarbons and branched-chain hydrocarbons
5. What are the bond angles around a carbon atom that is bonded to the following:
   a) four atoms   b) three atoms   c) two atoms
6. What is the major problem associated with representing organic compounds by two-dimensional structural formulas?

7. Describe two ways in which the octane rating of gasoline can be increased.

8. What is meant by each of the following terms:
   a) fractionation   b) cracking   c) reforming

9. What is the difference between an alkane and an alkyl group?

10. How are the boiling points of a homologous series of organic compounds related?

11. What is a polymer? Give an example.

12. How do the addition reactions of alkynes differ from the addition reactions of alkenes?

13. Describe the structure of the benzene molecule.

14. What evidence suggests that carbon–carbon double bonds are not present in the benzene molecule?

PROBLEMS 15. Compound A melts at 801 °C and is very soluble in water, whereas compound B melts at 24 °C and is insoluble in water. Which of these two compounds is most likely to be organic?

16. If organic and inorganic compounds were known from the time of the alchemists, why is Wöhler often referred to as the father or organic chemistry?

17. Pair up those formulas below which represent the same compound:

   a) $CH_3-CH_2-CH_2-CH_2-CH_3$

   e) $CH_3-CH-CH_2-CH_2-CH_3$
      $\quad\quad\quad |$
      $\quad\quad\quad CH_3$

   b) $CH_3-CH_2-CH-CH_3$
      $\quad\quad\quad\quad\quad |$
      $\quad\quad\quad\quad\quad CH_3$

   f) $CH_3-CH_2-CH_2-CH-CH_2-CH_3$
      $\quad\quad\quad\quad\quad\quad\quad\quad\quad |$
      $\quad\quad\quad\quad\quad\quad\quad\quad\quad CH_3$

   c) $CH_2-CH_2-CH_2-CH_3$
      $\,|$
      CH_3

   g) $CH_3-CH_2-CH_2-CH-CH_3$
      $\quad\quad\quad\quad\quad\quad\quad\quad |$
      $\quad\quad\quad\quad\quad\quad\quad\quad CH_2-CH_3$

   $\quad\quad\quad CH_3$
   $\quad\quad\quad |$
   d) $CH_3-CH-CH_2-CH_3$

18. Write the condensed formula for each possible structural isomer of
   a) C_4H_{10} b) C_6H_{14} c) C_7H_{16}
   Hint: there are two isomers of a), five of b), and nine of c)

19. Give the IUPAC name for each of the following alkanes:

a) 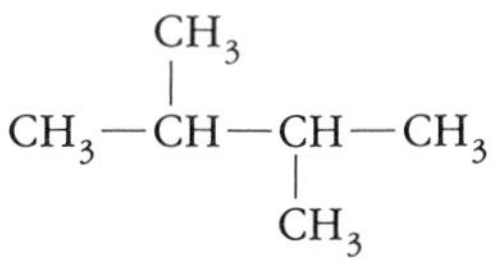
$$CH_3-CH-CH-CH_3$$
with CH_3 above the second carbon and CH_3 below the third carbon

a)
$$\overset{\displaystyle CH_3}{\underset{\displaystyle CH_3}{CH_3-CH-CH-CH_3}}$$

b) 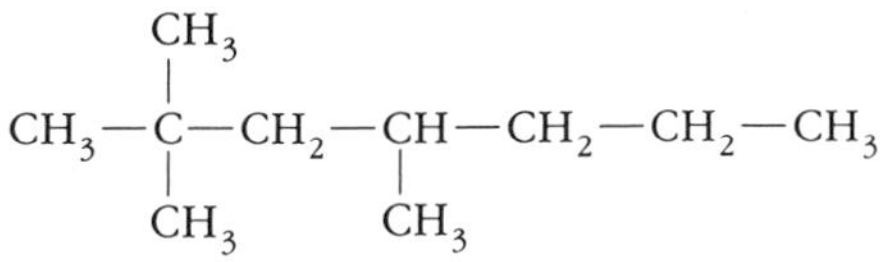
$$\overset{\displaystyle CH_3}{CH_3-\underset{\displaystyle CH_3}{C}-CH_2-\underset{\displaystyle CH_3}{CH}-CH_2-CH_2-CH_3}$$

c)
$$CH_2-CH-CH_3$$
$$|\qquad|$$
$$CH_2-CH_2$$

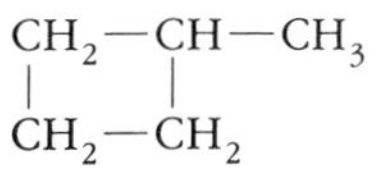

d) 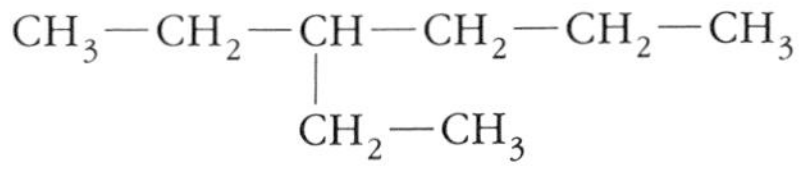
$$CH_3-CH_2-\underset{\displaystyle CH_2-CH_3}{CH}-CH_2-CH_2-CH_3$$

e) 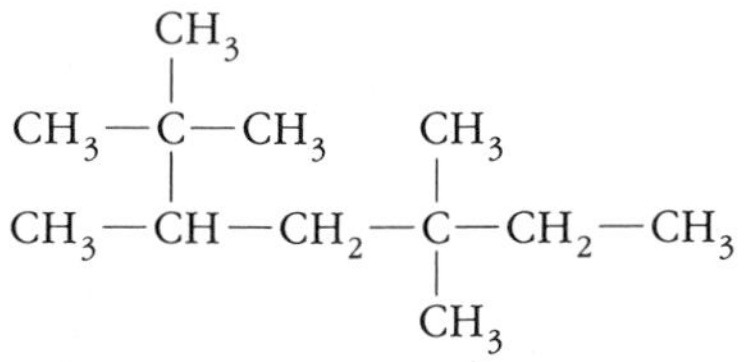
$$\overset{\displaystyle CH_3}{CH_3-\underset{\displaystyle |}{C}-CH_3}\qquad CH_3$$
$$CH_3-CH-CH_2-\underset{\displaystyle CH_3}{\overset{\displaystyle |}{C}}-CH_2-CH_3$$

20. Determine the IUPAC name corresponding to each of the following alkanes:

a) 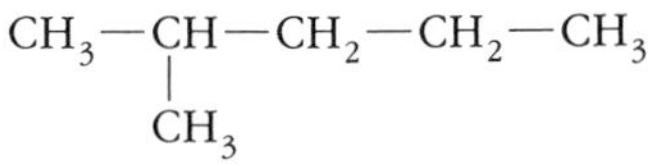
$$CH_3-\underset{\displaystyle CH_3}{CH}-CH_2-CH_2-CH_3$$

b) 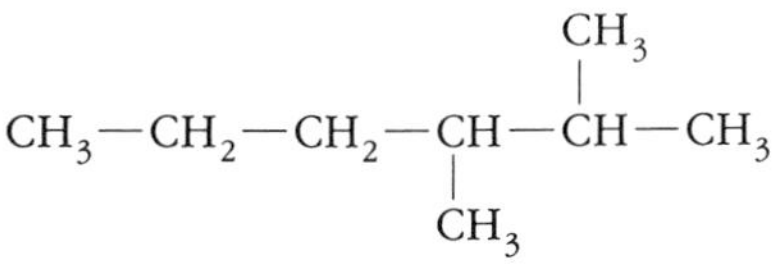
$$CH_3-CH_2-CH_2-CH-\underset{\displaystyle CH_3}{\overset{\displaystyle CH_3}{CH}}-CH_3$$

c) 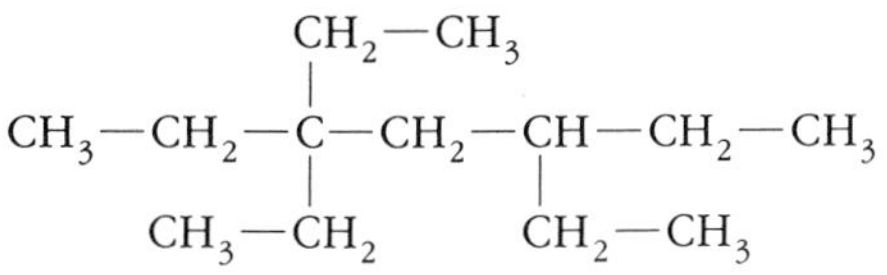
$$CH_3-CH_2-\overset{\displaystyle CH_2-CH_3}{\underset{\displaystyle CH_3-CH_2}{C}}-CH_2-\underset{\displaystyle CH_2-CH_3}{CH}-CH_2-CH_3$$

d) 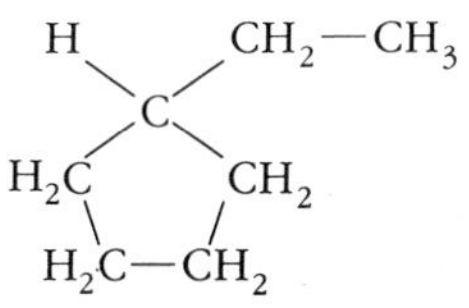
$$\begin{array}{c}
H\qquad\qquad CH_2-CH_3\\
\diagdown\quad\diagup\\
C\\
\diagup\quad\diagdown\\
H_2C\qquad CH_2\\
\diagdown\qquad\diagup\\
H_2C-CH_2
\end{array}$$

$$\text{e)} \quad CH_3-CH_2-\overset{\overset{\displaystyle CH_3}{|}}{CH}-CH_2-\overset{\overset{\displaystyle CH_3}{|}}{\underset{\underset{\displaystyle CH_2-\overset{\overset{\displaystyle CH_2-CH_3}{|}}{CH}-CH_3}{|}}{C}}-CH_3$$

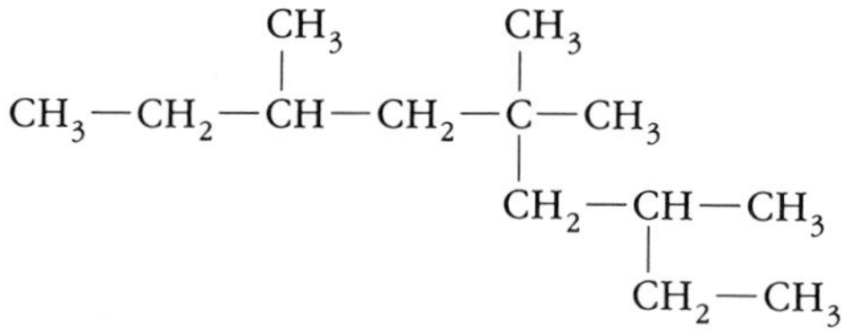

21. Write the structural formula for each of the following alkanes:

a) 3,4-dimethylnonane   c) ethylcyclopentane

b) 3-ethylpentane   d) 2,2,3,3-tetramethylbutane

22. Write the condensed formula for each of the following alkanes:

a) 2-methylhexane   c) cyclobutane

b) 3,5-dimethylheptane   d) 1,3,5-trimethylcyclohexane

23. Give the IUPAC name for each of the following alkenes:

a) $CH_3-CH=CH-CH_3$

b) 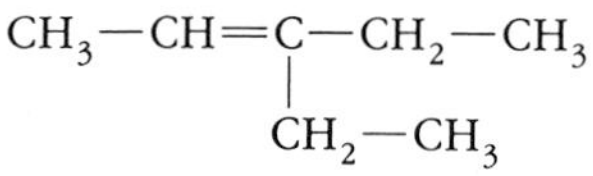 $CH_3-CH=\overset{\overset{\displaystyle CH_2-CH_3}{|}}{C}-CH_2-CH_3$

c) $CH_3-\overset{\overset{\displaystyle CH_3}{|}}{C}=CH-CH_2-CH_3$

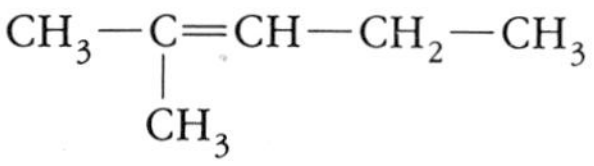

d) 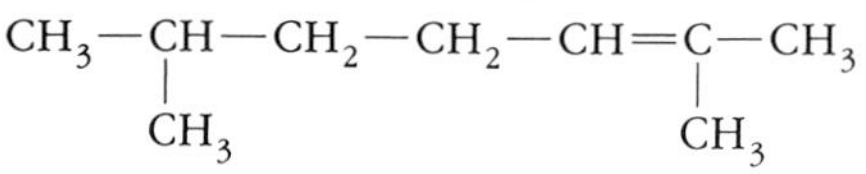 $CH_3-\overset{\overset{\displaystyle CH_3}{|}}{CH}-CH_2-CH_2-CH=\overset{\overset{\displaystyle CH_3}{|}}{C}-CH_3$

e) 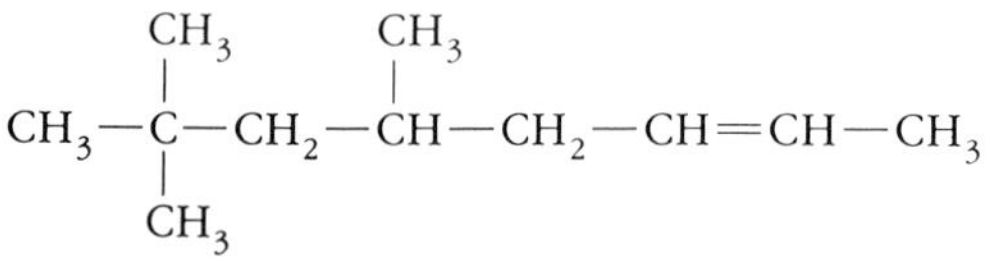 $CH_3-\overset{\overset{\displaystyle CH_3}{|}}{\underset{\underset{\displaystyle CH_3}{|}}{C}}-CH_2-\overset{\overset{\displaystyle CH_3}{|}}{CH}-CH_2-CH=CH-CH_3$

24. What is the IUPAC name for each of the alkenes shown below:

a) $CH_3-CH=CH_2$

b) 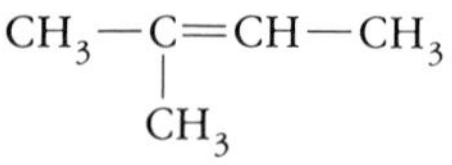 $CH_3-\overset{\overset{\displaystyle CH_3}{|}}{C}=CH-CH_3$

c) $CH_3-CH_2-CH_2-CH_2-CH=CH-CH_3$

d) 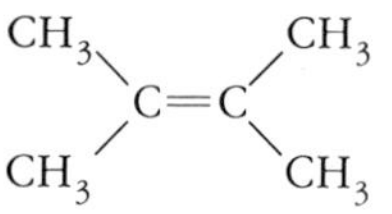 $\underset{CH_3}{\overset{CH_3}{\diagdown}}\!\!\!\underset{\diagup}{\diagup}C=C\underset{\diagdown}{\overset{\diagup}{\diagup}}\!\!\!\underset{CH_3}{\overset{CH_3}{}}$

e)

$$CH_3-CH_2-\overset{\overset{\displaystyle CH_2-CH_3}{|}}{C}=\overset{\overset{\displaystyle }{|}}{\underset{\underset{\displaystyle CH_2-CH_3}{|}}{C}}-CH_2-CH_2-CH_3$$

25. Two of the compounds shown in Problem 23 exhibit geometric isomerism. For each one draw the structures of the two isomers and name them accordingly.

26. Which one of the alkenes listed in Problem 24 exhibits *cis–trans* isomerism? Draw the structures of the isomers and give the appropriate IUPAC names.

27. a) Draw the condensed formula for each of the alkenes having the formula C_4H_8. Which of these alkenes can exist as *cis–trans* isomers?

   b) What other structures can you draw that correspond to the formula C_4H_8? Give the IUPAC name for each structure that you draw.

28. Write the condensed formula of each of the alkenes having the molecular formula C_5H_{10}. Which of these alkenes exhibit geometrical isomerism?

29. Write the condensed formula for each of the following alkenes:

   a) 1-hexene
   b) cyclohexene
   c) *cis–*2-butene

   d) 4,4-dimethyl-2-pentene
   e) 4-ethyl-3-octene

30. Write the condensed formula for each of the alkenes listed below:

   a) 1-butene
   b) *trans–*2-pentene
   c) 5,6-dimethyl-3-octene

   d) 3-ethyl-1-pentene
   e) 2,3-dimethyl-2-butene

31. Give the IUPAC name for each of the following alkynes:

   a) $HC\equiv C-CH_2-CH_2-CH_3$

   b) $CH_3-C\equiv C-\overset{\overset{\displaystyle }{|}}{\underset{\underset{\displaystyle CH_3}{|}}{CH}}-CH_3$

   c) $CH_3-C\equiv C-\overset{\overset{\displaystyle CH_3}{|}}{\underset{\underset{\displaystyle CH_3}{|}}{C}}-CH_2-CH_3$

   d) $CH_3-CH_2-C\equiv C-\overset{\overset{\displaystyle }{|}}{\underset{\underset{\displaystyle CH_3}{|}}{CH}}-CH_2-\overset{\overset{\displaystyle CH_3}{|}}{\underset{\underset{\displaystyle }{}}{CH}}-CH_3$

   e) $CH_3-C\equiv C-(CH_2)_3-\overset{\overset{\displaystyle }{|}}{\underset{\underset{\displaystyle CH_3}{|}}{CH}}-CH_3$

32. What is the IUPAC name of each alkyne shown below:

a) $CH_3-C\equiv C-CH_3$

b) 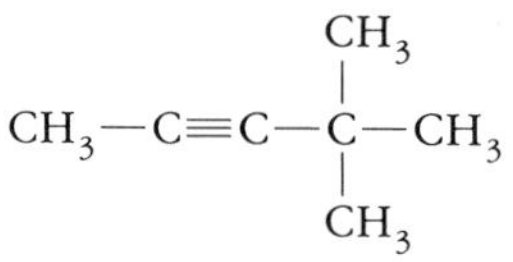
$$CH_3-C\equiv C-\overset{\overset{\displaystyle CH_3}{|}}{\underset{\underset{\displaystyle CH_3}{|}}{C}}-CH_3$$

c)
$$CH_3-CH_2-\overset{\overset{\displaystyle }{|}}{\underset{\underset{\displaystyle CH_3}{|}}{CH}}-C\equiv C-CH_3$$

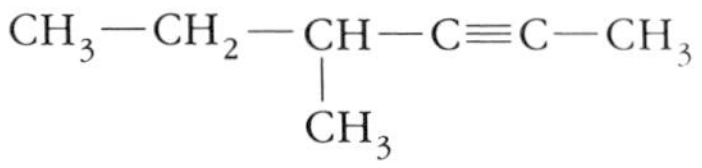

d) 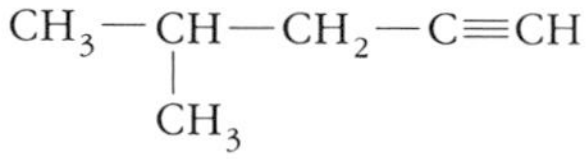
$$CH_3-\overset{\overset{\displaystyle }{|}}{\underset{\underset{\displaystyle CH_3}{|}}{CH}}-CH_2-C\equiv CH$$

e) 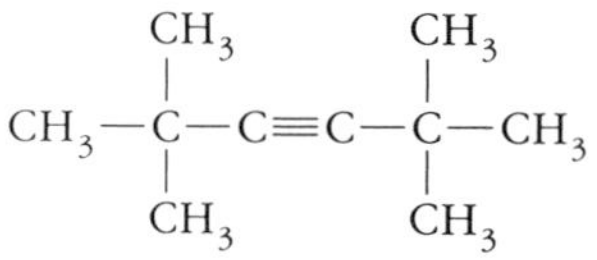
$$CH_3-\overset{\overset{\displaystyle CH_3}{|}}{\underset{\underset{\displaystyle CH_3}{|}}{C}}-C\equiv C-\overset{\overset{\displaystyle CH_3}{|}}{\underset{\underset{\displaystyle CH_3}{|}}{C}}-CH_3$$

33. Write the condensed formula for each of the following alkynes:
   a) 1-heptyne
   b) 3-hexyne
   c) 3,4-dimethyl-1-pentyne
   d) 2,3-dimethyl-4-octyne
   e) 2,2,5,5-tetramethyl-3-hexyne

34. Write the condensed formula for each of the alkynes below:
   a) 3-pentyne
   b) 5-methyl-1-hexyne
   c) 4,4-dimethyl-2-pentyne
   d) 3,3-diethyl-1-octyne
   e) 3,3-dimethyl-1-butyne

35. a) Write the condensed formula for each possible alkyne having the molecular formula C_4H_6.
    b) What other condensed formulas can you draw that correspond to a molecular formula of C_4H_6?

36. Write the condensed formula for each alkyne having the molecular formula C_5H_8.

37. Classify the following compounds as alkanes, alkenes, alkynes or aromatics:

a) 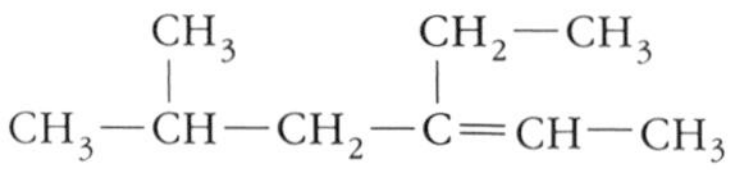
$$CH_3-\overset{\overset{\displaystyle CH_3}{|}}{CH}-CH_2-\overset{\overset{\displaystyle CH_2-CH_3}{|}}{C}=CH-CH_3$$

b) 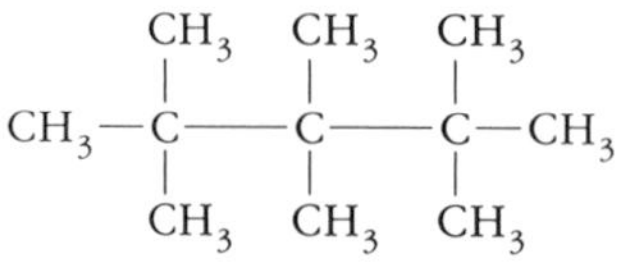
$$CH_3-\overset{\overset{\displaystyle CH_3}{|}}{\underset{\underset{\displaystyle CH_3}{|}}{C}}-\overset{\overset{\displaystyle CH_3}{|}}{\underset{\underset{\displaystyle CH_3}{|}}{C}}-\overset{\overset{\displaystyle CH_3}{|}}{\underset{\underset{\displaystyle CH_3}{|}}{C}}-CH_3$$

c) 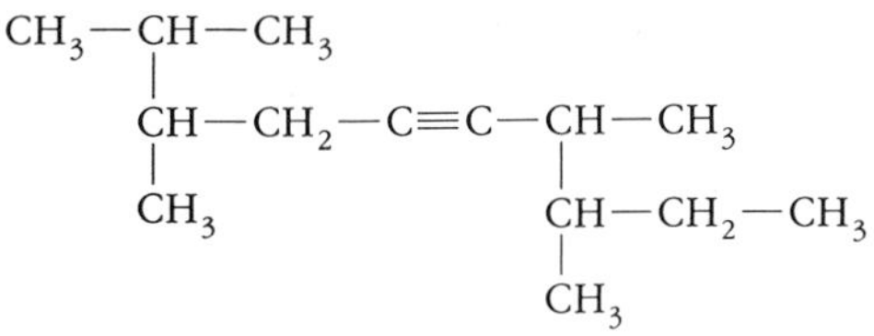 $CH_3-CH-CH_3$
$|$
$CH-CH_2-C\equiv C-CH-CH_3$
$|$ $|$
CH_3 $CH-CH_2-CH_3$
                  $|$
                  CH_3

d) 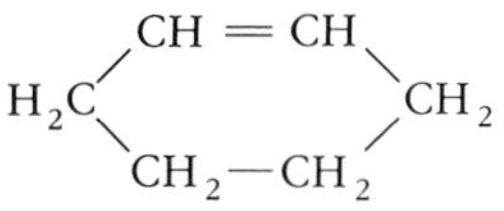
$$CH = CH$$
H_2C CH_2
$$CH_2-CH_2$$

e) 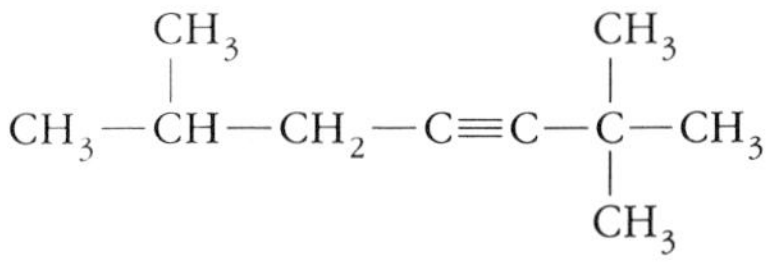 $CH_3-\overset{\displaystyle CH_3}{\overset{|}{CH}}-CH_2-C\equiv C-\overset{\displaystyle CH_3}{\underset{\displaystyle CH_3}{\overset{|}{\underset{|}{C}}}}-CH_3$

f) 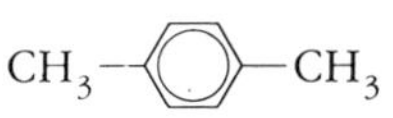 $CH_3-\hexagon-CH_3$

38. Identify the class or family to which each of the following compounds belongs:
a) 3,4-dimethylcycloheptene
b) 1,3,5-trimethylbenzene
c) 4-decyne
d) isopropylbenzene
e) 1,2,3,4,5,6-hexamethylcyclohexane

39. Identify the error(s) in each of the following condensed formulas:

a) 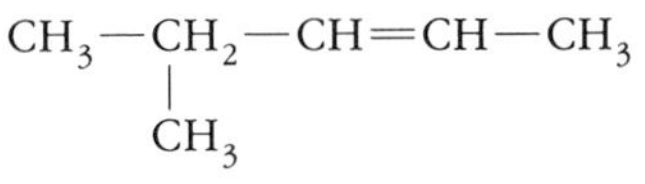 $CH_3-CH_2-CH=CH-CH_3$
          $|$
          CH_3

b) 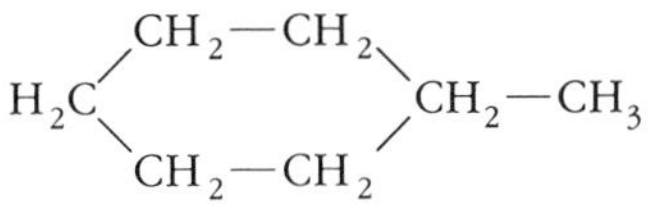
$$CH_2-CH_2$$
H_2C CH_2-CH_3
$$CH_2-CH_2$$

c) 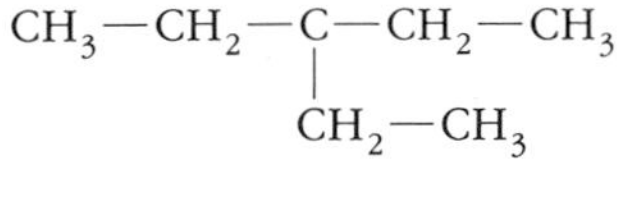 $CH_3-CH_2-\overset{\displaystyle}{\underset{\displaystyle CH_2-CH_3}{\overset{|}{C}}}-CH_2-CH_3$

d) 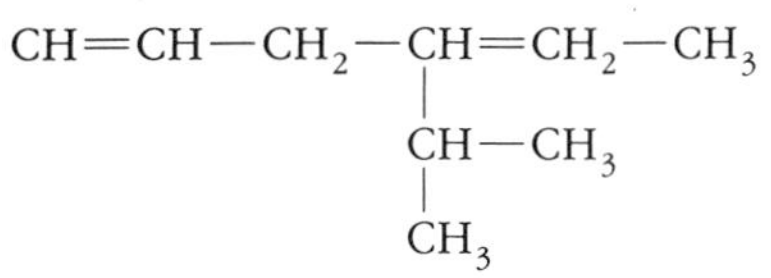 $CH=CH-CH_2-\overset{}{\underset{\displaystyle CH-CH_3}{\overset{|}{CH}}}=CH_2-CH_3$
                    $|$
                    CH_3

e) $CH_3-CH_2-CH-CH_2-CH_3$

40. Identify the error(s) in each of the following IUPAC names. Provide the correct name wherever possible.
    a) 2,4-diethylpentane
    b) 4-methyl-3-hexyne
    c) 3,5,5-trimethylhexane
    d) 2-isopropylbutane
    e) 1,1,4,4-tetramethyl-2-pentene

41. Write a balanced equation for each of the following reactions:
    a) 2-pentene + bromine (in carbon tetrachloride)
    b) propene burning in oxygen
    c) 3, 4-dimethyl-3-hexene + hydrogen in the presence of a platinum catalyst.
    d) 1-butyne and excess bromine (in carbon tetrachloride)

42. Write a balanced equation for each of the following reactions:
    a) propane burning in oxygen
    b) propyne and excess hydrogen in the presence of a nickel catalyst
    c) benzene + chlorine and an iron catalyst
    d) 2-methyl-1-butene + bromine (in carbon tetrachloride)

43. Draw the structure of
    a) a cyclic alkene containing five carbon atoms in the ring
    b) a branched-chain alkane containing four carbon atoms
    c) a straight-chain alkane that is isomeric with 2,2,4-trimethylpentane

44. Draw the structure of
    a) two four-carbon alkenes that do not exhibit *cis–trans* isomerism
    b) a saturated five-carbon cycloalkane containing a methyl substituent
    c) the *cis–* and *trans–* isomers of a four-carbon alkene
    d) three cyclic isomers of the compound drawn in b)

45. Assuming that the average composition of gasoline can be represented by the formula C_8H_{18}
    a) write a balanced equation for the reaction of gasoline with oxygen
    b) calculate the volume of carbon dioxide gas produced at 20 °C and 101 kPa pressure from the combustion of 1.00 L of gasoline (density 0.69 g·mL^{-1})

46. If 1.0×10^2 g of calcium carbide is to be used to generate acetylene in the laboratory by its reaction with water
    a) what volume of water (density 1.00 g·mL^{-1}) will be needed to completely react with the calcium carbide?
    b) what volume of ethyne (acetylene gas), measured at STP, will be produced when the two reactants are mixed?

SUGGESTED PROJECTS

1. What is the International Union of Pure and Applied Chemistry (IUPAC)? Find out where it is located, what its functions are and who supports it.

2. Molecular models enable us to obtain a much better understanding of the three-dimensional nature of organic compounds. Obtain a set of molecular models and construct examples of each of the four classes of hydrocarbons that we have studied in this chapter. Prepare a display of these models, giving information about the names, properties and uses of each of the compounds exhibited.

3. In addition to gasoline and other fuels, petroleum can be converted into a wide variety of useful products ranging from edible oil products, such as powdered coffee whiteners or whipped cream substitutes, to plastics and man-made fibres. The production of chemicals from petroleum (i.e. the petrochemical industry) is very important to the Canadian economy. Prepare a report on this industry, giving details of the range of petrochemical products that are made in Canada.

C H A P T E R **15**

Organic Chemistry II

15.1   *Common Functional Groups*
15.2   *Alcohols*
15.3   *Ethers*
15.4   *Aldehydes and Ketones*
15.5   *Carboxylic Acids*
15.6   *Esters*
15.7   *Organic Compounds Containing Nitrogen*
15.8   *Organic Compounds Containing Halogens*
15.9   *Amino Acids*
15.10 *Carbohydrates*
        Feature: Chemical Communication
15.11 *Review of the IUPAC Naming System for Organic Compounds*

In the previous chapter we discussed organic compounds that contain only carbon and hydrogen. Most organic compounds also contain at least one other element. In this chapter we will describe some of the classes of organic compounds that contain oxygen, nitrogen, or a halogen in addition to carbon and hydrogen. We will introduce you to the naming system used for these compounds, and discuss some of their chemical reactions and industrial uses. Since organic chemistry is closely related to biochemistry, the chemistry of life, we have also included a discussion of some biologically important compounds such as sugars, fats, and proteins.

Common Functional Groups   *15.1*

In Chapter 14 we saw that the presence of a specific functional group determines the class or family to which a compound belongs. The most common functional groups and classes are listed in Table 15.1.

After we have discussed compounds that contain only one functional group, we will look briefly at some slightly more complex compounds in which two or more functional groups are present. Many of these compounds have important biological roles.

458

TABLE 15.1 *Common Functional Groups*

Functional Group	Class or Family
none	alkane
$\text{C}=\text{C}$	alkene
$-\text{C}\equiv\text{C}-$	alkyne
(benzene ring)	aromatic
$-\text{C}-\text{OH}$	alcohol
$-\text{C}-\text{O}-\text{C}-$	ether
$-\text{C}-\overset{\text{O}}{\underset{\|}{\text{C}}}-\text{C}-$	ketone
$-\text{C}\overset{\text{O}}{\underset{\text{H}}{\diagup}}$	aldehyde
$-\text{C}\overset{\text{O}}{\underset{\text{OH}}{\diagup}}$	carboxylic acid
$-\text{C}\overset{\text{O}}{\underset{\text{O}-\text{C}-}{\diagup}}$	ester
$-\text{C}-\text{NH}_2$	amine
$-\text{C}-\text{X}$	alkyl halide

(where X can represent
the element F, Cl, Br, or I.)

15.1 Use Table 15.1 to identify the **family** or **class** of compounds to which each of the following belongs:

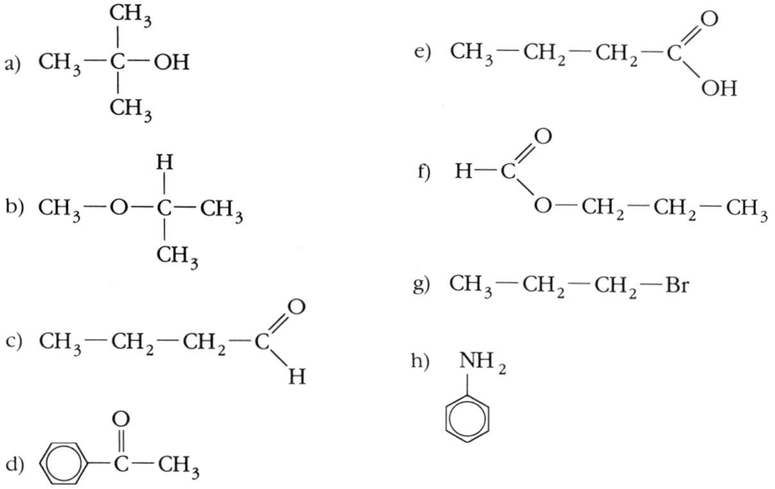

a)
$$CH_3-\underset{\underset{CH_3}{|}}{\overset{\overset{CH_3}{|}}{C}}-OH$$

e)
$$CH_3-CH_2-CH_2-C\underset{OH}{\overset{O}{\diagup}}$$

b)
$$CH_3-O-\underset{\underset{CH_3}{|}}{\overset{\overset{H}{|}}{C}}-CH_3$$

f)
$$H-C\underset{O-CH_2-CH_2-CH_3}{\overset{O}{\diagup}}$$

g) $CH_3-CH_2-CH_2-Br$

c)
$$CH_3-CH_2-CH_2-C\underset{H}{\overset{O}{\diagup}}$$

h) NH$_2$ (benzene ring)

d) (benzene ring)$-\overset{\overset{O}{\|}}{C}-CH_3$

SOLUTION

a) This molecule contains an —OH group and is therefore an alcohol.

b) The first group can be written as H$_3$C—. If we do this we see that we have a C—O—C group, which means the compound is an ether.

c) The presence of a $-C\overset{O}{\underset{H}{\diagup}}$ group makes this compound an aldehyde.

d) The benzene ring tells us that this is an aromatic compound.

The presence of a C—$\overset{\overset{O}{\|}}{C}$—C group also means that the compound is a ketone. Thus we would classify this compound as an aromatic ketone. It is a simple example of a compound that contains two functional groups.

e) From Table 15.1, we see that a compound containing a $-C\overset{O}{\underset{OH}{\diagup}}$ group is classified as a carboxylic acid.

f) Compounds containing the $-C\overset{O}{\underset{O-C}{\diagup}}$ group belong to the ester family.

g) This compound appears to be an alkane in which one hydrogen atom has been replaced by a halogen. Such compounds are called alkyl halides.

h) Two functional groups are present in this compound. The benzene ring indicates that the compound is aromatic. The —NH$_2$ group is the characteristic group of an amine. Thus this compound is correctly identified as being an aromatic amine.

QUESTIONS

1. Classify the following compounds according to the functional groups present:

a) $CH_3-CH_2-\overset{\overset{\displaystyle O}{\|}}{C}-CH_2-\underset{\underset{\displaystyle CH_3}{|}}{CH}-CH_3$

b) $CH_3-\underset{\underset{\displaystyle Br}{|}}{CH}-CH_3$

c) $CH_3-\overset{\overset{\displaystyle CH_3}{|}}{\underset{\underset{\displaystyle NH_2}{|}}{C}}-CH_2-\underset{\underset{\displaystyle CH_3}{|}}{CH}-CH_3$

d) $CH_3-CH=CH-\underset{\underset{\displaystyle CH_2-CH_3}{|}}{CH}-CH_2-CH_3$

e) $CH_3-\underset{\underset{\displaystyle CH_3}{|}}{CH}-CH_2-\overset{\overset{\displaystyle O}{\diagup\!\!\diagdown}}{C}\diagdown_{O-CH_2-CH_3}$

2. Identify

a) the ester group in $CH_3-\overset{\overset{\displaystyle O}{\|}}{C}-CH_2-\overset{\overset{\displaystyle O}{\diagup}}{C}\diagdown_{O-CH_2-CH_3}$

b) the alcohol hydroxyl group in the amino acid serine

$HO-CH_2-\overset{\overset{\displaystyle H}{|}}{\underset{\underset{\displaystyle NH_2}{|}}{C}}-\overset{\overset{\displaystyle O}{\diagup}}{C}\diagdown_{OH}$

c) the oxygen of an ether linkage in the herbicide 2,4-D

Alcohols

15.2

As we briefly mentioned in Section 14.5, members of the alcohol family all contain a **hydroxyl group** (—OH). The IUPAC names of the two simplest members of this family are obtained by dropping the -e from the name of the alkane containing the same number of carbon atoms and replacing it with the new ending -ol. Thus

$$
\underset{\text{ethanE}}{\begin{array}{c} \text{H} \quad \text{H} \\ | \quad | \\ \text{H}-\text{C}-\text{C}-\text{H} \\ | \quad | \\ \text{H} \quad \text{H} \end{array}} \qquad \underset{\text{minus E plus OL gives}}{\longrightarrow} \qquad \underset{\text{ethanOL}}{\begin{array}{c} \text{H} \quad \text{H} \\ | \quad | \\ \text{H}-\text{C}-\text{C}-\text{OH} \\ | \quad | \\ \text{H} \quad \text{H} \end{array}}
$$

An alcohol containing three or more carbon atoms requires the use of a number to identify unambiguously the position of the hydroxyl group in the molecule. We obtain this number by numbering the carbon chain so that the carbon atom to which a hydroxyl group is attached is given the lowest possible number. In the IUPAC name, this number is separated from the rest of the name using a hyphen:

$$
\underset{\text{1-propanol}}{\begin{array}{c} \text{H} \quad \text{H} \quad \text{H} \\ | \quad | \quad | \\ \text{H}-\text{C}-\text{C}-\text{C}-\text{OH} \\ | \quad | \quad | \\ \text{H} \quad \text{H} \quad \text{H} \end{array}} \qquad\qquad \underset{\text{2-propanol}}{\begin{array}{c} \text{H} \quad \text{H} \quad \text{H} \\ | \quad | \quad | \\ \text{H}-\text{C}-\text{C}-\text{C}-\text{H} \\ | \quad | \quad | \\ \text{H} \quad \text{OH} \quad \text{H} \end{array}}
$$

Both of the above alcohols contain straight carbon chains. When the chain is branched, then the position of any substituent is indicated by a number that can be assigned only after we have selected the appropriate carbon chain for our base name. Under the IUPAC system, we select the longest carbon chain to which the hydroxyl group is directly attached.

In the compound whose structure is shown below, the longest carbon chain contains five atoms. This might lead us to choose the base name pentane. However, the longest chain to which the hydroxyl group is directly attached contains only four carbon atoms. Therefore, the base name is **butane**.

$$
\begin{array}{c}
\text{H} \quad \text{H} \qquad\quad \text{H} \qquad\quad \text{H} \quad \text{H} \\
| \quad | \qquad\quad | \qquad\quad | \quad | \\
\text{H}-\text{C}-\text{C}\rule{1.2cm}{0.4pt}\text{C}\rule{1.2cm}{0.4pt}\text{C}-\text{C}-\text{H} \\
| \quad | \qquad | \qquad | \quad | \\
\text{H} \quad \text{H} \quad \text{H}-\text{C}-\text{H} \quad \text{H} \quad \text{H} \\
\qquad\qquad\qquad | \\
\qquad\qquad\qquad \text{OH}
\end{array}
$$

The presence of a hydroxyl group tells us that we have an alcohol, so we drop the -e from butane and replace it with the ending -ol to obtain **butanol**. As the hydroxyl group is attached to one end of the chain, we modify the name to **1-butanol**. An ethyl substituent is attached to the second carbon atom in the chain. Therefore, the full name of the compound is **2-ethyl-1-butanol**.

EXAMPLE   **15.2**   Name the following alcohols using the IUPAC system:

a) $CH_3-CH-CH_2-CH_3$
           $|$
           OH

c) CH_3
             $|$
    CH_3-C-OH
             $|$
            CH_3

b) $CH_3-CH-CH_2-OH$
           $|$
          CH_3

SOLUTION   a) The longest continuous carbon chain to which the hydroxyl group is attached contains four carbon atoms. This gives us the base name **butane**. As we have an —OH group, we change this to **butanol**. The hydroxyl group is present on the second carbon atom in the chain, hence the full name is **2-butanol**. (NOTE: If the carbon atoms were numbered from the other end, we would obtain the name 3-butanol. This would be incorrect as the position of the hydroxyl group must be indicated with the lowest possible number.)

b) The longest continuous carbon chain to which the hydroxyl group is attached contains three carbon atoms. This gives us the base name **propane**. Counting from the right, the hydroxyl group is attached to the first carbon atom in the chain and therefore we modify the name to **1-propanol**. The methyl group is attached to the second carbon atom; thus, the full name is **2-methyl-1-propanol**. (NOTE: Numbering from the other end of the molecule would again produce an incorrect answer, 2-methyl-3-propanol.)

c) As the longest continuous carbon chain to which the hydroxyl group is attached contains three carbon atoms, the base name is again **propane**. We have a hydroxyl group attached to carbon atom two; thus, the base name is modified to **2-propanol**. A methyl substituent is also present at carbon atom two; hence the full name is **2-methyl-2-propanol**.

The three alcohols in Example 15.2 provide a further illustration of isomerism. The compounds each have the molecular formula $C_4H_{10}O$, but have different structures. Note the different arrangements of groups around the carbon atom to which the hydroxyl group is attached. In 2-methyl-1-propanol there is only one alkyl group attached to the carbon bearing the hydroxyl group. Alcohols of this type are classed as **primary alcohols**.

In 2-butanol, two alkyl groups are attached to the carbon atom bearing the hydroxyl group, giving us a **secondary alcohol**. The three alkyl groups attached to the hydroxyl- bearing carbon atom in 2-methyl-2-propanol mean that this is a **tertiary alcohol**.

The slight structural variations between primary, secondary, and tertiary alcohols result in some differences in reactivity that need not concern us in this text. However, *all alcohols* react with sodium metal to produce hydrogen gas and a base. For example, with ethanol in excess, a solution of sodium ethoxide is produced:

$$2 \text{ CH}_3\text{CH}_2\text{OH} \ + \ 2 \text{ Na} \longrightarrow 2 \text{ CH}_3\text{CH}_2\text{ONa} \ + \ \text{H}_2$$

ethanol   sodium ethoxide
(a base)

Notice the similarity between the above reaction and that between sodium and water.

$$2 \text{ H}_2\text{O}_{(\ell)} \ + \ 2 \text{ Na}_{(s)} \longrightarrow 2 \text{ NaOH}_{(aq)} \ + \ \text{H}_{2\,(g)}$$

Ethanol (CH₃CH₂OH)

Ethanol, also known as ethyl alcohol or grain alcohol, was probably the first organic compound to attain widespread use. It has been suggested that civilization and the art of fermentation both began in the Middle East on the banks of the Tigris and Euphrates rivers around 7000 B.C.

In the preparation of beer and many alcoholic beverages, the starch in rice, barley, potatoes, corn, or wheat is first converted in solution to fermentable sugars. Fruit juices, which naturally possess fermentable sugars, are used to make wine. The sugars are converted by yeast enzymes into ethanol and carbon dioxide in a complex process called **fermentation**. Carbon dioxide is released with such vigour during the initial stages of this process that the solution appears to boil. (The term "fermentation" comes from the Latin word *fevere*, "to boil".) The proportion of ethanol in the final solution depends in part on both the concentration of fermentable sugars in the original solution and the degree to which fermentation is allowed to proceed. When the ethanol content reaches between 12–18%, depending on the yeast variety used, the yeast cells are inhibited from making more ethanol and begin to die. The proportion of ethanol in the final solution can then only be further increased by distilling it from the solution.

The fermentation process also produces trace amounts of other organic compounds. These compounds, which give each alcoholic beverage its characteristic flavour and odour, are produced from the nonstarch components of the raw materials or from the yeast. Trace compounds are also usually responsible for the headaches associated with drinking excessive quantities of alcohol. If large amounts of alcohol are consumed rapidly, death can result. Regular intake of smaller quantities of alcohol can cause brain and liver damage.

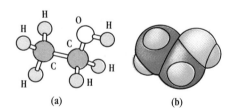

Figure 15.1

The shape of the ethanol molecule
a) as a ball-and-stick model
b) as a space-filling model

Ethanol is used as a starting material in the manufacture of many important organic chemicals. There is also an increasing interest in the use of ethanol as a fuel for automobiles.

The industrial synthesis of ethanol involves an addition reaction between ethene and water:

$$CH_2=CH_{2\,(g)} + H_2O_{(\ell)} \xrightarrow{\text{catalyst}} CH_3CH_2OH_{(\ell)}$$

The product consists of a mixture of 95% ethanol and 5% water. Absolute (100%) ethanol is produced by adding calcium oxide to react with the water, and then distilling off the ethanol:

$$H_2O_{(\ell)} + CaO_{(s)} \longrightarrow Ca(OH)_{2\,(s)}$$

Ethanol produced in this manner is exempt from federal taxes if it is not intended for use in an alcoholic beverage. Denatured alcohol is industrial alcohol that has had benzene or methanol added to it in order to make it unsuitable as a beverage.

Methanol (CH₃OH)

The properties of methanol, also known as methyl alcohol, methyl hydrate, or wood alcohol, are significantly different from those of ethanol.

Until 1923, methanol was obtained by heating wood in the absence of air (hence the name wood alcohol), but nowadays the industrial preparation of methanol involves the reaction of hydrogen with carbon monoxide at high temperatures and pressures in the presence of a catalyst:

$$CO_{(g)} + 2\,H_{2\,(g)} \xrightarrow[\text{ZnO/Cr}_2\text{O}_3]{350°C/200\,\text{atm}} CH_3OH_{(\ell)}$$

Methanol is used as a solvent for paint, as an ingredient in paint stripper, as windshield-wiper fluid, and as the starting material for the synthesis of formaldehyde. Methanol is very poisonous: ingestion of 15 mL will cause blindness, and 30 mL can be fatal. Many deaths have resulted from the consumption of home-made distilled beverages that contained significant amounts of methanol. Because methanol is readily absorbed through the skin and lungs, it should not be used as a rubbing alcohol, nor should its vapour be inhaled.

2-Propanol (CH₃CHOHCH₃)

Rubbing alcohol consists mainly of 2-propanol. Unlike methanol, it is not absorbed through the skin and is therefore toxic only when ingested. The common name for 2-propanol is isopropyl alcohol.

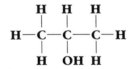

2-propanol (isopropyl alcohol)

Figure 15.2
Methanol is often referred to as methyl hydrate.

1,2-Ethanediol (CH₂OHCH₂OH)

1,2-Ethanediol (CH$_2$OHCH$_2$OH)

Commonly known as ethylene glycol, this compound is used as an anti-freeze agent in automobile radiators. A molecule of ethylene glycol has two hydroxyl groups, one attached to each of the two carbon atoms:

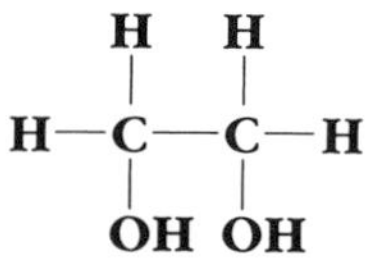

1,2-ethanediol (ethylene glycol)

1,2,3-Propanetriol (CH₂OHCHOHCH₂OH)

1,2,3-Propanetriol (CH$_2$OHCHOHCH$_2$OH)

This alcohol has many commercial uses. It is a component of many cosmetics, and is used as a sweetening agent, as a solvent for medicines, and in the preparation of plastics and synthetic fibres. Its common name is glycerol.

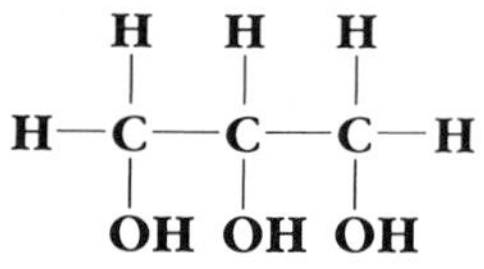

1,2,3-propanetriol (glycerol)

If glycerol (or glycerin, as it is sometimes called) is treated with a mixture of sulfuric and nitric acids, a yellow liquid called nitroglycerin is produced. Nitroglycerin can explode without warning, but when it is absorbed into diatomaceous earth and packed in tubes, it may be handled safely until detonated. The material in the tubes is known as *dynamite*, and is used extensively in the construction industry. The reaction involved in the preparation of this powerful explosive is as follows:

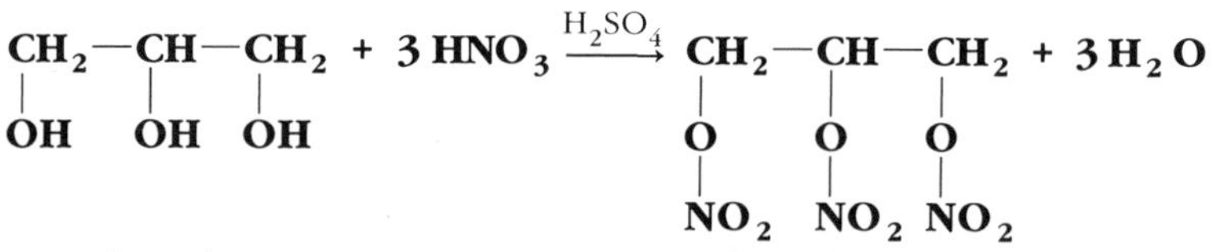

glycerol

glycerol trinitrate
(nitroglycerin)

QUESTIONS

3. Draw the structure for each of the eight alcohols with the formula $C_5H_{12}O$. Give the IUPAC name for each.

4. Draw the structure of each of the following alcohols:
   a) 3-hexanol   b) 2-methyl-3-hexanol   c) 2,3-dimethyl-2-hexanol.

5. Identify whether each structure drawn in response to Question 3 represents a primary, secondary, or tertiary alcohol.

Ethers

15.3

Water, alcohols, and ethers are all structurally related. If an alcohol is regarded as being formed by replacing one of the hydrogen atoms in a water molecule with an alkyl group, then an **ether** can be imagined as being formed by replacing both hydrogen atoms in a water molecule by alkyl groups. These two alkyl groups may be identical or different:

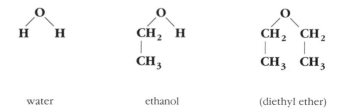

water   ethanol   (diethyl ether)

Ethers are generally known by their common names rather than by their IUPAC names. In the former system, the word "ether" is preceded by the names of the alkyl groups connected to the oxygen atom. Thus, in the compound CH_3CH_2—O—CH_2CH_3, the two ethyl groups attached to the oxygen atom lead to a common name of diethyl ether.

In the IUPAC system, the longer alkyl group is selected as the parent hydrocarbon. The other alkyl group and the oxygen atom constitute an **alkoxy group** which is regarded as being a substituent of the main carbon chain. The alkoxy groups are named according to the number of carbon atoms in the substituent. This is illustrated below.

TABLE 15.2 *Formation of Alkoxy Groups from Alkyl Groups*

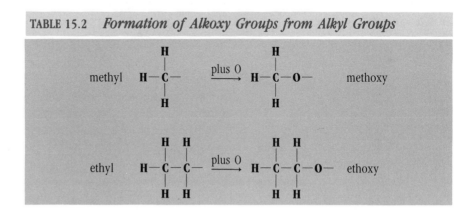

Thus diethyl ether, CH_3CH_2—O—CH_2CH_3, is viewed as being an ethane molecule in which one hydrogen atom has been replaced by an ethoxy group. Its IUPAC name is therefore ethoxyethane.

EXAMPLE **15.3** Give the IUPAC name for each of the following ethers:

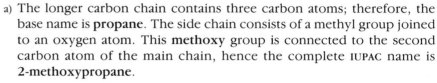

a) $CH_3—O—CH—CH_3$
$\qquad\qquad\quad\ |$
$\qquad\qquad\ CH_3$

b) $CH_3—CH_2—O—CH_2—CH_2—CH_2—CH_3$

SOLUTION a) The longer carbon chain contains three carbon atoms; therefore, the base name is **propane**. The side chain consists of a methyl group joined to an oxygen atom. This **methoxy** group is connected to the second carbon atom of the main chain, hence the complete IUPAC name is **2-methoxypropane**.

b) The longer carbon chain contains four carbon atoms and therefore the base name of this compound is **butane**. The side chain consists of an ethyl group joined to an oxygen atom. This **ethoxy** group is connected to the first carbon atom in the main chain; therefore the complete IUPAC name for this compound is **1-ethoxybutane**.

As a family, ethers are similar to the alkanes in their chemical and physical properties. They are used extensively as solvents because of their low reactivity and their ability to dissolve a wide range of compounds.

Figure 15.3
Diethyl ether is used in engine starting fluids.

Ethoxyethane (CH₃CH₂OCH₂CH₃)

At one time diethyl ether was widely used as an anesthetic. Because of its side effects (nausea and irritation of the lungs) it has been replaced by less toxic compounds.

Automobile starting fluids and lock de-icers contain high percentages of diethyl ether. *Care should be taken when handling these materials as mixtures of diethyl ether and air readily explode.*

QUESTIONS

6. Give the common and IUPAC names for the following
compound: $CH_3—O—CH_2—CH_3$
7. Draw the structure of 2-ethoxybutane.

Aldehydes and Ketones

15.4 Aldehydes and ketones contain an oxygen atom joined by a double bond to a carbon atom. This type of arrangement is called a **carbonyl group**. In an **aldehyde**, the carbonyl group is always bonded to a hydrogen atom. In a **ketone**, the carbonyl group is always bonded to two other carbon atoms.

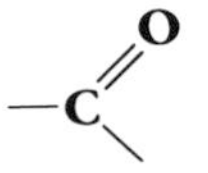

carbonyl group · propanal (an aldehyde) · propanone (a ketone)

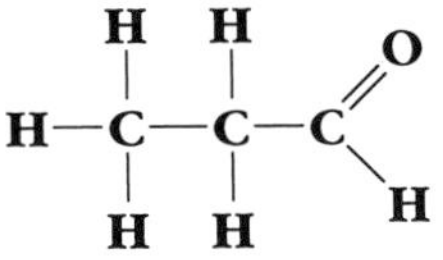

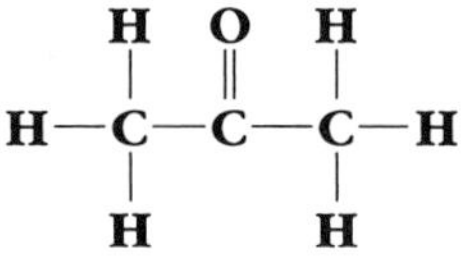

When naming an aldehyde or ketone by the IUPAC system we select the base name by picking out the longest carbon chain that contains the carbon atom of the carbonyl group. The final -*e* of this (alkane) base name is changed to -*al* if the compound is an aldehyde, and to -*one* if it is a ketone. Thus, you should now understand how we obtained the names propanal and propanone for the two compounds shown above. You may notice that neither of these names contains a number. If an aldehyde does not contain any substituents (e.g. alkyl groups), no number is required, since the carbonyl group will always be at the end of the carbon chain used to form the base name. This can be seen by examining the number of bonds in the functional group. If a substituent is present we indicate its position in the usual manner, taking care to number the longest chain starting at the carbonyl carbon atom.

In most ketones a number is required to indicate the position of the carbonyl group. This number is determined by numbering the carbon chain containing the carbonyl group in such a way that the carbonyl carbon atom is given the lowest possible number. This number precedes the base name in the final IUPAC name. You may wonder, then, why the ketone shown above is called propanone rather than 2-propanone. The answer is that the *2* would be superfluous. If the carbonyl group was at position 1 or 3 we would have an aldehyde (propanal) rather than a ketone; thus no number is necessary. If a ketone contains a substituent, it is indicated in the usual way. Remember, however, that it is the carbonyl group that determines in which direction the carbon chain is numbered. Example 15.4 illustrates how these rules are applied.

EXAMPLE **15.4** Name the following compounds using the IUPAC system:

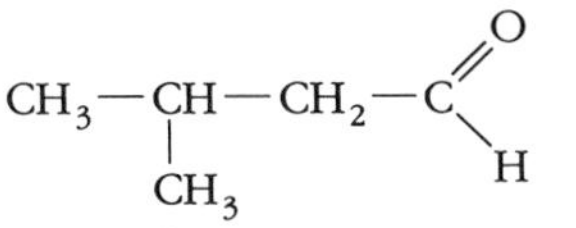

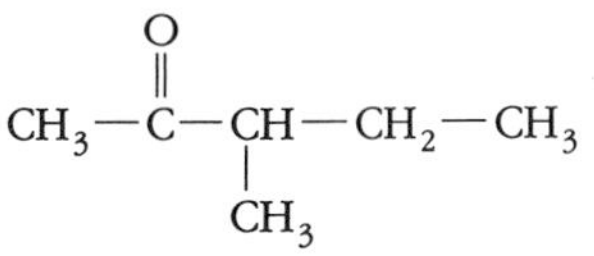

SOLUTION a) As the longest carbon chain containing the carbonyl carbon atom is four carbon atoms long, the base name of this compound is **butane**. The compound is an aldehyde; the ending is therefore changed from -*e* to -*al* giving us **butanal**. In an aldehyde, the numbering must start at the carbonyl carbon atom. Thus, the methyl substituent is attached to carbon atom number three. As it is not normally necessary to indicate the position of the carbonyl group when naming an aldehyde, the IUPAC name for this compound is **3-methylbutanal**.

b) The longest carbon chain containing the carbonyl carbon atom is five carbon atoms long, giving us the base name **pentane**. The compound is a ketone, with the carbonyl carbon atom being the second carbon atom in the chain. Hence the base name is modified to **2-pentanone**. We have a methyl substituent attached to the third carbon in the chain, therefore the full name is **3-methyl-2-pentanone**. (The name obtained by numbering from the other end of the molecule, 3-methyl-4-pentanone, is incorrect.)

When building the common name for ketones, the word "ketone" is preceded by the names of the alkyl groups attached to the carbonyl group. Some examples illustrating this system are shown below.

TABLE 15.3 *Naming of Ketones*

Structure	IUPAC Name	Common Name
$CH_3-\overset{\overset{\displaystyle O}{\|}}{C}-CH_3$	propanone	dimethyl ketone (acetone)
$CH_3-\overset{\overset{\displaystyle O}{\|}}{C}-CH_2-CH_3$	butanone	methyl ethyl ketone

Methanal (CH₂O)

The simplest aldehyde, methanal, is also known as formaldehyde. It is a gas at room temperature. A 40% aqueous solution of methanal, known as formalin, is used as a preservative, disinfectant, antiseptic, and bactericide. A solid polymer of methanal known as paraformaldehyde is produced when a formalin solution is allowed to evaporate slowly. This solid provides a convenient method of storage, as formaldehyde gas can be liberated by simply heating the polymer.

Ethanal (CH₃CHO)

The next simplest aldehyde, ethanal (acetaldehyde), forms a polymer consisting of four CH₃CHO molecules joined together. This polymer, known as metaldehyde, is used as a solid fuel in camp stoves. It is also used in slug pellets because its highly toxic vapour kills slugs and snails:

Aromatic Aldehydes

The aromatic aldehyde vanillin is responsible for the aroma of vanilla. However, the major ingredient in artificial vanilla extract is the synthetic

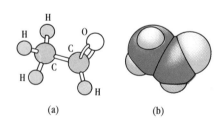

Figure 15.4

The shape of the ethanal (acetaldehyde) molecule

a) as a ball-and-stick model

b) as a space-filling model

compound ethovan, since its aroma is about five times stronger than that of vanillin. Note that the only structural difference between the two compounds is the extra CH_2 unit in ethovan:

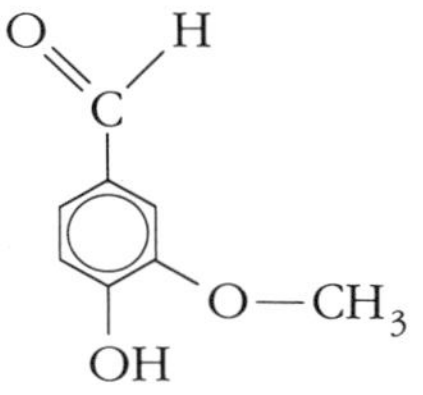

vanillin 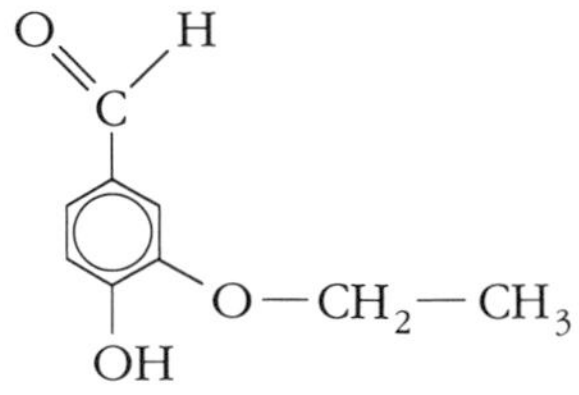   ethovan

Propanone (CH_3COCH_3)

Propanone is the simplest member of the ketone family. In the past it was prepared by the thermal decomposition of calcium acetate and was known as acetone:

$$(CH_3COO)_2Ca_{(s)} \xrightarrow{\Delta} CaCO_{3\,(s)} + CH_3-\overset{\displaystyle O}{\overset{\|}{C}}-CH_{3\,(\ell)}$$

Today, propanone, or acetone, is prepared on a large scale by the fermentation of corn and molasses. Fermentation of these substances would normally produce ethanol, but the reaction can be modified so that acetone is the major product.

Acetone is widely used as a solvent because it is miscible with water as well as with most nonpolar organic liquids. It is also found in the human body as a product of metabolism. However, the concentration of acetone in the blood rarely rises above 10 ppm, as it is readily oxidized to carbon dioxide and water. Some forms of diabetes affect this oxidation process and acetone can then be detected in the urine and on the breath.

QUESTIONS

8. Draw the structure of each of the following:
   a) 3-pentanone   c) butanal
   b) 2,4-dimethyl-3-hexanone   d) 2-methylpentanal

9. Name the following compounds by the IUPAC system:

a) 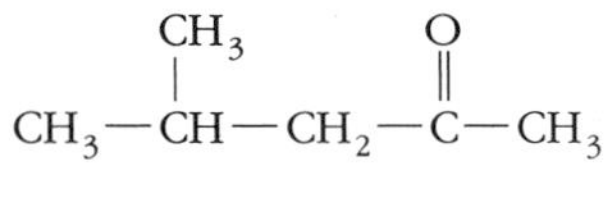
$$CH_3-\overset{\displaystyle CH_3}{\overset{|}{C}H}-CH_2-\overset{\displaystyle O}{\overset{\|}{C}}-CH_3$$

b) 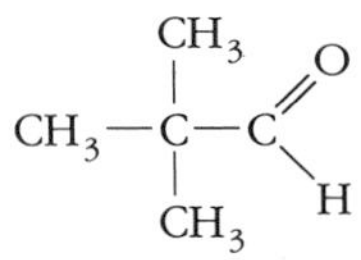
$$CH_3-\overset{\displaystyle CH_3}{\underset{\displaystyle CH_3}{\overset{|}{\underset{|}{C}}}}-\overset{O}{\underset{H}{C}}$$

Carboxylic Acids

15.5 Acids have been defined as compounds that produce H^+ ions in solution. Organic acids all contain the carboxyl functional group and are usually referred to as **carboxylic acids**. The **carboxyl group** is a combination of the carbonyl and hydroxyl groups. In general, carboxylic acids are much weaker than the common inorganic acids.

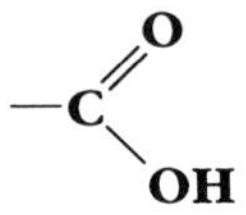

the carboxyl functional group

Carboxylic acids are named in a manner similar to aldehydes. We select the longest carbon chain containing the carboxyl carbon atom to give us the base name. The presence of the carboxyl group is shown by changing the ending of the base name from -e to -oic acid. The carboxyl carbon atom will always be at the end of the chain selected for our base name. Therefore we begin with this carbon atom when we number the chain for the purpose of indicating the positions of any substituents. The following example illustrates the IUPAC system of naming carboxylic acids.

EXAMPLE

15.5 Name the following acids using the IUPAC system:

a)

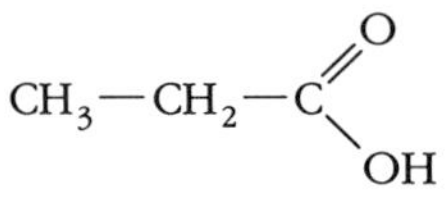

b)

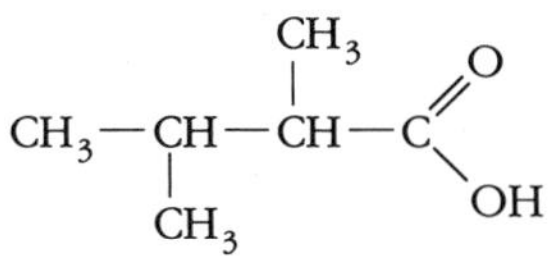

SOLUTION

a) The carbon chain containing the carboxyl group is three carbon atoms long, therefore the base name of this compound is **propane**. As there are no substituents present, we simply replace the final -e of propane with -oic acid to obtain the name **propanoic acid**. Notice that no number is needed to indicate the position of the carboxyl group, as it must be located at the end of the chain.

b) The longest carbon chain containing the carboxyl group is four carbons long; thus the base name is **butane**. Replacement of the -e of butane with -oic acid gives us **butanoic acid**. Counting the carboxyl carbon as carbon number one, we see that substituents are attached at carbon atoms two and three. Hence, the complete name of this compound is **2,3-dimethylbutanoic acid**.

A carboxylic acid, like an inorganic acid, will undergo a neutralization reaction with a base to form water plus the corresponding salt. Only the hydrogen atom that is bonded to the oxygen atom in the carboxylic acid takes part in such neutralization reactions. Thus the equation for the reaction of ethanoic acid with sodium hydroxide solution is

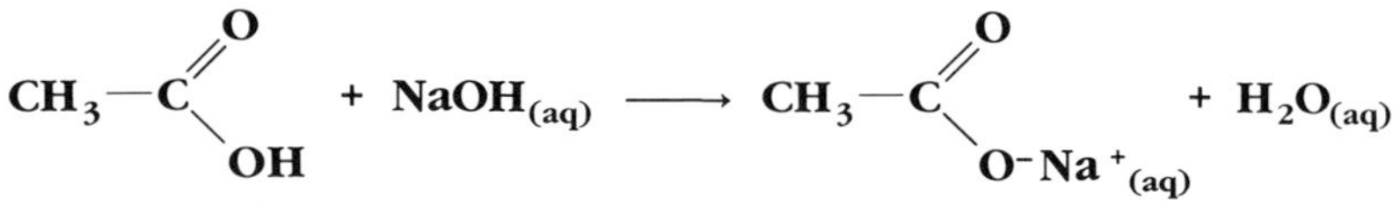

$$CH_3-C\overset{\displaystyle O}{\underset{\displaystyle OH}{\diagup}} + NaOH_{(aq)} \longrightarrow CH_3-C\overset{\displaystyle O}{\underset{\displaystyle O^- Na^+{}_{(aq)}}{\diagup}} + H_2O_{(aq)}$$

ethanoic acid   sodium ethanoate
(acetic acid)   (sodium acetate)

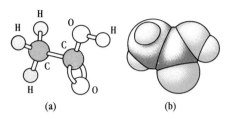

Figure 15.5

The shape of the ethanoic (acetic) acid molecule, CH_3CO_2H
a) as a ball-and-stick model
b) as a space filling model

The simplest carboxylic acid is methanoic acid, HCO_2H. Its common name, formic acid, is derived from the Latin word *formica*, meaning "ant". (The stinging sensation from an ant bite is caused by the effects of formic acid on skin cells.) Formic acid and formaldehyde are produced in the body when methanol is ingested. The toxic effects of drinking methanol are thought to arise from the body's production of these compounds rather than from the methanol itself. The overall reaction is illustrated below:

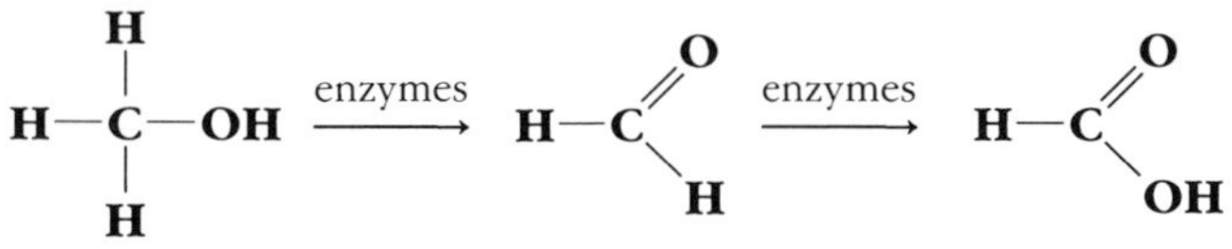

$$H-\overset{\displaystyle H}{\underset{\displaystyle H}{\overset{\displaystyle |}{\underset{\displaystyle |}{C}}}}-OH \xrightarrow{\text{enzymes}} H-C\overset{\displaystyle O}{\underset{\displaystyle H}{\diagup}} \xrightarrow{\text{enzymes}} H-C\overset{\displaystyle O}{\underset{\displaystyle OH}{\diagup}}$$

methanol   methanal   methanoic acid
     (formaldehyde)   (formic acid)

Ethanoic acid, CH_3CO_2H, is the next simplest member of the carboxylic acid family. It is better known by its trivial name, acetic acid. The properties of acetic acid were described in Section 12.10.

Butanoic acid ($CH_3CH_2CH_2CO_2H$), which has a disagreeable odour, is found in rancid butter. This is the origin of its trivial name, butyric acid. Butanoic acid is also a component of human perspiration and is partly responsible for the odour of stale perspiration in clothing.

Hexanoic, octanoic, and decanoic acid are also known as caproic, caprylic, and capric acid, respectively. All have distinctive odours. These acids are found in the butter prepared from goat's milk.

The sodium and potassium salts of acids such as hexadecanoic acid (palmitic acid, $CH_3(CH_2)_{14}CO_2H$) and octadecanoic acid (stearic acid, $CH_3(CH_2)_{16}CO_2H$) are used as soaps. Sodium benzoate, the sodium salt of benzoic acid (an aromatic carboxylic acid), is widely used as a food preservative. It is formed by the reaction of sodium hydroxide with benzoic acid.

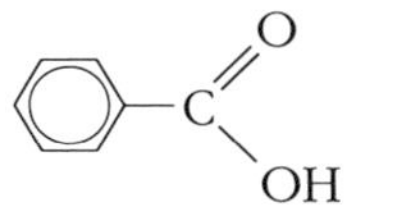

benzoic acid

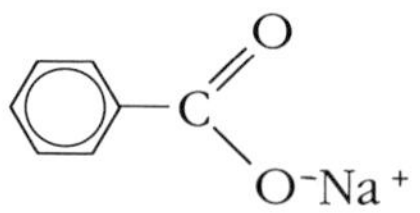

sodium benzoate

Figure 15.6

The structure of benzoic acid and sodium benzoate.

QUESTIONS

10. Name the following compounds according to the IUPAC system:

a) 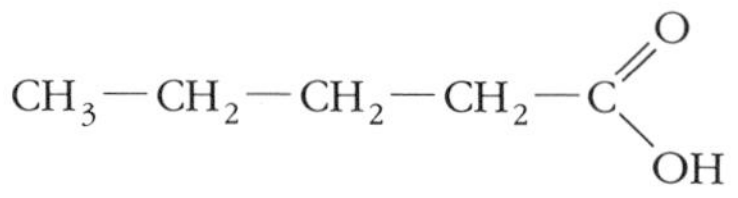 $CH_3-CH_2-CH_2-CH_2-C\overset{\displaystyle O}{\underset{\displaystyle OH}{\big\langle}}$

b) 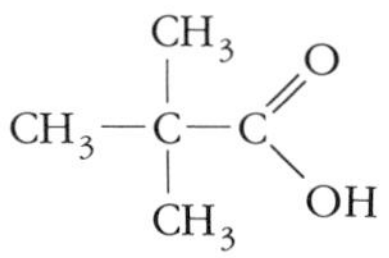 $CH_3-\overset{\displaystyle CH_3}{\underset{\displaystyle CH_3}{C}}-C\overset{\displaystyle O}{\underset{\displaystyle OH}{\big\langle}}$

11. Draw the condensed formula for each of the following carboxylic acids:
    a) heptanoic acid   b) 3-methylpentanoic acid

12. Write an equation to show the formation of sodium benzoate from benzoic acid and sodium hydroxide.

Esters

15.6

Esters are important derivatives of carboxylic acids. They can be prepared by the reaction of a carboxylic acid with an alcohol in the presence of a catalyst such as sulfuric acid. Two examples are shown below:

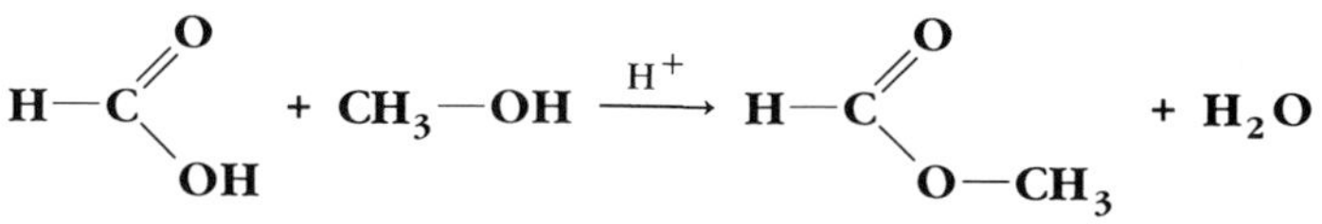

methanoic acid   methanol   methyl methanoate

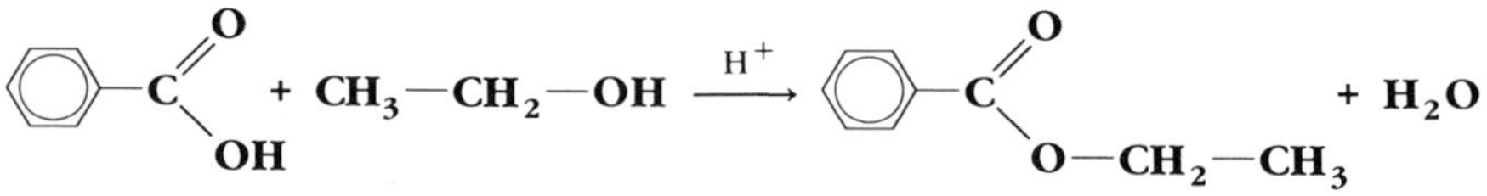

benzoic acid   ethanol   ethyl benzoate

In the IUPAC naming system, the base name of an ester is the carboxylic acid from which it is derived. The -oic ending of the name of the acid is replaced by the ending -oate. This name is then preceded by the name of the alkyl group attached to the singly-bonded oxygen atom of the carboxyl group.

Like the carboxylic acids from which they are derived, many esters are still called by their common names. The following example illustrates the naming of esters by both the IUPAC and common naming systems.

EXAMPLE   **15.6**   Give both the IUPAC and common name of each of the following esters.

a) $H-C \overset{O}{\underset{O-CH_2-CH_3}{\big\langle}}$

b) $CH_3-C \overset{O}{\underset{O-CH_3}{\big\langle}}$

c) $CH_3-CH_2-C \overset{O}{\underset{O-CH_2-CH_2-CH_3}{\big\langle}}$

SOLUTION   a) *The IUPAC name.*   This ester is derived from methanoic acid; hence, the base name is **methanoate**. Since an **ethyl** group is attached to the singly bonded oxygen atom of the carboxyl group, the complete name is **ethyl methanoate**.

The common name.   The common name of methanoic acid is formic acid. To obtain the common name of this ester, we follow essentially the same procedure that we used to derive the IUPAC name. The ending of the acid's name is changed from *-ic* to *-ate*, and this name is preceded by the name of the alkyl group attached to the oxygen of the carboxyl group. Thus, the common name for this compound is **ethyl formate**.

b) *The IUPAC name.*   This ester is derived from the carboxylic acid containing two carbon atoms, ethanoic acid. From this, the base name **ethanoate** is derived. In this ester a **methyl** group is attached to the singly bonded oxygen of the carboxyl group; thus, the complete name for the compound is **methyl ethanoate**.

The common name.   Acetic acid is the common name for ethanoic acid. Thus, the common or trivial name of this ester is **methyl acetate**.

c) *The IUPAC name.*   This ester is derived from the carboxylic acid containing three carbon atoms, i.e. propanoic acid. Therefore the base name of the ester is **propanoate**. The alkyl group attached to the oxygen atom of the carboxyl group consists of an unbranched, three-carbon chain, i.e. a **propyl** group. The name of the ester is therefore **propyl propanoate**.

The common name.   The common name for propanoic acid is propionic acid. We conclude therefore that the common name for this ester is **propyl propionate**.

Flavours and Aromas

Esters are responsible for many of the characteristic tastes and smells of our foods. A small change in structure can produce a very large change in smell. Table 15.4 shows the structure of a number of esters and lists the aromas associated with them.

Esters have the general formula

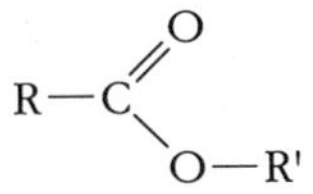

$$R-C\begin{array}{c}O\\\\\\O-R'\end{array}$$

where R and R' represent alkyl groups.

TABLE 15.4 **Structure and Aroma of Some Esters**

R	R'	Aroma	IUPAC Name
CH_3-	$\begin{array}{c}CH_3\\|\\-CH_2CH_2CHCH_3\end{array}$	banana	3-methylbutyl ethanoate
CH_3-	$-CH_2(CH_2)_6CH_3$	orange	octyl ethanoate
CH_3-	$-CH_2CH_2CH_3$	pear	propyl ethanoate
CH_3CH_2-	$\begin{array}{c}CH_3\\|\\-CH_2CHCH_3\end{array}$	rum	2-methylpropyl propanoate
$CH_3(CH_2)_2-$	$-CH_2CH_3$	pineapple	ethyl butanoate
$CH_3(CH_2)_2-$	$-CH_3$	apple	methyl butanoate

Fats

Esters, in the form of various fats, are components of food. Fats are triesters formed from three molecules of carboxylic acid and one molecule of glycerol. Such triesters are known as **triglycerides**. The process by which they are formed is illustrated in the equation below. The **R** represents the alkyl group of the carboxylic acid:

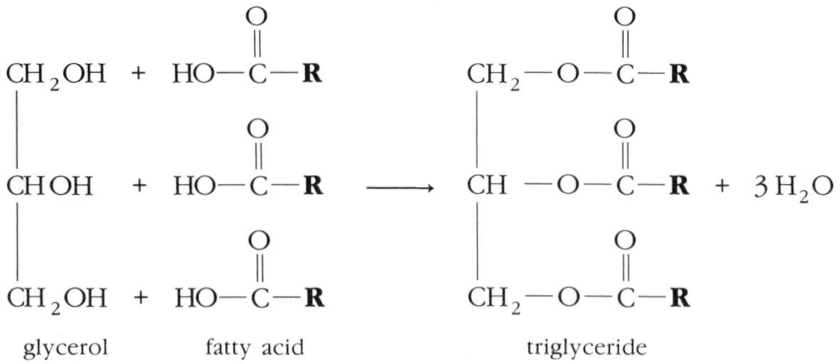

glycerol   fatty acid   triglyceride

Animal and vegetable fats are triglycerides in which **R** is a long-chain alkyl group containing from ten to twenty carbon atoms. The term "fat" tends to be reserved for triglycerides obtained from animal sources. These fats are usually solids. Triglycerides obtained from vegetable material are normally liquids at room temperature and are called oils.

We can classify triglycerides as being *saturated* or *unsaturated*, depending on the nature of the **R** group. If all the carbon–carbon bonds in this group are single, the fat is said to be saturated. In unsaturated fats, the **R** group contains one or more carbon–carbon double or even triple bonds. In general, the melting point of a fat is related to the number of double bonds present. The more double bonds there are in the compound, the lower the melting point. Studies show that diets containing large amounts of saturated animal fats may result in a build-up of blood cholesterol. This can eventually cause high blood pressure and heart trouble.

Pure vegetable oil is composed mainly of unsaturated triglycerides. While this is good from a dietary point of view, these oils cannot easily be spread on bread or toast. In the manufacture of margarine, hydrogen is added across some of the carbon–carbon double bonds. The oils become more saturated and the melting point is raised, producing a butter-like consistency. However, saturation is not carried to completion, since the result would be a crystalline solid. The body's enzymes are better able to deal with unsaturated triglycerides because of the greater reactivity of the carbon–carbon double bond.

Acetylsalicylic Acid

Acetylsalicylic acid (aspirin) is an ester formed by the reaction of acetic acid with the hydroxyl group of salicylic acid.

acetic acid   salicylic acid   acetylsalicylic acid (aspirin)

Acetylsalicylic acid reduces fever, helps to relieve pain, and reduces swelling in injured tissues. Exactly how it does this is still unclear. Prolonged use of acetylsalicylic acid can result in internal bleeding due to the action of the acid on the lining of the stomach.

QUESTIONS

13. There are two esters with the formula $C_3H_6O_2$.
    a) Draw their structures.
    b) Give their IUPAC names.
    c) Identify the alcohol and carboxylic acid used in their preparation.

14. Olive oil contains a variety of triglycerides, the majority of which have been formed (at least in part) from oleic acid. Oleic acid has the formula $C_{18}H_{34}O_2$ and contains a double bond between carbon atoms 9 and 10. Draw the structure of oleic acid. (In this compound the groups around the double bond have a *cis-* arrangement.)

Organic Compounds Containing Nitrogen

<u>15.7</u>

Nitrogen is found in a wide variety of organic compounds. Although nitrogen can form a double or triple bond with carbon, in this text we shall restrict our discussion to those compounds containing carbon–nitrogen single bonds.

In Section 15.3 we said that we could consider alcohols and ethers to be formed by replacing the hydrogen atoms of water with one or two alkyl groups respectively. Likewise, the family of organic nitrogen-containing compounds called **amines** can be considered as being formed by replacing one or more of the hydrogen atoms of ammonia with alkyl groups. Thus, by successively replacing the three hydrogen atoms of ammonia with methyl groups we obtain the primary, secondary, and tertiary amines shown below:

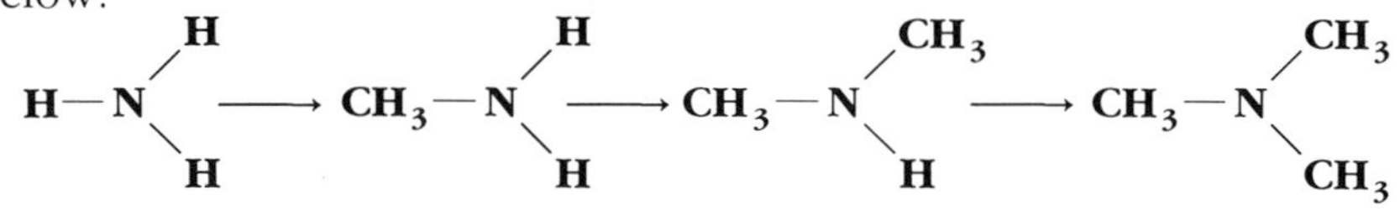

$$H-N\begin{smallmatrix}H\\\\H\end{smallmatrix} \longrightarrow CH_3-N\begin{smallmatrix}H\\\\H\end{smallmatrix} \longrightarrow CH_3-N\begin{smallmatrix}CH_3\\\\H\end{smallmatrix} \longrightarrow CH_3-N\begin{smallmatrix}CH_3\\\\CH_3\end{smallmatrix}$$

| ammonia | methylamine (a primary amine) | dimethylamine (a secondary amine) | trimethylamine (a tertiary amine) |

In alcohols, the terms primary, secondary, and tertiary are used to describe the number of alkyl groups attached to the *carbon atom* bearing the hydroxyl group. However, with amines, these terms refer to the number of alkyl groups bonded to the *nitrogen atom*. Thus a **primary amine** has one alkyl group bonded to the nitrogen atom, a **secondary amine** has two, and a **tertiary amine** has three. In this text we shall be concerned mainly with primary amines.

Amines can be named using a number of different systems. The most frequently used system gives the name(s) of the alkyl group(s) attached to the nitrogen atom followed by the ending *-amine*. This is the system that we used above.

In the IUPAC system, the NH_2 substituent is known as an **amino group**, and primary amines are named as substituted alkanes. Thus the compound $CH_3—CH_2—CH_2—CH_2—NH_2$ is called 1-aminobutane. This system is rarely used for simple amines, but is very useful for more complex compounds.

EXAMPLE

15.7

Give an acceptable name for each of the following:

a) $CH_3—CH_2—CH_2—NH_2$ b) $CH_3—CH_2—NH—CH_2—CH_3$

SOLUTION

a) Here we have a three-carbon unbranched propyl group attached to an amino group. This compound could therefore be called **propylamine**. The IUPAC name for this compound is **1-aminopropane**.

b) This secondary amine has two ethyl groups attached to the nitrogen atom. Thus it is commonly called **diethylamine**, and this is the name that we shall use.

The simplest amines all have a fishy odour and many of them can be isolated from herring as well as from other species of fish. Methylamine is a colourless gas and, like all amines, is basic. We can see a similarity between the reactions of amines and those of ammonia:

$$NH_{3\ (g)} + HCl_{(g)} \longrightarrow NH_4^+ Cl^-_{(s)}$$

ammonium chloride

$$CH_3NH_{2\ (g)} + HCl_{(g)} \longrightarrow CH_3NH_3^+ Cl^-_{(s)}$$

methylammonium chloride

The amine in which the amino group is directly attached to a benzene ring is called aniline. Aniline is the starting material for the manufacture of a large number of industrially important compounds, especially dyes, many of which contain the —N=N— linkage.

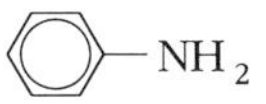

aniline

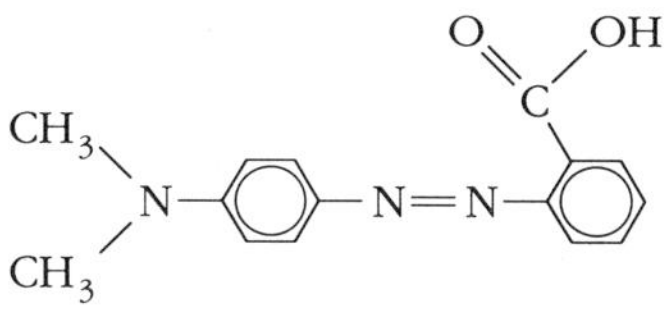

methyl red

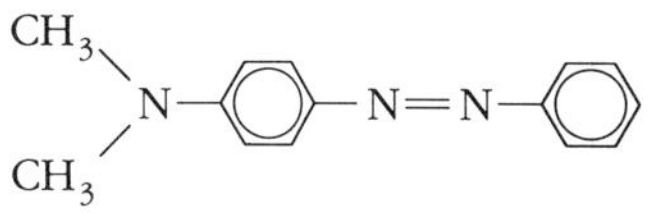

butter yellow

Figure 15.7
The structure of aniline and of two dyes derived from it.

QUESTIONS

15. Draw the structure of each of the following amines and indicate whether each one is primary, secondary, or tertiary:
  a) 3-aminopentane   b) triethylamine

16. Write an equation for the reaction of aniline with hydrochloric acid.

Organic Compounds Containing Halogens

15.8

The family of compounds known as the **alkyl halides** can be considered to be alkanes in which one hydrogen atom has been replaced by a halogen atom. Alkyl halides can be named using either the IUPAC or common system:

1. *The IUPAC system:* Here we use the same rules that we used for naming alkanes. The halogen atom is treated as a substituent and is identified by combining the terms *fluoro-, chloro-, bromo-,* or *iodo-* with the name of the alkane.

2. *The common system:* In this system the name of the alkyl group is followed by the name of the halogen, whose ending is changed from *-ine* to *-ide.*

The application of both of these systems to simple alkyl halides is illustrated below:

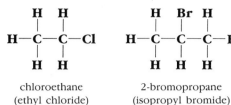

chloroethane
(ethyl chloride)

2-bromopropane
(isopropyl bromide)

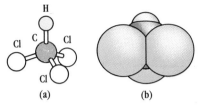

Figure 15.8

*The shape of trichloromethane
(chloroform) molecule
a) as a ball-and-stick model
b) as a space-filling model*

Trichloromethane (CHCl₃)

The common name for this compound is chloroform. It was once used as an inhalation anesthetic in surgery. It was also used to remove caffeine from coffee. However it is no longer used for these purposes because recent tests have shown that chloroform causes cancer in laboratory animals.

The chloroform molecule is shown in Figure 15.8. Like methane, chloroform has a tetrahedral shape. From the space-filling model you can see that chlorine atoms are much larger than hydrogen atoms.

Tetrachloromethane (CCl₄)

The common name for this compound is carbon tetrachloride. It was formerly used as a dry-cleaning agent and as an industrial solvent for removing grease. Like chloroform, carbon tetrachloride is now regarded as a health hazard and should only be used in areas with good ventilation.

Because of its low boiling point and the high density of its vapour, carbon tetrachloride was once used in fire extinguishers. It is no longer used for this purpose because it produces the toxic substance phosgene (COCl₂) when it is burned. (Phosgene gas was used as a chemical-warfare agent during World War I.)

Freons

A large variety of organic compounds containing both fluorine and chlorine have been used as refrigerants and as propellants in aerosol cans. These gases, collectively known as *freons*, have low toxicities and are very stable. Their stability has caused a serious environmental problem in that they do not react with substances in the lower atmosphere but gradually diffuse to the stratosphere (16–20 km above the earth). Here they react with and decompose the ozone (O₃) layer. As mentioned in Section 9.7, the normal role of the ozone layer is to absorb most of the ultraviolet radiation given off by the sun and prevent it from reaching the earth. Scientists believe that if the concentration of ozone is decreased, more ultraviolet radiation will reach the surface of the earth and cause an increase in skin cancer. Consequently, many countries have banned the use of freons in aerosol cans to try to protect the vital ozone layer.

DDT and PCBs

Other chlorine-containing organic compounds that have been shown to be harmful include dichlorodiphenyltrichloroethane (DDT) and polychlorinated biphenyls (PCBs).

DDT is an insecticide that was used extensively in the fight against the malaria-carrying mosquito in tropical climates and in the control of insects. Its use is now severely restricted in most provinces.

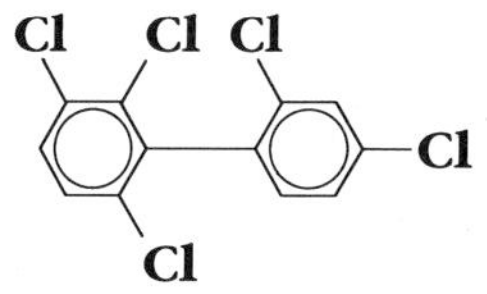

a typical PCB 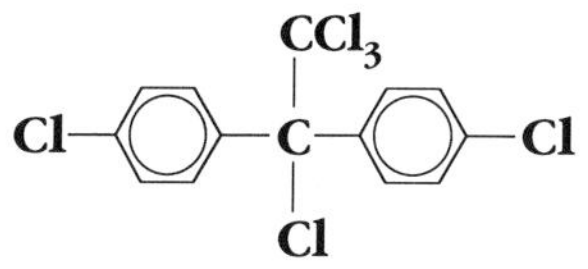   dichlorodiphenyltrichloroethane (DDT)

DDT does not decompose readily and tends to accumulate in the fatty tissues of animals, fish, and birds. In birds, this results in the formation of eggs with very thin shells. Consequently, very few of these eggs hatch.

At one time, PCBs were considered "wonder chemicals" because of their chemical stability, insulating properties, fire-resistant characteristics and indestructibility. They were used in a variety of products such as hydraulic fluids, pesticides, and carbon paper. Since they do not decompose readily, PCBs tend to accumulate in the environment, and have now been linked to a number of human health problems including birth defects, liver damage, and cancer. Because of this their production was banned by the Canadian government in 1980.

QUESTIONS

17. Give the IUPAC name for each of the following compounds:

a)

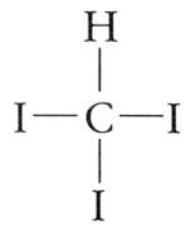

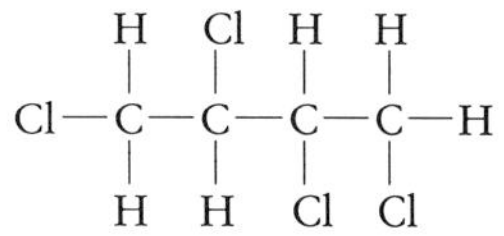

b)

c)

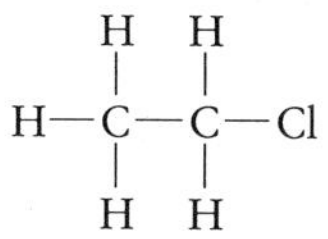

18. Draw the structure of each of the following compounds:
   a) 1,1,1-trichloropropane
   b) 1,2,3,4,5,6-hexachlorocyclohexane
   c) 3-bromopentane

Amino Acids   ## 15.9

Most of the organic compounds we have discussed up to this point contain only one functional group. A large proportion of all organic molecules are **bifunctional**, containing two functional groups. The α-**amino acids**, which contain both an amino (NH_2) group and a carboxyl (CO_2H) group, are an example. The α in the name α-amino acid indicates that the amino group and the carboxyl group are both attached to the same carbon atom.

$$H-\overset{\overset{\displaystyle H}{|}}{\underset{\underset{\displaystyle NH_2}{|}}{C}}-CO_2H \qquad CH_3-\overset{\overset{\displaystyle H}{|}}{\underset{\underset{\displaystyle NH_2}{|}}{C}}-CO_2H \qquad HO-CH_2-\overset{\overset{\displaystyle H}{|}}{\underset{\underset{\displaystyle NH_2}{|}}{C}}-CO_2H$$

glycine alanine serine

The α-amino acids have an important biological role. They are intermediates in metabolic pathways and are used as building blocks for larger molecules such as peptides and proteins.

Peptides and Proteins

A simple amine will react with a carboxylic acid to form an **amide**:

$$CH_3-\overset{\overset{\displaystyle O}{\|}}{C}\diagdown_{OH} + \overset{\diagup H}{\underset{\diagdown H}{N}}-CH_2-CH_3 \xrightarrow{\Delta} CH_3-\overset{\overset{\displaystyle O}{\|}}{C}\diagdown_{\underset{\underset{\displaystyle H}{|}}{N}-CH_2-CH_3} + H_2O$$

carboxylic acid   amine   amide

Similarly, the amino group of one amino acid can react with the carboxyl group of another amino acid to produce a **dipeptide**:

$$NH_2-\overset{\overset{\displaystyle H}{|}}{\underset{\underset{\displaystyle H}{|}}{C}}-\overset{\overset{\displaystyle O}{\|}}{C}\diagdown_{OH} + \overset{\diagup H}{\underset{\diagdown H}{N}}-\overset{\overset{\displaystyle H}{|}}{\underset{\underset{\displaystyle CH_3}{|}}{C}}-CO_2H \longrightarrow NH_2-\overset{\overset{\displaystyle H}{|}}{\underset{\underset{\displaystyle H}{|}}{C}}-\overset{\overset{\displaystyle O}{\|}}{C}-NH-\overset{\overset{\displaystyle H}{|}}{\underset{\underset{\displaystyle CH_3}{|}}{C}}-CO_2H + H_2O$$

(glycine)   (alanine)   a dipeptide (glycylalanine)

A dipeptide still contains a free amino group and a free carboxyl group. Each of these can react with additional amino acids to produce a **polypeptide**. Polypeptides, with well-defined sequences of amino acids, are found in all living organisms and are called **proteins**.

Every cell in an organism contains many different peptides and proteins, each with a specific function. Large amounts of protein are found in eggs, meat, and milk. When these foods are consumed, their proteins are broken down by digestive enzymes (usually proteins also) into individual amino acids. These acids are then absorbed into the bloodstream and transferred to the various regions of the body. There they combine to form new proteins that are used to build new cells and larger structures such as hair and muscle.

Carbohydrates

15.10

Simple carbohydrates or **monosaccharides** (also called sugars) have the general formula $(CH_2O)_n$. They are polyhydroxyl compounds, glucose and fructose being typical examples:

glucose

fructose

sucrose

Table sugar, or sucrose, is also a carbohydrate; however, sucrose is classed as a **disaccharide** as it can be broken down into two simpler monosaccharides. Some organisms, most notably yeast and bees, can convert sucrose into a mixture of glucose and fructose. This mixture, called invert sugar, is sweeter than sucrose alone because of the presence of the free fructose (the sweetest sugar). Honey consists mainly of invert sugar.

Glucose, which is found in blood, is the repeating unit in starch and cellulose, both of which are examples of **polysaccharides**. The only difference between starch and cellulose is the way in which the glucose units are linked together.

Cellulose is an architectural polysaccharide that gives strength to the stems and branches of plants. Dry leaves contain about 20% cellulose; wood, 50% cellulose; and cotton, 90% cellulose. Starch is a nutritional polysaccharide that is found in many of our foodstuffs (e.g. potatoes and wheat). Human beings can digest starch but not cellulose. Grazing animals such as cattle and sheep cannot digest cellulose directly, but their digestive tracts contain colonies of bacteria that break down cellulose into smaller molecules. These molecules can then be used up by the animals for food. Eating would be much simpler if the human digestive system contained the same bacteria as that of grazing animals — a bowl of grass and a bag of sawdust would then make a meal that was both inexpensive and tasty!

Chemical Communication

An area of research that is both challenging to scientists and appealing to the imagination of many other people is the investigation of the means by which insects, plants, and other organisms communicate with one another. Chemists and biologists often work together in this field. Most of our knowledge about this type of communication has resulted from work carried out in the last 25 years.

Semiochemicals are responsible for the transfer of messages between members of the same species, or between members of two different species. These messages include warnings of danger, indications of a readiness to mate, and so on. The three main subclasses of semiochemicals are pheromones, allomones, and kairomones.

Pheromones are released by one member of a species to bring about a specific behavioural response or physiological change in other members of the same species. Pheromones are often mixtures of two or more substances rather than a single pure substance.

Two types of pheromones that have been identified are releaser pheromones and primer pheromones. Releaser pheromones cause an instantaneous behavioural response in the recipient. The most common examples are sex pheromones. One of the components of the sex pheromone of the cabbage looper, *Trichoplusia ni*, is *cis*-7-dodecenyl acetate:

This compound is secreted by the female cabbage looper and causes the male to fly towards the female responsible for the secretion. If the concentration of the secretion is high enough, copulation takes place.

Primer pheromones produce long-term physiological changes. The best-known example of a primer pheromone is the "queen substance" produced by queens of the honeybee, *Apis mellifera*. A typical colony of honeybees consists of one queen, several hundred drones (males), and thousands of workers (underdeveloped females). The queen bee is the only fully developed female in the colony and she maintains this status by secreting the queen substance. This substance prevents the development of the ovaries of the workers and keeps them infertile. The active ingredient of queen substance is *trans*-9-oxo-2-decenoic acid:

An *allomone* is produced by one species and detected by another. It gives the producing species some kind of advantage. Allomones are often secreted for defensive purposes. Over nineteen hundred years ago, the Roman scholar Pliny recorded that plants growing beneath walnut trees became poisoned. We now know that this occurs because the leaves of the walnut tree store a nontoxic glycoside which is converted to a substance called juglone when the leaves fall to the ground. Juglone is toxic to other plants. It appears that the walnut tree produces this toxin to prevent other plants from using its supply of water and nutrients.

Kairomones are substances that are a disadvantage to the organism that produces the chemical message, usually through normal metabolism. In this category we include secretions that attract predators to their prey and herbivores to their food. An example is lactic acid (2-hydroxypropanoic acid), which is produced by human beings and attracts the yellow fever mosquito, *Aedes aegypti*:

Although most known pheromones, allomones, and kairomones relate to chemical communication in plants and insects, some researchers have identified pheromones that influence the behaviour of mammals such as dogs, hamsters, and rodents. Many more interesting discoveries are sure to follow in the near future.

Review of the IUPAC Naming System for Organic Compounds

15.11

To conclude this chapter, we shall summarize the IUPAC rules for naming the various classes of organic compounds introduced.

Alcohols

All alcohols contain the hydroxyl group (—OH). We indicate the presence of this functional group with the ending *-ol*. In addition, the lowest possible number is used to indicate the carbon atom to which the hydroxyl group is attached:

$$CH_3-CH_2-CH_2-CH_2-OH$$

1-butanol

$$CH_3-\underset{\underset{OH}{|}}{CH}-CH_2-CH_3$$

2-butanol

If an alkyl substituent is attached to the longest carbon chain bearing the hydroxyl group, the name of the alkyl group precedes the base name of the alcohol. The point of attachment of the alkyl group is indicated by a number:

$$CH_3-\underset{\underset{CH_3}{|}}{CH}-CH_2-\underset{\underset{OH}{|}}{CH}-CH_3$$

4-methyl-2-pentanol

Ethers

Ethers contain an oxygen atom that links two alkyl groups. The longer alkyl group is used as the base name. The oxygen atom and the shorter alkyl group are then regarded as a single substituent which is named by replacing the *-yl* ending of the name of the alkyl group with the ending *-oxy*. Thus the CH_3—O— group is called methoxy and the name of the compound CH_3—O—CH_2—CH_2—CH_3 is 1-methoxypropane.

Aldehydes and Ketones

Both aldehydes and ketones contain a carbonyl group consisting of a carbon atom and an oxygen atom joined by a double bond (C=O). In an aldehyde, a hydrogen atom is bonded to the carbon atom of the carbonyl group, whereas in a ketone the carbonyl carbon atom is bonded to two other carbon atoms. We name compounds belonging to both of these families by first picking out the longest carbon chain that contains the carbonyl carbon atom. In the case of an aldehyde, the ending of the base (alkane) name is changed from -e to -al. No number is needed to indicate the position of the carbonyl group since it is always at the end of the carbon chain:

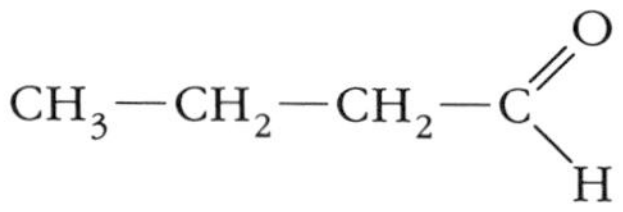

$$CH_3-CH_2-CH_2-C\overset{\displaystyle O}{\underset{\displaystyle H}{\diagup}}$$

butanal

To name a ketone we follow a similar procedure, but now the ending of the base (alkane) name is changed to -one. The position of the carbonyl carbon atom in the chain is indicated, if necessary, using the lowest possible number:

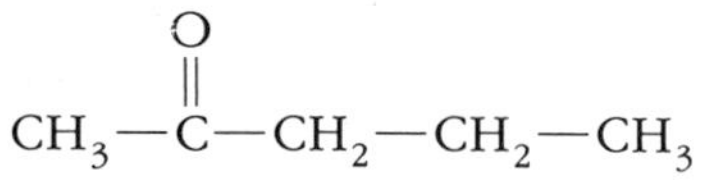

$$CH_3-\overset{\displaystyle O}{\overset{\|}{C}}-CH_2-CH_2-CH_3$$

2-pentanone

The presence of substituents in these compounds can be indicated in the usual manner (see Alcohols, above).

Carboxylic Acids

The functional group present in carboxylic acids is the carboxyl group, $-CO_2H$. When naming carboxylic acids the base (alkane) name is obtained by choosing the longest carbon chain that includes the carboxyl carbon atom. The ending of the base name is changed from -e to -oic acid. No number is required to indicate the position of the carboxyl group as it is automatically at the end of the chain:

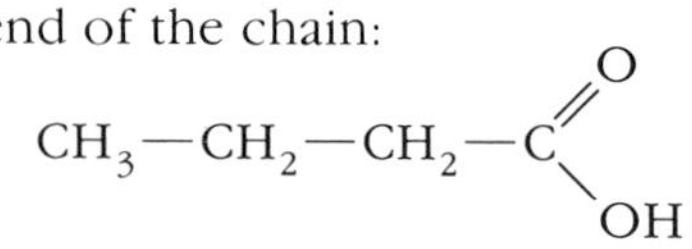

$$CH_3-CH_2-CH_2-C\overset{\displaystyle O}{\underset{\displaystyle OH}{\diagup}}$$

butanoic acid

Again, the presence of a substituent can be indicated as previously described.

Esters

An ester is very similar in structure to a carboxylic acid, except that the hydrogen of the carboxyl group is replaced by an alkyl group. When naming these compounds we first note the name of the carboxylic acid from which the ester is derived, but we change the ending from -oic acid to -oate. This part of the name is preceded by the name of the alkyl group that is attached to the singly-bonded oxygen of the carboxyl group. For example, the compound methyl propanoate can be considered to be derived from propanoic acid and methanol. Here the carboxyl hydrogen atom has been replaced by a methyl group:

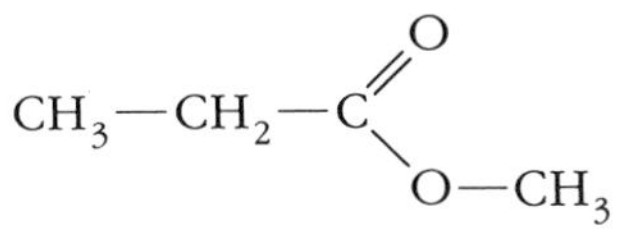

$$CH_3-CH_2-C{\overset{\displaystyle O}{\underset{\displaystyle O-CH_3}{}}}$$

methyl propanoate

Amines

When naming a primary amine according to the IUPAC system we treat the compound as if it were an alkane substituted with an amino (NH_2) group. The position of attachment of the amino group to the carbon chain is indicated using the lowest possible number:

$$CH_3-\underset{\underset{\displaystyle NH_2}{|}}{CH}-CH_2-CH_3$$

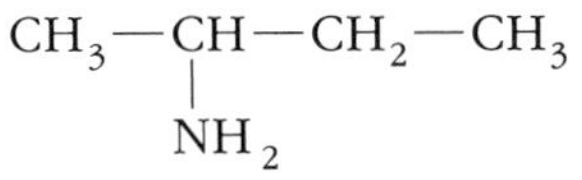

2-aminobutane

Organic Compounds Containing Halogens

Halogen-containing compounds are named as alkanes in which a hydrogen atom has been substituted by a halogen atom. To indicate the presence of a halogen, we use the prefix *fluoro-, chloro-, bromo-,* or *iodo-*. The position at which the halogen atom is attached to the main chain is indicated using the lowest possible number:

$$CH_3-CH_2-CH_2-CH_2-Cl \qquad CH_3-\underset{\underset{\displaystyle Cl}{|}}{CH}-CH_2-CH_3$$

1-chlorobutane   2-chlorobutane

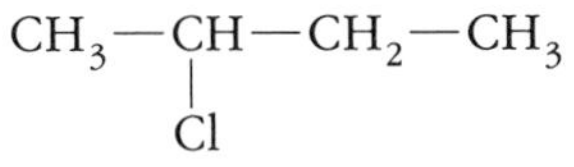

It is quite common to have more than one halogen atom present in a molecule. To indicate the number of halogen atoms present we use the prefixes *di-, tri-, tetra-, penta-, hexa-,* etc:

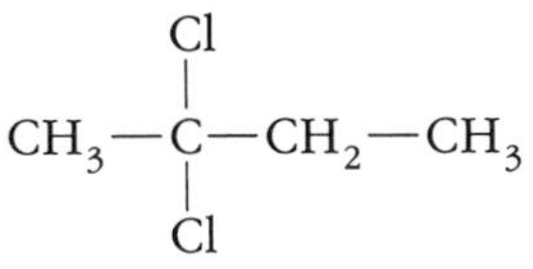

$$CH_3-\underset{\underset{\displaystyle Cl}{|}}{\overset{\overset{\displaystyle Cl}{|}}{C}}-CH_2-CH_3$$

2,2-dichlorobutane

EXAMPLE   **15.8**   Give the IUPAC name of each of the following compounds:

a) 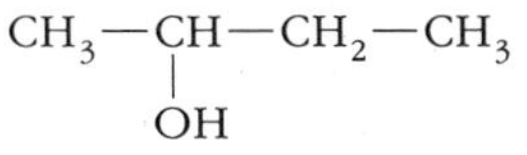 $CH_3-\underset{\underset{\displaystyle OH}{|}}{CH}-CH_2-CH_3$

b)

$$CH_3-C\overset{\displaystyle O}{\underset{\displaystyle O-CH_2-CH_2-CH_3}{\Big\backslash\!\!/}}$$

c)

$$CH_3-\underset{\underset{\displaystyle O-CH_3}{|}}{\overset{\overset{\displaystyle H}{|}}{C}}-CH_2-CH_3$$

d)

$$H-\underset{\underset{\displaystyle Br}{|}}{\overset{\overset{\displaystyle H}{|}}{C}}-\underset{\underset{\displaystyle H}{|}}{\overset{\overset{\displaystyle H}{|}}{C}}-\underset{\underset{\displaystyle Br}{|}}{\overset{\overset{\displaystyle Br}{|}}{C}}-H$$

SOLUTION   a) The carbon chain is four carbon atoms long, which gives us **butane** as our base name. The hydroxyl group is attached to the second carbon in the chain. The name of the compound is therefore **2-butanol**.

b) This compound is an ester derived from the two-carbon carboxylic acid, ethanoic acid. The alkyl group attached to the single-bonded oxygen of the carboxyl group is a propyl group. The name of this ester is therefore **propyl ethanoate**.

c) The presence of an oxygen atom linking two alkyl groups identifies this compound as an ether. The longest alkyl group (four carbons long) is selected to give us the base name **butane**. We regard this chain as being substituted with a methoxy (CH_3-O-) group at the second carbon atom; thus, the name of the compound is **2-methoxybutane**.

d) This compound consists of a three-carbon chain (propane) with three bromine atoms attached. Of these bromine substituents, two are bonded to the first carbon atom in the chain and the other one is bonded to the third carbon atom. Hence the compound is called **1,1,3-tribromopropane**. Note that we numbered the carbon chain from the right rather than the left in order to keep the numbers as low as possible.

QUESTIONS

19. Give the IUPAC name of each of the following compounds:

a)

$$CH_3-\underset{\underset{\displaystyle CH_3}{|}}{CH}-\underset{\underset{\displaystyle CH_3}{|}}{CH}-C\overset{\displaystyle O}{\underset{\displaystyle H}{\Big\backslash\!\!/}}$$

c)

$$CH_3-\underset{\underset{\displaystyle CH_3}{|}}{CH}-C\overset{\displaystyle O}{\underset{\displaystyle OH}{\Big\backslash\!\!/}}$$

b) CH_3-CF_3

d)

$$CH_3-\underset{\underset{\displaystyle NH_2}{|}}{CH}-CH_2-CH_2-CH_3$$

Summary

- The family or class to which a given organic compound belongs is determined by the functional group(s) present in that compound.

- Alcohols contain a hydroxyl group and can be classified as primary, secondary, or tertiary, depending on the number of alkyl groups attached to the carbon atom that is bonded to the hydroxyl group. The IUPAC name of an alcohol always ends with *-ol*.

- Ethers contain an oxygen atom bonded to two alkyl groups. The chemical and physical properties of ethers are similar to those of the alkanes.

- Aldehydes and ketones both contain a carbonyl group, which consists of an oxygen atom joined to a carbon atom by a double bond. An aldehyde has at least one hydrogen attached to the carbonyl carbon atom. A ketone has only other carbon atoms directly attached to the carbonyl carbon atom. The IUPAC name of an aldehyde always ends with *-al* whereas the ending of the IUPAC name of a ketone is *-one*.

- Carboxylic acids contain a carboxyl group, $-CO_2H$. Like mineral acids, carboxylic acids undergo neutralization reactions with bases to form water plus the corresponding salts. The IUPAC name of a carboxylic acid always ends with *-oic acid*.

- Esters can be considered to be formed by replacing the hydrogen of a carboxyl group with an alkyl group. The name of this alkyl group gives us the first part of the ester's name. The second part of the name is derived from the name of the carboxylic acid from which the ester is considered to be formed.

- Fats are triesters derived from three units of carboxylic acid and one unit of glycerol. Unsaturated fats contain one or more carbon–carbon double bonds. Saturated fats contain no carbon–carbon double bonds.

- Amines consist of one or more alkyl groups bonded to a nitrogen atom. They are classified as primary, secondary, or tertiary according to the number of alkyl groups attached to the nitrogen atom.

- Alkyl halides can be considered to be alkanes in which one of the hydrogen atoms has been replaced by a halogen atom.

- Amino acids are bifunctional. They contain two functional groups, an amino group and a carboxyl group. The α-amino acids are biologically important as they are building blocks from which proteins are made.

- Simple carbohydrates (or monosaccharides) have the general formula $(CH_2O)_n$. Examples are glucose and fructose, both having the formula $C_6H_{12}O_6$.

aldehyde
alkoxy group
alkyl halide
amide
amine
α-amino acid
amino group
bifunctional
carbohydrate
carbonyl group
carboxyl group
carboxylic acid
dipeptide
disaccharide
ester
ether

fermentation
hydroxyl group
ketone
monosaccharide
peptide
polypeptide
polysaccharide
primary alcohol
primary amine
protein
secondary alcohol
secondary amine
tertiary alcohol
tertiary amine
triglycerides

ANSWERS TO SECTION QUESTIONS

1. a) ketone   c) amine   e) ester
   b) alkyl halide   d) alkene

2. a)

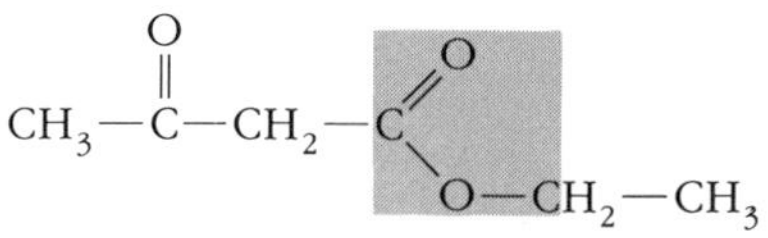

$$CH_3-\overset{O}{\overset{||}{C}}-CH_2-\overset{O}{\overset{||}{C}}-O-CH_2-CH_3$$

b)

$$HO-CH_2-\overset{H}{\underset{NH_2}{\overset{|}{C}}}-\overset{O}{\overset{||}{C}}-OH$$

c)

[structure: dichlorophenoxy ring]$-O-CH_2-\overset{O}{\overset{||}{C}}-OH$, with Cl substituents

3.

$$CH_3-CH_2-CH_2-CH_2-\underset{OH}{\overset{|}{CH_2}},\quad \text{1-pentanol}$$

$$CH_3-CH_2-CH_2-\underset{OH}{\overset{|}{CH}}-CH_3,\quad \text{2-pentanol}$$

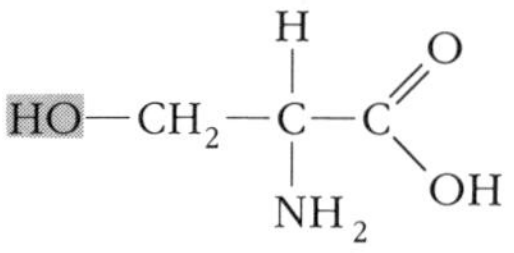

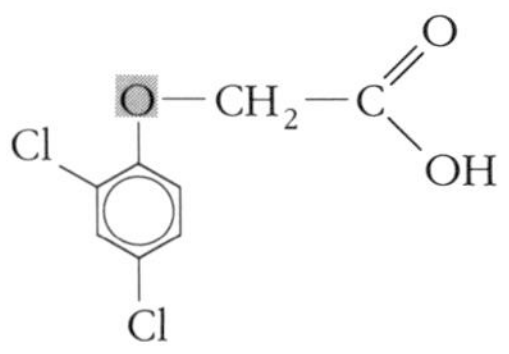

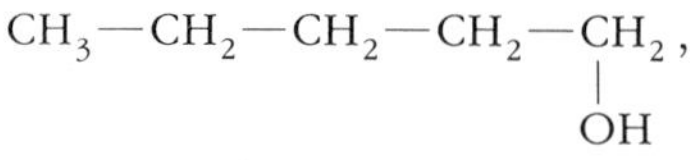

$$CH_3-CH_2-\underset{OH}{\overset{|}{CH}}-CH_2-CH_3,\quad \text{3-pentanol}$$

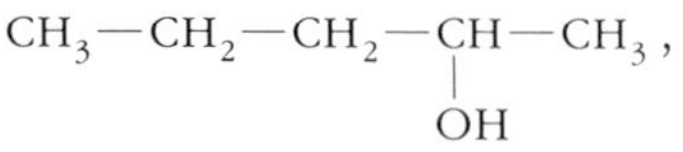

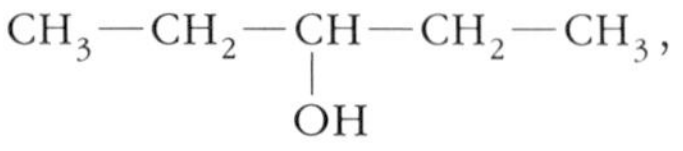

$$CH_3-\underset{OH}{\overset{CH_3}{\overset{|}{\underset{|}{C}}}}-CH_2-CH_3,\quad \text{2-methyl-2-butanol}$$

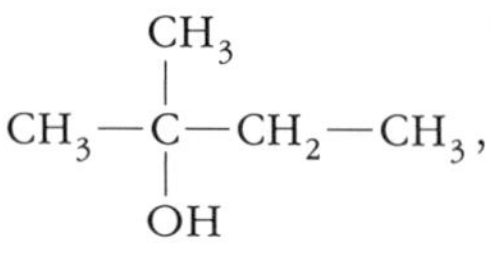

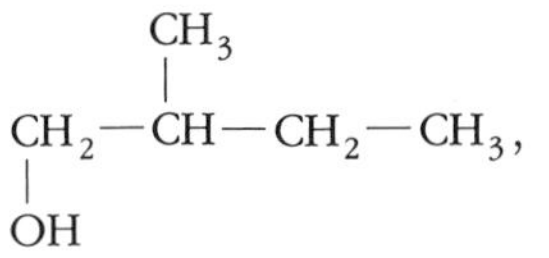

$$CH_2-CH-CH_2-CH_3, \quad \text{2-methyl-1-butanol}$$

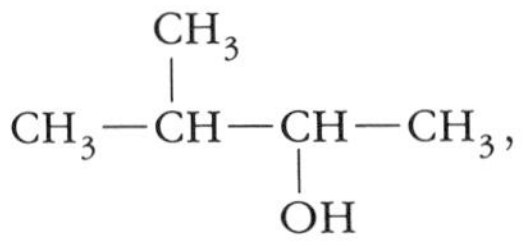

with CH₃ above CH, OH below CH₂:

CH₃ (top)
$$CH_2-\underset{|}{\overset{|}{CH}}-CH_2-CH_3, \quad \text{2-methyl-1-butanol}$$
OH (bottom)

$$CH_3-CH-CH-CH_3, \quad \text{3-methyl-2-butanol}$$ 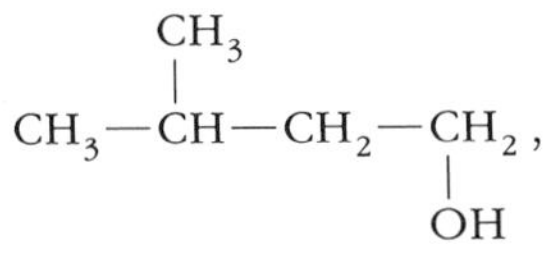
with CH₃ above first CH, OH below second CH

$$CH_3-CH-CH_2-CH_2, \quad \text{3-methyl-1-butanol}$$ 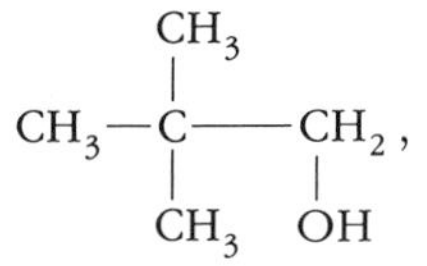
with CH₃ above CH, OH below last CH₂

$$CH_3-C-CH_2, \quad \text{2,2-dimethyl-1-propanol}$$
with CH₃ above C, CH₃ and OH below

4. a) 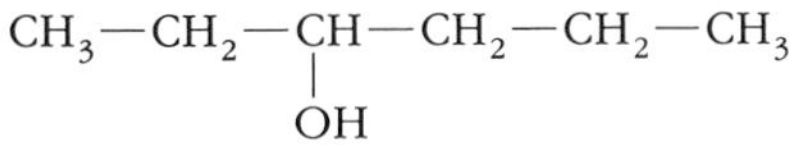 $CH_3-CH_2-CH-CH_2-CH_2-CH_3$
with OH below CH

b) 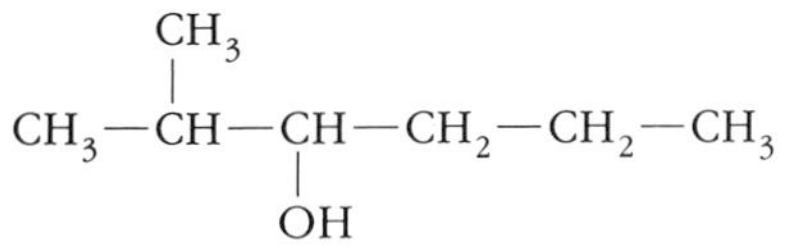
CH₃
$CH_3-CH-CH-CH_2-CH_2-CH_3$
with OH below second CH

c)
CH₃ CH₃
$CH_3-C-CH-CH_2-CH_2-CH_3$
with OH below C

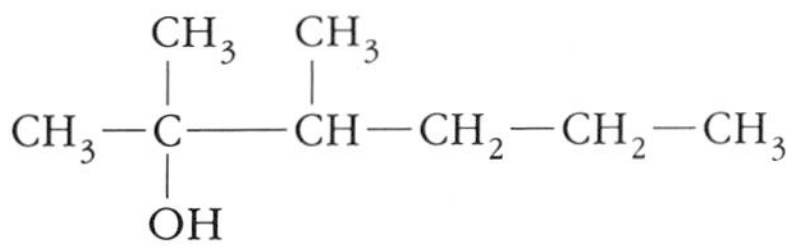

5. *Primary:* 1-pentanol, 2-methyl-1-butanol, 3-methyl-1-butanol, and 2,2-dimethyl-1-propanol
Secondary: 2-pentanol, 3-pentanol, and 3-methyl-2-butanol
Tertiary: 2-methyl-2-butanol

6. Ethyl methyl ether; methoxyethane

7. 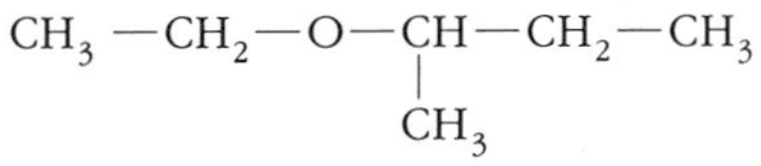 $CH_3-CH_2-O-CH-CH_2-CH_3$
with CH₃ below CH

8. a) 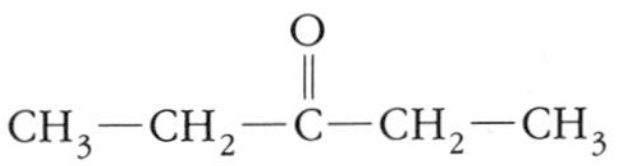
O
‖
$CH_3-CH_2-C-CH_2-CH_3$

b)

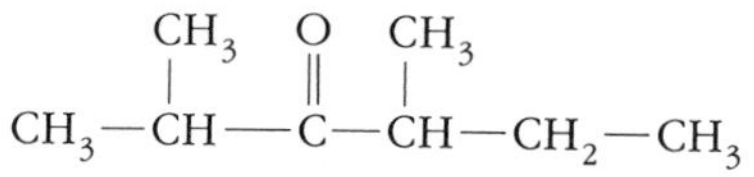

$$CH_3-\underset{\underset{\displaystyle CH_3}{|}}{CH}-\underset{\underset{\displaystyle }{\|}}{\overset{\overset{\displaystyle O}{}}{C}}-\underset{\underset{\displaystyle CH_3}{|}}{CH}-CH_2-CH_3$$

c)

$$CH_3-CH_2-CH_2-C\overset{\displaystyle O}{\underset{\displaystyle H}{\diagup}}$$

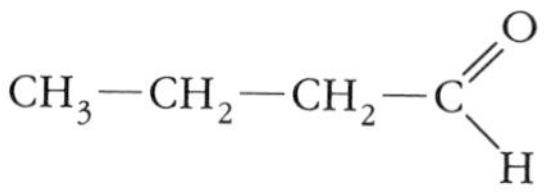

d)

$$CH_3-CH_2-CH_2-\underset{\underset{\displaystyle CH_3}{|}}{CH}-C\overset{\displaystyle O}{\underset{\displaystyle H}{\diagup}}$$

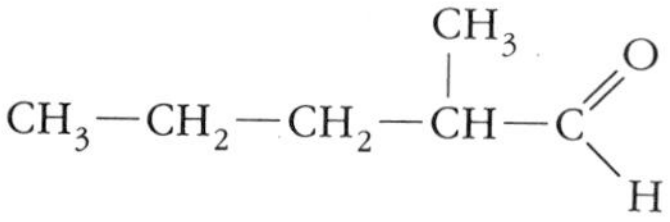

9. a) 4-methyl-2-pentanone   b) 2,2-dimethylpropanal

10. a) pentanoic acid   b) 2,2-dimethylpropanoic acid

11. a)

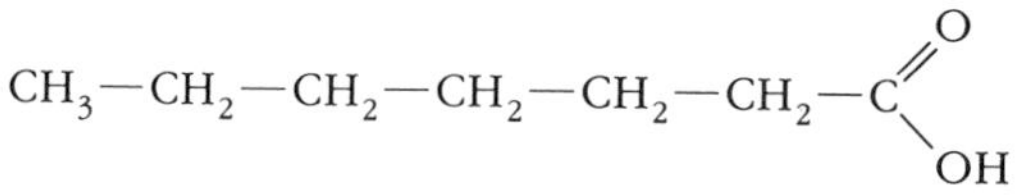

$$CH_3-CH_2-CH_2-CH_2-CH_2-CH_2-C\overset{\displaystyle O}{\underset{\displaystyle OH}{\diagup}}$$

b)

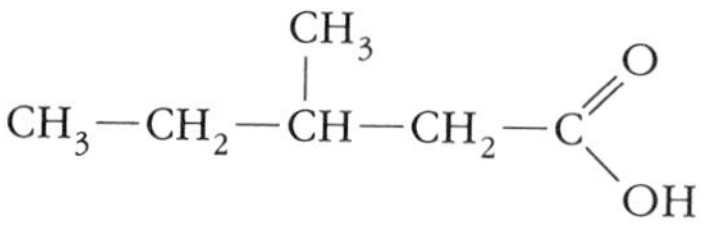

$$CH_3-CH_2-\underset{\underset{\displaystyle CH_3}{|}}{CH}-CH_2-C\overset{\displaystyle O}{\underset{\displaystyle OH}{\diagup}}$$

12.

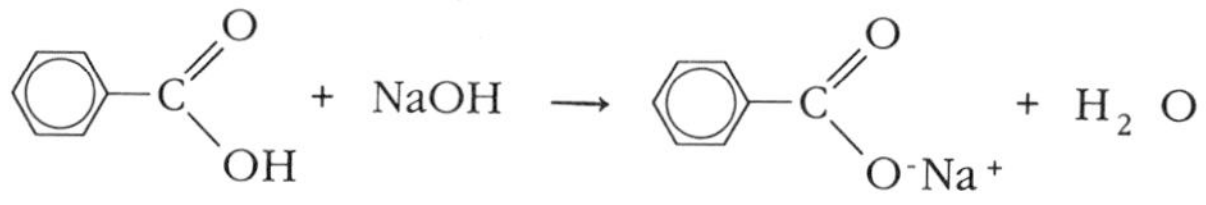

$$\bigcirc\!\!-C\overset{\displaystyle O}{\underset{\displaystyle OH}{\diagup}} \;+\; NaOH \;\longrightarrow\; \bigcirc\!\!-C\overset{\displaystyle O}{\underset{\displaystyle O^-Na^+}{\diagup}} \;+\; H_2O$$

13. a)

$$CH_3-C\overset{\displaystyle O}{\underset{\displaystyle O-CH_3}{\diagup}} \qquad H-C\overset{\displaystyle O}{\underset{\displaystyle O-CH_2-CH_3}{\diagup}}$$

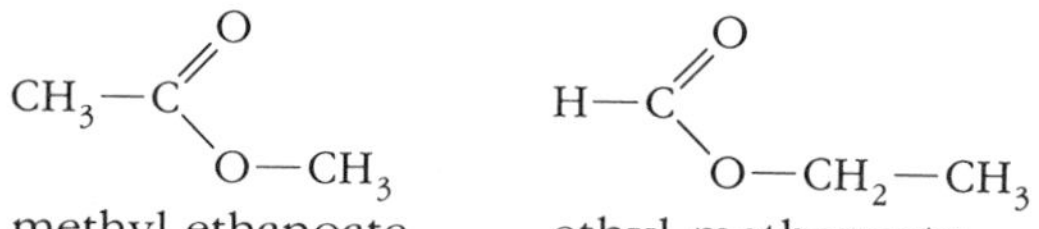

b) methyl ethanoate   ethyl methanoate
c) methanol, ethanoic acid; ethanol, methanoic acid

14.

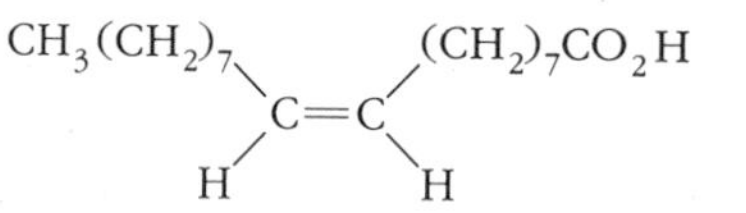

$$\underset{H}{\overset{CH_3(CH_2)_7}{\diagdown}}C=C\underset{H}{\overset{(CH_2)_7CO_2H}{\diagup}}$$

15. a)

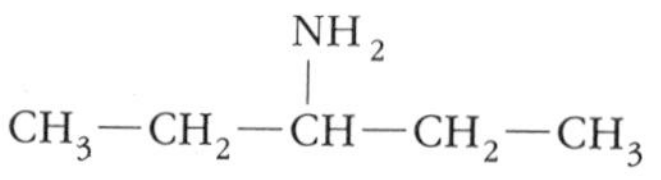

$$CH_3-CH_2-\underset{\underset{\displaystyle }{|}}{\overset{\overset{\displaystyle NH_2}{|}}{CH}}-CH_2-CH_3$$

a primary amine

b)

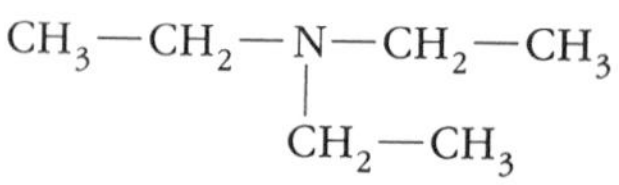

$$CH_3-CH_2-\underset{\underset{\displaystyle CH_2-CH_3}{|}}{N}-CH_2-CH_3$$

a tertiary amine

16.

$$\bigcirc\!\!-NH_2 + HCl \;\longrightarrow\; \bigcirc\!\!-NH_3^+Cl^-$$

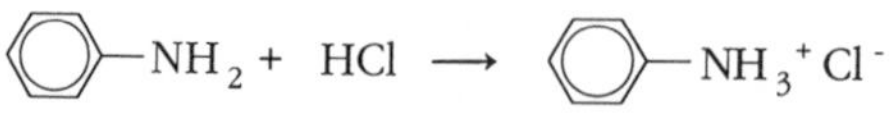

17. a) triiodomethane   b) chloroethane   c) 1,2,3,4-tetrachlorobutane

18. a)

$$Cl-\underset{\underset{\displaystyle Cl}{|}}{\overset{\overset{\displaystyle Cl}{|}}{C}}-\underset{\underset{\displaystyle H}{|}}{\overset{\overset{\displaystyle H}{|}}{C}}-\underset{\underset{\displaystyle H}{|}}{\overset{\overset{\displaystyle H}{|}}{C}}-H$$

b)

c)

$$H-\underset{\underset{\displaystyle H}{|}}{\overset{\overset{\displaystyle H}{|}}{C}}-\underset{\underset{\displaystyle H}{|}}{\overset{\overset{\displaystyle H}{|}}{C}}-\underset{\underset{\displaystyle H}{|}}{\overset{\overset{\displaystyle Br}{|}}{C}}-\underset{\underset{\displaystyle H}{|}}{\overset{\overset{\displaystyle H}{|}}{C}}-\underset{\underset{\displaystyle H}{|}}{\overset{\overset{\displaystyle H}{|}}{C}}-H$$

19. a) 2,3-dimethylbutanol   c) 2-methylpropanoic acid
b) 1,1,1-trifluoroethane   d) 2-aminopentane

COMPREHENSION QUESTIONS

1. Draw the functional group(s) present in each of the following classes of organic compounds:
a) aldehydes   d) carboxylic acids   g) alcohols
b) primary amines   e) ketones   h) amino acids
c) ethers   f) esters

2. What is the difference between primary, secondary, and tertiary alcohols? Give an example of each.

3. What is the difference between wood alcohol, grain alcohol, and rubbing alcohol?

4. What is denatured alcohol?

5. What is the difference between an aldehyde and a ketone?

6. What two classes of compounds react together to produce an ester?

7. a) What is the difference between a saturated and an unsaturated triglyceride (fat)?
b) Why can eating large amounts of saturated animal fats be harmful?

8. What is the difference between a fat and an oil?

9. What is the difference between primary, secondary, and tertiary amines? Give an example of each.

10. Of what repeating chemical units are the following composed:
a) proteins   b) cellulose and starch

11. Name the two monosaccharides that combine to form the disaccharide, sucrose.

12. Briefly describe the similarities and differences between the two most important polysaccharides, starch and cellulose.

13. Give the name and condensed formula of each of the following:
    a) a compound used to preserve biological specimens
    b) the acid found in ant bites
    c) the acid found in vinegar
    d) the simplest α-amino acid

14. Provide the name and formula for each of the following:
    a) a common drug used to relieve headaches
    b) a compound used as an antifreeze in car radiators
    c) two organic compounds formerly used as anesthetics

15. Name one use for each of the following organic compounds:
    a) aniline   b) methanol   c) 1,2,3-propanetriol (glycerol)

16. Give one use for each of the following chemicals:
    a) metaldehyde   b) propanone (acetone)   c) sodium benzoate

17. Identify the functional group(s) present in each of the compounds shown below:

a)

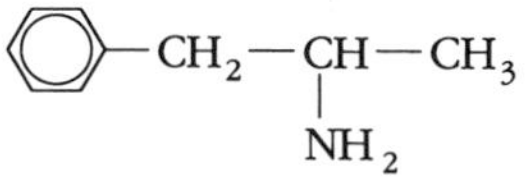

$$\text{C}_6\text{H}_5-\text{CH}_2-\underset{\underset{\text{NH}_2}{|}}{\text{CH}}-\text{CH}_3$$

benzedrine
(an amphetamine)

b)

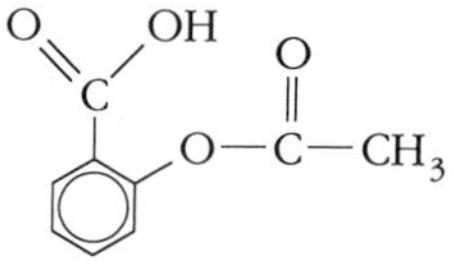

acetylsalicylic acid
(aspirin)

c)

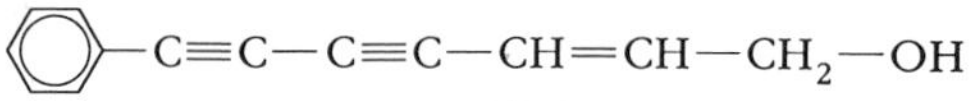

$$\text{C}_6\text{H}_5-\text{C}\equiv\text{C}-\text{C}\equiv\text{C}-\text{CH}=\text{CH}-\text{CH}_2-\text{OH}$$

compositol
(a compound produced by the plant *Coreopsis*)

d)

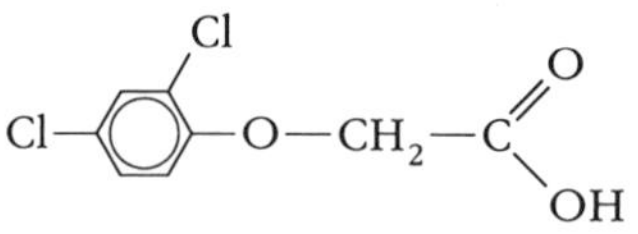

2,4-D
(a herbicide that kills broad-leaved plants)

e)

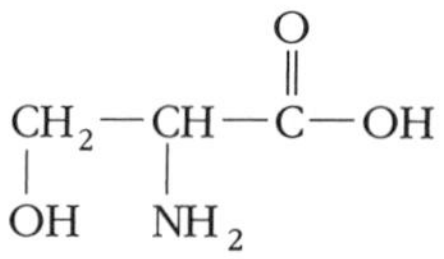

$$\underset{\underset{\text{OH}}{|}}{\text{CH}_2}-\underset{\underset{\text{NH}_2}{|}}{\text{CH}}-\overset{\overset{\text{O}}{\|}}{\text{C}}-\text{OH}$$

serine (a common α-amino acid)

18. Identify the family of compounds (e.g. alkane, ester, aromatic) to which each of the following belong:

a) 2-methyl-2-propanol   d) 4-methylpentanal

b) 2-methyl-3-hexanone   e) 3-methoxypentane

c) ethyl benzoate

(NOTE: Some may belong to more than one family.)

19. What is the minimum number of carbon atoms that must be present in each of the following:

a) a secondary alcohol   c) a secondary amine

b) a tertiary alcohol   d) a tertiary amine

20. Draw the structure and give the IUPAC name for all the possible alcohols with the formula C_4H_9OH. Identify each as a primary, secondary, or tertiary alcohol.

21. Draw the structure and give both the common and IUPAC names of each of the three ethers with the formula $C_4H_{10}O$.

22. a) Draw the structure and provide the IUPAC and common name of the ether with the formula C_2H_6O.

b) Which common organic compound, belonging to a different family or class, has the same formula as the ether in a)? Draw the structure of this compound and give its IUPAC name.

23. Draw the structure and give the IUPAC name of both an aldehyde and a ketone with the formula C_3H_6O.

24. Two aldehydes and one ketone have the formula C_4H_8O. Draw the structures of these compounds and name each one according to the IUPAC system.

25. Provide either the IUPAC or common name for each of the following:

a) $CH_3-CH_2-C \overset{\displaystyle O}{\underset{\displaystyle H}{\diagdown}}$

b) $CH_3-CH-CH_2-CH_3$
    $\quad\quad\ \ \overset{|}{NH_2}$

c) $CH_3-CH_2-CH_2-C \overset{\displaystyle O}{\underset{\displaystyle OH}{\diagdown}}$

d) $CH_3-CH-CH_2-CH_2-CH_3$
    $\quad\quad\ \ \overset{|}{OH}$

e) $CH_3-CH-C \overset{\displaystyle O}{\underset{\displaystyle OH}{\diagdown}}$
    $\quad\quad\ \overset{|}{CH_3}$

f) 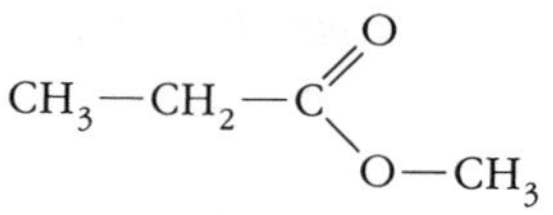 $CH_3-CH_2-C{\overset{\displaystyle O}{\underset{\displaystyle O-CH_3}{\Vert}}}$

g) 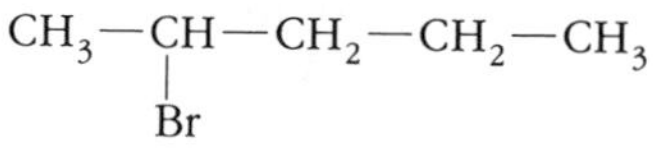 $CH_3-\underset{\underset{\displaystyle Br}{|}}{CH}-CH_2-CH_2-CH_3$

h) 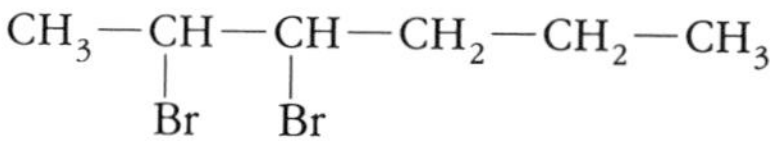 $CH_3-\underset{\underset{\displaystyle Br}{|}}{CH}-\underset{\underset{\displaystyle Br}{|}}{CH}-CH_2-CH_2-CH_3$

i) $CH_3-O-CH_2-CH_2-CH_2-CH_2-CH_3$

j) 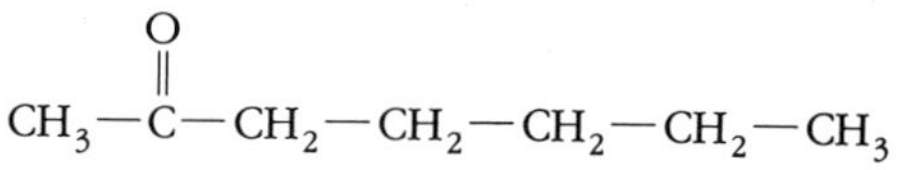 $CH_3-\overset{\displaystyle O}{\overset{\displaystyle \Vert}{C}}-CH_2-CH_2-CH_2-CH_2-CH_3$

26. Give either the IUPAC or common name for each of the following:

a) 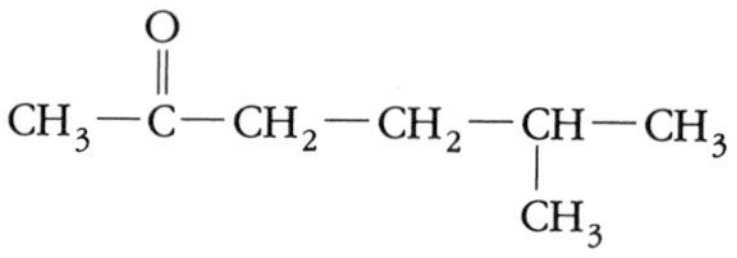 $CH_3-\overset{\displaystyle O}{\overset{\displaystyle \Vert}{C}}-CH_2-CH_2-\underset{\underset{\displaystyle CH_3}{|}}{CH}-CH_3$

b) 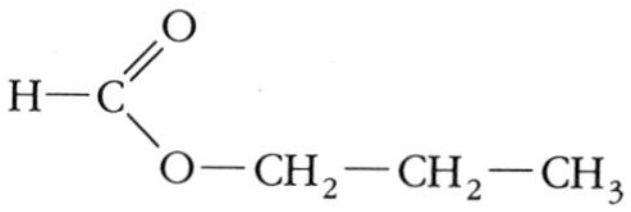 $H-C{\overset{\displaystyle O}{\underset{\displaystyle O-CH_2-CH_2-CH_3}{\Vert}}}$

c) $(CH_3)_3 N$

d) 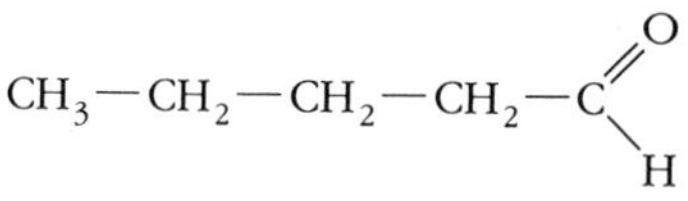 $CH_3-CH_2-CH_2-CH_2-C{\overset{\displaystyle O}{\underset{\displaystyle H}{\Vert}}}$

e) 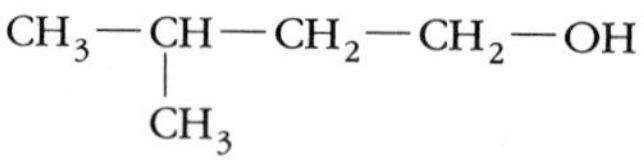 $CH_3-\underset{\underset{\displaystyle CH_3}{|}}{CH}-CH_2-CH_2-OH$

f) CH_3-O-CH_3

g) 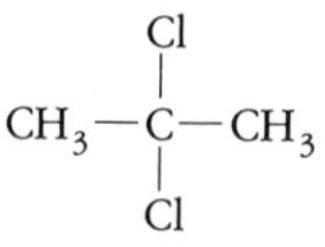 $CH_3-\overset{\overset{\displaystyle Cl}{|}}{\underset{\underset{\displaystyle Cl}{|}}{C}}-CH_3$

h) $CH_3-CH_2-NH_2$

i) $CH_3-CH-CH-CH_3$
     | |
    CH_3 OH

j) $CH_3-CH_2-CH_2-CH_2-CH_2-C\overset{O}{\underset{OH}{\diagup\!\!\!\backslash}}$

27. Draw the condensed formula for each of the following compounds:
    a) 2-pentanone
    b) methyl propanoate
    c) triethylamine
    d) hexanoic acid
    e) 2,2-dichlorobutane

28. Draw the condensed formula for each of the compounds named below:
    a) ethyl butanoate
    b) 1-butanol
    c) 2-methylpentanoic acid
    d) 4-methyl-2-hexanone
    e) 2-methoxypropane

29. Draw the condensed formula of each carboxylic acid and ester that has the molecular formula $C_4H_8O_2$.

30. Draw the condensed formula of each carboxylic acid and ester with the molecular formula $C_5H_{10}O_2$.

31. Write a balanced equation for
    a) the preparation of methanal (formaldehyde) by the oxidation of methanol at high temperature in the presence of a catalyst (the other product is water vapour)
    b) the neutralization of methanoic (formic) acid by potassium hydroxide

32. Write a balanced equation for
    a) the reaction between trimethylamine and hydrochloric acid
    b) the reaction between 1 mol of 1,2-ethanediol and 2 mol of ethanoic (acetic) acid

33. Write a balanced equation for the reaction that occurs between each of the following pairs of compounds:
    a) methanoic (formic) acid and ethanol
    b) ethanoic (acetic) acid and methanol

34. Write a balanced equation to show how each of the following esters could be prepared in the laboratory:

    a) $CH_3-C\overset{O}{\underset{O-CH_2-CH_3}{\diagup\!\!\!\backslash}}$

    b) $CH_3-CH_2-CH_2-C\overset{O}{\underset{O-(CH_2)_4-CH_3}{\diagup\!\!\!\backslash}}$

    c) $CH_3-C\overset{O}{\underset{O-(CH_2)_7-CH_3}{\diagup\!\!\!\backslash}}$

35. Because of the high density of its vapour, carbon tetrachloride was at one time used in fire extinguishers. Calculate the density of carbon tetrachloride, $CCl_{4 (g)}$, at 200 °C and 101.3 kPa.

36. Would it be possible to ship natural gas (methane) from the Arctic by filling balloons with the gas and flying them south? (HINT: Find the density of methane at 5 °C and standard atmospheric pressure and compare it with the value for air, $1.2 \ g \cdot L^{-1}$, under these conditions.)

37. Gasoline containing about 5% ethanol is currently available in certain parts of North America for use as an automobile fuel.
    a) Write a balanced equation for the reaction of ethanol with oxygen gas. The products are $CO_{2 (g)}$ and $H_2O_{(g)}$.
    b) Calculate the volume of oxygen gas, at 20 °C and 101.3 kPa of pressure, necessary to burn 1.00 L of ethanol. The density of ethanol is $0.789 \ g \cdot L^{-1}$.

38. The balanced equation for the explosive reaction of nitroglycerin is
    $$4 \ C_3H_5(ONO_2)_3 \longrightarrow 12 \ CO_{2 (g)} + O_{2 (g)} + 6 \ N_{2 (g)} + 10 \ H_2O_{(g)}$$
    If 5.0 g of nitroglycerin explodes in a 1.0 L container, calculate the resulting pressure inside the container if the final temperature is 45 °C.

39. Analysis shows that a certain organic compound has the following composition (by mass): 29.30% carbon, 5.74% hydrogen, 64.96% bromine.
    a) Determine the empirical formula of this compound.
    b) What is the molecular mass of this compound if its molecular formula is the same as its empirical formula?

40. An organic halogen-containing compound was found to have the following composition by mass: 49.02% carbon, 2.74% hydrogen, 48.24% chlorine. If the molecular mass of this compound is $145 \ g \cdot mol^{-1}$, what is its molecular formula?

SUGGESTED PROJECTS

1. The pharmaceutical industry produces a wide variety of chemicals for medicinal purposes. Using reference books, write an essay on some of the chemicals produced by this industry and their use in medicine.

2. In this text we have discussed structural isomerism and geometrical (*cis–trans*) isomerism. A third type of isomerism, optical isomerism, is displayed by certain organic compounds. Research this subject and write a report on optical isomerism. Discuss why it is important in biological systems.

3. Steroids are a group of naturally occurring organic compounds. Find out all you can about the structures of these compounds and the roles they play in the human body.

4. Prepare and purify a number of organic esters that have distinctive aromas. Organize a display of these compounds, including information on their structures and method of preparation. Be sure you are aware of the necessary safety precautions before preparing these compounds. This will require checking with your instructor.

The Canadian Chemical Industry

There is much more to chemistry than mixing chemicals in a laboratory. Modern lifestyles depend on steel, plastics, high-grade fertilizers, and many other materials that are not found in nature. Industries prepare most of these materials by utilizing large-scale chemical processes that convert naturally occurring raw materials into the desired end products.

However, with greater industrialization and the parallel increase in demand for electrical energy come new problems that threaten both our environment and the quality of working life. As we examine some Canadian chemical industries we will stress not only the chemical processes involved but some of the issues we have to face in our industrialized society.

The Origins of the Canadian Chemical Industry 16.1

One of the basic requirements of settlers in any new country is a source of iron for making cooking utensils, farm implements, and other tools. Iron, like many other metals, is produced in **smelters** that combine chemical processes with high temperatures in order to produce molten metals. The first known iron smelter in Canada was established by the Vikings, circa 1000 A.D., at what is now L'Anse aux Meadows, Newfoundland. However, we have to look to 1736 and the establishment of the iron smelter at St. Maurice, Quebec, as the first example of the large-scale production of iron in Canada.

The origins of the Canadian petrochemical industry can also be traced back to the days before Confederation. In the middle of the 19th century, the oil lamps used in North America normally burned whale oil. Since the American Civil War resulted in a shortage of this commodity, it became necessary for Canadians to find an alternative fuel with which to light their lamps.

Abraham Gesner, a Nova Scotian geologist, had previously shown that lamps could be fuelled by kerosene, a product that can be obtained from coal. However, kerosene could also be produced from petroleum, and Gesner introduced a chemical method for refining kerosene that involved the use of sulfuric acid. By 1864, there were 27 small refineries producing kerosene in the Petrolia–Oil Springs area of Ontario. These refineries depended on sulfuric acid that was imported by lake schooner from Cleveland, Ohio. However, in rough weather the schooner captains would often throw the containers of sulfuric acid overboard, as they were concerned that the containers might break or spill. As a result, the Petrolia refineries were frequently short of sulfuric acid.

Two railroad employees, T.H. Smallman and W. Bowman, realized that the solution to the problem was to build a sulfuric acid plant near the Petrolia refinery. This plant, which opened at London, Ontario in 1867, marked the founding of the Canada Chemical Company, now Allied Chemical (Canada) Ltd.

Industrial Chemistry

16.2 There are some major differences between small-scale laboratory work and large-scale industrial chemistry. A few of these differences are identified below.

Figure 16.1
An erroneous image of an industrial chemical plant.

Cost

In industry, cost is of major importance. In order for a chemical industry to survive, the value of its product must be more than the total cost of producing it. Production costs include the price of raw materials, transportation, depreciation and maintenance of the plant, labour, and energy. Even then, the selling price of the product is not determined by simply adding a profit margin to the production cost. Consumer demand and competition in the marketplace must also be taken into account.

An understanding of these factors is essential if we are to understand why a given chemical plant is located in a specific country or region. Three key factors that must be taken into consideration are discussed below.

1. **The availability of an ample supply of raw materials**
   Transportation costs can be minimized by processing impure raw materials near their source of supply. This is a major reason why Canadian oil refineries and metal smelters are often located close to oil or mineral deposits. The development of large, bulk-cargo ships that can move huge volumes of raw materials at very low cost has reduced the importance of this consideration.

2. **The proximity of an inexpensive energy source**
   Many chemical processes consume vast quantities of energy, often in the form of electricity. The cost of this energy is usually a major factor in determining the cost of the final product. In Canada, we have an ample supply of electric power.

3. **A large domestic market for the product**
   Canada has a small domestic market for chemical products and therefore many international or U.S. companies would prefer to locate manufacturing plants in the United States, where there is a much larger domestic market. Without its vast natural resources and relatively abundant low-cost energy, it is doubtful whether Canada could maintain a viable chemical industry.

Scale

In the laboratory, we mix reactants together in a glass beaker or test tube in order to obtain a small amount of product. In industry, much larger quantities of material are used. Consequently, it is preferable to organize an industrial plant so that its product can be prepared on a continual basis. Furthermore, although glass is an excellent material for small laboratory containers, its fragility makes it impractical for the large-scale storage tanks, pipes, and reaction containers required by industry. These are usually contructed of steel.

When planning to produce a chemical on an industrial scale it is important to beware of problems that may seem minor when the same chemical is produced on a smaller scale, as in the case of a test-tube reaction. For example, the release of a small amount of heat or gas in a test-tube reaction could indicate the possibility of a massive build-up of heat or pressure in a large, sealed, reactor vessel. To avoid problems of this nature a pilot plant, which is a scaled-down version of the proposed plant, is usually built before construction begins on the plant itself. Problems can then be identified and any necessary modifications made and tested before hundreds of millions of dollars are spent.

Waste Disposal

We can often dispose of the small quantities of waste chemicals produced in a school laboratory by washing them down the drain with large volumes of water. However, the disposal of the large amounts of chemical wastes produced in an industrial process can cause serious environmental problems. Many chemical plants were built long before environmental pollution became a major concern. It is often both difficult and costly to install anti-pollution devices in these older plants. Sometimes it is more economical to close such plants down and build new ones, frequently in different locations. Unfortunately such moves often result in social upheaval and loss of employment in the communities that were home to the older plants.

The three major types of wastes produced by chemical industries are gases, which can cause air pollution; liquids, which can cause water and soil pollution; and solids, which are often dumped at some convenient location. Chemical manufacturers are interested in finding uses for these by-products — if a use can be found the disposal problem will be solved and the plant will become more cost-effective.

Aluminum 16.3

Although aluminum is the most abundant metallic element in the earth's crust, it is not easy to obtain in pure form. Aluminum is very high in the activity series, and is therefore extremely difficult to separate from the other elements with which it is combined in nature. In addition, most aluminum compounds are found in clay. To date, we have not yet developed a commercially viable process for extracting aluminum from this source.

Bauxite, an ore consisting mainly of hydrated aluminum oxide, is still the only source from which we can commercially extract aluminum. About 30% of the world's bauxite is mined in Australia, but Canada's three main sources are Brazil and Guyana in South America, and Guinea in West Africa. Bauxite typically contains about 50% aluminum oxide and about 15% silicon dioxide and iron(III) oxide. The remainder is mainly water.

Aluminum smelters in Canada are located close to inexpensive sources of electricity because one of the major costs in aluminum extraction is the cost of energy. Nearby deep-water ports are important as a means of delivering raw materials and shipping the refined metal.

TABLE 16.1	*Aluminum Smelters in Canada*	
Province	Number of Smelters	Aluminum Production, 1984 (tonnes)
Quebec	6	966 000
British Columbia	1	268 000

When bauxite ore arrives in Canada, the first step is to remove the impurities. This is done by reacting a hot solution of sodium hydroxide with the bauxite. The aluminum oxide in the bauxite reacts with the base to give a solution of sodium aluminate. The aluminate anion is a polyatomic oxyanion, analogous to the chromate and permanganate anions.

$$2\ NaOH_{(aq)}\ +\ Al_2O_{3\ (s)} \longrightarrow 2\ NaAlO_{2\ (aq)}\ +\ H_2O_{(\ell)}$$

The iron and silicon oxides present in the ore do not react with sodium hydroxide, but remain as a red, insoluble sludge. This sludge, called 'red mud', is filtered out of the solution of sodium aluminate. When the remaining solution is cooled, the reverse reaction takes place:

$$2\ NaAlO_{2\ (aq)}\ +\ H_2O_{(\ell)} \longrightarrow Al_2O_{3\ (s)}\ +\ 2\ NaOH_{(aq)}$$

The solid aluminum oxide, which at this point exists as the trihydrate $Al_2O_3 \cdot 3H_2O$, is then separated from the sodium hydroxide solution by filtration. The penultimate step in the overall process is to heat the solid aluminum oxide trihydrate to over 1000 °C in order to remove the residual water:

$$Al_2O_3 \cdot 3H_2O_{(s)} \xrightarrow{\Delta} Al_2O_{3\ (s)}\ +\ 3\ H_2O_{(g)}$$

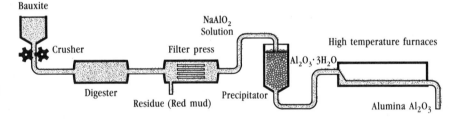

Figure 16.2

A flowchart showing steps in the production of pure aluminum oxide from bauxite.

In the final step of the process, aluminum metal is produced from aluminum oxide by **electrolysis**; that is, by passing an electric current through aluminum oxide. As you are probably aware, household electricity is supplied at 110 V, and currents of about 200 A are adequate for most domestic purposes. By way of contrast, the voltage used in the electrolysis of aluminum oxide is very low — about 4.5 V. However, the current required is very high, about 100 000 A. It is for this reason that aluminum smelters are located close to sources of cheap electric power.

In the electrolytic process itself, the aluminum oxide is dissolved in cryolite, Na_3AlF_6, at a temperature of about 1000 °C. This is accomplished

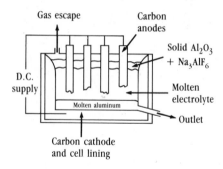

Gas escape

Carbon anodes

Solid Al_2O_3 + Na_3AlF_6

D.C. supply

Molten aluminum

Molten electrolyte

Outlet

Carbon cathode and cell lining

Figure 16.3

A schematic of the electrolytic cell used in the extraction of aluminum.

in a steel container called a 'pot'. Large carbon rods are then lowered into the pot and an electric current is passed through the molten solution from the carbon lining of the pot to the carbon rods.

In order to understand what happens in this process, we must consider the aluminum oxide present in the molten solution as consisting of free aluminum ions and free oxide ions. The negatively charged oxide ions are attracted to the positively charged carbon rods. There, they lose electrons and react with carbon atoms to give carbon dioxide gas. As the carbon rods decompose during the process to form carbon dioxide, the rods must be replaced on a continuing basis:

$$2 \; O^{2-} \; + \; C_{(s)} \longrightarrow CO_{2 \; (g)} \; + \; 4e^-$$

Similarly, the positively charged aluminum ions are attracted towards the negatively charged carbon lining of the pot, where they gain electrons to form aluminum metal:

$$Al^{3+} \; + \; 3e^- \longrightarrow Al_{(\ell)}$$

As aluminum melts at 659 °C and is denser than the molten cryolite–aluminum oxide solution, it forms a layer at the bottom of the pot. This liquid aluminum is siphoned off periodically and transferred to a holding furnace, where it is kept liquid until it is poured into moulds to form ingots or castings. About 70% of the aluminum produced in Canada is exported, most of it to the United States. Significant quantities are also sent to Japan and China.

Figure 16.4

Approximate quantities of reactants and products involved in the aluminum smelting process.

carbon ($^1/_2$ kg)

bauxite (4 kg)

electricity (5.6 × 10⁷ J)

aluminum smelter

carbon dioxide (1.25 kg)

aluminum (1 kg)

red mud ($^1/_2$ kg)

Uses of Aluminum

The importance of aluminum as a metal is second only to that of iron. Although aluminum is high in the activity series, a microthin, tough coating of aluminum oxide forms over the surface of aluminum metal when it is exposed to air. This protects the metal from further attack by oxygen.

Aluminum has a low density, 2.7 g·cm⁻³, and is therefore used in applications where weight is an important factor, such as in aircraft bodies. However, as aluminum is not a very strong metal, it is usually alloyed with other elements to give it more strength. One aluminum alloy used in the manufacture of aircraft consists of 94.4% aluminum, 4.5% copper, 1.0% magnesium, and 0.1% manganese.

Aluminum is a good conductor of electricity and was once used in residential wiring. Too often, however, improper connections were made

Figure 16.5
The bodies of commercial aircraft are constructed from aluminum alloys.

between existing copper wiring and the new aluminum wiring. As corrosion can occur at such junctions, electrical fires were often the unfortunate result. Consequently aluminum wiring has been disallowed for residential use.

Aluminum is also a very good conductor of heat, and is therefore used to make cooking utensils. Its malleability and light weight make it ideal for use in the form of aluminum foil. It is also used extensively to make containers for many consumer drinks. However, acid foods should not be cooked in aluminum pans, nor should acid liquids be stored in aluminum containers. The aluminum reacts with the acid to produce the Al^{3+} ion. Excessive intake of this ion is now suspected to be one of the contributing factors in Alzheimer's disease.

As we have seen, the production of aluminum metal from bauxite requires enormous quantities of electricity. On the other hand, only 5% of this energy is required to recycle aluminum. Thus, recycling aluminum (particularly cans) is an important way of conserving our energy resources and reducing our expenditures on imported raw materials.

Environmental Issues

There are three major pollution problems associated with the production of aluminum. Two of these are the large amounts of carbon dioxide gas and red mud (silicon and iron oxides) that are produced as by-products. For every kilogram of aluminum produced, almost 1.25 kg of carbon dioxide is released into the atmosphere. Some scientists fear that excessive amounts of atmospheric carbon dioxide could lead to a "greenhouse effect", a warming up of the earth's climate with potentially disastrous results.

Charles Hall and the Extraction of Aluminum

Metallic aluminum was first isolated in 1827 by the German chemist Friedrich Wöhler. The method involved displacing the aluminum from one of its salts using a metal that was above aluminum in the activity series. For example, when potassium was used the reaction was:

$$3\ K_{(s)}\ +\ AlCl_{3\ (s)} \xrightarrow{\Delta} 3\ KCl_{(\ell)}\ +\ Al_{(\ell)}$$

When the reaction mixture was cooled, both the potassium chloride and the aluminum metal solidified. The potassium chloride was removed from the reaction mixture by dissolving it in water, leaving a residue of aluminum metal.

Although Wöhler could have used sodium metal as an alternative to potassium in the above reaction, neither method proved economical, as sodium and potassium were both difficult and expensive to obtain.

Figure 16.6
Charles M. Hall (1863–1914).

Charles M. Hall was born in Ohio in 1863 and became a chemistry student at Oberlin College, Ohio. During a lecture on aluminum, Hall's professor predicted both financial and social rewards for the inventor of an inexpensive method for producing aluminum on an industrial scale. Hall decided to devote all his spare time to developing such a process. He read everything that had been published on aluminum, and conducted experiments in his parents' woodshed. One day in 1886, Hall rushed into his professor's office and presented him with a handful of aluminum buttons that he had prepared by a new electrochemical method. Two years later, Hall set up a small company to produce aluminum on a commercial scale. The company later became ALCOA, the Aluminum Company of America.

Unknown to Hall, a French chemist named Paul Héroult (also born in 1863) had devised a similar process for extracting aluminum. As a result, the procedure is now called the Hall–Héroult process.

The financial rewards that Hall had anticipated were delayed because of a series of challenges to the patents that he filed on the process. However, these challenges were eventually settled in Hall's favour and in 1914 he died a rich man. As a result of the introduction of the Hall–Héroult process, the price of aluminum dropped from about $10/kg in 1886 to about $1.50/kg in 1893.

In his work Hall collaborated with his older sister Julia, who had also studied chemistry. Unfortunately, she received no credit for her contribution to the discovery of the extraction process.

Figure 16.7
The first aluminum nuggets isolated by the modern electrochemical process. Until the discovery of this process in 1886, aluminum was a rare and expensive metal.

Disposal of the red mud is difficult. The mud is very basic because it contains sodium hydroxide from the extraction process. Although the mud has a high iron content, it is not economical to extract the iron. At present, the mud is allowed to settle in ponds. The aqueous layer containing the sodium hydroxide is then removed and either recycled or neutralized. If the sodium hydroxide is neutralized, the water can be run off into rivers or lakes. The dried mud is then used for landfill and for creating new farmland.

The third pollution problem associated with aluminum production is the hydrogen fluoride gas emitted when traces of water react with the cryolite. Hydrogen fluoride causes major damage to vegetation, not only because it is an acid, but also because the fluoride ion is toxic in high concentrations. Fortunately, the acidic hydrogen fluoride gas can be removed by passing the waste gases through powdered aluminum oxide:

$$Al_2O_{3\ (s)} \ + \ 6\ HF_{(g)} \longrightarrow 2\ AlF_{3\ (s)} \ + \ 3\ H_2O_{(g)}$$

One advantage of removing hydrogen fluoride in this manner is that after a certain proportion of the aluminum oxide has reacted, the aluminum fluoride–aluminum oxide mixture can be fed back into the pot in which the electrolysis is carried out. Thus, in principle, no aluminum or fluoride is wasted.

QUESTIONS

1. Why are Canadian aluminum smelters located in Quebec and British Columbia rather than in other provinces such as Saskatchewan or Prince Edward Island?

2. Write the balanced chemical equation for the neutralization reaction that occurs between an acid oxide and a base during the extraction of aluminum metal from bauxite.

Iron and Steel

16.4

Iron is the most widely used of all the metallic elements. Unlike aluminum, iron is comparatively easy to obtain from its ores because of its low position in the activity series. Methods of extracting iron have been known for thousands of years. In fact, the chemical reactions used to extract iron today are the same ones that were used in the past. What has changed is the scale of the extraction process and the quality of the product.

Three main raw materials are used in the production of iron. The most important, naturally, is iron ore, which is impure iron(III) oxide. Canada has large deposits of iron ore. About 50% of our annual production is mined in Newfoundland, 35% in Quebec, and 10% in Ontario. About 60% of the iron ore mined in Canada is shipped out of the country, much of it going to the United States. Most of the remaining 40% is converted into steel.

The two additional raw materials required to extract iron from its ore are coal and limestone. We shall see the roles played by these two materials as we examine the details of the extraction process.

TABLE 16.2 *Steel Production in Canada*		
Province	**Number of Mills**	**Steel Production, 1982 (tonnes)**
Nova Scotia	1	1 000 000
Quebec	5	1 809 000
Ontario	8	16 730 000
Manitoba	1	240 000
Saskatchewan	1	680 000
Alberta	2	392 000
British Columbia	1	175 000

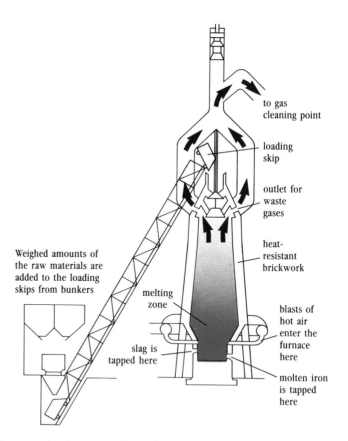

Figure 16.8
A schematic of the blast furnace.

The first step in the extraction of iron is to turn coal, which is a complex mixture of compounds containing carbon, hydrogen, and other elements, into **coke**, an impure form of carbon. This is accomplished by heating the coal in airtight ovens for about twenty hours at a temperature of about 1200 °C. In this process, elements other than carbon are released as a mixture of gases, leaving coke (carbon) as a solid. The gases which are produced are collected, separated into their components, and then used in other chemical processes.

The iron ore, coke, and limestone are loaded into a **blast furnace** which consists of a steel cylinder about 30 m high and 10 m in diameter. The cylinder is lined with special bricks. Air heated to 540 °C is pumped into the bottom of the furnace. The coke is ignited and burns to produce carbon monoxide according to the following equation:

$$2 \, C_{(s)} \; + \; O_{2 \, (g)} \longrightarrow 2 \, CO_{(g)}$$

The hot carbon monoxide gas reacts with the iron(III) oxide to produce carbon dioxide gas and liquid iron. The liquid iron collects at the bottom of the furnace, where the temperature is about 1600 °C. It is run off periodically:

$$3 \, CO_{(g)} \; + \; Fe_2O_{3 \, (s)} \longrightarrow 2 \, Fe_{(\ell)} \; + \; 3 \, CO_{2 \, (g)}$$

So far we have not considered the purpose of adding the third raw material, limestone. One of the major impurities in iron ore is sand (silicon dioxide). Limestone (calcium carbonate) is added to the blast furnace to remove this impurity. At the temperature of the furnace, the calcium carbonate decomposes into solid calcium oxide and gaseous carbon dioxide:

$$CaCO_{3 \, (s)} \xrightarrow{\;\Delta\;} CaO_{(s)} \; + \; CO_{2 \, (g)}$$

Calcium oxide is a basic oxide and reacts with the silicon dioxide, an acidic oxide, to produce calcium silicate:

$$CaO_{(s)} \; + \; SiO_{2 \, (s)} \longrightarrow CaSiO_{3 \, (\ell)}$$

Calcium silicate is less dense than liquid iron. It floats on top of the iron and can be run off through a tap higher up on the furnace than the outlet through which the iron is removed (Figure 16.8). An unwanted by-product such as calcium silicate is called **slag**.

The iron produced in a blast furnace is only about 90–95% pure. The main impurities are carbon, sulfur, phosphorus, manganese, and silicon. These impurities are removed in an oxygen furnace.

The **oxygen furnace** is filled with liquid metal from the blast furnace and some calcium oxide, produced from calcium carbonate, is added. A high-speed blast of pure oxygen is then blown onto the metal through a water-cooled lance. This converts the impurities in the liquid metal to their oxides. Carbon dioxide and sulfur dioxide escape as gases. The other (acidic) oxides combine with the basic calcium oxide to form calcium salts. These salts form a slag similar to that produced in the blast furnace. When the slag is removed the iron that remains contains only small, controlled quantities of impurities. This nearly pure iron, which contains traces of carbon, is now called **steel**. The steel is poured off into molds where it is allowed to solidify.

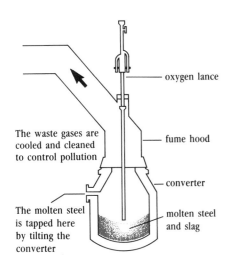

oxygen lance

The waste gases are cooled and cleaned to control pollution

fume hood

converter

The molten steel is tapped here by tilting the converter

molten steel and slag

Figure 16.9
Cross-section of an oxygen furnace.

Uses of Iron

Pure iron is a soft metal that rusts easily. Neither of these properties is particularly desirable in a metal, so why is iron so widely used? The two major reasons are that it is comparatively inexpensive to produce, and that by adding different quantities of other elements, major changes can be made to the properties of the resulting alloy.

A small quantity of carbon (0.1% to 2.0%) is present in the steels that are in widest use. Carbon steel, as it is known, is much harder than pure iron. Stainless steel is made by adding chromium. The addition of about 5% chromium reduces the rate of rusting by about 80%. If the chromium content is raised to 16%, the problem of rusting is almost completely eliminated.

The best permanent magnets are made from steel alloys containing nickel and cobalt, the two other magnetic metals. About 15% silicon is added to iron that will be used for chemical-resistant piping; and an alloy containing iron, nickel, cobalt, molybdenum, and tungsten is used to obtain the hardness and corrosion-resistant properties required of surgical knives.

Environmental Problems

The steel industry consumes vast quantities of air and water. Air is required to provide the oxygen that is consumed in the blast furnace where coke is converted to carbon monoxide and carbon dioxide. The quantities of carbon monoxide produced are so high that it can be used as a fuel for other parts of the plant. After the carbon monoxide is burned, the carbon dioxide gas that forms can be released into the atmosphere.

Water is used for two main purposes in the iron and steel industry. The first is to clean the gases that are released from the furnaces. These gases contain a large quantity of dust in the form of limestone, iron ore, and coke particles. This dust would cause serious air pollution problems if released directly into the atmosphere. The gases are therefore passed through water, where the solid dust particles are retained in suspension. The solids are then allowed to settle out. Any smaller particles remaining in suspension are removed by filtration.

The second use for water is to cool the red-hot coke that is produced from coal. Pollutants must be removed from the water used for either of these purposes before it can be returned to the environment.

QUESTIONS

3. Why are most of Canada's steelmaking facilities concentrated in Ontario, particularly in the Great Lakes region?
4. Why was it considered feasible to operate a steel mill in Cape Breton?
5. Identify the following:
    a) two combination reactions that take place inside a blast furnace
    b) one decomposition reaction that takes place inside a blast furnace

The Lake Erie Steel Works

It is easy to condemn industry for causing excessive pollution and environmental damage, but we must remember that environmental concerns have only become widespread in the last two or three decades. Many industrial plants date back fifty or more years, and add-on pollution control devices are expensive to install and often inefficient. Rather than modifying an existing plant, the best solution to environmental pollution problems is often to develop an entirely new plant that can be equipped with the most modern anti-pollution features.

An example of what can be done is provided by Stelco's steel plant at Nanticoke on Lake Erie. Planning for this completely new smelter began in 1962. Before any construction started, Stelco, the Ontario Ministry of the Environment, the Ministry of Natural Resources, and Ontario Hydro collaborated to study the water, air, vegetation, and wildlife of the region. These studies identified potential problems that could be avoided. For example, the lakeside dock was originally planned as a rock-filled structure. Since one of the studies showed that this type of structure would interfere with local fish movements,

a bridge was used instead. The studies also provided data on air and water quality that could be compared with values measured after the plant was in operation. It would then be clear what effects the operation of the plant was having on air and water quality.

Design of the Nanticoke plant also called for a major effort in water-quality control. Now in operation, over 90 % of the water used in the plant is recycled. The beneficial effects of this are that the demand for water from Lake Erie is reduced and the volume of water that requires treatment before being returned to the lake is kept to a minimum. Thus the Lake Erie plant uses only about 5000 L of water to produce a tonne of steel, whereas some older Hamilton plants require as much as 75 000 L of water per tonne of steel produced. New ways to purify the water that is returned to Lake Erie have been devised and the quality of this water is tested on a regular basis.

The costs of the pollution control devices installed by Stelco were so high that they added about 11 % ($90 million) to the capital cost of the plant. This represents one example of the new costs of doing business for our heavy industries. On the other hand it represents substantial savings in environmental cleanup on the part of both federal and provincial governments.

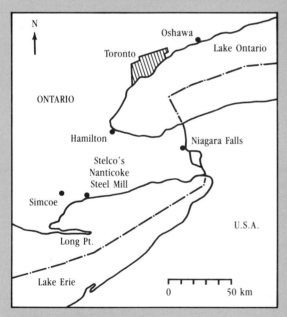

Figure 16.10
The location of the Nanticoke steel plant.

Figure 16.11
The Nanticoke steel plant.

Sulfur and Sulfuric Acid

16.5

The key raw material used in the manufacture of sulfuric acid is sulfur. In Canada and France, sulfur is obtained from natural gas containing a high proportion of hydrogen sulfide. This type of natural gas is referred to as **sour gas**. The hydrogen sulfide is separated from the hydrocarbons which make up the bulk of the natural gas. One-third of the hydrogen sulfide is burned to produce sulfur dioxide:

$$2\ H_2S_{(g)}\ +\ 3\ O_{2\,(g)}\ \longrightarrow\ 2\ H_2O_{(\ell)}\ +\ 2\ SO_{2\,(g)}$$

Sulfur is then produced as a yellow powder from the reaction between the sulfur dioxide and the remaining hydrogen sulfide:

$$2\ H_2S_{(g)}\ +\ SO_{2\,(g)}\ \xrightarrow{\ Al_2O_3\ }\ 3\ S_{(s)}\ +\ 2\ H_2O_{(\ell)}$$

TABLE 16.3 *Canadian Production of Sulfur from Sour Gas*

Province	Number of Plants	Capacity, 1983 (tonnes)
Saskatchewan	1	2 500
Alberta	47	9 800 000
British Columbia	2	570 000

Since about 80% of the sulfur produced in Canada is exported, sulfur is an important source of foreign exchange. Countries that import Canadian sulfur include the United States, Australia, and China. Each of these countries uses their imported sulfur in the manufacture of sulfuric acid.

The Frasch Process for the Extraction of Sulfur

Although most of the sulfur in Canada is produced from sour gas, in other parts of the world elemental sulfur is found in vast undergound deposits. Herman Frasch, the first chemist to work for the Imperial Oil Company, devised a simple method for bringing the sulfur in these deposits to the surface. This method is now known as the **Frasch process**.

Knowing that sulfur melts at 120 °C, Frasch proposed that water, heated under pressure to a temperature of about 180 °C, be pumped down into the sulfur deposits to melt the sulfur. Compressed air could then be pumped into the deposits to force the melted sulfur to the surface. To accomplish this, Frasch devised a well-pipe system consisting of three concentric pipes. Superheated water is pumped down the outside pipe and compressed air down the centre pipe. The mixture of liquid sulfur, water, and air comes to the surface through the other pipe.

The liquid sulfur obtained from the Frasch process is poured into huge moulds that are up to 400 m long, 60 m wide, and 15 m high. When full,

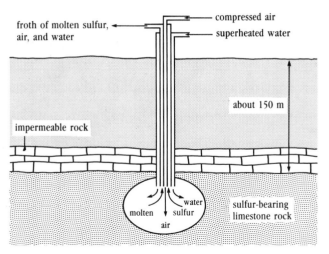

Figure 16.12
The Frasch process for extracting sulfur from underground deposits.

each mould contains about 400 000 t of sulfur. After the sulfur has solidified, the forms around each mould are removed and the solid sulfur is broken up and transported to its destination.

The Conversion of Sulfur to Sulfuric Acid

The first step in the production of sulfuric acid from sulfur involves burning sulfur to produce sulfur dioxide:

$$S_{(s)} + O_{2(g)} \longrightarrow SO_{2(g)}$$

Sulfur dioxide is a major by-product formed during the extraction of a number of metals from their ores. In Canada, over half the sulfur dioxide used in the production of sulfuric acid is obtained from sources such as the nickel smelter operating in Copper Cliff, Ontario, and the lead/zinc smelter in Trail, B.C.

To obtain sulfuric acid, sulfur dioxide must first be converted to sulfur trioxide. This conversion requires a high temperature and a catalyst, vanadium(V) oxide:

$$2\,SO_{2(g)} + O_{2(g)} \xrightarrow[400\,°C]{V_2O_5} 2\,SO_{3(g)}$$

In theory we could simply add the acidic oxide, sulfur trioxide, to water and obtain sulfuric acid. However, in industry it is more convenient to pass the gas into a tower down which concentrated sulfuric acid is flowing. The sulfur trioxide reacts with the sulfuric acid to form pyrosulfuric acid, $H_2S_2O_7$:

$$H_2SO_{4(\ell)} + SO_{3(g)} \longrightarrow H_2S_2O_{7(\ell)}$$

The pyrosulfuric acid is then added to water to produce sulfuric acid:

$$H_2S_2O_{7(\ell)} + H_2O_{(\ell)} \longrightarrow 2\,H_2SO_{4(\ell)}$$

For every two moles of sulfuric acid produced, one mole is recycled to absorb more sulfur trioxide.

TABLE 16.4 *Sulfuric Acid Production Capacity in Canada*		
Province	Number of Plants	Capacity, 1983 (tonnes)
New Brunswick	1	160 000
Quebec	5	848 000
Ontario	5	1 977 000
Manitoba	1	150 000
Saskatchewan	1	45 000
Alberta	5	2 263 000
British Columbia	3	765 000

Uses for Sulfuric Acid

About 70% of the sulfuric acid produced in Canada is used in the manufacture of fertilizers. Uranium processors, pulp and paper mills, and metal smelters and refiners are also major users of this acid.

In fertilizer production, sulfuric acid is required for the synthesis of both nitrogen- and phosphorus-containing fertilizers. For example, ammonium sulfate is an important nitrogen-containing fertilizer that can be produced by reacting sulfuric acid with the ammonia formed as a by-product during the conversion of coal to coke.

$$2\ NH_{3\ (aq)}\ +\ H_2SO_{4\ (aq)}\ \longrightarrow\ (NH_4)_2SO_{4\ (aq)}$$

Naturally occurring calcium phosphate rock is used as a source of phosphorus in the manufacture of phophorus-containing fertilizer. Calcium phosphate itself cannot be used as a fertilizer, as it is completely insoluble in water. However, if calcium phosphate-containing rock is treated with sulfuric acid, the more soluble calcium dihydrogen phosphate, $Ca(H_2PO_4)_2$, is produced:

$$Ca_3(PO_4)_{2\ (s)}\ +\ H_2SO_{4\ (\ell)}\ \longrightarrow\ Ca(H_2PO_4)_{2\ (s)}\ +\ 2\ CaSO_{4\ (s)}$$

This mixture of calcium dihydrogen phosphate and calcium sulfate is called superphosphate. The manufacture of superphosphate is an important part of Canada's fertilizer production.

Environmental Issues

Two main pollution problems are encountered in the production of sulfuric acid. First, some of the sulfur dioxide escapes without being converted to sulfur trioxide. This sulfur dioxide emission, which represents about 0.3% of the sulfur used, is difficult to reduce. The second problem is that some of the sulfuric acid can escape as a fine mist during production. All new sulfuric acid plants have mist eliminators to reduce the emission of sulfuric acid.

New Uses for Sulfur

In Canada, the amount of sulfur produced from sour gas far exceeds the amount required for the manufacture of sulfur-containing chemicals such as sulfuric acid. In order to find new uses for all the excess sulfur being produced, the Sulfur Development Institute of Canada (SUDIC) was formed. This is a non-profit Canadian corporation, funded by both the Federal and Alberta governments.

The major success of the Institute to date has been the development of an asphalt paving mix in which some of the asphalt is replaced by sulfur. Using sulfur in this way not only reduces paving costs, but also results in a better, more durable highway surface. Almost one million tonnes of this sulfur-asphalt mix had been used by the end of 1982, over half of it in the state of Wisconsin.

Another potential use of sulfur is in sulfur concrete. In this material, the sulfur completely replaces the cement component of the concrete. Sulfur concrete has many advantages over ordinary concrete, including greater strength and increased resistance to acids. There are great possibilities for producing and using SUDIC-developed sulfur concrete in the Middle East, which has large stockpiles of sulfur but few of the raw materials required for the manufacture of cement.

Figure 16.13
Paving with a sulfur–asphalt mix in northern B.C.

Figure 16.14
A low-cost house constructed of sulfur concrete building blocks, Quebec.

QUESTIONS

6. Why is Canada a major exporter of sulfur but not of sulfuric acid?
7. Why is Alberta a major producer of sulfuric acid?
8. Why is Ontario a major producer of sulfuric acid?
9. Identify three combination reactions that are involved in the production of sulfuric acid from sulfur.

Phosphorus and Phosphoric Acid 16.6

Although phosphoric acid is rarely used in the high school chemical laboratory, it is an extremely important industrial chemical. The starting material used in the manufacture of this acid is phosphate rock, which consists mainly of calcium phosphate. About 40% of the world's phosphate rock comes from the United States, the majority coming from Florida. Over half of the known deposits of this rock are located in the Morocco–Sahara region.

In the manufacture of phosphoric acid, phosphate rock is first converted to elemental phosphorus. In addition to the phosphate rock, this process requires coke, sand (impure silicon dioxide), and electrical energy. As with the manufacture of aluminum, a source of low-cost electricity is a major consideration when selecting a location for a phosphorus-producing plant. Also, as large quantities of phosphate rock have to be imported, it is essential that the plant be located near a deep-water port.

The conversion of phosphate rock to elemental phosphorus takes place in basically two steps in a very large electric furnace where each electrode has a mass of about 60 t. First, the calcium phosphate reacts with silicon dioxide (sand) to give calcium silicate and tetraphosphorus decaoxide. The tetraphosphorus decaoxide then reacts with carbon (coke) to give phosphorus:

$$2\ Ca_3(PO_4)_{2\ (s)}\ +\ 6\ SiO_{2\ (s)}\ \xrightarrow{\Delta}\ 6\ CaSiO_{3\ (\ell)}\ +\ P_4O_{10\ (\ell)}$$

$$P_4O_{10\ (\ell)}\ +\ 10\ C_{(s)}\ \longrightarrow\ P_{4\ (g)}\ +\ 10\ CO_{(g)}$$

Since at high furnace temperatures phosphorus is a gas, the mixture of phosphorus and carbon monoxide gases is passed through condensing towers where the phosphorus condenses to a liquid. Next, the liquid phosphorus is transferred to holding tanks that are kept warm to prevent the phosphorus from solidifying (the melting point of phosphorus is 44 °C).

Several substances with commercial uses are obtained as by-products of the phosphorus production process. For example, most of the carbon monoxide is used as a fuel in the furnaces that are used to dry the raw materials:

$$2\ CO_{(g)}\ +\ O_{2\ (g)}\ \longrightarrow\ 2\ CO_{2\ (g)}$$

In addition, the calcium silicate slag that is tapped from the furnace can be used as road fill. Finally, some of the phosphorus produced in the furnace reacts with iron impurities in the phosphate rock to form iron(III) phosphide, FeP, otherwise known as ferrophosphorus. This dense compound separates out at the bottom of the furnace, where it is removed and

Figure 16.15

A schematic of the production of phosphorus.

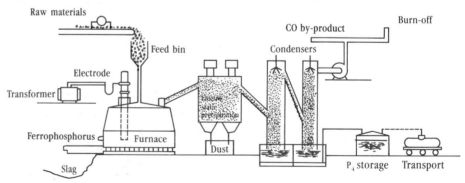

sold to steelmaking plants for use in making specialty steels, such as the one used for making rail car brake shoes.

Since phosphorus ignites spontaneously in air, it is transported in specially designed ships. During transportation, the phosphorus is maintained in liquid form by storing it in large tanks around which warm water is circulated.

Figure 16.16

The Albright Explorer, the world's first bulk-phosphorus carrier, which was launched in 1969. This ship's four steel tanks each carry 1200 t of liquid phosphorus.

Figure 16.17

Approximate quantities of reactants and products involved in the production of 1 kg of elemental phosphorus.

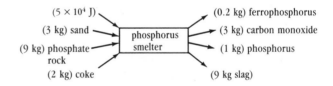

TABLE 16.5	*Phosphorus Production in Canada*	
Province	**Number of Plants**	**Phosphorus Production, 1984 (tonnes)**
Newfoundland	1	60 000
Quebec	1	22 500

The Production of Phosphoric Acid

The production of pure phosphoric acid from elemental phosphorus is a very simple process. First, a spray of molten phosphorus is burned in air to produce tetraphosphorus decaoxide as follows:

$$P_{4\,(\ell)} + 5\,O_{2\,(g)} \longrightarrow P_4O_{10\,(g)}$$

Nauru — The World's Richest Island

The Republic of Nauru, located in the Pacific Ocean, has an area of only 21 km², yet it is one of the world's major suppliers of phosphate rock. Between one and two million tonnes of phosphate rock are mined here each year, providing a gross national product of about $200 million annually. This represents about $25 000 for each of the 8000 inhabitants, 58% of whom are native Nauruans. As a consequence of this wealth, Nauruan households have all the conveniences and luxuries of modern living, from washing machines to VCR's to motor vehicles. Education is both free and compulsory for all children from age six to sixteen, and the government provides a comprehensive welfare system and free medical treatment for all residents.

Although living on an island in the Pacific and having a guaranteed income may sound like an idyllic life, the residents of Nauru have a number of problems. One immediate difficulty is that the inhabitants have little incentive to work or study. Obesity and alcohol abuse are common. A longer-term problem is that the phosphate deposits will be exhausted by about 1995.

Extraction of the phosphate is a bit like dentistry. The ore is scooped up from between enormous toothlike stalks of coral limestone, some of which are about 25 m high. These barren pinnacles of coral will be all that is left of 80% of the island's surface when the deposits are exhausted.

In order to provide a future for the islanders, the larger part of the income from phosphate sales is now placed in a

Figure 16.18
The Republic of Nauru.

Phosphate Royalties Trust, a fund that is similar to the Alberta Heritage Fund. The Nauruans are hoping that it will be feasible to use this money to level the pinnacles and cover them with imported topsoil. They believe that this will not only restore the appearance of the island, but also produce agricultural land that will provide a long-term source of employment for the islanders. An alternative plan would be to relocate the Nauruan population to some other, currently uninhabited, Pacific island.

This gaseous oxide is then reacted with water to give phosphoric acid:

$$P_4O_{10\,(g)} \ + \ 6\,H_2O_{(\ell)} \longrightarrow 4\,H_3PO_{4\,(\ell)}$$

If only impure phosphoric acid is required, then a double displacement reaction between phosphate rock and an excess of sulfuric acid is used instead:

$$Ca_3(PO_4)_{2\,(s)} \ + \ 3\,H_2SO_{4\,(aq)} \longrightarrow 3\,CaSO_{4\,(s)} \ + \ 2\,H_3PO_{4\,(aq)}$$

Uses of Phosphoric Acid

Impure phosphoric acid is used in the manufacture of ammonium phosphate fertilizer. Pure phosphoric acid is used in the manufacture of food additives and detergents.

TABLE 16.6 *Ammonium Phosphate Fertilizer Production in Canada*

Province	Number of Plants	Annual Capacity, 1984 (tonnes)
New Brunswick	1	150 000
Ontario	2	210 000
Alberta	4	625 000
British Columbia	2	164 000

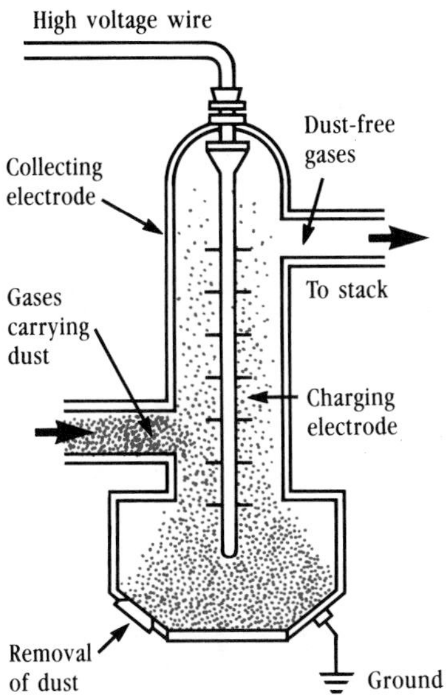

High voltage wire

Collecting electrode

Gases carrying dust

Removal of dust

Dust-free gases

To stack

Charging electrode

Ground

Figure 16.19

Diagram of a Cottrell electrostatic precipitator.

Environmental Problems

Two major pollution problems are associated with the manufacture of elemental phosphorus. First, the water used in the plant becomes contaminated with phosphorus. A purification system must be used before this water can be discharged into the surrounding lakes or rivers. Secondly, phosphate rock contains some solid fluorides. These fluorides are converted to gaseous fluorides in the furnace. If these gases escape into the environment, they can cause major damage to plants and animals. The fumes emitted from a phosphorus-producing plant must be cleaned until only carbon dioxide gas remains for release into the atmosphere.

Electrostatic precipitators are used to remove about 99% of the dust particles present in the plant's emission. In these precipitators, the exhaust gases are passed between small high-voltage electrodes. The high voltage ionizes the solid dust particles present in the gases. The ionized particles are attracted by collector plates bearing an opposite charge. The deposits are disposed of along with other solid wastes.

In the manufacture of impure phosphoric acid, a major environmental problem is the disposal of the large amount of calcium sulfate that is produced as a by-product. Some of this calcium sulfate can be used in the manufacture of gypsum wallboard, but most of it has to be stockpiled as there is little industrial demand for this substance.

QUESTIONS

10. Why are Canada's phosphorus plants located in Quebec and Newfoundland?

11. Table 16.6 details four provinces in which ammonium phosphate fertilizer is produced. For each province, give two reasons why you think it might have been advantageous to locate a plant there.

12. Identify the two combination reactions that take place during the preparation of pure phosphoric acid.

13. If a phosphorus-carrying ship were involved in a collision, what would be the major environmental hazard?

Long Harbour, Newfoundland — A Case Study in Pollution

In December 1968 the Electric Reduction Company (ERCO) opened a plant to produce elemental phosphorus at Long Harbour, Newfoundland. At the beginning of February 1969 there were reports of dead herring in the area. In late April of the same year, divers conducted an investigation and found several million dead cod on the sea floor of Long Harbour Inlet. In May of 1969 the plant was closed temporarily while scientists investigated the matter.

The Fisheries Research Board of Canada began to analyze the problem as soon as the first reports of dead fish were received. Tests ruled out the possibility of disease, and it soon became apparent that the problem was caused by liquid wastes from the ERCO plant. It was established that elemental phosphorus in the waste water was causing the fish to die and that a phosphorus concentration as low as ten parts per billion could be fatal to fish.

Once the source of the problem was determined, the next task was to reclaim as much of the released phosphorus as possible. Much of the phosphorus had settled into the mud at the bottom of the inlet. With the help of divers, a hydraulic dredge was used to lift the contaminated mud, which was then returned to the plant for treatment. Another task was to ensure that water contaminated with phosphorus would not escape from the plant when it reopened. This was accomplished by designing and constructing a chemical treatment system that enabled water to be recycled back into the plant after the removal of most of the phosphorus.

Why was this pollution problem not anticipated before the plant was constructed? The extraction process being used in the plant was new, and major pollution control efforts had been directed at air pollution rather than water pollution. At the time, dilution of the liquid waste with sea water was considered to be sufficient to prevent problems. Also, at that time there had been no in-depth studies on the toxicity of phosphorus to marine life. Finally, in 1968 anti-pollution legislation was much weaker than it is today.

Figure 16.20
The phosphorus plant at Long Harbour, Newfoundland.

Figure 16.21
Collecting samples of sediment for analysis.

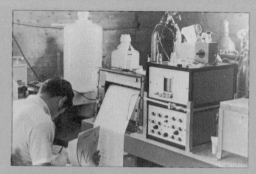

Figure 16.22
Analyzing samples for phosphorus pollution.

Uranium Dioxide

16.7

Canada, which has the second-largest deposits of uranium in the world, is the second-largest producer and the largest exporter of uranium in the western hemisphere. Uranium is found as its oxide, one of the most important sources being the mineral uraninite. Such deposits typically contain only 0.1–0.2% uranium, although in Saskatchewan some bodies of ore have been found to contain up to 40% uranium.

Figure 16.23
Giant rotating cylinders containing steel balls are used to grind uranium-bearing ores into a fine powder prior to chemical processing.

TABLE 16.7	*Uranium production in Canada*	
Province	Number of mines	Annual Production, 1983 (tonnes of pure uranium)
Ontario	3	4800
Saskatchewan	3	2300

The first step in the extraction of uranium is to grind the ore to the consistency of fine sand. The chemical treatment that follows partly depends on the ore's composition, but eventually a salt in which uranium is present as a polyatomic anion is produced. This is then shipped to the uranium-processing plant in Blind River, Ontario, where the salt, which is often referred to as "yellowcake", is thermally decomposed into the oxide U_3O_8. This oxide is subsequently dissolved in nitric acid to give uranyl nitrate, $UO_2(NO_3)_2$. After the impurities have been removed, the uranyl nitrate solution is evaporated, and the resulting solid uranyl nitrate hexahydrate is strongly heated to give uranium(VI) oxide, UO_3:

Figure 16.24
Principal uranium deposits in Ontario and Saskatchewan.

$$2\ UO_2(NO_3)_2 \cdot 6H_2O_{(s)} \xrightarrow{\Delta} 2\ UO_{3\ (s)} + 4\ NO_{2\ (g)} + O_{2\ (g)} + 6\ H_2O_{(g)}$$

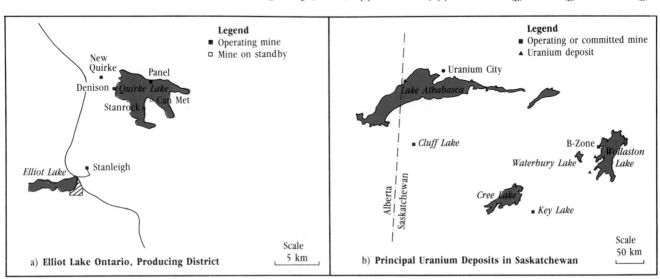

a) **Elliot Lake Ontario, Producing District**

Legend
■ Operating mine
□ Mine on standby

New Quirke
Panel
Denison
Quirke Lake
Can Met
Stanrock
Elliot Lake
Stanleigh

Scale 5 km

b) **Principal Uranium Deposits in Saskatchewan**

Legend
■ Operating or committed mine
▲ Uranium deposit

Uranium City
Lake Athabasca
Cluff Lake
B-Zone
Waterbury Lake
Wollaston Lake
Cree Lake
Key Lake
Alberta
Saskatchewan

Scale 50 km

The uranium(VI) oxide is then transferred to Port Hope, Ontario for further processing. The first stage in processing involves a reaction between the uranium(VI) oxide and hydrogen gas to produce uranium(IV) oxide, UO_2:

$$UO_{3 (s)} + H_{2 (g)} \longrightarrow UO_{2 (s)} + H_2O_{(g)}$$

This is the form of uranium used in Canada's CANDU nuclear reactors; however, since most of our uranium exports are eventually used in non-CANDU systems, a different compound of uranium (UF_6) is usually required for these markets. Uranium(IV) oxide is converted to uranium(VI) fluoride by the following two-stage process:

$$UO_{2 (s)} + 4 HF_{(aq)} \longrightarrow UF_{4 (s)} + 2 H_2O_{(\ell)}$$
$$UF_{4 (s)} + F_{2 (g)} \longrightarrow UF_{6 (s)}$$

Uses of Uranium

The major use of uranium is as a fuel in nuclear reactors. About 80% of the uranium produced in Canada is exported to countries such as France that depend heavily on nuclear power as a source of electricity.

A certain amount of uranium is used in its pure metallic form. Although uranium is radioactive, its level of radiation is very low. Because uranium is very dense (1.7 times denser than lead), it is used to make counterweights for use in aircraft, as these occupy less space than lead counterweights of the same mass.

One considerably useful property of uranium is its ability to absorb radiation. A sheet of uranium 1 cm thick will block radiation as effectively as a slab of concrete twelve times as thick. Thus, highly radioactive elements used in engineering and medicine are often stored in containers made of uranium metal.

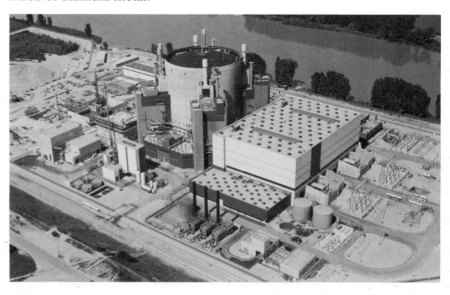

Figure 16.25
The Super-Phénix nuclear power plant near Grenoble, France.

The Production of Aluminum

As aluminum is high in the activity series, it is extremely difficult and expensive to extract from its ores by chemical means. Instead, an electrical method is used. Canada is one of the world's largest producers of refined aluminum, mainly because of the availability of low-cost electricity and deep-water ports. Aluminum producers have built their smelters close to large hydroelectric power stations in Quebec and British Columbia to obtain the electrical energy required for the smelting process.

Bauxite, an impure form of aluminum oxide, is the primary source of aluminum. Most of Canada's supply comes by ship from Brazil, Guyana, Guinea, and Jamaica.

A deep-water port, such as this one at La Baie, Quebec, is required for the delivery of ore.

Pure aluminum oxide is a fine, white powder. Although most of this compound is destined for the smelting process, it is also used as an abrasive in toothpaste and in sandpaper, and in the production of ceramic material in spark plugs and dishware.

The first step in the aluminum smelting process is to convert the bauxite ore into pure aluminum oxide (alumina). About one tonne of alumina is obtained from two tonnes of bauxite. The reagent used in this step is sodium hydroxide solution. The Vaudreuil works in Jonquière, Quebec uses new technology for drying the purified aluminum oxide.

The Grande-Baie smelter at La Baie, Quebec is one of the most advanced in the world. It incorporates sophisticated technology for protecting the environment, improving the quality of life in the workplace, and conserving energy.

The alumina is analyzed for the presence of impurities such as oxides of titanium and vanadium.

PLATE 10 — THE PRODUCTION OF ALUMINUM

Large pipes remove toxic fumes and dust and convey them to a scrubber unit.

The purified aluminum oxide is placed in heated electrolytic cells, or pots. An electric current passed through the cell causes decomposition of the oxide. At the temperature of the cell, aluminum is a liquid.

Molten aluminum is periodically siphoned from the pots into crucibles.

The molten aluminum is poured either into moulds, as shown here, or into giant crucibles. In the moulds, it is allowed to cool and solidify; in the crucibles, it is kept in a molten state until it is ready to be used for fabrication into sheet metal or piping.

Properties of the most common alloys

Specific properties are obtained by the careful addition of small quantities of alloying elements, sometimes singly but usually in combination. Total alloying elements seldom exceeds 10%. The table below shows only a few major examples.

| Symbols | ● Average | ● Good | ● Excellent |

Alloying Elements	Strength	Corrosion Resistance	Workability	Major Uses
Magnesium/Silicon Mg/Si	●	●	●	Architecture
Magnesium/Manganese Mg/Mn	●	●	●	Beverage cans
Copper/Magnesium/Manganese Cu/Mg/Mn	●	●	●	Aircraft, space vehicles
Silicon/Nickel/Copper Si/Ni/Cu	●	●	●	Pistons. Alloys for use at high temperature
Magnesium Mg	●	●	●	Marine products
Copper/Lead/Bismuth Cu/Pb/Bi	●	●	●	Bearings - Outstanding workability
Titanium Ti	N.A.	N.A.	N.A.	Grain refining
Zinc Zn	●	●	●	Cathodic protection; Tubing for air conditioners

Other alloying elements such as cadmium, chromium and boron impart specific characteristics.

Because of its low density, aluminum is used in pure or alloy form in aircraft, buses and cars. It is also familiar in household utensils and appliances.

A road-rail transporter is used to convey molten aluminum in the giant crucible from the smelter to the sheet fabricating plant.

At the Saguenay works in Jonquière, Quebec, molten aluminum is converted directly to sheet metal.

Low-cost electricity, such as that from the Shipshaw hydroelectric power station in Quebec, is essential for the aluminum industry.

PLATE 12 — THE PRODUCTION OF ALUMINUM

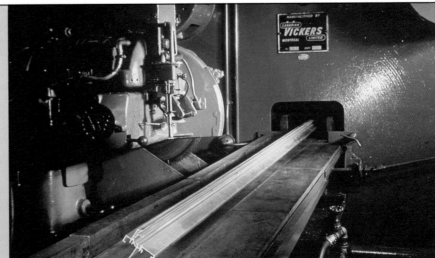

Much of the aluminum produced is
sold in semi-finished form to
industries in Canada or other
countries.

Oil Sands

Canada has large deposits of oil sands in Alberta and Saskatchewan. These consist of a mixture of sand, clay, water, and bitumen (the oil component), which resembles tar in both appearance and consistency. There is enough oil in these sands to supply our needs for about 250 years at the current rate of oil consumption. Unfortunately, extracting the oil is a difficult and expensive process.

Environmental damage is a major concern in the oil sands industry. Large areas of land must be excavated to obtain the oil sand, leaving barren areas behind. Under provincial environmental regulations, all disturbed areas must be reclaimed and revegetated.

Principal Canadian oil sands deposits.

The Syncrude operation-mine (foreground), plant (centre), and tailings pond (background).

PLATE 14 — OIL SANDS

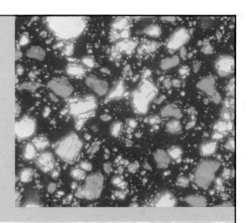

Oil sands contain up to 18% bitumen, but the average bitumen content is about 10%. The oil-soaked sands are not solid, but can be easily broken and crumbled.

A microscopic view of oil sand, containing particles of sand and clay.

Bucket-wheel excavators at work in the open-pit Suncor mine.

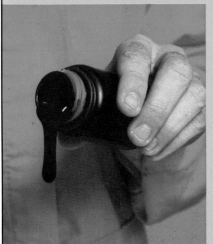

At room temperature, bitumen is highly viscous and pours very slowly.

The extraction of bitumen from the sands begins in revolving, boxcar-sized tumblers which separate the oil from the other components. Vast quantities of water are used in this process. Waste water is pumped into a tailings pond where the suspended solids settle out. Any remaining bitumen can be skimmed from the surface and the water is then recycled.

Chemists are conducting research to devise better methods of oil production and to examine the potential of converting bitumen into more useful light oils.

Chemical engineers are developing techniques for extracting bitumen from deep oil sand deposits. After the methods have been perfected, the technology can be sold to other countries that have oil sand deposits. These nations include Venezuela, the Soviet Union, the United States, and the Malagasy Republic.

After separation, the thick oil must be chemically decomposed to make it commmercially useful. In this process, known as coking, heat is used to break down the large molecules to produce lighter oils and coke (impure carbon). These fluid coking units at the Syncrude plant are the largest in the world.

Prevention of air pollution also poses problems since the bitumen contains sulfur compounds. During coking some of the sulfur is converted to the acid gas, sulfur dioxide. A sulfur recovery plant is therefore necessary to reduce the gas emissions.

The oil sands of Peace River, Cold Lake, and Wabasca, Alberta, and of Melville Island and Fort Good Hope in the Northwest Territories, lie far below the earth's surface. New technology will be needed to extract the oil from these sands. Experimental pilot plants such as this one use physical extraction methods, such as steam injection, to make the oil less viscous. Other plants use chemical methods.

Vast numbers of seedlings are needed for the task of reforestation.

PLATE 16 — OIL SANDS

Environmental Issues

Rocks that contain uranium also contain radon, the only radioactive noble gas. Radon gas is particularly hazardous because it can be absorbed by the lungs and cause lung cancer. Uranium miners are in danger of being exposed to large quantities of radon gas. Thus, for each tonne of ore produced underground, between thirteen and sixteen tonnes (1×10^7 L) of fresh air is circulated through each mine. This sweeps the radon gas from the mine into the atmosphere, where it joins the radon released from the surface rocks in the Canadian Shield.

The major environmental problem associated with uranium production is the quantity of waste material that is generated. For every tonne of uranium oxide produced, about 900 t of partially radioactive waste rock remains, although this ratio is very much lower for some of the richer Saskatchewan ores. These wastes are generally allowed to settle in ponds. Although uranium wastes are now treated with greater care than they were in the past, accidents can still occur. For example, in January 1984 a break occurred in the dam of a holding pond at Key Lake, Saskatchewan, and about 9×10^6 L of slightly radioactive waste water escaped and contaminated the surrounding frozen muskeg.

QUESTIONS

14. In the production of uranium(VI) fluoride from uranium ore, identify
    a) a combination reaction
    b) a decomposition reaction
    c) a neutralization reaction between a basic oxide and an acid

Titanium Dioxide

16.8 All the chemicals that we have discussed so far in this chapter are produced in Canada on a relatively large scale. In addition, Canada also produces a number of other chemicals on a much smaller scale. These also play an important role in the national economy. For example, titanium(IV) oxide, usually called titanium dioxide, represents about 10% of the annual dollar sales of the Canadian inorganic chemical industry. This is true not because large quantities of the oxide are produced, but because it commands a high price.

The province of Quebec has the world's second-largest supply of ilmenite, an ore that contains iron and titanium. After the iron has been removed in a smelter, the remaining slag contains about 60% titanium dioxide. Concentrated sulfuric acid is used to dissolve this compound:

$$TiO_{2\,(s)} + H_2SO_{4\,(\ell)} \longrightarrow TiOSO_{4\,(aq)} + H_2O_{(\ell)}$$

Figure 16.26
The titanium dioxide plant at Varennes, Quebec.

Next, the solid impurities are removed by filtration and hot water is added to the solution of titanyl sulfate, $TiOSO_{4(aq)}$, to give a precipitate of titanium dioxide:

$$TiOSO_{4\,(aq)} + 2\,H_2O_{(\ell)} \longrightarrow TiO_2 \cdot H_2O_{(s)} + H_2SO_{4\,(aq)}$$

Since the titanium dioxide is formed as the hydrate, $TiO_2 \cdot H_2O$, a drying step is necessary to produce a marketable product:

$$TiO_2 \cdot H_2O_{(s)} \xrightarrow{\Delta} TiO_{2\,(s)} + H_2O_{(g)}$$

TABLE 16.8	*Titanium Dioxide Production in Canada*	
Province	Location	Annual Production, 1984 (tonnes)
Quebec	Varennes	36 000
Quebec	Tracy	36 000

Uses of Titanium Dioxide

Titanium dioxide is a chemically inert, white pigment that is used as a whitener in a number of products. About 50% of the titanium dioxide produced annually is used in white paint, and about 25% is used as a coating for white paper. Another 10% is used to give plastics a white colour. Similarly, the whitewalls of tires are coloured by titanium dioxide.

Approximately 10% of all titanium dioxide is converted to titanium, an extremely strong, low-density metal used in the aerospace industry. However, the conversion of titanium dioxide to titanium metal is not carried out in Canada and we must rely on imported titanium metal for our own aerospace industry.

Environmental Issues

Large quantities of waste material are produced during the refining of titanium dioxide. Even after most of the iron is removed from the ilmenite ore by the initial smelting process, the remaining slag holds a significant proportion of iron. After the slag is treated with sulfuric acid and the titanium dioxide precipitated by the addition of hot water, the solution that remains is very acidic and contains a high concentration of iron(II) sulfate. At present it is not economically feasible either to extract the iron from this solution or to reclaim the sulfuric acid. One company, Trioxide Canada Ltd., has experimented with a process that involves adding lime to the acidic wastes to produce gypsum (calcium sulfate).

Since gypsum is used in the production of wallboard, plaster of Paris, and Portland cement, it appears that this would be an extra source of revenue for the company. As it turns out, gypsum is cheaper to mine than it is to produce by the above method. For example, gypsum from the surface

Figure 16.27
Titanium metal is used for the construction of high-performance aircraft such as this Lockheed SR-71A that holds many of the world's speed and altitude records.

Figure 16.28
Loading gypsum at St. George's, Newfoundland.

mines in Flat Bay, Newfoundland, is loaded directly into ships at St. George's by way of a long conveyor system. Over seventy percent of our gypsum is exported to U.S. markets.

QUESTIONS

15. Identify the following reactions that occur in the production of titanium dioxide:
    a) a reaction between a basic oxide and an acid
    b) a reaction in which a precipitate is formed

16. What factors affect the economics of the recovery of gypsum from acidic wastes formed during the production of titanium dioxide?

Summary

- Industrial chemistry differs from laboratory chemistry in that:
  a) the cost of production is much higher
  b) continuous production methods are used
  c) the disposal of waste products is of major concern

- Chemical plants are usually located:
  a) close to a source of the required raw materials
  b) where energy costs can be minimized
  c) where there is a large domestic market for the products

- If raw materials are imported or if finished products are to be exported, industrial plants are usually located close to deep-water ports.

- Aluminum is produced by the electrolysis of aluminum oxide obtained from bauxite.

- Aluminum and its alloys are used in products where weight is an important consideration.

- Iron is obtained from iron ore consisting mainly of iron(III) oxide. The oxide is reduced to metallic iron in a blast furnace.

- Steel is an alloy that consists of nearly pure iron and traces of carbon and other elements.

- In Canada, sour gas is an important source of sulfur. Sulfur can be converted to sulfur dioxide and subsequently to sulfuric acid. The sulfur dioxide produced by smelting metal is also used to produce sulfuric acid.

- The major use of the sulfuric acid produced in Canada is in the manufacture of fertilizers.

- Phosphoric acid can be obtained from phosphate rock in two ways. Pure phosphoric acid is produced by first extracting elemental phosphorus from the phosphate rock, converting the element to the oxide, and then reacting the oxide with water. Impure phosphoric acid is produced by reacting phosphate rock with sulfuric acid.

- Impure phosphoric acid is mainly used in the preparation of phosphate fertilizers. Pure phosphoric acid is used in detergents and in the manufacture of food additives.

- Uranium ore, consisting mainly of U_3O_8, is converted by a series of reactions to uranium dioxide, UO_2, for use in Canadian nuclear reactors or to uranium(VI) fluoride, UF_6, for export.

- Titanium dioxide is separated from its ore, ilmenite, by reacting the ore with sulfuric acid to produce a soluble sulfate and then adding hot water to precipitate the oxide. It is used as white pigment.

- Titanium metal is important in the aerospace industry because of its strength and low density.

KEY WORDS		
	bauxite	oxygen furnace
	blast furnace	slag
	coke	smelter
	electrolysis	sour gas
	electrostatic precipitator	steel
	Frasch process	

ANSWERS TO
SECTION QUESTIONS

1. Aluminum smelters are located in Quebec and British Columbia because of the availability of cheap hydroelectric power and the existence of deep-water ports in these provinces.

2. $2\ NaOH_{(aq)}\ +\ Al_2O_{3\ (s)} \longrightarrow 2\ NaAlO_{2\ (aq)}\ +\ H_2O_{(\ell)}$

3. At least four factors can be considered to be important:
  a) The Great Lakes are a source of the vast amounts of water required by the steel industry.
  b) Ports on the Great Lakes can be used to receive shipments of iron ore and distribute the steel that is produced.
  c) Many of the industries that use steel as a raw material are located in Ontario.
  d) Ontario has deposits of limestone and iron ore.

4. Cape Breton has large coal deposits and deep-water ports that facilitate the transportation of incoming iron ore and outgoing steel.

5. a) $2\ C_{(s)}\ +\ O_{2\ (g)} \longrightarrow 2\ CO_{(g)}$
  $CaO_{(s)}\ +\ SiO_{2\ (s)} \longrightarrow CaSiO_{3\ (\ell)}$
  b) $CaCO_{3\ (s)} \longrightarrow CaO_{(s)}\ +\ CO_{2\ (g)}$

6. It is easier and cheaper to transport sulfur than to transport sulfuric acid.

7. There are vast quantities of sour gas available in Alberta.

8. Ontario has many smelting industries which produce sulfur dioxide.

9. The combination reactions are the following:
  $S_{(s)}\ +\ O_{2\ (g)} \longrightarrow SO_{2\ (g)}$
  $2\ SO_{2\ (g)}\ +\ O_{2\ (g)} \longrightarrow 2\ SO_{3\ (g)}$
  $H_2SO_{4\ (\ell)}\ +\ SO_{3\ (g)} \longrightarrow H_2S_2O_{7\ (\ell)}$

10. The most essential raw material, phosphate rock, can be shipped from its source in Florida to deep-water ports in Quebec and Newfoundland. These ports can also be used to ship the phosphorus which is produced. Quebec, in particular, has abundant low-cost hydroelectric power.

11. a) New Brunswick is located reasonably close to a source of phosphate rock (Florida). In addition, it has deep-water ports, a supply of locally-produced sulfuric acid, and an agricultural base.
  b) Ontario has the advantage of locally produced sulfuric acid. In addition, phosphate rock can be imported via the Great Lakes and the demand for fertilizer from farmers in Southern Ontario is considerable.
  c) Alberta produces sulfuric acid. As an agricultural province, it also exhibits a high demand for fertilizer.
  d) British Columbia, like Ontario, produces sulfuric acid via sulfur dioxide from its smelters. It has deep-water ports and an important agricultural base.

12. $P_{4\ (\ell)}\ +\ 5\ O_{2\ (g)} \longrightarrow P_4O_{10\ (g)}$
  $P_4O_{10\ (g)}\ +\ 6\ H_2O_{(\ell)} \longrightarrow 4\ H_3PO_{4\ (\ell)}$

13. If the accident split the phosphorus tanks, the phosphorus would ignite, causing an enormous fire. However, were the ship to sink, the water would extinguish the fire. There would still be long term environmental problems for the fishing industry due to phosphorus absorption, as there was in Long Harbour, Newfoundland.

14. a) $UF_{4(s)} + F_{2(g)} \longrightarrow UF_{6(s)}$

b) $2\,UO_2(NO_3)_2 \cdot 6H_2O_{(s)} \longrightarrow 2\,UO_{3(s)} + 4\,NO_{2(g)} + O_{2(g)} + 6\,H_2O_{(g)}$

c) $UO_{2(s)} + 4\,HF_{(aq)} \longrightarrow UF_{4(s)} + 2\,H_2O_{(\ell)}$

15. a) $TiO_{2(s)} + H_2SO_{4(\ell)} \longrightarrow TiOSO_{4(aq)} + H_2O_{(\ell)}$

b) $TiOSO_{4(aq)} + 2\,H_2O_{(\ell)} \longrightarrow TiO_2 \cdot H_2O_{(s)} + H_2SO_{4(\ell)}$

16. Factors include the cost of the lime required to neutralize the acidic wastes and the cost of delivering the final product to market.

COMPREHENSION QUESTIONS

1. List three main reasons for locating a specific chemical plant in a particular region.

2. Describe three differences between preparing a chemical in a laboratory and carrying out the same process on an industrial scale.

3. Why is aluminum difficult to obtain in pure form?

4. Describe two important uses of aluminum.

5. What are the three major pollution problems associated with the production of aluminum?

6. What two essential raw materials, in addition to iron ore, are consumed in the production of iron?

7. What is the difference between iron and steel?

8. Name two alloys of steel and give their properties.

9. Why is an abundant supply of water so important to a steel-producing plant?

10. What is sour gas? How can it be safely put to use?

11. What are the main uses for sulfuric and phosphoric acid in Canada?

12. In this chapter we have described the extraction of aluminum from bauxite, the production of iron and steel, and the manufacture of sulfuric acid, phosphoric acid, uranium dioxide, and titanium dioxide. Which of these industries requires:
    a) large quantities of electricity
    b) large quantities of water
    c) facilities for the disposal of large quantities of waste material
    d) special precautions to prevent environmental pollution

13. What are the major uses of uranium?

14. Describe some of the specific problems associated with extracting uranium.

15. Why are the deposits of ilmenite in Quebec so important to the Canadian economy?

16. List some of the uses of titanium and its compounds.

PROBLEMS

17. Write the equation for each step in the extraction of
a) aluminum from bauxite   b) iron from iron ore

18. Write the equation for each step in the production of
a) sulfur from hydrogen sulfide   b) sulfuric acid from sulfur

19. The properties of iron change significantly when other elements are added to form alloys. Briefly explain the advantage(s) obtained by adding each of the following elements to iron:
a) carbon   b) chromium   c) silicon

20. Why are aluminum and titanium used in the manufacture of aircraft?

21. Why do elemental phophorus and the compounds of uranium require special handling and transportation methods?

22. Write the equation for each step in the production of
a) phophorus from calcium phosphate
b) pure phosphoric acid from phosphorus

23. Write the equation for each step in the production of
a) ammonium phosphate from calcium phosphate (phosphate rock)
b) uranium(VI) fluoride from uranium(IV) oxide

24. Explain briefly why iron has been used for thousands of years, whereas aluminum has only been used for about one hundred years.

25. The extraction of elemental phosphorus from phosphate rock is a good example of a chemical process that produces a number of useful by-products. What are the useful by-products that are produced in this process, and to what uses are these substances put?

26. A 5.00×10^3 t shipment of bauxite contains 47.3% aluminum oxide trihydrate. What is the maximum mass of aluminum metal that could be extracted from this mass of bauxite?

27. What mass of pure sulfuric acid can be produced from 1.00×10^2 t of sulfur? What volume of $1.00 \text{ mol} \cdot \text{L}^{-1}$ sulfuric acid could be prepared?

28. Taking the total annual Canadian production of phosphorus as 72 500 t, what mass of carbon monoxide is produced each year by this industry? What volume of gas does this represent at 25 °C and 101 kPa?

29. What volume of oxygen, measured at STP, would be required for the complete combustion of 5.00×10^3 t of sulfur? What volume of sulfur dioxide would be produced in the process?

SUGGESTED PROJECTS

1. The economic viability of an industry often depends on using the waste products from one process as the raw materials for another. This creates secondary industries. Find examples of secondary industries that have been created in your province and prepare a report on them.

2. Canada is a major exporter of raw materials. In many cases, we export raw materials and import finished products made from them. Find an example of such an industry and write a report on it. Suggest reasons why it might be impractical to process, in Canada, the raw materials from which the industry's products are made.

3. Choose a sector of the chemical industry that has not been covered in this chapter and write a report on it. Indicate the raw materials required and their place of origin. Detail the industry's energy requirements, the environmental problems associated with the manufacturing process, and the location of the markets for the product.

4. Like any other industry, the chemical industry exists in order to make profits. As a consequence, most industrial research concentrates on finding new uses for either existing products, or waste materials from the manufacturing process. On the other hand, much of the pure research carried out in universities is not driven by such commercial interests and must be supported by government agencies such as the National Research Council. Write a report on this agency, showing some of the ways in which it supports chemical research in Canada.

5. Corporate responsibility is a term that is used to imply that industry has a responsibility to provide safe products and to avoid unnecessary pollution of the environment. Prepare a report that would suggest ways in which industry and the various levels of government can work together to share the burden of costs associated with maintaining a safe and clean environment.

17

Nuclear Chemistry

In our discussion of atomic structure in Chapter 3, we emphasized the way in which electrons are arranged around the nucleus of an element. We saw that this electron arrangement determined each element's chemical properties. Nuclear chemistry is concerned with changes that occur *within* the nucleus. These changes result in the transformation of one element to another and are always accompanied by the emission of radiation. We shall begin our study of nuclear chemistry by examining the different types of radiation that can be emitted.

The Common Types of Nuclear Radiation   17.1

In 1896 the French scientist Antoine-Henri Becquerel placed some uranium salts on glass plates coated with light-sensitive material. Even though the plates had previously been wrapped in black paper, the light-sensitive material darkened. As no light could have penetrated the paper, Bequerel deduced that the uranium must have emitted rays capable of penetrating the paper and darkening the light-sensitive surface of the plates. Becquerel called the production of these kinds of rays **radioactivity**.

In later experiments, Ernest Rutherford showed that two different types of rays were produced by radioactive materials. One type was easily stopped by any solid material, such as paper. Rutherford called these *alpha rays*. The other rays, which were one-hundred times more penetrating than alpha rays, he called *beta rays*. Subsequently a third type of ray called a *gamma ray*, was identified by Paul Villard. Gamma rays proved to be even more penetrating than beta rays.

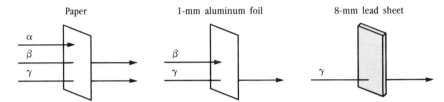

Figure 17.1

The penetrating ability of alpha (α), beta (β), and gamma (γ) rays. Skin will stop alpha rays, but not beta or gamma rays.

Alpha Rays

An **alpha ray** is a beam of helium nuclei; that is, helium atoms that have lost their two valence electrons. Particles of this type consist of two protons and two neutrons, and therefore have a charge of +2. We can represent these alpha particles using the format introduced in Section 3.4. The atomic number is shown as a subscript to the lower left of the chemical symbol and the mass number as a superscript to the upper left. When discussing nuclear chemistry we are usually only concerned with nuclei. Thus the overall charge on an ion is usually ignored, and for an alpha particle the symbol ^4_2He is preferred to the alternative $^4_2He^{2+}$.

Beta Rays

A **beta ray** is a beam of electrons. These electrons result from a transformation within the nucleus during which a neutron changes into a proton and an electron. In earlier chapters, we represented an electron as e^-. Although this is a useful way of depicting an electron in conventional chemistry, the slightly different format, $^0_{-1}e$, is preferred for nuclear chemistry. The zero in this representation indicates that the electron has a negligible mass when compared to a proton or neutron. The subscript represents the charge, which is negative for an electron.

Gamma Rays

A **gamma ray** is a high-energy form of electromagnetic radiation. Like other types of electromagnetic radiation, gamma rays are transmitted in the form of waves. Energy emitted or absorbed as gamma rays can be represented as $^0_0\gamma$. The zero subscript and superscript show that a gamma ray has neither mass nor charge.

In addition to alpha, beta, and gamma rays, other types of radiation have also been identified as being emitted by certain nuclei. This radiation includes streams of protons (symbol $_1^1\text{p}$ or $_1^1\text{H}$), and streams of neutrons (symbol $_0^1\text{n}$). One rather unusual type of radiation consists of a stream of positive electrons ($_{+1}^{0}\text{e}$), usually called **positrons**.

TABLE 17.1 *Common Forms of Radiation and Their Symbols*

Name	Symbol
Alpha particle (helium nucleus)	$_2^4\text{He}$
Beta particle (electron)	$_{-1}^{0}\text{e}$
Gamma ray	$_0^0\gamma$
Proton	$_1^1\text{p}$ or $_1^1\text{H}$
Neutron	$_0^1\text{n}$
Positron (positive electron)	$_{+1}^{0}\text{e}$

Nuclear Equations

17.2 When we balance a conventional chemical equation, we take care to ensure that each type of atom occurs the same number of times on each side of the equation. During a nuclear reaction nuclei change their identity, so we cannot balance an equation for these reactions in the usual way. Instead we balance mass number and the total nuclear charge.

The simplest nuclear reactions involve the **radioactive decay** (or decomposition) of radioactive isotopes. When such a decay occurs, radiation is emitted by the nucleus. If alpha or beta particles are given off, new elements are formed. On the other hand, neutrons and gamma rays have no charge, and their loss from the nucleus does not change the atomic number of the nucleus or its identity. Thus a radioactive element is only transformed into another element when a charged particle is emitted during the decay process.

As an example, let us consider the decomposition of tritium, a rare isotope of hydrogen that has one proton and two neutrons in its nucleus. In the decay process, tritium releases a beta particle and changes into an isotope of helium containing one neutron and two protons. Tritium can be represented as $_1^3\text{H}$ and the helium isotope as $_2^3\text{He}$. We represent a beta particle (i.e. an electron) as $_{-1}^{0}\text{e}$. The nuclear equation is therefore

$$_1^3\text{H} \longrightarrow\ _2^3\text{He}\ +\ _{-1}^{0}\text{e}$$

In order for the equation to be balanced, the sum of the mass numbers on each side of the equation must be the same. We can see that this is the case. Similarly, the total nuclear charge on each side of the equation must also be the same. When we add the charges we see that $1 = 2 + (-1)$.

Although we may think of neutrons and protons as being unchangeable, this is not true. For example, the above decay process involves the conversion of one of the neutrons within the tritium nucleus to a proton and an electron. During the conversion, the electron is expelled from the nucleus.

When we write a nuclear equation we usually show only particles that have mass and/or charge. Thus such equations give no indication as to whether or not a gamma ray is emitted during the reaction.

If we know the type of radiation produced during the simple radioactive decay of a radioactive isotope, we should be able to predict the identity and mass number of the element that will be produced.

EXAMPLE   **17.1**   One of the radioactive isotopes of radon, radon-222, releases one alpha particle per nucleus as it decays into another element. What element is formed and what is its mass number?

SOLUTION   Initially, we can write the equation as

$$^{222}_{86}\text{Rn} \longrightarrow \, ^{4}_{2}\text{He} \; + \; ?$$

The sum of the mass numbers and the sum of the atomic numbers on each side of the equation must be the same. Therefore the element that is produced must have a mass number of 218 and an atomic number of 84. From the Periodic Table we see that the element with atomic number 84 is polonium (Po). Thus the symbolic representation of the isotope that is produced is $^{218}_{84}\text{Po}$. The full nuclear equation for the process that occurs is therefore

$$^{222}_{86}\text{Rn} \longrightarrow \, ^{4}_{2}\text{He} \; + \; ^{218}_{84}\text{Po}.$$

Similarly, if we know the atomic number and the mass number of the isotope produced during the simple radioactive decay of a given nucleus, we can deduce the type of radiation released during the decay process.

EXAMPLE   **17.2**   A radioactive isotope of oxygen, oxygen-15, undergoes radioactive decay to form nitrogen-15. What type of radiation is released during this process?

SOLUTION   We can represent this process as follows:

$$^{15}_{8}\text{O} \longrightarrow \, ^{15}_{7}\text{N} \; + \; ?$$

The particles that are produced must have a mass number of zero and an atomic number, or nuclear charge, of +1. By referring to Table 7.1 we see that the positron ($^{0}_{+1}\text{e}$) is the only particle that fits this description. The complete equation is therefore

$$^{15}_{8}\text{O} \longrightarrow \, ^{15}_{7}\text{N} \; + \; ^{0}_{+1}\text{e}$$

Radioactive Series

Although most radioactive isotopes change directly into a stable isotope during a decay process, certain isotopes with high atomic numbers go through a series of decay steps before a stable isotope is reached. The product of each intermediate step is itself radioactive, and the series of isotopes produced during a given sequence of decay processes is called a **radioactive series**. The radioactive series for uranium is a good example.

Uranium exists in nature as two isotopes, uranium-235 (percent abundance, 0.7%) and uranium-238 (percent abundance, 99.3%). Uranium-238 undergoes radioactive decay by releasing an alpha particle to form thorium-234:

$$^{238}_{92}U \longrightarrow {}^{234}_{90}Th + {}^{4}_{2}He$$

However, thorium-234 is also radioactive and releases a beta particle to form protactinium-234:

$$^{234}_{90}Th \longrightarrow {}^{234}_{91}Pa + {}^{0}_{-1}e$$

Protactinium, is radioactive, as is the product of its decay, uranium-234. These decays continue in a series of steps, each step involving the release of an alpha particle or a beta particle. After a total of fourteen steps a stable isotope, lead-206, is finally obtained. Similar radioactive series exist for other actinon isotopes.

Figure 17.2

The uranium-238 radioactive decay series. As can be seen, at certain points in the series two alternative routes are available. Ultimately, however, the final product is always lead-206.

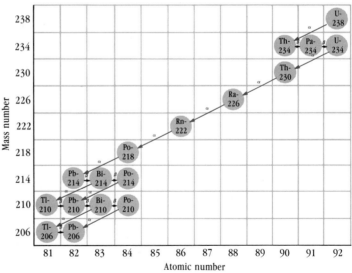

QUESTIONS

1. Complete the following nuclear equations:

   a) $^{190}_{75}Re \longrightarrow {}^{190}_{76}Os + ?$

   b) $^{214}_{83}Bi \longrightarrow {}^{4}_{2}He + ?$

   c) $^{120}_{49}In \longrightarrow {}^{0}_{-1}e + ?$

   d) $^{162}_{69}Tm \longrightarrow {}^{0}_{+1}e + ?$

   e) $^{9}_{3}Li \longrightarrow {}^{8}_{3}Li + ?$

The Rate of Nuclear Change   _17.3_

In 1899 Rutherford and one of his co-workers, Frederick Soddy, noted that the amount of radiation emitted by a radioactive substance decreased over time, and that the rate of decrease depended on the identity of the substance.

In order to understand why this is so, let us analyze what happens when a radioactive isotope decays in a single step to a non-radioactive isotope.

If we begin by measuring the initial level of radiation being produced by our hypothetical sample, we can then determine the time that it takes for this level of radiation to decrease by half, i.e. to 50% of the original level. Let us say that it takes twenty seconds for this to happen. What we would then observe is that during the next twenty seconds the radiation level would again decrease by half; that is, to one-fourth of the original level. Similarly, over the next twenty-second period the radiation level would again decrease by half, so that after a total elapsed time of sixty seconds the radiation level would have decreased to one-eighth of the initial value.

As the level of radiation being emitted from a sample must be directly proportional to the number of radioactive nuclei present, this simple experiment tells us that, for this particular isotope, the number of radioactive nuclei present is halved every twenty seconds. In other words, after twenty seconds only 50% of our original nuclei remains, while after forty seconds only 25% remains, and so on. The time required for half of the nuclei in a given sample of a radioactive isotope to decay is called the **half-life** of the isotope. Isotopic half-lives range from fractions of a second to billions of years (Table 17.2).

TABLE 17.2	_Half-Life of Selected Isotopes_			
Isotope	**Half-Life***		**Isotope**	**Half-life***
$^{238}_{92}U$	4.51×10^9 y		$^{251}_{100}Fm$	7 h
$^{14}_{6}C$	5730 y		$^{11}_{6}C$	20.5 min
$^{60}_{27}Co$	5.27 y		$^{15}_{6}C$	2.5 s
$^{131}_{53}I$	8.05 d		$^{212}_{84}Po$	3×10^{-7} s

* y = year, d = day, h = hour, min = minute, s = second

As a more concrete example of half-life let us again consider the case of tritium, $^{3}_{1}H$, which has a half-life of 12.3 years and decays according to the equation

$$^{3}_{1}H \longrightarrow ^{0}_{-1}e + ^{3}_{2}He$$

If we started out with 8×10^{23} tritium nuclei, half of these would have decayed into helium-3 after 12.3 years. We would then be left with 4×10^{23}

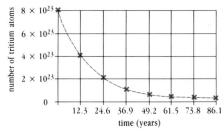

Figure 17.3
The decay of a sample of tritium. With the passage of each 12.3-year period, the number of tritium nuclei remaining is halved.

tritium nuclei. After a further 12.3 years the number of tritium nuclei would again be halved, this time to 2×10^{23}. By this time, a total of 6×10^{23} helium-3 nuclei would have been produced. At the end of the third 12.3-year period, 1×10^{23} tritium nuclei would remain, and so the process would continue.

In order to introduce the concept of half-life, we used an example of a radioactive element that decayed directly into a stable isotope in a single step. If we had studied an isotope that goes through a series of decay steps, we would have recorded the *total* radiation emitted by *each* of the radioactive isotopes involved in the decay sequence. In such situations it is much more difficult to determine the half-life of a particular isotope in the decay series.

The following example shows how we can use the half-life of a radioactive isotope to determine how much of a given sample of that isotope will remain after a certain time has elapsed.

EXAMPLE   *17.3*   Iodine-131 has a half-life of eight days. It decays to xenon-131 and produces beta particles. If we started with 2.000 g of iodine-131, what mass of iodine-131 would remain after 32 days?

SOLUTION   The number of elapsed half-lives is determined as follows:

$$32 \text{ days} \times \frac{1 \text{ half-life}}{8 \text{ days}} = 4 \text{ half-lives}$$

For each half-life, the mass of iodine-131 will decrease by one-half. Therefore the mass remaining after four half-lives will be

$$2.000 \text{ g} \times (\tfrac{1}{2})^4 = 0.1 \text{ g}$$

QUESTIONS

2. Oxygen-20 has a half-life of 14 s. If we start with a 64 g sample, what mass of oxygen-20 will remain after 56 s?

3. Cobalt-60 is used in cancer treatment. If three-quarters of a sample of cobalt-60 decays in 10.5 years, what is the half-life of the isotope?

Radiation Dosage   *17.4*

The effect of radiation on living organisms is a major concern. As we mentioned in Section 17.1, each type of radiation differs in its ability to penetrate materials. Thus the various types of radiation can cause different degrees of damage to living tissue. In general, alpha rays are blocked by the outer layers, beta rays are more penetrating, and gamma rays are extremely penetrating.

Maria Mayer and the Structure of the Nucleus

Maria Göppert Mayer was born in Upper Silesia (then part of Germany) in 1906. Early in life, she developed an interest in mathematics, but after entering the University of Göttingen in 1924 she changed her field of study to atomic physics. Göttingen was then a leading centre for the study of nuclear physics. Mayer emigrated to the U.S.A. in 1930.

Mayer was curious about why some nuclei were more stable than others. In 1948, she developed the Shell Model of the Nucleus to explain nuclear structure and stability in terms of shells of protons and neutrons within the nucleus.

This model is similar to the Bohr model of the atom that we used to explain the arrangement of electrons within an atom in terms of energy levels. The shell model developed by Mayer is still used to help us understand the properties and behaviour of different nuclei. As a result of her work, Mayer shared the Nobel Prize for physics in 1963.

Figure 17.4
Maria Göppert Mayer (1906–1972)

The half-life of an isotope is also an important factor when we consider the effect that the isotope might have on a living organism. Isotopes with short half-lives decompose rapidly and release radiation at a *faster rate* than isotopes with longer half-lives. An isotope with a short half-life is thus more dangerous to handle than an isotope with a very long half-life.

The effects of radiation are measured in terms of the energy absorbed by a sample of body tissue. The SI unit used to measure this energy is called a rad, from **r**adiation **a**bsorbed **d**ose. A **rad** is equal to the absorption of 10^{-5} J of energy by 1 g of tissue.

However, when we are dealing with the effect of radiation on biological cells, the *amount* of radiation received is not the only factor that must be considered. The *type* of radiation is also important. For example, one rad of neutron radiation causes about ten times more damage to a cell then one rad of X-rays. Thus in biological applications we frequently encounter a second unit for expressing radiation dosage, the rem. A **rem** is the amount of radiation absorbed (measured in rads), multiplied by a factor that depends on the type of radiation. For X-rays, γ-rays, and β-rays (electrons) the factor is 1; for neutrons the factor varies from 3 to 10 (depending upon the energy of the neutrons); and for α-rays (helium nuclei) the factor is 20.

TABLE 17.3 *Average Exposure to Radiation per Year*

Natural background (Calgary)	6.4×10^{-2} rem
Natural background (Fredericton)	5.1×10^{-2} rem
Natural body constituents	2.4×10^{-2} rem
Living in stone or brick house	7×10^{-3} rem
Watching TV	4×10^{-4} rem
Chest X-ray (maximum)	4×10^{-3} rem

Workers in nuclear power plants or in laboratories where radioactive materials are handled carry detectors that measure the amount of radiation to which they are exposed. Maximum permissible exposure levels have been established, and workers who are exposed to this level are assigned to duties elsewhere so they will not come into further contact with radioactive materials. The maximum exposure allowed is 5 rem per year. By way of contrast, an exposure of 500 to 1000 rem over a very short period would be lethal.

The Synthesis of New Nuclei

17.5 When most nuclei are bombarded with a stream of high-energy particles, a nuclear reaction takes place and different nuclei are produced. One method of initiating such a reaction is to use a **particle accelerator**. When an accelerated particle such as a neutron strikes one of the target nuclei, the nucleus can split into two or more smaller nuclei. Splitting a nucleus in this manner is called **nuclear fission**. Alternatively, an accelerated particle can be captured by a target nucleus to produce a larger nucleus. This process is known as **nuclear fusion**. Nuclear fission and fusion are both examples of **artificial transmutation**; that is, they are artificial processes by which one element is changed into another.

Nuclear Fission

In 1934, Enrico Fermi, an Italian physicist, bombarded certain elements with beams of neutrons. He found that different elements were produced. Some of the isotopes formed had atomic numbers higher than those of the target elements. When Fermi tried this experiment with uranium-238 he was hoping to create a new element with atomic number 93. Fermi expected a neutron to be absorbed by the uranium-238 nucleus to give uranium-239, which he thought would then be rapidly transformed into the new element, X, with the release of an electron:

$$^{238}_{92}\text{U} + {}^{1}_{0}\text{n} \longrightarrow {}^{239}_{92}\text{U}$$

$$^{239}_{92}\text{U} \longrightarrow {}^{239}_{93}\text{X} + {}^{0}_{-1}\text{e}$$

However, the expected reaction did not occur. Over the next three years, Fermi and his co-workers had no success in identifying the products of the reaction. It was not until 1939 that two German physicists, Lise Meitner and her nephew Otto Frisch, reported that instead of forming an element with a higher atomic number, the neutrons were splitting the uranium-238 nuclei to produce nuclei of lower atomic number. They also reported that considerable quantities of energy were released in this nuclear fission process.

Another important observation was that the fission of uranium-238 did not always yield the same two products. From a single sheet of uranium that had been bombarded with neutrons it was possible to identify a wide range of products, including bromine, krypton, rubidium, strontium, molybdenum, antimony, tellurium, iodine, xenon, cesium, and barium.

Nuclear Chain Reactions

Uranium-238 does not undergo fission as readily as its less abundant isotope, uranium-235. One of the many reactions that occur when uranium-235 is bombarded with neutrons is

$$^{235}_{92}U + ^{1}_{0}n \longrightarrow ^{141}_{56}Ba + ^{92}_{36}Kr + 3\,^{1}_{0}n$$

As we can see from the equation, when a single neutron collides with a uranium-235 nucleus, two nuclei with lower atomic numbers are formed, together with three neutrons. If these neutrons then collide with other nearby uranium nuclei, these nuclei will also subdivide and release still more neutrons (Figure 17.5).

A self-sustaining sequence of nuclear fission reactions is called a **nuclear chain reaction**. Under controlled conditions, a chain reaction can be used to produce a steady quantity of heat in a nuclear fission reactor. However, if these controls are removed, an explosion or meltdown may result.

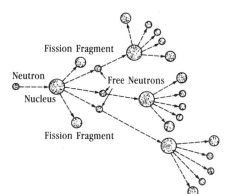

Figure 17.5
The start of a nuclear chain reaction.

QUESTIONS

4. Complete the following nuclear equations involving fission reactions:

a) $^{235}_{92}U + ^{1}_{0}n \longrightarrow ^{87}_{35}Br + ? + 3\,^{1}_{0}n$

b) $^{235}_{92}U + ^{1}_{0}n \longrightarrow ^{103}_{42}Mo + ? + 2\,^{1}_{0}n$

c) $^{235}_{92}U + ^{1}_{0}n \longrightarrow ^{90}_{37}Rb + ^{144}_{55}Cs + ?$

The Energy Changes that Accompany Nuclear Reactions

17.6

In the preceding section we mentioned that Meitner and Frisch reported that considerable quantities of energy were released by nuclear fission reactions. We also mentioned that under controlled conditions fission reactions could be used to produce a steady quantity of heat in a nuclear reactor. Now we shall see why nuclear reactions are capable of producing far greater quantities of energy than the conventional chemical reactions that we have studied in previous chapters.

Very precise measurements show that the mass of a helium nucleus is 4.0015 u. However, if we take the sum of the masses of each of the four particles in a helium nucleus, 2 protons (2 × 1.0073 u) and 2 neutrons (2 × 1.0087 u), we obtain a value of 4.0320 u. This difference (here 0.0305 u) between the total mass of the separate particles within a nucleus and the mass of the nucleus itself is called the **mass defect**. We can explain the origin of mass defect by using Einstein's proposition that energy and matter are equivalent. According to Einstein, energy (E) and mass (m) are related by the simple formula

$$E = mc^2$$

where c is the speed of light (3.00×10^8 m·s^{-1}).

Using this relationship, we could say that the mass "missing" from a helium nucleus is accounted for by the energy released when two protons and two neutrons come together to form such a nucleus. Conversely, we could argue that, if we want to break up a helium nucleus into its component particles i.e. two protons and two neutrons, we would require energy equivalent to 0.0305 u.

EXAMPLE **17.4** The mass lost when a mole of helium nuclei is formed from two moles of protons and two moles of neutrons is 0.0305 g. Calculate how much energy would be required to break up a mole of helium nuclei into its constituent particles.

SOLUTION Before starting the calculation, we must identify the units that we will use. The SI unit of energy is the joule, defined in the base units kg·m^2·s^{-2}. The speed of light (c) is measured in m·s^{-1}. The change in mass will have to be expressed in kilograms. Therefore

$$0.0305 \text{ g} = 0.0305 \text{ g} \times \frac{1 \text{ kg}}{1000 \text{ g}} = 3.05 \times 10^{-5} \text{ kg}$$

Substituting values for mass and the speed of light into Einstein's equation gives

$$E = 3.05 \times 10^{-5} \text{ kg} \times (3.00 \times 10^8 \text{ m·s}^{-1})^2$$
$$= 2.75 \times 10^{12} \text{ kg·m}^2\text{·s}^{-2} \times \frac{1 \text{ J}}{1 \text{ kg·m}^2\text{·s}^{-2}}$$
$$= 2.75 \times 10^{12} \text{ J}$$

There is an increase in mass as the reaction takes place:

$$^4_2\text{He} \longrightarrow 2\,^1_1\text{p} + 2\,^1_0\text{n}$$

This means that energy must be added in order for the reaction to occur. This added energy results in the increase in mass.

As we have just seen, a very large amount of energy (2.75×10^{12} J) is required in order to break down one mole of helium nuclei into two moles of protons and two moles of neutrons. The energy required to break any nucleus into its constituent protons and neutrons is called the **binding energy** of that nucleus. Since energy and mass are related by Einstein's equation $E = mc^2$, the greater the mass defect of a nucleus, the greater will be its binding energy.

Mass Defect and Binding Energy

The size of the mass defect of a nucleus depends upon the number of particles present in the nucleus, although the two quantities are not directly proportional. The nuclear mass of $^{16}_{8}O$ (sixteen particles, 15.9905 u) is less than double that of $^{8}_{4}Be$ (eight particles, 8.0031 u). These figures tell us that, if we were to combine two beryllium-8 nuclei to form one oxygen-16 nucleus, there would be an overall decrease in mass, and energy would be released:

$$2\ ^{8}_{4}Be \longrightarrow\ ^{16}_{8}O\ +\ \textbf{energy}$$
$$\textbf{16.0062 u} \longrightarrow \textbf{15.9905 u}\ +\ \textbf{energy}$$
$$(2 \times 8.0031\ u)$$

Let us see if the outcome is similar when we are dealing with nuclei with much higher atomic numbers. Suppose we combine together two strontium-92 nuclei in order to produce one osmium-184 nucleus. Here we find that the mass of the product (183.9112 u) is greater than the mass of the reactants (2×91.8898 u = 183.7796 u). In other words, mass must be created by the absorption of a large amount of energy in order for this transformation to occur:

$$2\ ^{92}_{38}Sr\ +\ \textbf{energy} \longrightarrow\ ^{184}_{76}Os$$
$$\textbf{183.7796 u}\ +\ \textbf{energy} \longrightarrow \textbf{183.9112 u}$$
$$(2 \times 91.8898\ u)$$

By studying these and many other examples, we find that mass is generally lost and energy released when nuclei with low atomic numbers combine to form a nucleus with an atomic number of 26 or less. However, when nuclei combine to produce a nucleus with an atomic number greater than 26, there is an increase in mass. Such combinations can only be achieved when extremely large amounts of energy are supplied.

QUESTIONS

5. Calculate how much energy would be released when two moles of $^{8}_{4}Be$ nuclei combine to form one mole of $^{16}_{8}O$ nuclei. The mass decrease is 0.0157 g.

6. To heat 100 g of water from 10 °C to 100 °C, about 38 kJ of heat energy is required. If this energy is supplied by a nuclear reaction, what mass would have to be converted into energy?

Fusion Reactions

17.7 When two nuclei combine in a nuclear reaction, a fusion reaction occurs. In some cases, one or more subatomic particles are released in the process. Fusion reactions take place in the extremely hot interiors of stars, and are the source of the heat and light energy provided by our sun. Although scientists believe that several reactions take place in our sun, the most important involves the transformation of hydrogen-1 to helium-4:

$$^1_1\text{H} + {}^1_1\text{H} \longrightarrow {}^2_1\text{H} + {}^0_{+1}\text{e}$$

$$^2_1\text{H} + {}^1_1\text{H} \longrightarrow {}^3_2\text{He}$$

$$^3_2\text{He} + {}^3_2\text{He} \longrightarrow {}^4_2\text{He} + 2\,{}^1_1\text{H}$$

Every second, about 6×10^8 t (600 million t) of our sun's hydrogen is converted to helium. The sun has enough hydrogen to last for several billion years. However, when the hydrogen is almost all used up, the core of the sun will shrink. The sun's temperature will then rise from its present level of 1.5×10^7 K to about 10^8 K. At this point, the helium-4 nuclei will start combining to form carbon-12 and oxygen-16 according to the following equations:

$$^4_2\text{He} + {}^4_2\text{He} \longrightarrow {}^8_4\text{Be}$$

$$^8_4\text{Be} + {}^4_2\text{He} \longrightarrow {}^{12}_6\text{C}$$

$$^{12}_6\text{C} + {}^4_2\text{He} \longrightarrow {}^{16}_8\text{O}$$

Our sun is not likely to reach the temperature of 8×10^8 K required to initiate the fusion reactions that would produce nuclei with atomic numbers greater than eight. It is more likely that the sun will become a white-dwarf star consisting of a carbon–oxygen core surrounded by a shell of helium. Eventually its temperature will begin to decline. As it does so, the sun will slowly die in much the same way that a dying ember fades in a fireplace once the fire has gone out.

The Origin of the Elements

We have just examined a future scenario for our sun. Not all stars meet their end in this way. Stars much more massive than our sun are able to sustain the high temperatures required to initiate the fusion reactions that result in the formation of all the elements up to and including iron (atomic number 26).

You will recall that the formation of nuclei above atomic number 26 requires vast amounts of energy. Since the dying star cannot supply this energy, fusion ceases at this point and the star begins to collapse. As it does so, the star's density increases as its nuclei are pulled closer together. Eventually the repulsive forces acting between the nuclei cause a gigantic explosion called a *supernova*. During such a supernova great amounts of energy are released. Nuclei capture free neutrons and all natural elements above iron are formed. The elements present in our solar system are thought to have been formed by the death of such stars.

The Transuranium Elements

Elements that occur after uranium in the Periodic Table, i.e. those elements with an atomic number greater than 92, do not occur in nature. These elements, usually referred to as the synthetic or **transuranium elements**, are produced by nuclear reactions in which a target nucleus is bombarded with suitable particles such as neutrons. The first two transuranium elements to be produced in this manner were neptunium (atomic number 93) and plutonium (atomic number 94). These elements were named after the planets Neptune and Pluto which lie beyond Uranus in our solar system. Uranium, as you may have deduced, was named after Uranus.

Neptunium-239 was obtained in 1940 by bombarding uranium-238 nuclei with neutrons. The uranium-239 initially produced in this reaction rapidly decays to produce neptunium-239, as follows

$$^{238}_{92}U + ^{1}_{0}n \longrightarrow ^{239}_{92}U$$

$$^{239}_{92}U \longrightarrow ^{239}_{93}Np + ^{0}_{-1}e$$

Similarly, plutonium-238 was first obtained in 1942 according to the following process:

$$^{238}_{92}U + ^{2}_{1}H \longrightarrow ^{238}_{93}Np + 2\,^{1}_{0}n$$

$$^{238}_{93}Np \longrightarrow ^{238}_{94}Pu + ^{0}_{-1}e$$

You will notice that this process involves the use of deuterium nuclei (deuterons, $^{2}_{1}H$) as bombarding particles. Other particles used to bring about similar transmutations include α-particles, carbon nuclei, and oxygen nuclei:

$$^{242}_{96}Cm + ^{4}_{2}He \longrightarrow ^{245}_{98}Cf + ^{1}_{0}n$$

$$^{246}_{96}Cm + ^{12}_{6}C \longrightarrow ^{254}_{102}No + 4\,^{1}_{0}n$$

$$^{249}_{98}Cf + ^{18}_{8}O \longrightarrow ^{263}_{106}Unh + 4\,^{1}_{0}n$$

In 1982 it was reported that a single atom of element 109 (unnilennium, symbol Une) had been prepared through the fusion of an iron projectile nucleus and a bismuth target.

Figure 17.6
For his work on synthesis of new elements, notably plutonium-239, Glenn Seaborg was awarded the 1951 Nobel Prize for chemistry.

QUESTIONS

7. Complete the following nuclear equations:

a) $^{27}_{13}Al + ^{4}_{2}He \longrightarrow ^{1}_{1}H + ?$ d) $^{116}_{48}Cd + ^{4}_{2}He \longrightarrow ^{1}_{0}n + ?$

b) $4\,^{1}_{1}H \longrightarrow 2\,^{0}_{+1}e + ?$ e) $^{249}_{98}Cf + ^{11}_{5}B \longrightarrow 6\,^{1}_{0}n + ?$

c) $^{118}_{50}Sn + ^{1}_{0}n \longrightarrow ?$

Nuclear Reactors

17.8   As we have seen, nuclear reactions are accompanied by the release of large amounts of energy. Nuclear engineers have attempted to harness this energy by building power stations in which the heat energy released by a nuclear reaction is converted to electrical energy. The nuclear reactions take place in a **nuclear reactor**. The heat is absorbed by a liquid or gas, which is then passed through a heat exchanger in order to generate steam. The steam then passes to a turbine connected to an electrical generator. Although it is theoretically possible to have both fission and fusion reactors, to date no viable fusion reactor has been developed.

The Basic Requirements of a Fission Reactor

Most nuclear reactors utilize the chain reactions that take place when uranium-235 nuclei are bombarded with neutrons. As we mentioned earlier, uranium-235 undergoes fission much more readily than uranium-238. Because natural uranium contains only 0.7% uranium-235, large amounts of ore must be processed in order to obtain even a small quantity of fissionable material.

When bombarded by neutrons, uranium-235 nuclei release some of their own neutrons. The released neutrons move too quickly to be captured by neighbouring uranium nuclei, and therefore a chain reaction does not occur. To slow down these fast moving neutrons, a moderator such as graphite or water is used. The **moderator** causes the neutrons to move more slowly so they can be trapped by the target uranium-235 nuclei. When these nuclei trap neutrons they become unstable and split into two smaller nuclei, releasing two or three more neutrons in the process. A chain reaction can then occur, producing many different fission products. Two typical reactions are

$$_0^1n + {}_{92}^{235}U \longrightarrow {}_{37}^{90}Rb + {}_{55}^{144}Cs + 2\,_0^1n + \text{energy}$$

$$_0^1n + {}_{92}^{235}U \longrightarrow {}_{35}^{87}Br + {}_{57}^{146}La + 3\,_0^1n + \text{energy}$$

Fission Reactor Designs

The main purpose of the moderator is to slow down fast-moving neutrons. However, the hydrogen nuclei in water absorb some of the neutrons. Consequently, the proportion of uranium-235 in water-moderated reactors must be increased (enriched) in order to supply enough neutrons to sustain the chain reaction. Increasing this proportion is a difficult and expensive process. Nevertheless, most reactors in the United States and Europe use **enriched uranium** as a fuel and water as a moderator.

Similar reactors are used to power most nuclear ships. Construction costs for these ships are very high because of their reactor-powered engines. However, such ships only require refuelling once every two to five years.

Figure 17.7
The Soviet Union's nuclear-powered ice-breaker, Arktika (12 000 t). This huge, extremely powerful vessel can cruise through ice up to 3 m thick.

A large number of U.S. naval vessels, especially submarines, are now nuclear-powered. Nuclear-powered ships have also been constructed for non-military purposes. The Soviet Union, for example, has a fleet of nuclear-powered ice-breakers.

The CANDU Reactor

In the Canadian-designed **CANDU** (Canadian Deuterium-Uranium) **reactor**, natural uranium is used as the fuel. Although this fuel is cheaper than enriched uranium, its use means that regular water cannot be used as the moderator, since the hydrogen nuclei would absorb too many neutrons to allow a chain reaction to proceed. Instead the CANDU reactor uses heavy water, which absorbs very few neutrons. **Heavy water** consists of water molecules in which the hydrogen-1 atoms (^1_1H) have been replaced by deuterium atoms (^2_1H).

The process by which water molecules containing deuterium atoms are separated from those containing normal hydrogen atoms is very expensive. Any saving in cost obtained by using natural uranium instead of enriched uranium is offset by the cost of producing heavy water.

Figure 17.8
The Pickering nuclear power station is equipped with CANDU reactors.

The Advantages and Disadvantages of the CANDU System.

In most nuclear power plants, the reactors have to be shut down in order to replace spent fuel. One advantage of the CANDU system is that refuelling

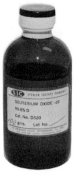

Figure 17.9
A bottle of heavy water (deuterium oxide).

Figure 17.10
A schematic of the CANDU *system.*

Figure 17.11
The destroyed unit 4 of the Chernobyl nuclear power station near Kiev.

can be carried out without this inconvenience. A second advantage of the CANDU reactor design is that it can be easily modified to use thorium-232 as a fuel.

The major disadvantage of the CANDU reactor arises from the collision of neutrons with the uranium-238 nuclei present in the fuel. These collisions cause a nuclear reaction that produces plutonium-239, and plutonium-239 can be used to construct nuclear weapons. Consequently, the Canadian government now refuses to sell CANDU reactors to any country that it feels is likely to use plutonium for military purposes.

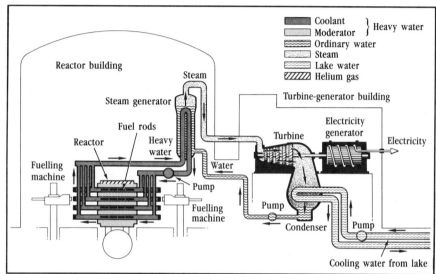

The Safety of Nuclear Reactors

No doubt you have heard about the major nuclear accidents at Three-Mile Island and Chernobyl. In both accidents, a loss of cooling water caused the temperature inside the reactor to increase rapidly. At Three-Mile Island, the reactor was surrounded by a thick-walled containment building preventing the escape of most of the radioactive materials. At Chernobyl, the reactor was contained in a normal building. Additionally, the graphite moderator caught fire and contributed to the problem.

Could accidents like these happen in Canada? In Canadian nuclear power stations, such as the one at Pickering, Ontario, the reactor is located in a thick-walled containment building that is connected to a vacuum building (the large drum-shaped building seen in Figure 17.8). During an emergency, any pressure build-up would be vented into this building. The CANDU reactor is thus considered to have a fundamentally safer design than other nuclear reactors. However, human error, substandard materials, and unanticipated events can lead to accidents in even the most carefully designed plants.

The question of whether or not Canada should build more CANDU reactors and become more dependent on nuclear energy is a controversial one.

The decisions that we make now may affect future generations. Is the use of nuclear energy an acceptable risk? All Canadians would do well to give this issue some careful consideration.

The Pros and Cons of Nuclear Power

In Canada, we are fortunate to have four major sources of energy that can be used for the large-scale production of electricity: water, oil, coal, and nuclear energy. The use of water as a source of energy is limited to provinces such as British Columbia, Manitoba, Ontario, Quebec, and Newfoundland, where there are plentiful supplies of inland water, or to regions like the Bay of Fundy, where tidal water can be used. The other regions must derive their energy supply from the other alternatives: oil, coal, and nuclear energy.

Nuclear power is an attractive option in Canada because we have very large deposits of uranium. In power plants that burn coal and oil, the cost

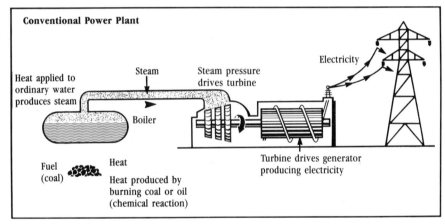

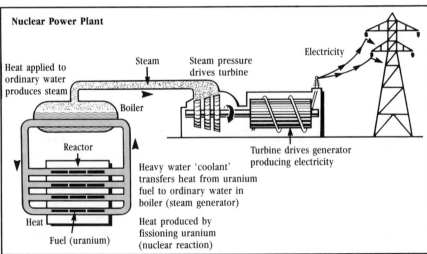

Figure 17.12

Comparison of a conventional electrical generating station with a nuclear power plant.

of the fuel comprises a large and often unpredictable portion of the final cost of the electricity. From an environmental point of view, power plants that burn coal and oil produce large quantities of carbon dioxide and sulfur dioxide. Carbon dioxide is of concern because its build-up in the atmosphere might lead to major climatic changes, while sulfur dioxide is the major cause of acid rain. Although the technology is now available to build coal-burning plants that produce minimal amounts of air pollution, both the initial cost and the operating costs of such plants are quite high.

The cost of constructing a nuclear power station is relatively high because it is a much more complex operation than a conventional oil- or coal-fired power plant. In addition, legislation requires safety features to protect both the nuclear power-plant workers and the environment from radiation. Incorporating these features also leads to increased costs.

A major problem faced by the owners of nuclear power plants is how to dispose of used fuel. It is important to realize that nuclear fuel is not consumed in the same way that gasoline is consumed by a car. Even after it has lost its usefulness, used nuclear fuel is still present in a reactor. This spent fuel consists of a wide variety of elements produced from the fission of uranium-235. Many of the isotopes produced are highly radioactive and have short half-lives. Others have long half-lives and produce low levels of radiation for very long periods. If the used fuel is stored for several months, the nuclei with short half-lives will almost all decompose, but those with long half-lives will remain. In fact, nuclear waste must be stored safely for thousands of years before its radiation level will decrease significantly. One method being considered involves sealing the waste into a synthetic rock called "Synroc". Discs of Synroc would then be buried about 4 km beneath the earth's surface in stable rock formations. It is hoped that a disposal system of this type will protect the environment from contamination.

A second problem connected with the disposal of nuclear waste results from the capture of neutrons by uranium-238 nuclei. When uranium-235 captures a neutron, fission results. However, if a uranium-238 nucleus is hit by a slow-moving neutron, fusion occurs and uranium-239 is formed:

$$^{238}_{92}\text{U} + ^{1}_{0}\text{n} \longrightarrow ^{239}_{92}\text{U}$$

This isotope has a half-life of only 23 min. It decays by releasing a beta particle to form neptunium-239:

$$^{239}_{92}\text{U} \longrightarrow ^{239}_{93}\text{Np} + ^{0}_{-1}\text{e}$$

Neptunium-239 has a half-life of two days and also undergoes beta decay to form plutonium-239:

$$^{239}_{93}\text{Np} \longrightarrow ^{239}_{94}\text{Pu} + ^{0}_{-1}\text{e}$$

Plutonium-239 has a half-life of 24 000 years and therefore poses a long-term problem. As mentioned before, this particular isotope can be used to manufacture fission bombs. Only a few kilograms of plutonium-239 are required to make a nuclear bomb. Thus, for countries with nuclear reactors, the disposal of plutonium-239 is a security problem as well as a safety problem.

The Commercial Use of Fusion Power

For more than thirty years scientists have been working to find a way of harnessing the energy released by nuclear-fusion reactions. In order to initiate such reactions, a high concentration of nuclei must be maintained at a temperature of about 5.8×10^6 K. As such high temperatures would vaporize any solid instantly, the reacting nuclei have to be held within very strong magnetic fields instead of within conventional metal or concrete containers. Only if these conditions can be realized is it possible to obtain more energy from the fusion reaction than is used in heating the nuclei and providing the necessary magnetic fields.

In Canada, an experimental fusion reactor has been built at Varennes, near Montreal. From the experiments carried out using this reactor, scientists hope to learn how a fusion reaction can be sustained for more than the present limit of a few seconds. The fusion reaction which appears to be the most viable from a commercial point of view involves the fusion of deuterium ($^2_1$H) and tritium ($^3_1$H):

$$^2_1\text{H} + ^3_1\text{H} \longrightarrow ^4_2\text{He} + ^1_0\text{n} + \text{energy}$$

Fusion reactions offer several potential advantages over fission reactions. To begin with, the quantity of fuel needed is much less. While a large fission plant needs about 150 t of uranium per year, the same energy output could be obtained in a fusion reaction from about 0.6 t of deuterium and tritium. In terms of the availability of raw materials, the world's water supplies contain enough deuterium to provide fusion power for millions of years. The other reactant, tritium, can be easily obtained from deuterium by neutron bombardment.

The radiation produced by the used fuel from a fission reactor presents a disposal problem, but the major product (helium-4) of the fusion reaction just described is non-radioactive. Nevertheless, there are other radiation problems associated with fusion reactors. First, tritium is very radioactive and must be contained within the reactor at all times. Second, and perhaps of greater importance, is the fact that this fusion reaction produces neutrons, many of which will collide with the nuclei of the materials used in the construction of the reactor to produce radioactive nuclei. Thus the reactor itself will become increasingly radioactive, and this will present problems for personnel working at the site. Disposal of the reactor after it is no longer useful will also be difficult. Work is therefore underway to produce materials that are less likely to produce radioactive isotopes when bombarded by neutrons.

We are still a long way from the successful development of a fusion reactor. In fact, we may be well into the next century before a satisfactory design is available. Nevertheless, research needs to be done now in order to assure continuing energy supplies.

8. Identify two of the differences between a CANDU reactor and a conventional nuclear fission reactor.

9. Give two reasons why most Canadian nuclear power stations are located in Ontario.

10. Besides Ontario, which other provinces have commercial nuclear reactors?

Applications 17.9 of Nuclear Chemistry

Nuclear chemistry has been applied to a number of fields, including medicine, biology and biochemistry, geology, and archaeology. Several typical applications in these fields are described below.

Medicine. In medicine, radioactive isotopes are used to diagnose and treat disease. In the treatment of certain types of cancer, gamma radiation is used to kill cancerous cells. Cobalt-60 is often used as the source of the γ-radiation. This isotope is prepared by placing the only natural isotope of cobalt, cobalt-59, in a nuclear reactor. Here cobalt-59 absorbs a neutron to produce cobalt-60:

$$^{59}_{27}\text{Co} + ^{1}_{0}\text{n} \longrightarrow ^{60}_{27}\text{Co}$$

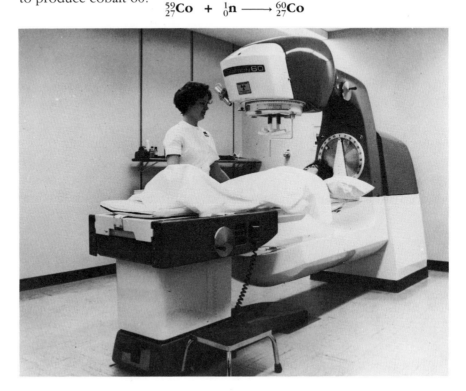

Figure 17.13

Cobalt-60 is used in the treatment of certain types of cancer.

About 90% of the cobalt-60 used throughout the world is produced in Canada. Cobalt-60 has a half-life of about five years and releases both beta and gamma rays:

$$^{60}_{27}\text{Co} \longrightarrow {}^{60}_{28}\text{Ni} + {}^{0}_{-1}\text{e} + {}^{0}_{0}\gamma$$

Biology and Biochemistry. To help us understand the biochemical processes that take place in plants and animals we use radioactive tracers. A **radioactive tracer** is a radioactive isotope that can be substituted for the more abundant, non-radioactive isotope involved in some biochemical processes. Once substituted, the radioactive tracer and the compounds formed by it can be tracked through the respective plant or animal system.

Carbon-14, for example, can be used to study photosynthesis in plants. We can place a plant in a container filled with radioactive carbon dioxide. The plant absorbs the radioactive carbon dioxide just as it would normal carbon dioxide. We can then follow the progress of the radioactive carbon atoms by monitoring the emission of β-rays as the carbon-14 nuclei decay:

$$^{14}_{6}\text{C} \longrightarrow {}^{14}_{7}\text{N} + {}^{0}_{-1}\text{e}$$

Chemistry. Nuclear reactions can be used in both qualitative and quantitative chemical analysis. A very sensitive technique, known as **neutron activation analysis**, is used to determine elemental concentrations as low as one part per billion. In neutron activation analysis, the sample is placed in a small nuclear reactor where it is bombarded with neutrons. This transforms many of the nuclei into radioactive isotopes. The sample, which is now radioactive, is removed from the reactor and the rays it emits are studied. Each radioactive isotope produces rays with very precise wavelengths characteristic of that isotope. For example, natural gold consists of one isotope: gold-197. When exposed to neutrons, gold-198 is produced which further decays by the emission of both beta and gamma rays:

$$^{197}_{79}\text{Au} + {}^{1}_{0}\text{n} \longrightarrow {}^{198}_{79}\text{Au}$$

$$^{198}_{79}\text{Au} \longrightarrow {}^{198}_{80}\text{Hg} + {}^{0}_{-1}\text{e} + {}^{0}_{0}\gamma$$

The γ-rays have a wavelength of 3.01×10^{-12} m (3.01 pm). If we measure the intensity of the γ-rays of this wavelength we are able to find the concentration of gold in the sample.

Geology and Archeology. We can use our knowledge of radioactive isotopes to determine the age of rock formations. One isotope that is useful in this regard is potassium-40. This isotope decays as shown below via a mechanism called electron capture:

$$^{40}_{19}\text{K} + {}^{0}_{-1}\text{e} \longrightarrow {}^{40}_{18}\text{Ar}$$

Potassium-40 has a half-life of 1.3×10^9 years. The age of a potassium-containing rock can be calculated by determining the ratio of potassium-40 to argon-40 present. While the rock is in molten form inside the earth, the argon gas can escape. However, once the rock has solidified near the surface of the earth, any atoms of argon produced by the decay of potassium-40 will be trapped in the rock. If we melt a sample of this rock in the laboratory, we can measure the volume of argon released. We then compare the amount of gas released with the amount of potassium-40 remaining in the rock. This comparison gives us a good estimate of the time that has elapsed since the rock solidified.

Potassium-argon dating can be used for objects that are millions of years old, but comparatively young materials will not have produced sufficient argon to allow them to be dated by this method. For these materials, carbon-14 or tritium dating is used. Carbon-14, with a half-life of 5720 years, is especially useful for dating wood specimens; tritium, with a half-life of 12.3 years, is used for dating water samples.

QUESTIONS

11. Which radioactive dating method could have been used to date the rock samples that the Apollo astronauts brought back from the Moon?

The Destructive Side of Nuclear Energy

17.10

The transformation of matter into energy by nuclear reactions can be used for destructive as well as constructive purposes. A fission bomb (popularly called an atomic bomb) consists of uranium-235 or plutonium-239 surrounded by a layer of ordinary explosive. When the explosive is detonated, the uranium or plutonium is compressed into a small single lump in which a chain reaction can take place. Unlike the chain reactions that are used in nuclear reactors, this reaction is not controlled, and an enormous explosion results.

A temperature of millions of kelvins is required to detonate a fusion bomb (a hydrogen bomb). The only 'easy' way to achieve this temperature level is to set off a fission reaction first. Thus every fusion bomb also contains a small fission bomb. The fusion reaction, once begun, releases much more energy than a fission reaction, and the resulting explosion is greater than that of a fission bomb.

The effects of nuclear warfare would be disastrous. The total explosive power of existing nuclear weapons is great enough to destroy the world several times over. Studies indicate that hundreds of millions of people would die as a result of even a limited nuclear war. In addition, scientists now believe that the dust and smoke from the explosions and fires would result in darkness over most of the earth's surface. This darkness could last for months or even years, preventing heat and light from the sun from reaching the earth. Without this light and heat, temperatures would drop to well below freezing even at the equator, and plants would not be able to survive. Without plants for food, any surviving animals or humans would not live very long in this aptly named "nuclear winter".

Figure 17.14
A plutonium bomb similar to this one was dropped on Nagasaki in 1945. The blast killed or maimed nearly 100 000 people.

A nuclear war would also destroy the ozone layer in the upper atmosphere that protects us from the sun's ultraviolet rays. Thus, the "nuclear winter" would be followed by an equally inhospitable "ultraviolet spring".

Summary

- Nuclear chemistry is concerned with changes that occur in the nucleus of an atom.

- The nucleus of a radioactive isotope can emit several types of radiation. Common types include alpha, beta, and gamma rays.

- A balanced nuclear equation has the same total mass and the same total nuclear charge on each side of the equation.

- Radioactive isotopes may decay through a series of steps before a stable isotope is produced.

- The time required for half the atoms of a radioactive isotope to decay is called the half-life of the isotope.

- The effects of radiation are measured in terms of the energy released when the rays are stopped by a sample of matter. The harmful effects of radiation depend upon the type of radiation and the half-life of the isotope.

- Most nuclei can be changed by bombarding them with particles. The nuclei can either split into smaller nuclei (fission), or capture the bombarding particles to form larger nuclei (fusion).

- The energy released by the sun and other stars is due to a series of nuclear reactions that take place within them.

- Nuclear reactions involve the transformation of a small amount of matter into a large amount of energy.

- The energy produced by nuclear reactions may be converted into electrical energy through the use of a nuclear reactor.

- The CANDU reactor is a Canadian-designed nuclear reactor.

- Nuclear chemistry has been applied to many fields including medicine, geology, and archeology.

- Nuclear weapons have been designed that utilize both nuclear fission and nuclear fusion.

KEY WORDS

alpha ray	nuclear fission
artificial transmutation	nuclear fusion
beta ray	nuclear reactor
binding energy	particle accelerator
CANDU reactor	positron

enriched uranium
gamma ray
half-life
heavy water
mass defect
moderator
neutron activation analysis
nuclear chain reaction

rad
radioactive decay
radioactive series
radioactive tracer
radioactivity
rem
transuranium elements

ANSWERS TO SECTION QUESTIONS

1. a) $^{190}_{75}Re \longrightarrow ^{190}_{76}Os + ^{0}_{-1}e$

b) $^{214}_{83}Bi \longrightarrow ^{4}_{2}He + ^{210}_{81}Tl$

c) $^{120}_{49}In \longrightarrow ^{0}_{-1}e + ^{120}_{50}Sn$

d) $^{162}_{69}Tm \longrightarrow ^{0}_{+1}e + ^{162}_{68}Er$

e) $^{9}_{3}Li \longrightarrow ^{8}_{3}Li + ^{1}_{0}n$

2. 4.0 g

3. As ¾ of the cobalt-60 decays in 10.5 years, ¼ must remain after this time. Two half-lives must have elapsed; therefore the half-life is 5.25 years.

4. a) $^{235}_{92}U + ^{1}_{0}n \longrightarrow ^{87}_{35}Br + ^{146}_{57}La + 3\,^{1}_{0}n$

b) $^{235}_{92}U + ^{1}_{0}n \longrightarrow ^{103}_{42}Mo + ^{131}_{50}Sn + 2\,^{1}_{0}n$

c) $^{235}_{92}U + ^{1}_{0}n \longrightarrow ^{90}_{37}Rb + ^{144}_{55}Cs + 2\,^{1}_{0}n$

5. 1.41×10^{12} J

6. 4.2×10^{-10} g

7. a) $^{27}_{13}Al + ^{4}_{2}He \longrightarrow ^{1}_{1}H + ^{30}_{14}Si$

b) $4\,^{1}_{1}H \longrightarrow 2\,^{0}_{+1}e + ^{4}_{2}He$

c) $^{118}_{50}Sn + ^{1}_{0}n \longrightarrow ^{119}_{50}Sn$

d) $^{116}_{48}Cd + ^{4}_{2}He \longrightarrow ^{1}_{0}n + ^{119}_{50}Sn$

e) $^{249}_{98}Cf + ^{11}_{5}B \longrightarrow 6\,^{1}_{0}n + ^{254}_{103}Lw$

8. The CANDU reactor uses natural uranium as a fuel and heavy water as a moderator. Conventional reactors use enriched uranium as fuel and "ordinary" water as the moderator.

9. Ontario has a shortage of other energy sources (e.g. coal and oil) and a convenient source of uranium.

10. New Brunswick and Quebec also have nuclear power plants.

11. Potassium-argon dating.

1. Describe the nature of each of the three common types of radiation: alpha, beta, and gamma.

2. What happens to the number of protons and neutrons in a nucleus when it undergoes decay by releasing beta particles?

3. How does balancing a nuclear equation differ from balancing a conventional chemical equation?

4. Explain the term "radioactive series".

5. Define the term "half-life".

6. What is the difference between a rad and a rem?

7. What two factors determine the effect of radiation on body tissue?

8. Explain the difference between a fission reaction and a fusion reaction. Give an example of each.

9. Briefly describe how a nuclear reactor converts nuclear fuel into electrical energy.

10. What are the advantages and disadvantages of the use of nuclear power compared to the use of water or fossil fuels to produce electricity?

11. What are the advantages and disadvantages of a CANDU reactor compared to a conventional nuclear reactor?

12. Explain the role of a moderator in a nuclear reactor.

13. List four applications of nuclear chemistry to areas other than the production of energy in nuclear reactors and the manufacture of nuclear weapons.

14. Describe two of the difficulties involved in the development of a commercial fusion reactor.

15. Why is the disposal of nuclear waste containing plutonium-239 considered to be a particular problem?

16. Why is it more dangerous to handle a radioactive isotope with a short half-life than one with a long half-life?

17. Why are radioactive isotopes with short half-lives unlikely to occur naturally?

18. Why can we combine only nuclei with low atomic numbers in a fusion reactor?

PROBLEMS 19. Determine whether each of the following equations represents a natural decay process or an artificial transmutation. In the case of a natural decay, identify the type of particle that is emitted (e.g. alpha particle, positron, etc.). If the process is a transmutation, determine whether a fission or fusion reaction is involved.

a) $^{234}_{90}\text{Th} \longrightarrow {}^{234}_{91}\text{Pa} + {}^{0}_{-1}\text{e}$

b) $^{54}_{26}\text{Fe} + {}^{1}_{1}\text{H} \longrightarrow {}^{54}_{27}\text{Co} + {}^{1}_{0}\text{n}$

c) $^{101}_{46}Pd \longrightarrow {}^{101}_{45}Rh + {}^{0}_{+1}e$

d) $^{238}_{92}U + {}^{14}_{7}N \longrightarrow {}^{247}_{99}Es + 5 {}^{1}_{0}n$

e) $^{10}_{5}B + {}^{1}_{0}n \longrightarrow {}^{3}_{1}H + 2 {}^{4}_{2}He$

20. State which of the following equations represent natural decay processes and which represent artificial transmutations. Identify the type of particle emitted in each of the natural decay processes.

a) $^{216}_{85}At \longrightarrow {}^{212}_{83}Bi + {}^{4}_{2}He$

b) $^{89}_{36}Kr \longrightarrow {}^{88}_{36}Kr + {}^{1}_{0}n$

c) $^{59}_{27}Co + {}^{1}_{0}n \longrightarrow {}^{60}_{27}Co$

d) $^{235}_{92}U + {}^{1}_{0}n \longrightarrow {}^{90}_{38}Sr + {}^{143}_{54}Xe + 3 {}^{1}_{0}n$

e) $^{24}_{11}Na \longrightarrow {}^{24}_{12}Mg + {}^{0}_{-1}e$

21. Complete each of the following equations:

a) $^{18}_{10}Ne \longrightarrow {}^{0}_{+1}e + ?$

b) $^{212}_{86}Rn \longrightarrow {}^{208}_{84}Po + ?$

c) $^{6}_{2}He \longrightarrow {}^{6}_{3}Li + ?$

d) $^{214}_{83}Bi \longrightarrow {}^{4}_{2}He + ?$

e) $^{207}_{84}Po \longrightarrow {}^{207}_{83}Bi + ?$

22. Identify the missing particle in each of the following equations:

a) $^{226}_{88}Ra \longrightarrow {}^{222}_{86}Rn + ?$

b) $^{12}_{6}C + ? \longrightarrow {}^{13}_{7}N + {}^{0}_{0}\gamma$

c) $^{31}_{15}P + {}^{4}_{2}He \longrightarrow {}^{34}_{17}Cl + ?$

d) $^{120}_{49}In \longrightarrow {}^{0}_{-1}e + ?$

e) $^{31}_{15}P + {}^{4}_{2}He \longrightarrow ? + {}^{1}_{1}H + {}^{1}_{0}n$

23. The following equations each represent a fusion reaction that can occur in the sun and other stars. Identify the missing particle in each equation.

a) $^{12}_{6}C + {}^{12}_{6}C \longrightarrow {}^{23}_{12}Mg + ?$

b) $^{18}_{8}O + ? \longrightarrow {}^{15}_{7}N + {}^{4}_{2}He$

c) $^{3}_{2}He + {}^{4}_{2}He \longrightarrow ? + {}^{0}_{0}\gamma$

24. Artificial transmutation can be brought about by bombarding target nuclei with a variety of particles. Identify the isotope produced in each of the equations below:

a) $^{253}_{99}Es + {}^{4}_{2}He \longrightarrow {}^{1}_{1}H + ?$

b) $^{98}_{42}Mo + {}^{1}_{0}n \longrightarrow {}^{0}_{-1}e + ?$

c) $^{244}_{96}Cm + {}^{4}_{2}He \longrightarrow ? + {}^{1}_{1}p + 2 {}^{1}_{0}n$

25. Iodine-132 is used in the treatment of thyroid conditions. It has a half-life of 2.33 hours. How much of an 8.0 mg sample of this isotope would remain after 9.32 hours?

26. The half-life of fermium-253 is 4.5 days. If you start with 1.00 g of this isotope, how much would remain after 45 days?

27. Uranium-233 undergoes alpha decay to form thorium-229. The mass loss during this reaction is 0.0055 g for each mole of uranium used. What is the total energy released when 1.00 mol of uranium-233 decays in this manner?

28. When 1.00 mol of plutonium-239 is bombarded with neutrons there is a decrease in mass of 0.188 g. How much energy is released in the reaction?

$$^{239}_{94}\text{Pu} + {}^{1}_{0}\text{n} \longrightarrow {}^{90}_{38}\text{Sr} + {}^{144}_{58}\text{Ce} + 2\,{}^{0}_{-1}\text{e} + 6\,{}^{1}_{0}\text{n}$$

29. In order to convert 1.00 kg of water at 25 °C into steam at 100 °C we would require a heat input of 2.57 MJ. What mass would have to be converted to energy if the required 2.57 MJ is to be provided by a nuclear reaction?

30. The sun is estimated to produce 3.6×10^{23} kJ of energy every second. What mass must be converted to energy each second in order to sustain this output?

31. Technetium-99 is used in medicine as a radioactive tracer because it concentrates in abnormal heart tissue. The presence of this isotope is detected by measuring the beta radiation that is produced as it decays. Write a balanced nuclear equation for this decay process.

32. Gold-188 decays by positron emission. Write a balanced nuclear equation to describe this process.

33. Write a balanced nuclear equation for each step in the radioactive decay series from uranium-238 to lead-214 (Figure 17.2).

34. Write a balanced nuclear equation for each step in the uranium-238 decay series from lead-214 to lead-206 (Figure 17.2).

35. Why is there no such thing as a pure radioactive isotope?

36. Why would you expect the chemical properties of carbon-14 to be the same as those of carbon-12?

SUGGESTED PROJECTS

1. Nuclear radiation is a cause of cancer, yet it is also used in the treatment of certain types of cancer. Write a report on this apparent contradiction.

2. "Nuclear winter" and the "greenhouse effect" are two gloomy prospects for the future of our planet. Find out what each of these terms means and which activities could bring on these phenomena. Be prepared to take part in a group discussion on the consequences of nuclear winter and the greenhouse effect, and on our ability to survive them.

3. Is nuclear power a viable means of meeting Canada's future energy requirements? Is it a viable means for providing energy for the rest of the world? If so, what should be Canada's role? What are some of the alternative energy sources that should be considered? Write a report or hold a class discussion on these issues.

4. Write an essay on the life cycle of stars and their role in the formation of elements through fusion reactions.

5. In order to synthesize new elements by bombarding target nuclei with positively charged particles such as protons or helium nuclei, the bombarding particle must be accelerated to a very high velocity. Write a report on the different types of particle accelerators and their use in this and other fields.

6. Nuclear waste disposal is one of the most fundamental problems for us to solve. Debates over "burial" locations are raised almost monthly in our major newspapers. Investigate this issue and prepare a formal report on both the short term and long term solutions that are being proposed.

Appendix I

Electronegativity Values for the Main Group Elements (to two decimal places)

Name	Symbol	Value	Name	Symbol	Value
Aluminum	Al	1.61	Lead	Pb	2.10
Antimony	Sb	2.05	Lithium	Li	0.98
Arsenic	As	2.18	Magnesium	Mg	1.31
Astatine	At	2.20	Nitrogen	N	3.04
Barium	Ba	0.89	Oxygen	O	3.44
Beryllium	Be	1.57	Phosphorus	P	2.19
Bismuth	Bi	2.02	Polonium	Po	2.00
Boron	B	2.04	Potassium	K	0.82
Bromine	Br	2.96	Radium	Ra	0.90
Calcium	Ca	1.00	Rubidium	Rb	0.82
Carbon	C	2.55	Selenium	Se	2.55
Cesium	Cs	0.79	Silicon	Si	1.90
Chlorine	Cl	3.16	Sodium	Na	0.93
Fluorine	F	3.98	Strontium	Sr	0.95
Francium	Fr	0.70	Sulfur	S	2.58
Gallium	Ga	1.81	Tellurium	Te	2.10
Germanium	Ge	2.01	Thallium	Tl	1.83
Hydrogen	H	2.20	Tin	Sn	1.88
Indium	In	1.78	Xenon	Xe	2.60
Iodine	I	2.66			

Appendix II

Atomic Masses of the Elements

Name	Symbol	Atomic Number	Atomic Mass (u)*	Name	Symbol	Atomic Number	Atomic Mass (u)*
Actinium	Ac	89	227.03	Bromine	Br	35	79.90
Aluminum	Al	13	26.98	Cadmium	Cd	48	112.41
Americium	Am	95	(243)	Calcium	Ca	20	40.08
Antimony	Sb	51	121.75	Californium	Cf	98	(249)
Argon	Ar	18	39.95	Carbon	C	6	12.01
Arsenic	As	33	74.92	Cerium	Ce	58	140.12
Astatine	At	85	(210)	Cesium	Cs	55	132.91
Barium	Ba	56	137.33	Chlorine	Cl	17	35.45
Berkelium	Bk	97	(247)	Chromium	Cr	24	52.00
Beryllium	Be	4	9.01	Cobalt	Co	27	58.93
Bismuth	Bi	83	208.98	Copper	Cu	29	63.55
Boron	B	5	10.81	Curium	Cm	96	(247)

Name	Symbol	Atomic Number	Atomic Mass (u)*	Name	Symbol	Atomic Number	Atomic Mass (u)*
Dysprosium	Dy	66	162.50	Potassium	K	19	39.10
Einsteinium	Es	99	(254)	Praseodymium	Pr	59	140.91
Erbium	Er	68	167.26	Promethium	Pm	61	(147)
Europium	Eu	63	151.96	Protactinium	Pa	91	231.04
Fermium	Fm	100	(253)	Radium	Ra	88	226.03
Fluorine	F	9	19.00	Radon	Rn	86	(222)
Francium	Fr	87	(223)	Rhenium	Re	75	186.21
Gadolinium	Gd	64	157.25	Rhodium	Rh	45	102.91
Gallium	Ga	31	69.72	Rubidium	Rb	37	85.47
Germanium	Ge	32	72.59	Ruthenium	Ru	44	101.07
Gold	Au	79	196.97	Samarium	Sm	62	150.36
Hafnium	Hf	72	178.49	Scandium	Sc	21	44.96
Helium	He	2	4.00	Selenium	Se	34	78.96
Holmium	Ho	67	164.93	Silicon	Si	14	28.09
Hydrogen	H	1	1.008	Silver	Ag	47	107.87
Indium	In	49	114.82	Sodium	Na	11	22.99
Iodine	I	53	126.90	Strontium	Sr	38	87.62
Iridium	Ir	77	192.22	Sulfur	S	16	32.06
Iron	Fe	26	55.85	Tantalum	Ta	73	180.95
Krypton	Kr	36	83.80	Technetium	Tc	43	(98)
Lanthanum	La	57	138.91	Tellurium	Te	52	127.60
Lawrencium	Lr	103	(257)	Terbium	Tb	65	158.93
Lead	Pb	82	207.20	Thallium	Tl	81	204.38
Lithium	Li	3	6.94	Thorium	Th	90	232.04
Lutetium	Lu	71	174.97	Thulium	Tm	69	168.93
Magnesium	Mg	12	24.30	Tin	Sn	50	118.69
Manganese	Mn	25	54.94	Titanium	Ti	22	47.88
Mendelevium	Md	101	(256)	Tungsten	W	74	183.85
Mercury	Hg	80	200.59	Unnilennium	Une	109	(266)
Molybdenum	Mo	42	95.94	Unnilhexium	Unh	106	(263)
Neodymium	Nd	60	144.24	Unniloctium	Uno	108	(265)
Neon	Ne	10	20.18	Unnilpentium	Unp	105	(260)
Neptunium	Np	93	237.05	Unnilquadium	Unq	104	(257)
Nickel	Ni	28	58.69	Unnilseptium	Uns	107	(262)
Niobium	Nb	41	92.91	Uranium	U	92	238.03
Nitrogen	N	7	14.01	Vanadium	V	23	50.94
Nobelium	No	102	(254)	Xenon	Xe	54	131.29
Osmium	Os	76	190.20	Ytterbium	Yb	70	173.04
Oxygen	O	8	16.00	Yttrium	Y	39	88.91
Palladium	Pd	46	106.42	Zinc	Zn	30	65.38
Phosphorus	P	15	30.97	Zirconium	Zr	40	91.22
Platinum	Pt	78	195.08				
Plutonium	Pu	94	(242)				
Polonium	Po	84	(210)				

*The values have been rounded to two figures after the decimal point (except for hydrogen, which has three). Approximate values for the atomic masses of non-naturally occurring elements are given in parentheses.

Glossary of Terms

abundance (i) the percentage of all the atoms of a given element that occurs as a particular isotope; (ii) the extent to which an element or compound occurs in the universe, atmosphere, or Earth's crust.

accuracy a measure of how closely a result, or the arithmetic mean of a set of results, approaches the true, or accepted, value.

acid rain rainfall with a pH of less than 5.6; the acidity arises from the presence of acidic oxides dissolved in the rainwater.

acid salt a salt which still contains one or more of the hydrogen atoms of the acid from which it was formed; examples include $NaHSO_4$ and KH_2PO_4.

acid–base titration a procedure in which we measure the volume of acid (or base) of known concentration required to neutralize a given volume of base (or acid) of unknown concentration.

acid according to the Arrhenius definition, an acid is a substance that will produce hydrogen ions when dissolved in water; acids turn blue litmus paper red.

acidic oxide an oxide which will produce an acidic solution when dissolved in water; oxides of nonmetals, such as CO_2 and P_4O_{10}, are acidic oxides.

actinons the fourteen elements (atomic number 90–103) that follow actinium in the seventh row of the Periodic Table.

activity series a table of metallic elements (plus hydrogen) arranged in such a way that any element in the table will displace ions of the elements below it from aqueous solutions of their salts.

actual yield the actual mass of product formed in a given chemical reaction.

addition polymer a very large molecule formed by adding together many small molecules; the joining of many molecules of ethene to form polythene is an example.

addition reaction a reaction in which a reagent adds across a multiple bond, as in the reaction between ethene and bromine:

$$\underset{H}{\overset{H}{>}}C=C\underset{H}{\overset{H}{<}} + Br_2 \longrightarrow H-\underset{Br}{\overset{H}{\underset{|}{C}}}-\underset{Br}{\overset{H}{\underset{|}{C}}}-H$$

additives a term generally used to describe chemicals which are added to consumer products.

alcohols a family of organic compounds in which a hydroxyl group (—OH) is attached to a carbon atom, as in ethanol, CH_3—CH_2—OH.

aldehyde an organic compound in which the carbon of the carbonyl group is attached to a hydrogen atom.

aliphatic an organic compound that is not aromatic.

alkaki metals the elements in Group IA of the Periodic Table.

alkaline earth metals the elements in Group IIA of the Periodic Table.

alkane a hydrocarbon containing only carbon–carbon and carbon–hydrogen single bonds.

alkene a hydrocarbon that contains at least one carbon–carbon double bond.

alkoxy group a structural unit in which an alkyl group is bonded to oxygen:

$$CH_3-CH_2-O-CH_2-CH_2-CH_2-CH_3 \quad \text{1-ethoxybutane}$$

alkyl group a structural unit consisting of a number of carbon and hydrogen atoms joined by single bonds; alkyl groups can be considered to be formed by removing a hydrogen atom from an alkane:

$$H-\underset{H}{\overset{H}{\underset{|}{\overset{|}{C}}}}-H \longrightarrow H-\underset{H}{\overset{H}{\underset{|}{\overset{|}{C}}}}-$$

methane   methyl group
(an alkane)   (an alkyl group)

alkyl halide an organic compound which can be considered to be formed by replacing one of the hydrogen atoms of an alkane with a halogen:

$$H-\underset{H}{\overset{H}{\underset{|}{\overset{|}{C}}}}-H \qquad H-\underset{H}{\overset{H}{\underset{|}{\overset{|}{C}}}}-Cl$$

methane   chloromethane
(an alkane)   (an alkyl halide)

alkyne a hydrocarbon that contains at least one carbon–carbon triple bond.

allotrope a different molecular form of the same element; ozone (O_3) and dioxygen (O_2) are allotropes of oxygen.

alpha ray a stream of helium nuclei, $_2^4He^{2+}$.

amide an organic compound containing the following functional group:

$$-C\overset{\displaystyle O}{\underset{\displaystyle N}{\Big\diagdown}}$$

amine an organic nitrogen-containing compound.

α-amino acid an organic compound in which an amino group ($-NH_2$) and a carboxyl group ($-CO_2H$) are attached to the same carbon atom:

$$CH_3-\overset{\displaystyle H}{\underset{\displaystyle NH_2}{C}}-C\overset{\displaystyle O}{\underset{\displaystyle OH}{\Big\diagup}}\qquad \text{alanine}$$

amino group a structural unit consisting of two hydrogen atoms bonded to a nitrogen atom ($-NH_2$).

anion a negatively charged species formed when a neutral atom gains one or more additional electrons:
$Cl + e^- \longrightarrow Cl^-$

aqueous solution a solution in which water is the solvent.

aromatic an organic compound containing the benzene structural unit.

artificial transmutation a process in which the atomic nucleus of one element is transformed into an atomic nucleus of a second element; artificial transmutation can be brought about by either nuclear fission or nuclear fusion.

atom as defined by Dalton, an atom is a small, indivisible particle of which all elements are composed; although atoms can be broken down into a number of subatomic particles, the atom remains the smallest particle of an element that can exist and still exhibit the properties of that element.

atomic mass may be regarded as (i) the relative mass of an atom on a scale which sets the (relative) atomic mass of a carbon-12 atom as exactly 12; (ii) the absolute mass of an atom measured in unified atomic mass units, symbol μ, with $1\ \mu$ being defined as one-twelfth of the mass of a single atom of carbon-12.

atomic number the number of protons present in the nucleus of one atom of a given element.

atomic radius the distance from the centre of the nucleus to the valence level of the electrons; atomic radii are measured in picometres; $1\ pm = 10^{-12}\ m$.

Avogadro's hypothesis equal volumes of all gases, measured at the same temperature and pressure, contain the same number of molecules.

Avogadro's number the number 6.02×10^{23}; this is the number of particles (atoms, molecules) present in one mole of any substance.

balancing equations a procedure used to ensure that there is an equal number of each atom on both sides of a chemical equation.

ball-and-stick model a type of molecular model used to show the three-dimensional nature of chemical compounds.

bar a unit used, particularly by meteorologists, to express pressure; $1\ bar = 100\ kPa$.

barometer an instrument used for measuring atmospheric pressure.

base as defined by Arrhenius, a base is a substance that will produce hydroxide ions when dissolved in water; bases turn red litmus paper blue.

base unit in SI, all measurements are related to the seven base units of length, mass, time, temperature, electric current, light intensity, and amount of substances.

basic oxide an oxide which produces a basic solution when dissolved in water; metal oxides such as CaO, MgO, and Li_2O are basic oxides.

bauxite the most important aluminum-containing ore; bauxite is hydrated aluminum oxide.

benzene ring the structural unit present in aromatic compounds; a benzene ring is represented by a hexagon containing a circle to indicate that the six carbon–carbon bonds in the ring are identical:

beta ray a stream of electrons; certain radioactive nuclei decay by emitting beta rays.

bifunctional a term used to describe organic compounds that contain two functional groups.

binary acid an acid composed of hydrogen and one other non-metallic element.

binary compound a compound composed of two elements, as in sodium chloride, NaCl, and sulfur dioxide, SO_2.

binding energy the energy that would be released if we were able to form a given nucleus by combining the appropriate numbers of neutrons and protons; the binding energy (E) of a nucleus can be determined using the formula $E = mc^2$, where m is the mass defect, and c is the speed of light.

biochemical reaction any natural chemical reaction that occurs in a living thing.

blast furnace a furnace used in industry to extract iron from its ore.

boiling point the temperature at which the vapour pressure of a liquid is equal to the prevailing atomospheric pressure.

bond the forces that hold atoms together in compounds, bonds are ususally described as being either ionic or covalent.

Boyle's law at constant temperature, the volume of a fixed mass of gas is inversely proportional to its pressure.

branched-chain compound an organic compound in which one or more alkyl groups are attached to the main carbon chain:

$$CH_3 - CH - CH - CH_2 - CH_3 \qquad \text{2,3-dimethylpentane}$$

with CH_3 groups above the second and third carbons and CH_3 below the third carbon.

Brownian motion the constant motion of colloidal particles caused by collisions between the particles themselves and the supporting medium.

burette a piece of laboratory glassware used for the precise measurement of liquid volumes.

by-product a secondary, or minor product formed during a chemical reaction.

CANDU reactor the CANDU (Canadian Deuterium Uranium) reactor uses natural uranium as its fuel and heavy water as the moderator.

carbohydrate simple carbohydrates (also called monosaccharides) have the general formula $(CH_2O)_n$; more complex carbohydrates (disaccharides, trisaccharides) correspond to formulas of the type $C_n(H_2O)_{n-1}$, and $C_n(H_2O)_{n-2}$.

carbonyl group a structural unit consisting of a carbon atom joined to an oxygen atom by a double bond.

carboxyl group a structural unit consisting of a carbon atom attached to a hydroxyl group by a single bond, and to an oxygen atom by a double bond.

carboxylic acid an organic compound containing the carboxyl functional group.

catalyst a substance that increases the rate of a chemical reaction, but is itself unchanged at the end of the reaction.

catenation the ability of atoms to join together to form long chains or rings; carbon exhibits this ability more that any other element.

cation a positively charged species formed when a neutral atom loses one or more electrons: $Na \longrightarrow Na^+ + e^-$.

Charles' Law at constant pressure, the volume of a fixed mass of gas is directly proportional to its Kelvin temperature.

chemical change a change that results in the formation of a new substance.

chemical equation a shorthand method used by chemists to represent a chemical reaction.

chemical property a property that can only be observed when a chemical change takes place.

classical system of nomenclature a system for naming chemical compounds that was originally introduced by Guyton de Morveau; although still used extensively, classical nomenclature is gradually being replaced by the IUPAC system.

coke an impure form of carbon, produced by heating coal for about 20 hours in airtight ovens at 1200 °C.

colloid clusters of molecules suspended in a medium; the clusters are invisible to the naked eye and cannot be removed from the solution by filtration; unlike suspensions, colloids do not settle out when left standing.

combination reaction a reaction in which two or more substances combine to form a more complex substance:
$$Li_2O + CO_2 \longrightarrow Li_2CO_3.$$

combined gas equation an equation obtained by combining the Laws of Boyle, Charles, and Gay-Lussac; temperature must be expressed in kelvins:
$$\frac{P_1 V_1}{T_1} = \frac{P_2 V_2}{T_2}$$

combustion reaction a reaction between an organic compound and oxygen that produces carbon dioxide and water.

common name a non-systematic name for a compound.

compound a substance that can be broken down into two or more simpler substances by means of a chemical change.

concentrated solution (i) a relative term used when comparing the concentrations of two chemically similar solutions — the solution with the higher concentration is referred to as being the more concentrated solution; (ii) a term used to describe certain solutions of generally known concentration — a concentrated solution of hydrochloric acid is generally accepted as having a concentration of 12 mol·L^{-1}.

concentration a means of expressing the amount of solute present in a given volume of solution; usually expressed in moles per litre ($mol \cdot L^{-1}$).

condensation the process of changing from the gas phase to the liquid phase.

condensed formula a shorthand method of showing the structures of organic compounds without including all the bonds; the condensed formula for pentane, C_5H_{12}, is

$$CH_3 - CH_2 - CH_2 - CH_2 - CH_3$$

continuous spectrum the pattern of colours observed when a narrow beam of white light is passed through a prism.

conversion factor a means of showing the relationship between two quantities expressed in different units.

coordinate covalent bond a covalent bond in which the two bonding electrons are both provided by the same atom.

covalent bond the attractive force that holds together two atoms which share a pair of electrons; covalent bonds are formed between atoms of nonmetallic elements.

cracking a process used in the petroleum industry to break down long-chain alkanes into alkenes and alkanes of lower molecular mass.

crystal lattice a term used to describe the three-dimensional array of positive and negative ions in an ionic compound.

cyclic hydrocarbon a hydrocarbon in which a number of the carbon atoms are joined together in a ring:

methylcyclopentane

decomposition reaction a chemical reaction in which a complex substance is broken down into one or more simpler substances: $CaCO_3 \longrightarrow CaO + CO_2$.

deliquescent a term used to describe a substance that absorbs moisture from the air very quickly and eventually dissolves in the absorbed water.

density mass per unit volume; the density of a substance may be determined by dividing the mass by the volume.

derived unit a unit formed by combining SI base units; a simple example is the cubic metre (m^3).

diatomic molecule a molecule consisting of two atoms held together by a covalent bond.

dilute solution (i) a relative term used when comparing the concentrations of two chemically similar solutions — the solution with the lower concentration is referred to as a dilute solution; (ii) meaning "not a concentrated solution".

dilution the process of adding solvent to a solution in order to reduce the concentration of solute.

dipeptide an organic compound formed by the combination of two α-amino acids.

disaccharide a carbohydrate that can be broken down into two (identical or different) monosaccharide molecules; sucrose, $C_{12}H_{22}O_{11}$, is an example of a disaccharide.

dissociate to break down into ions when dissolved in water:

$$HCl_{(g)} \xrightarrow{\text{dissolve in } H_2O} H^+_{(aq)} + Cl^-_{(aq)}$$

double bond two pairs of electrons (a total of four) shared between two atoms; two double bonds are present in a molecule of carbon dioxide: O C O.

double displacement reaction a reaction between two ionic compounds in which the cation of one compound changes places with the cation of a second compound; the net effect of such a reaction is that the positive ions exchange their negative partners: $NaCl_{(aq)} + AgNO_{3\,(aq)} \longrightarrow NaNO_{3\,(aq)} + AgCl_{(s)}$.

electrolysis the process of bringing about a chemical reaction by passing an electric current through a solution or molten solid.

electrolyte a substance which, when dissolved in water, produces a solution that conducts an electric current.

electron a negatively charged particle of almost negligible mass.

electron affinity the energy released when an electron is added to a neutral gaseous atom to form a negative ion.

electron capture the capture of an inner-level electron by a nucleus; the net result is that one of the protons in the nucleus is converted to a neutron and a new element is formed:

$$^{40}_{19}K + ^{\ 0}_{-1}e^- \longrightarrow ^{40}_{18}Ar$$

electron configuration the number of electrons present in each of the occupied energy sublevels of an atom or ion; a neon atom has the electron configuration $1s^2 2s^2 2p^6$.

electronegativity a measure of the tendency of an atom to attract electrons when forming a covalent bond; the most commonly used values of electronegativity were assigned by Linus Pauling.

electrostatic precipitator a device used to reduce the amount of dust in the waste gas emissions from chemical plants; the dust particles are ionized and then collected on charged plates.

element a substance that cannot be broken down into simpler substances by any chemical means.

empirical formula a formula which shows the simplest whole number ratio of the atoms or ions present in a compound; CH_2 is the empirical formula of both ethene (C_2H_4) and cyclohexane (C_6H_{12}).

endothermic reaction a reaction that absorbs heat from the surroundings.

energy level as outlined by Bohr, the distance of an orbiting electron from an atomic nucleus; as we no longer consider electrons to orbit the nucleus, we can now regard an energy level as representing one of the allowable energies that an electron in a given atom may possess.

enriched uranium uranium in which the concentration of the uranium-235 isotope has been increased above the 0.7 % level.

enthalpy the energy a substance contains is called enthalpy (symbol H); during a chemical reaction the energy released or absorbed is referred to as the enthalpy change and is indicated by the symbol ΔH.

enzyme A complex molecule (usually a protein) that acts as a catalyst in biochemical reactions.

equation factor a factor which shows the relationship between the number of moles of the different chemicals involved in a reaction; the equation factors which relate water and hydrogen in the equation: $2 \text{ Na} + 2 \text{ H}_2\text{O} \longrightarrow \text{H}_2 + 2 \text{ NaOH}$ are:

$$\frac{2 \text{ mol H}_2\text{O}}{1 \text{ mol H}_2} \text{ and } \frac{1 \text{ mol H}_2}{2 \text{ mol H}_2\text{O}}$$

equilibrium reaction a reaction in which a certain amount of the reactants always remains, no matter how long the reaction mixture is allowed to stand; chemical equations which represent equilibrium reactions can be identified by the presence of a double arrow.

ester an organic compound in which the hydrogen of a carboxyl group has been replaced by an alkyl group (or a benzene ring).

ether an organic compound in which an oxygen atom is bonded to two carbon atoms.

evaporation the process of changing from the liquid phase to the gas phase at a temperature which is lower than the boiling point of the liquid.

exact number a number which can be considered to have an infinite number of significant figures.

excited state a state that occurs when an electron absorbs energy and is raised from its ground state to a higher energy level.

exothermic reaction a reaction which releases energy (heat) to the surroundings.

fermentation the enzyme-catalysed degradation of carbohydrates (starch and sugars) into ethanol and carbon dioxide.

formula equation a shorthand representation (also called molecular equation) of a chemical reaction in which each substance is represented by its chemical formula.

formula mass the mass of the smallest grouping of an ionic compound, usually expressed in unified atomic mass units.

formula unit the smallest conceivable unit of an ionic compound that would still have the properties of the compound.

fractionation a process used in the petroleum industry for separating crude petroleum into a number of fractions, each containing a large number of compounds having roughly similar boiling points.

Frasch process a method used to obtain sulfur from underground deposits of this element.

functional group a combination of atoms present in an organic compound that determines to which family (or class) of compounds a given substance belongs; the functional group present largely determines the properties of a compound.

gamma ray the form of electromagnetic radiation that has the highest energy.

gas one of the three common phases of matter, a gas has neither definite shape nor definite volume.

Gay-Lussac's Law at constant volume, the pressure of a fixed mass of gas is directly proportional to its Kelvin temperature.

Gay-Lussac's Law of Combining Volumes in any chemical reaction involving gases, the volumes of the reactants are always in small, whole-number ratios.

geometric (*cis–trans*) isomerism a type of isomerism that occurs in alkenes containing two different atoms or groups bonded to each of the double bonded carbon atoms; *cis–trans* isomerism occurs in compounds such as 2-pentene:

$$CH_3-CH_2 \diagdown \atop H \diagup C=C \diagup \atop H \diagdown CH_3 \quad \textit{cis-2-pentene}$$

$$CH_3-CH_2 \diagdown \atop H \diagup C=C \diagup \atop CH_3 \diagdown H \quad \textit{trans-2-pentene}$$

gravimetric analysis a method of determining the amount of a specific cation or anion in a solution by precipitating an insoluble compound of that ion; the technique can also be used to determine how much of a given element is present in a sample, or to establish the purity of a substance.

ground state the lowest energy level that an electron can occupy.

group a column of elements in the Periodic Table.

half-life the length of time that it takes for half the nuclei of a given radioactive isotope to decay.

halogen an element in Group VIIA of the Periodic Table.

halogen displacement series a listing of the halogens such that the elements higher in the series can displace ions of the elements below from any aqueous solution of their salts; chlorine (high in the series) can displace bromine (low in the series) from a solution of sodium bromide: $Cl_2 + 2\ NaBr \longrightarrow 2\ NaCl + Br_2$.

heavy water water in which the hydrogen atoms have been replaced by deuterium ($^2_1H_2O$) atoms.

heterogeneous mixture a mixture that does not have a uniform composition.

homogeneous mixture a mixture that has a uniform composition; such mixtures are often more simply referred to as solutions.

homologous series a family of organic compounds in which the composition of each member differs from the other by a $-CH_2$ unit.

hydrated salt a salt that forms crystals containing water molecules, as in copper(II) sulfate pentahydrate, $CuSO_4 \cdot 5H_2O$.

hydrocarbon an organic compound consisting of only carbon and hydrogen.

hydroxyl group the functional group ($-OH$) found in alcohols.

hygroscopic a term used to describe substances that absorb water but remain in the solid phase.

hypothesis a tentative explanation put forward in order to explain certain observations.

ideal gas equation an equation that relates the pressure, volume, and temperature of a gas to the number of moles (n) of gas present; R is the universal gas constant: $PV = nRT$

immiscible a term used to describe liquids that cannot be mixed together to form a solution; gasoline and water are immiscible.

initiator a compound that is used to start a polymerization reaction.

insoluble a term used to describe a solid that does not dissolve (or dissolves to the extent of 1 g·L^{-1} or less) in a given liquid.

ion a charged species formed by the addition or removal of one or more electrons from a neutral atom.

ionic bond the electrostatic attraction between ions of opposite charge.

ionic radius the distance from the nucleus to the outermost occupied energy level of an ion.

ionization energy the first ionization energy of an element is the amount of energy required to remove the most weakly held electron from a neutral gaseous atom of that element; similarly, the second ionization energy corresponds to the energy needed to remove the most weakly held electron from an ion with a +1 charge.

isomers compounds having the same molecular formula, but different structural formulas.

isotopes atoms whose nuclei contain the same number of protons, but different numbers of neutrons;

IUPAC system a system for naming chemical compounds; IUPAC is the International Union for Pure and Applied Chemistry.

Kelvin temperature scale a temperature scale developed by Lord Kelvin on which the melting point of ice is 273.15 K, and 0 K corresponds to absolute zero.

kelvin the unit used on the Kelvin temperature scale; a kelvin is of the same magnitude as a Celsius degree.

ketone a compound in which the carbon atom of a carbonyl group is bonded to two other carbon atoms:

$$CH_3-\overset{\overset{\displaystyle O}{\|}}{C}-CH_2-CH_3$$

kilopascal an SI unit of pressure; 101.3 kPa = 1 atm.

kinetic energy the energy possessed by a moving object; for any object in motion, the kinetic energy is given by $K = \frac{1}{2}mv^2$.

lanthanons the 14 elements (atomic number 58–71) that follow lanthanum in the sixth row of the Periodic Table.

law a rule that nature seems to follow; a law is a statement based on patterns of behaviour that allows us to predict events.

Law of Conservation of Mass in any chemical reaction, there is no detectable difference between the total mass of the reactants and the total mass of the products.

Law of Constant Composition any given compound has the same composition anywhere in the universe.

Law of Multiple Proportions when two elements can combine to form more that one compound, the masses of one element that will combine with a fixed mass of the other element are in small, whole-number ratios.

Law of Octaves when John Newlands arranged the elements known in 1864 in order of increasing atomic mass, he found that every eighth element formed part of a set of elements having similar chemical and physical properties; he called this pattern the Law of Octaves.

Law of Partial Pressures the total pressure of a mixture of gases is equal to the sum of the partial pressures of the component gases.

Le Système international d'unités (SI) a system of metric units which relates measurements to the seven base units of mass, length, time, temperature, electric current, light intensity, and amount of substance.

Lewis formula also called an electron-dot formula, a Lewis formula uses dots to show (i) the number of valence electrons possessed by an atom of a given element, and (ii) the distribution of electrons in a compound or ion.

limiting reagent in a chemical reaction, the limiting reagent determines the maximum amount of product(s) that can be formed; because of stoichiometric considerations, the limiting reagent is not necessarily the reagent present in the least amount.

line spectrum when light consisting of only a few wavelengths is passed through a prism, a spectrum in which each line corresponds to light of a single wavelength is produced.

linear molecule a molecule in which all the atoms are arranged in a straight line.

liquid one of the three common phases of matter; liquids are characterized by having a definite volume, but no definite shape.

liquid crystal one of the two less common phases of matter, liquid crystals are liquids with ordered structures.

lone pair a pair of valence electrons not involved in bonding; the oxygen atom of a water molecule has two lone pairs:

$$H \diagdown \overset{\cdot\cdot}{\underset{\cdot\cdot}{O}} \diagup H$$

main groups those groups in the Periodic Table whose group number includes the letter "A".

manometer a device used in the laboratory to measure the pressure of gas in a container.

mass the quantity of matter in a sample or object.

mass defect the difference between the mass of a nucleus and the total mass of its component subatomic particles.

mass number the sum of the number of protons and neutrons present in the nucleus of an atom.

mass percent a means of expressing the concentration of a solution:

$$\text{mass percent} = \frac{\text{mass of solute}}{\text{mass of solution}} \times 100\,\%$$

mass spectrometer a sophisticated instrument used for studying the structures of elements and compounds; one application is to determine precisely the mass and abundance of isotopes.

melting the process of changing from the solid phase to the liquid phase.

metal an element that is shiny and conducts heat and electricity.

methyl group an alkyl group consisting of three hydrogen atoms attached to a carbon atom.

metric prefix a group of letters, applied to the beginning of a unit, that represent a certain multiple of that unit in the metric system: one *kilo*metre = 1000 m.

metric system a system of measurement based on the decimal system.

miscible a term used to describe liquids that can be mixed together in any proportion to give a solution; water and alcohol are miscible.

mixture a mixture is composed of two or more substances that can be separated by physical methods; mixtures can be homogeneous or heterogeneous.

moderator a substance used to slow down fast-moving neutrons so that they can be captured by uranium nuclei and thereby initiate a nuclear fission reaction.

molarity a non-SI term (symbol M) used to indicate concentration in moles per litre.

molar mass the mass of one mole of any substance; the units of molar mass are $g \cdot mol^{-1}$.

molar volume the volume of one mole of any gas measured at STP; this volume is 22.4 L.

mole the SI unit (symbol mol) for amount of substance; it is defined as 6.02×10^{23} units or particles.

mole fraction a method of representing concentrations, the mole fraction of substance X in a mixture of X and Y is given by:

$$\text{mole fraction of X} = \frac{\text{moles of X}}{\text{moles of X} + \text{moles of Y}}$$

mole method a systematic approach to solving chemical problems, particularly those pertaining to the quantities of chemicals consumed or produced in a given chemical reaction.

molecular equation see *formula equation*.

molecular formula a formula which shows the actual number of atoms of each element in one molecule of a covalent compound.

molecular mass the mass of one molecule of a covalent compound, expressed in unified atomic mass units.

molecule the smallest particle of a covalent compound that can exist and still have the properties of that compound.

moles per litre the units in which it is most useful for chemists to express the concentration of a solution; the term indicates moles of solute per litre of solution.

monomer the compound(s) from which polymers are made; vinyl chloride $(CH_2\!=\!CHCl)$ is the monomer from which polyvinyl chloride, or PVC, is made.

monosaccharide a carbohydrate corresponding to the general formula $(CH_2O)_2$; glucose is an example.

net ionic equation an equation in which the ions that play no part in the reaction (the spectator ions) are omitted; the net ionic equation for the reaction between sodium chloride and silver nitrate is: $Ag^+_{(aq)} + Cl^-_{(aq)} \longrightarrow AgCl_{(s)}$.

neutral compound a compound that is neither acidic nor basic.

neutralization reaction a double displacement reaction in which water is produced; often defined as a reaction between an acid and a base to produce a salt and water.

neutron an electrically neutral particle found in atomic nuclei; the mass of a neutron is approximately equal to that of a proton.

neutron activation analysis an analytical technique used to determine elemental concentrations as low as one part per billion.

noble-gas configuration any species with a full valence shell of electrons is said to have a noble-gas configuration.

noble gas a member of the series of elements found in Group VIIIA (Group O) of the Periodic Table.

nonelectrolyte a substance which, when dissolved in water, produces a solution that does not conduct electricity.

nonmetal an element lacking the properties of a metal; nonmetals are found to the right of the thick, vertical, zig-zag line seen in most Periodic Tables.

nuclear chain reaction a self-sustaining sequence of nuclear fission reactions.

nuclear fission the splitting of an atomic nucleus into two or more smaller nuclei.

nuclear fusion the joining together of two atomic nuclei to produce a larger nucleus.

nuclear reactor the vessel, building, or group of buildings in which nuclear reactions take place.

nucleon a term used to describe both protons and neutrons.

nucleus the region at the centre of an atom in which the protons and neutrons are located; the diameter of the nucleus is about $1/_{10\,000}$ of the diameter of the atom.

octane rating a system for grading gasoline; the rating given indicates the quality of the gasoline as compared to mixtures of isooctane (octane rating 100) and heptane (octane rating 0).

oxidation number a positive or negative number assigned to an element, ion, or atom according to a set of arbitrary rules.

oxidation a process in which the oxidation number of a given atom or ion increases; when zinc metal reacts with hydrochloric acid to give zinc chloride, the oxidation number of zinc increases from zero to $+2$.

oxidation-reduction reaction chemical reactions in which two or more of the atoms involved undergo a change in oxidation number:

$$\underbrace{\overbrace{Zn \; + \quad 2\,HCl \quad \longrightarrow \quad ZnCl_2 \; + \; H_2}^{\text{oxidation}}}_{\text{reduction}}$$
$$\;\; 0 \qquad\; +1\;\; -1 \qquad\qquad +2\;\; -1 \qquad 0$$

oxyacid an acid that contains oxygen.

oxyanion a polyatomic anion that contains oxygen; the sulfate ion, SO_4^{2-} is an example.

oxygen furnace a furnace used to remove impurities during the conversion of iron into steel.

partial pressure in a mixture of gases, the contribution that each gas makes to the total pressure.

particle accelerator equipment that accelerates particles (e.g. neutrons) that are used to bombard target nuclei in an attempt to initiate nuclear reactions.

parts per million usually abbreviated to ppm, this is an expression used to indicate low concentrations:

$$\text{concentration (in ppm)} = \frac{\text{mass of solute}}{\text{mass of solution}} \times 10^6$$

pascal the SI unit of pressure; a pascal is defined as the force of one Newton acting on an area of 1 m^2.

peptide a compound formed by the joining together of a number of amino acid molecules; if the number of amino acid molecules is greater than 10, the product is usually called a polypeptide.

percentage yield a method of expressing how efficiently a reactant can be converted into product in a given chemical reaction:

$$\text{percentage yield} = \frac{\text{actual yield}}{\text{theoretical yield}} \times 100\%$$

period a row in the Periodic Table.

Periodic Law a law, developed by Mendeléev, which states that elements arranged in order of increasing atomic mass show a periodic repetition of properties.

Periodic Table a special table that lists the symbols of the elements in order of increasing atomic number.

pH scale a logarithmic scale used to express the hydrogen-ion concentration of a solution: $\text{pH} = -\log_{10}[\text{H}^+]$.

phenol a substance in which a hydroxyl group is attached to a benezene ring.

photosynthesis the process by which plants convert carbon dioxide and water into starch and oxygen.

physical change a process of change in which the identity of the substance undergoing the change remains the same.

pipette a piece of glassware used in the laboratory to measure precisely a predetermined volume of liquid.

planar molecule a molecule in which all the atoms lie in the same plane.

plasma a phase of matter in which an electrically neutral gas contains positive ions and electrons.

polar covalent bond a covalent bond formed between atoms with different electronegativities that has a certain amount of ionic character.

polyatomic ion an ion consisting of two or more atoms.

polymerization a reaction in which a large number of identical molecules join together to form a very large molecule.

polypeptide a compound of high molecular mass, formed by the joining together of more than 10 amino acid molecules; proteins are an example.

polysaccharide a carbohydrate of high molecular mass that can be broken down into a number of monosaccharide molecules.

positron a positively charged electron.

pounds per square inch a non-SI unit of pressure: 1 psi = 6.89 kPa.

precipitate a solid formed during a chemical reaction occuring in solution.

precision a measure of the agreement contained within a set of experimental results.

primary alcohol an alcohol in which the —OH group is bonded to a carbon with only one alkyl group attached.

primary amine an organic compound containing a nitrogen atom bonded to one carbon atom and two hydrogen atoms; a compound containing the $-\text{NH}_2$ (amino) group.

principal quantum number an integer (symbol n) used to identify energy levels in the Bohr model of the atom.

product a substance formed during a chemical reaction.

protein a molecule formed by a number of amino acid molecules joining together through the reaction of their carboxyl and amino groups.

proton a positively charged particle found in the nucleus of an atom.

pure substance matter that is uniform throughout and has a definite set of chemical and physical properties.

rad a unit used to express the level of nuclear radiation; a rad of radiation corresponds to the absorption of 10^{-5} J of energy by 1 g of tissue.

radioactive a term used to describe unstable isotopes that emit alpha, beta or gamma rays.

radioactive decay the natural conversion of the nucleus of one element into a nucleus of another element through the emission of alpha or beta radiation.

radioactive series when the product of one radioactive decay can itself decay into yet another radioactive species, the various isotopes formed belong to a radioactive series which is named after the starting element; in the uranium series, uranium-238 eventually decays to lead-206 through a series of 14 steps.

radioactive tracer a compound containing a radioactive atom which permits the fate of the compound to be followed through various chemical, biological, or physical processes.

radioactivity the process by which certain nuclei are transformed into nuclei of different elements by the emission of radiation.

random error an error caused by poor judgement on the part of the experimenter, or by some other uncontrollable factor.

reactant one of the substances taking part in a chemical reaction.

reagent in excess a reactant that is present in more than the stoichiometric amount; thus, not all of the reagent in excess is consumed in a chemical reaction.

reduction a process in which the oxidation number of an atom or ion decreases.

reforming a process used in the petroleum industry to convert straight-chain alkanes into branched-chain alkanes having higher octane ratings.

relative humidity a number that indicates the percentage of the maximum amount of water vapour present in a sample of air at a given temperature:

$$\text{relative humidity} = \frac{\text{pressure of water in the air at } T_1}{\text{vapour pressure of water at } T_1}$$

rem a measure of the biological effect of the different types of radiation on human tissue.

salt a compound consisting of a metallic element combined with one or more nonmetallic elements, or of a polyatomic cation combined with an anion; salts are usually formed by the reaction of an acid with a base.

saponification strictly speaking, the reaction between sodium hydroxide and a fat; however, this term is sometimes used to describe the reaction between sodium hydroxide and any ester.

saturated compound an organic compound, usually a hydrocarbon, that does not contain any double or triple bonds.

saturated solution a solution that contains the maximum amount of solute that can be dissolved at a given temperature.

scientific notation a convenient method of expressing very large and very small numbers by multiplying the significant figures by the appropriate power of ten; thus, 1 250 000 000 is written as 1.25×10^9.

secondary alcohol an alcohol in which the —OH group is bonded to a carbon with two alkyl groups attached.

secondary amine an organic compound containing a nitrogen atom that is bonded to two carbon atoms and one hydrogen atom; these compounds contain the —NH structural unit.

semimetal an element that has some of the properties of the metals and some of the properties of the nonmetals.

side chain a short chain of carbon atoms which is attached to the main carbon chain in a branched organic compound:

$$\overset{\displaystyle CH_2-CH_3}{\underset{\displaystyle CH_3-CH_2-CH_2-CH-CH_2-CH_2-OH}{|}}$$

3-ethyl-1-hexanol

significant figures the number of figures that indicates the precision of the measurement taken.

single bond a covalent bond consisting of a pair of electrons.

single displacement reaction a reaction in which one element replaces another element in an ionic compound:

$$Zn + CuSO_4 \longrightarrow ZnSO_4 + Cu$$

slag a by-product formed in the industrial extraction of a metal from its ore.

smelter a chemical plant in which one of the processes involves obtaining a metal from molten raw materials.

solid one of the three common phases of matter; solids have both a definite shape and a definite volume.

solidification the process of changing from a liquid to a solid.

solubility the mass of a given substance that can be dissolved in a specific solvent at a given temperature.

soluble when at least 10 g of a substance will dissolve in 1 L of a given solvent, the substance is said to be soluble in that solvent.

solute when a solution is prepared, the solute is dissolved in the solvent; when salt is dissolved in water, the salt is the solute.

solution a mixture of uniform composition, consisting of two components, the solute and the solvent.

solvent the substance in which a solute is dissolved in order to prepare a solution; when salt is dissolved in water, the water is the solvent.

sour gas natural gas that contains an appreciable amount of hydrogen sulphide.

space-filling model an exact model which shows the relative sizes of the atoms in a compound.

spectator ion an ion that does not take part in a reaction.

standard atmospheric pressure in SI, a pressure of 101.3 kPa; in other systems, 760 mm Hg and 14.7 lb·in⁻¹ are used.

steel an alloy of iron with a relatively small amount of carbon and often smaller amounts of other elements.

Stock system a system of naming inorganic compounds which specifies the oxidation number(s) of one or more of the elements involved; the compound $FeCl_3$ is called iron(III) chloride in the Stock system, the Roman numerals indicating that iron has an oxidation number of $+3$.

stoichiometric quantities molar quantities of reagents which, when reacted together, are completely consumed; balanced equations show stoichiometric quantities.

stoichiometry the application of mole calculations to determine the quantities of reagents used and the quantities of products formed in a chemical reaction.

straight-chain compound an organic compound in which there are no alkyl side chains.

structural formula a two-dimensional diagram showing the way in which the atoms are arranged in a molecule; lines are used to represent covalent bonds:

$$H-\underset{\underset{H}{|}}{\overset{\overset{H}{|}}{C}}-H \quad \text{methane}$$

structural isomers compounds which have the same molecular formula, but whose atoms are arranged differently:

$$CH_3-CH_2-CH_2-CH_3 \qquad CH_3-\underset{\underset{CH_3}{|}}{CH}-CH_3$$

butane

2-methylpropane

sublimation the process in which a substance passes directly from the solid phase to the gas phase (or vice-versa).

substituent an atom (other than hydrogen), or a group of atoms attached to the main carbon chain of an organic compound:

$$CH_3-\underset{\underset{Cl}{|}}{CH}-CH_2-CH_3 \quad \text{2-chlorobutane}$$

substitution reaction a term used mainly in organic chemistry to describe reactions in which an atom or group of atoms is replaced by a different atom or group of atoms.

suspension a mixture of a solid and a liquid that can be separated into its components by filtration.

systematic error a consistent factor which adversely affects all the results of an experiment in a similar manner.

systematic name a term which usually refers to the IUPAC name of an organic compound.

tertiary alcohol an alcohol in which the —OH group is bonded to a carbon with three alkyl groups attached.

tertiary amine an organic nitrogen-containing compound in which the nitrogen atom is bonded to three carbon atoms.

tetrahedral the geometrical shape of a molecule in which the four bonds attached to the central atom point to the four corners of a regular tetrahedron.

theoretical yield the maximum possible mass of product that could theoretically be produced in a given reaction.

theory an explanation of a variety of phenomena, supported by known laws and experimental evidence.

thermal decomposition a decomposition reaction brought about by heating the reactant.

thermochemistry the study of energy changes that accompany chemical reactions.

titration a laboratory technique used in quantitative analysis; see *acid–base titration*.

torr a non-SI unit of pressure; 1 torr = 1 mm Hg = 0.133 kPa.

total ionic equation a chemical equation involving one or more ionic compounds; each species that is dissociated is written in ionic form.

transition metals the elements in Groups IB through VIIIB of the Periodic Table.

transuranium elements the elements that follow uranium in the Periodic Table.

triad a group of three elements displaying a certain regularity in their properties; Dobereiner's observation of such triads (1829) was one of the first steps towards the development of the modern Periodic Table.

triglycerides esters of the compound glycerol having the general formula:

$$\underset{\underset{CH_2}{|}}{\overset{\overset{R}{|}}{\underset{\underset{O}{|}}{\overset{\overset{|}{C=O}}{}}}} \quad \underset{\underset{CH}{|}}{\overset{\overset{R}{|}}{\underset{\underset{O}{|}}{\overset{\overset{|}{C=O}}{}}}} \quad \underset{\underset{CH_2}{|}}{\overset{\overset{R}{|}}{\underset{\underset{O}{|}}{\overset{\overset{|}{C=O}}{}}}}$$

triple bond a bond that consists of three pairs of electrons:
$$N:::N$$

trivial name the non-systematic or common name of a chemical compound.

Tyndall effect the observation that when a beam of light is passed through a colloid, the beam becomes visible from the side.

unified atomic mass unit a unit (symbol u) defined as $\frac{1}{12}$ of the mass of an atom of carbon-12.

universal gas constant the constant (symbol R) in the ideal gas equation, $PV = nRT$; the value of R depends on the units used, but in SI is usually given as 8.31 kPa$\cdot$L$\cdot$mol$^{-1}\cdot$K^{-1}.

unsaturated hydrocarbon a hydrocarbon that contains at least one double bond, one triple bond, or one benzene ring.

valence electron an electron in the outermost occupied energy level of an atom; valence electrons are used by atoms to form bonds.

vapour pressure the pressure exerted at a given temperature by the gas molecules of a liquid or solid.

volume percent a method of expressing the concentration of solute present in a solution:

$$\text{volume percent of solute} = \frac{\text{volume of solute}}{\text{volume of solution}} \times 100\,\%$$

volumetric analysis a quantatative analytical technique that involves the precise measurement of the volume of standard solution required to react with a known volume of a solution of unknown concentration.

volumetric flask a piece of laboratory glassware used in the preparation of standard solutions.

volumetric pipette a piece of laboratory glassware used to deliver a precise volume of liquid.

word equation a method of representing a chemical reaction using both words and symbols.

Answers to Odd-Numbered Problems

Because of variation in the rounding-off procedure, you may observe slight differences between the answers given here and those that you obtain.

Chapter 1

11. a) heterogeneous mixture   c) heterogeneous mixture
    b) element   d) heterogeneous mixture

13. a) chemical   c) physical
    b) physical   d) chemical

15. a) physical   c) physical
    b) chemical   d) physical

17. a) nonmetal   d) nonmetal
    b) metal   e) metal
    c) metal

19. We cannot tell the difference by observation only. We have to compare the physical and chemical properties of the two liquids with those of known pure substances. For example, in comparing the boiling points of pure water and a salt solution, the solution would have the higher boiling point (above $100\,^\circ$C).

21. Yes, because density = mass/volume. Neither the mass nor the volume would change.

23. It would freeze upwards from the bottom until the lake was frozen solid.

25. An example of a series of 37 elements: Tl, La, As, Sn, Na, Am, Mg, Ga, At, Tc, Cf, Fr, Ra, Al, Lr, Rn, Ne, Es, Se, Er, Rb, Ba, Ac, Cl, Li, In, Np, Pt, Tm, Mo, Os, Sc, Ca, Ar, Rh, Ho, O

Chapter 2

13. precise

15. a) 3   b) 1   c) 4   d) 1   e) 3

17. a) 8.10×10^{-4} d) 1.000×10^{1}
    b) 5.83×10^{4} e) 1.780×10^{0}
    c) 5.836×10^{1}

19. a) negative   b) zero   c) positive

21. a) 0.040 30   d) 0.000 003 98
    b) 510.2   e) 600
    c) 40 200

23. a) 1.130×10^{1} d) 1.0138×10^{2}
    b) 1.51×10^{1} e) 5.41×10^{-3}
    c) 6.0×10^{-1}

24. 145.4 g

27. a) 2.17×10^{-1} d) 7.9×10^{2}
    b) 1.2×10^{-1} e) 3.93×10^{4}
    c) 1.37×10^{0} or 1.37

29. a) 18   d) 3.5
    b) 2.9   e) 1.5
    c) 0.28

31. a) $42\,\mu$g   d) 486 nm
    b) 3.8 mg   e) 14 mL
    c) 12.5 km   f) $2.5\,\mu$L

33. a) 5.4×10^{2} m   c) 2.800×10^{-1} m
    b) 1.5×10^{-2} L   d) 8.0×10^{-4} kg

35. a) 8.3×10^{2} cm^3 b) 5.8 cm

37. 1.8×10^{2} g

39. $10.8\,\text{g}\cdot\text{mL}^{-1}$

41. systematic error

43. time

Chapter 3

15.

	Protons	Neutrons	Electrons
a)	9	10	9
b)	8	10	8
c)	19	22	19
d)	92	146	92

17. 27 p, 33 n, 27 e;   phosphorus-30, 15 p;   bromine-81, 35 e

19. $^{86}_{38}$Sr, $^{87}_{38}$Sr, $^{88}_{38}$Sr

21. 121.76 u

23. 28.09 u

25. Cu-63, 69.5 %;   Cu-65, 30.5 %

27. 7.5×10^{-15} mol

29. a) 24.3 g   b) 40.0 g   c) 39.1 g

31. a) 10.7 mol   c) 54.3 mol
    b) 2.3×10^{-4} mol   d) 0.250 mol

33. a) 96.0 g c) 4.6×10^4 g
b) 0.6 g d) 97.1 g

35. a) 3.01×10^{24} c) 2×10^{14}
b) 6.0×10^{20} d) 1.29×10^{25}

37. a) 1.29×10^{23} atoms c) 3.82×10^{-3} g
b) 1.83×10^{24} atoms

39. Energy is absorbed by an atom (from a flame or electric source) causing an electron to be promoted to an excited state. When the electron returns to the ground state, it releases the energy in the form of light.

41. There are six in the spectrum, but only two in the visible region.

43. a) Li· b) ·$\ddot{\underset{..}{O}}$· c) ·Ca·

45. a) 3s b) 2p c) 1s d) 4d e) 3d

47. Check figure 3.27.

49. $1s^2 2s^2 2p^6 3s^2 3p^6 4s^2 3d^{10}$
$1s^2 2s^2 2p^6 3s^2 3p^6 4s^2 3d^{10} 4p^3$
$1s^2 2s^2 2p^6 3s^2 3p^6 4s^2 3d^{10} 4p^6 5s^1$
$1s^2 2s^2 2p^6 3s^2 3p^6 4s^2 3d^7$
$1s^2 2s^2 2p^6 3s^2 3p^6 4s^2 3d^{10} 4p^2$

Chapter 4

11. Precise atomic mass values had not been measured. As well, only half of the elements had been discovered.

13. a) the alkali metals c) the transition metals
b) the halogens d) the lanthanons

15. a) 2 b) 4 c) 1 d) 7

17. The naturally occurring isotopes of tellurium happen to have higher atomic masses (i.e. more neutrons) than the naturally occurring isotopes of iodine. This points out the importance of ordering elements by atomic number (i.e. by number of protons) instead of by atomic mass.

19. The melting point is about 230 °C, the boiling point about 310 °C.

21. a) arsenic b) aluminum c) astatine

23. a) sodium, aluminum c) hydrogen, helium
b) barium, magnesium

25. a) Group IIA, because the 1st and 2nd ionization energies are much lower than the 3rd ionization energy, indicating that there are only two valence electrons.
b) greater

Chapter 5

15. a) ionic c) ionic e) covalent
b) covalent d) ionic f) covalent

17. a) 1+ c) 0 e) 1−
b) 2+ d) 2− f) 1+ or 1−

19. a) Na^+ c) Ca^{2+} e) I^-
b) P^{3-} d) Cu^+

21. a) $1s^2$, He c) $1s^2 2s^2 2p^6 3s^2 3p^6$, Ar
b) $1s^2 2s^2 2p^6$, Ne d) $1s^2 2s^2 2p^6 3s^2 3p^6$, Ar

23. a) 3p, 4n, 2e c) 16p, 16n, 18e
b) 17p, 18n, 18e d) 13p, 14n, 10e

25. a) ·$\dot{B}$· e) $[Ca]^{2+}$
b) ·Mg· f) $[:\ddot{\underset{..}{N}}:]^{3-}$
c) :$\ddot{\underset{..}{A}}$r: g) $[:\ddot{\underset{..}{B}r}:]^-$
d) ·$\ddot{\underset{..}{I}}$:

27. a) $[Na]^+ [:\ddot{\underset{..}{I}}:]^-$ c) $3[Ca]^{2+} 2[:\ddot{\underset{..}{N}}:]^{3-}$
b) $2[K]^+ [:\ddot{\underset{..}{S}}:]^{2-}$

29. Ionic; yes, it would conduct electricity.

31. a) :$\ddot{\underset{..}{S}}$::$\ddot{C}$::$\ddot{\underset{..}{S}}$:

b) H:C:::N:

c) :$\ddot{\underset{..}{C}l}$: $\dot{P}$:$\ddot{\underset{..}{C}l}$:
    :$\ddot{\underset{..}{C}l}$:

33. a) Br—Br d) H—S—H

b) H—P—H e) S=C=S
      |
      H

f) H—C≡N

c)   Br
        |
    Br—C—Br
        |
        Br

g) O—S—O
       ‖
       O

35. a) δ^+ δ^- c) δ^-
       H—I   Cl
                  δ^- | δ^+ δ^-
                  Cl—C—Cl
   δ^+ δ^- δ^+ | δ^-
   b) H—S—H   Cl

37. a)

$$2[Na]^+ \left[\begin{matrix} \ddot{O} \\ C \\ \ddot{O}\ \ddot{O} \end{matrix} \right]^{2-}$$

b)

$$\left[\begin{matrix} H \\ H{:}\ddot{N}{:}H \\ H \end{matrix} \right]^+ \left[{:}\ddot{O}{:}H \right]^-$$

c)

$$[K]^+ \left[\begin{matrix} \ddot{O} \\ N \\ {:}\ddot{O}{:}\ \ddot{O}{:} \end{matrix} \right]^-$$

39. *Solid phase:* neither conducts electricity.

Liquid phase: ionic compounds conduct electricity; covalent compounds do not.

Aqueous solution: ionic compounds conduct electricity; with the exception of acid-forming compounds, covalent compounds do not conduct electricity.

Chapter 6

15. a) KI, potassium iodide
b) BaF_2, barium fluoride
c) $SnCl_2$, tin(II) chloride
$SnCl_4$, tin(IV) chloride
d) Li_2O, lithium oxide
e) ZnS, zinc sulfide

17. a) $CaSO_4$, calcium sulfate
b) Al_2O_3, aluminum oxide
c) $Pb_3(PO_4)_2$, lead(II) phosphate
d) $AlCl_3$, aluminum chloride
e) $Hg_2(NO_3)_2$, mercury(I) nitrate

19. a) potassium bromide
b) barium fluoride
c) sodium nitrate
d) calcium nitrite
e) sodium sulfate heptahydrate

21. a) carbon dioxide
b) barium chloride
c) dichlorine heptaoxide
d) tin(II) chloride
e) aluminum oxide

23. a) BF_3
b) K_2O
c) N_2O_4
d) $HgBr_2$
e) SiO_2

25. a) sulfate ion, $SO_4{}^{2-}$
b) cyanide ion, CN^-
c) hydroxide ion, OH^-
d) dichromate ion, $Cr_2O_7{}^{2-}$
e) acetate ion, $CH_3CO_2{}^-$

27. a) $:O{:}{:}\ddot{Xe}{:}{:}O:$

xenon dioxide

b)

sulfur hexafluoride

29. a) calcium sulfate
b) lead(II) nitrate
c) copper(II) acetate
d) sodium phosphate
e) aluminum hydroxide
f) zinc sulfite
g) ammonium perchlorate
h) lithium hypochlorite
i) magnesium nitrate
j) magnesium nitrite

31. a) K_2SO_4
b) NaCN
c) $PbCrO_4$
d) $Fe(OH)_3$
e) NH_4NO_3
f) $NaClO_3$
g) $(NH_4)_3PO_4$
h) $Zn(ClO_4)_2$
i) $FeSO_3$
j) $Mg(ClO)_2$

33. a) $BaCl_2 \cdot 2H_2O$, hydrated salt
b) $KHSO_4$, acid salt
c) $NaCl \cdot 4H_2O$, hydrated salt
d) $Ca(HCO_3)_2$, acid salt

35. a) lead(II) sulfide
b) silicon dioxide
c) calcium sulfate dihydrate

37. a) magnesium sulfate heptahydrate
b) sodium sulfate decahydrate
c) arsenic trichloride

39. a) $FeSO_4$, iron(II) sulfate
b) $SnCl_2$, tin(II) chloride
c) $Cu(NO_3)_2$, copper(II) nitrate

41. a) SF_6, sulfur hexafluoride
b) NO_2, nitrogen dioxide
c) I_2O_5, diiodine pentaoxide

43. Compounds formed with elements less electronegative than sulfur; in this case the oxidation number of sulfur is -2:

Li_2S	lithium sulfide
BeS	beryllium sulfide
B_2S_3	diboron trisulfide
CS_2	carbon disulfide

Compounds formed with elements more electronegative than sulfur; in these cases the oxidation number of sulfur is either $+4$ or $+6$:

S_3N_4	trisulfur tetranitride
SN_2	sulfur dinitride
SO_3	sulfur trioxide
SF_4	sulfur tetrafluoride
SF_6	sulfur hexafluoride

45. a) tungsten(VI) oxide, $+6$
b) vanadium(V) oxide, $+5$
c) cadmium oxide, $+2$ (cadmium, like zinc, has only one oxidation state)
d) manganese(VII) oxide, $+7$
e) cobalt(III) oxide, $+3$

Chapter 7

13. a) $262.9\,g\cdot mol^{-1}$ d) $233.3\,g\cdot mol^{-1}$
b) $207.4\,g\cdot mol^{-1}$ e) $85.0\,g\cdot mol^{-1}$
c) $68.2\,g\cdot mol^{-1}$

15. a) 8.46×10^{-1} mol c) 1.8×10^{-4} mol
b) 7.30 mol d) 5.0 mol

17. 29 mol

19. $169 per mol

21. a) 0.498 mol c) 8.3 mol
b) 1.45×10^{-8} mol

23. a) $9.78\,g$ d) $7.0\,g$
b) $34.4\,g$ e) $4.50\,g$
c) $99.9\,g$

25. a) $1.32 \times 10^{-2}\,g$ c) $7.16 \times 10^{-12}\,g$
b) $2.01 \times 10^9\,g$

27. a) boron b) sulfur dioxide c) urea

29. $4.7\,g$ of water, $15.3\,g$ of acetone

31. a) 3.08×10^{24} atoms (N.B. hydrogen is H_2)
b) 1.85×10^{24} atoms c) 3.38×10^{22} atoms

33. a) 72.3% Fe, 27.7% O b) 7.80×10^{27} atoms

35. a) 17.7% Na, 39.2% Cr, 43.1% O
b) 24.7% K, 34.7% Mn, 40.5% O
c) 20.2% Mg, 26.7% S, 53.2% O

37. a) $ZnCl_2$ c) PbN_2O_6 (i.e. $Pb(NO_3)_2$)
b) $FeBr_2$

39. $C_4H_{10}O$

41.

compound	empirical formula	molecular formula
1	BH_3	B_2H_6
2	B_2H_5	B_4H_{10}
3	B_5H_9	B_5H_9
4	B_5H_7	$B_{10}H_{14}$

43. Mn_2O_7

45. C_4H_5

47. $15.2\,g$

49. a) $64.0\,g\cdot mol^{-1}$
b) empirical formula = molecular formula = SO_2

Chapter 8

19. a) copper $+$ sulfur $\longrightarrow$ copper(II) sulfide
b) zinc $+$ hydrochloric acid $\longrightarrow$ zinc chloride $+$ hydrogen

21. a) $N_{2\,(g)} + 3\,H_{2\,(g)} \longrightarrow 2\,NH_{3\,(g)}$
b) $2\,NaN_{3\,(s)} \longrightarrow 2\,Na_{(\ell)} + 3\,N_{2\,(g)}$
c) $2\,Fe_2O_{3\,(s)} + 3\,C_{(s)} \longrightarrow 4\,Fe_{(s)} + 3\,CO_{2\,(g)}$
d) $Mg_3N_{2\,(s)} + 6\,H_2O_{(\ell)} \longrightarrow 3\,Mg(OH)_{2\,(s)} + 2\,NH_{3\,(g)}$
e) $H_2O_{(\ell)} + 3\,NO_{2\,(g)} \longrightarrow 2\,HNO_{3\,(aq)} + NO_{(g)}$

23. a) $3\,Mg_{(s)} + N_{2\,(g)} \longrightarrow Mg_3N_{2\,(s)}$
b) $H_2S_{(g)} + CuSO_{4\,(aq)} \longrightarrow CuS_{(s)} + H_2SO_{4\,(aq)}$
c) $MnO_{2\,(s)} + 4\,HCl_{(aq)} \longrightarrow Cl_{2\,(g)} + MnCl_{2\,(aq)} + 2\,H_2O_{(\ell)}$
d) $Ba_{(s)} + 2\,H_2O_{(\ell)} \longrightarrow Ba(OH)_{2\,(aq)} + H_{2\,(g)}$

25. a) $KOH_{(s)} \xrightarrow[\text{water}]{\text{dissolve in}} K^+_{(aq)} + OH^-_{(aq)}$

b) $MgBr_{2\,(s)} \xrightarrow[\text{water}]{\text{dissolve in}} Mg^{2+}_{(aq)} + 2\,Br^-_{(aq)}$

c) $HNO_{3\,(\ell)} \xrightarrow[\text{water}]{\text{dissolve in}} H^+_{(aq)} + NO^-_{3\,(aq)}$

d) $Al(NO_3)_{3\,(s)} \xrightarrow[\text{water}]{\text{dissolve in}} Al^{3+}_{(aq)} + 3\,NO^-_{3\,(aq)}$

e) $CuSO_{4\,(s)} \xrightarrow[\text{water}]{\text{dissolve in}} Cu^{2+}_{(aq)} + SO^{2-}_{4\,(aq)}$

27. a) no, Al is above Fe c) yes, H is below Sn
b) yes, Zn is below Mg

29. a) does not occur
b) $Cu_{(s)} + Hg(NO_3)_{2\,(aq)} \longrightarrow Hg_{(\ell)} + Cu(NO_3)_{2\,(aq)}$
c) $Br_{2\,(aq)} + MgI_{2\,(aq)} \longrightarrow MgBr_{2\,(aq)} + I_{2\,(aq)}$

31. a) yes, $CaCO_3$ calcium carbonate
b) yes, $Fe(OH)_3$ iron(III) hydroxide and $BaSO_4$ barium sulfate
c) no precipate formed

33. a) $S_{(s)} + O_{2\,(g)} \xrightarrow{\Delta} SO_{2\,(g)}$ (acidic oxide)
b) $CaO_{(s)} + H_2O_{(\ell)} \longrightarrow Ca(OH)_{2\,(s)}$ (base)
c) $Li_2O_{(s)} + CO_{2\,(g)} \longrightarrow Li_2CO_{3\,(s)}$ (salt)

35. a) $CuSO_{4\,(s)} \xrightarrow{\Delta} CuO_{(s)} + SO_{3\,(g)}$
b) $Zn(OH)_{2\,(s)} \xrightarrow{\Delta} ZnO_{(s)} + H_2O_{(g)}$
c) $PbCO_{3\,(s)} \xrightarrow{\Delta} PbO_{(s)} + CO_{2\,(g)}$

37. a) $Mg(OH)_{2\,(s)} + H_2SO_{4\,(aq)} \longrightarrow MgSO_{4\,(aq)} + 2\,H_2O_{(\ell)}$;
neutralization occurs

b) $3\,Na_2CO_{(aq)} + 2\,H_3PO_{4\,(aq)} \longrightarrow$
$\qquad\qquad 2\,Na_3PO_{4\,(aq)} + 3\,H_2O_{(\ell)} + 3\,CO_{2\,(g)}$;
CO_2 gas produced

c) $Pb(NO_3)_{2\,(aq)} + 2\,KCl_{(aq)} \longrightarrow PbCl_{2\,(s)} + 2\,KNO_{3\,(aq)}$;
precipitate $PbCl_2$ formed

d) $(NH_4)_2S_{(aq)} + FeSO_{4\,(aq)} \longrightarrow FeS_{(s)} + (NH_4)_2SO_{4\,(aq)}$;
precipitate $FeS_{(s)}$ formed

39. a) Al oxidized $(0 \longrightarrow +3)$
S reduced $(0 \longrightarrow -2)$

b) not a redox reaction

c) Zn oxidized $(0 \longrightarrow +2)$
Cu reduced $(+2 \longrightarrow 0)$

d) N of $[NH_4]^+$ oxidized $(-3 \longrightarrow +1)$
N of $[NO_3]^-$ reduced $(+5 \longrightarrow +1)$

41. a) double displacement   d) double displacement
b) single displacement   e) combination
c) decomposition

43. a) exothermic   c) endothermic
b) endothermic   d) exothermic

Chapter 9

15. Both Groups IA and VIIA contain very reactive elements. These will react with other substances in the environment to form compounds.

17. The alkali metals are strongly electropositive (they readily form cations). This trend increases as we go down the group. Hence, rubidium and cesium are the most reactive.
The halogens are strongly electronegative (they readily form anions). This trend increases as we go up the group. Hence, fluorine is the most reactive.

19.

Elements	Sodium	Phosphorus
Classification	metal	nonmetal
Appearance	shiny, silvery	white, waxy solid or red powder
Conductivity	conducts heat, electricity	does not conduct heat, electricity
Reaction with oxygen	burns	burns
Reaction with water	violent	none (in fact, white phosphorus is stored under water)

21. A = oxygen   D = neon
B = carbon   E = nitrogen
C = lithium

23. a) BeO, covalent   d) TeI_2, covalent
b) InI_3, ionic   e) SiF_4, covalent
c) Ce_2O_3, ionic

25. a)   H
$\quad$ H:$\ddot{Si}$:H
$\qquad$ H

c) $[\,H\!:\!\ddot{\underset{..}{N}}\!:\!H\,]^-$

b) $:\!\ddot{\underset{..}{O}}\!:\!N\!:::\!N\!:$

Chapter 10

11. 4.44 g

13. $\dfrac{2\ \text{mol KCl}_3}{2\ \text{mol KCl}}$ $\dfrac{2\ \text{mol KClO}_3}{3\ \text{mol O}_2}$ $\dfrac{2\ \text{mol KCl}}{3\ \text{mol O}_2}$

15. a) 0.75 mol   b) 1.0 mol   c) 4.5 mol

17. a) 1.80 g   c) 9.80 g

19. 2.00 g

21. 56.3 g

23. 706 g

25. 1.10 t

27. a) potassium sulfate in excess   b) 10.7 g

29. 0.439 g

31. sodium in excess, 81.9 % remains

33. a) 85.8 %   b) 2.68 g

35. 65.6 %

37. a) hydrogen in excess   b) 44.2 %

Chapter 11

13. a) 298 K   b) 423 K   c) 104 K   d) 1043 K

15. a) Pressure is caused by the impact of all the gas molecules on the container walls. Hence, in a mixture of gases, the total number of impacts is equal to the sum of the impacts of each of the component gases (i.e. the sum of the pressures of the component gases).

b) When the barrier is removed, the molecules of each gas are free to travel throughout the container. Thus the gases mix completely to form a solution.

c) The average kinetic energy of the molecules of a gas is $\frac{1}{2}mv^2$. At the same temperature, all gases have the same average kinetic energy. As the molar mass of carbon dioxide ($44\,g\cdot mol^{-1}$) is greater than that of oxygen ($32.0\,g\cdot mol^{-1}$), then the average velocity, v, must be less for carbon dioxide.

17. a) The greater number of particles will require a larger volume if the number of impacts, per unit surface area of the container walls, is to remain constant.

b) In the same volume, the greater number of particles will cause an increase in the number of impacts per unit surface area of the container walls. Hence, the pressure will increase.

19. a) 104.7 kPa   b) 785.4 mm Hg

21. $149\,m^3$

23. 96.6 L

25. a) 108 kPa   b) 199 kPa

27. 1.9×10^{-2} L (19 mL)

29. a) $-127\,°C$ b) 86.9 kPa   c) 0.116 L

31. a) 1.26×10^3 L   b) 2.80 L

33. 31.3 g

35. a) 0.539 g   b) $28\,°C$ c) 698 kPa

37. 9.65×10^5 g (or 965 kg)

39. $3.09\,g\cdot L^{-1}$

41. $83.8\,g\cdot mol^{-1}$ Kr

43. $147\,g\cdot mol^{-1}$

45. a) $C_7H_{14}O_2$ b) $130\,g\cdot mol^{-1}$ c) $C_7H_{14}O_2$

47. a) $77.9\,g\cdot mol^{-1}$ b) As

49. 333 kPa

51. 102 kPa He, 3 kPa Ne

53. 5.79×10^{-2} g

55. XeF_6

Chapter 12

19. Less than 1 g

21. a) very soluble   d) slightly soluble
    b) insoluble   e) very insoluble
    c) soluble

23. a) 8.30 % NaCl by mass   c) 18 % H_2SO_4 by mass
    b) 4.90 % $CaCl_2$ by mass

25. 58.3 % gold by mass

27. 21.0 % alcohol by volume

29. 0.805

31. a) $0.140\,mol\cdot L^{-1}$ c) $0.26\,mol\cdot L^{-1}$
    b) $0.402\,mol\cdot L^{-1}$

33. a) 4.00 g   b) 66 g

35. Place 6.02 g $MgSO_4$ in a 500.0 mL volumetric flask and fill to the mark with de-ionized or distilled water. Shake thoroughly.

37. $[Na_3PO_4] = 0.146\,mol\cdot L^{-1}$
    $[Na^+] = 0.438\,mol\cdot L^{-1}$
    $[PO_4{}^{3-}] = 0.146\,mol\cdot L^{-1}$

39. $[Cl^-] = 0.21\,mol\cdot L^{-1}$

41. a) Place 2.1 mL of the $12.0\,mol\cdot L^{-1}$ acid in a 250.0 mL volumetric flask and fill to the mark with de-ionized or distilled water. Shake thoroughly.
    b) Pour 150 mL of the $1.00\,mol\cdot L^{-1}$ solution of $CaCl_2$ into a 2.00 L graduated cylinder and fill to a volume of 1.50 L with de-ionized or distilled water.

47. a) below 7   b) equal to 7   c) above 7

49. a) 4.60   b) 11.00

Chapter 13

5. 0.318 g

7. 0.540 g

9. 0.540 L

11. $5.792 \times 10^{-2}\,mol\cdot L^{-1}$

13. a) $Zn_{(s)} + 2\,HNO_3{}_{(aq)} \longrightarrow Zn(NO_3)_2{}_{(aq)} + H_2{}_{(g)}$
    b) 0.668 g

15. a) 2.15×10^3 L
    b) 2.91×10^3 g SiO_2, 4.85×10^2 g C

17. 59.7 % pure $CaCl_2$

19. a) 15.0 L NH_3, 18.8 L O_2 b) 22.5 L

21. a) $138.2\,g\cdot mol^{-1}$ b) $39.1\,g\cdot mol^{-1}$ c) potassium

23. a) 30.0 g   b) 6.98 L

25. a) 2.51 L   b) 2.00 L

27. a) potassium chromate   b) 0.102 g

29. a) potassium sulfate   b) 10.7 g

31. $[H_2SO_4] = 0.137\,mol\cdot L^{-1}$, $[NaOH] = 0.201\,mol\cdot L^{-1}$

33. $Na_2CO_3 \cdot 10H_2O$

35. a) 4.98×10^{-3} mol   b) $139.3\,g \cdot mol^{-1}$ c) barium

Chapter 14

15. B

17. a) and c),   b) and d),   f) and g)

19. a) 2,3-dimethylbutane   d) 3-ethylhexane
b) 2,2,4-trimethylheptane   e) 2,2,3,5,5-pentamethylheptane
c) methylcyclobutane

21. a)

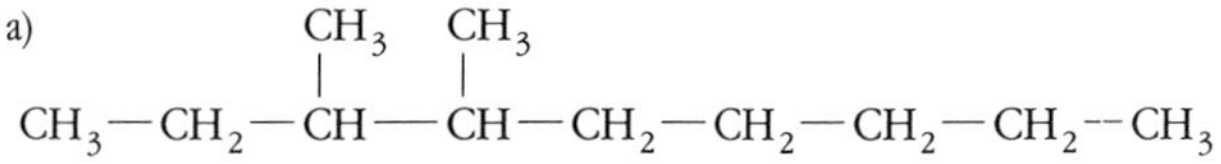

b)

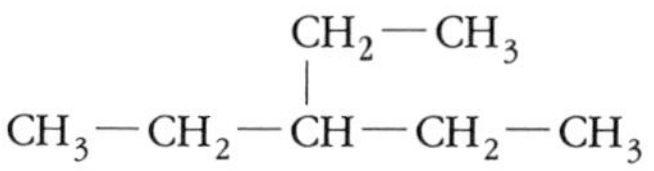

c)

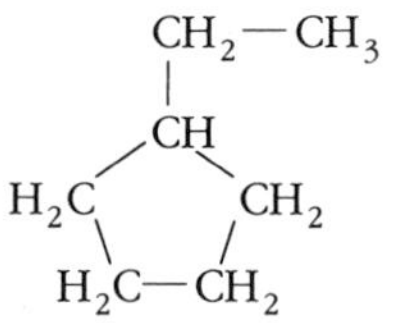

d)

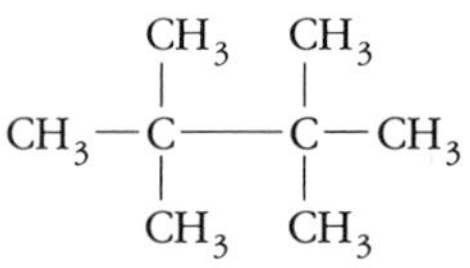

23. a) 2-butene   d) 2,6-dimethyl-2-heptane
b) 3-ethyl-2-pentene   e) 5,7,7-trimethyl-2-octene
c) 2-methyl-2-heptene

25. a)

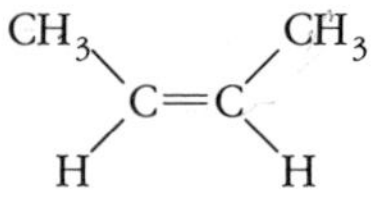

cis-2-butene

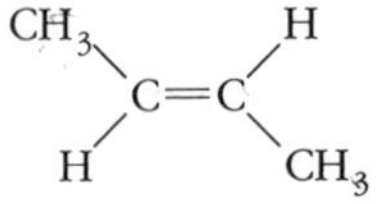

trans-2-butene

b)

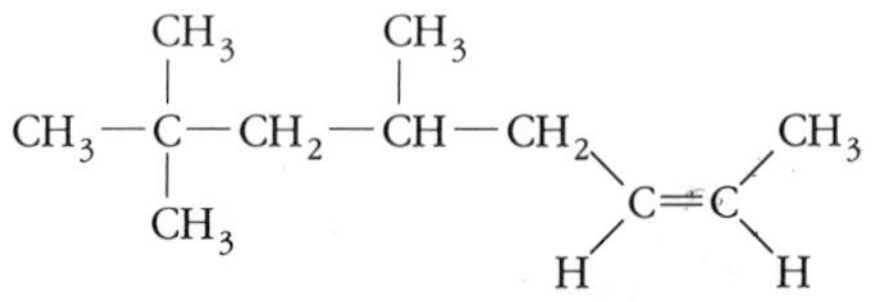

cis-5,7,7-trimethyl-2-octene

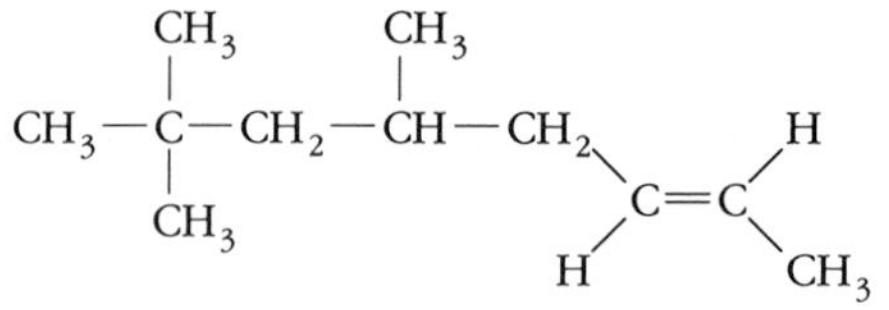

trans-5,7,7-trimethyl-2-octene

27. a) $CH_2{=}CH{-}CH_2{-}CH_3$
$CH_3{-}CH{=}CH{-}CH_3$ (exist as cis–trans isomers)
$CH_2{=}C{-}CH_3$
$\quad\quad\;\; |$
$\quad\quad\; CH_3$

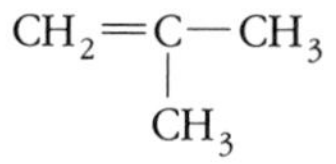

b)

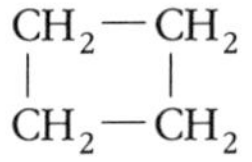

cyclobutane

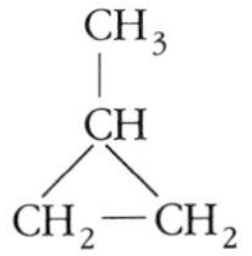

methylcyclopropane

29. a) $CH_2{=}CH{-}CH_2{-}CH_2{-}CH_2{-}CH_3$

b)

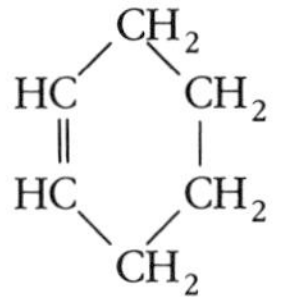

c)

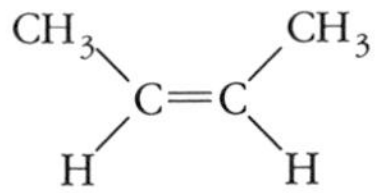

d)

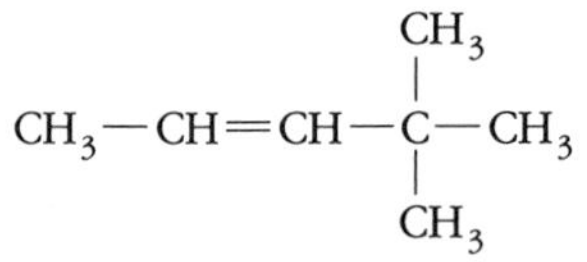

e) $CH_3{-}CH_2{-}CH{\equiv}C{-}CH_2{-}CH_2{-}CH_2{-}CH_3$
$\quad\quad\quad\quad\quad\quad\quad |$
$\quad\quad\quad\quad\quad\quad\; CH_2{-}CH_3$

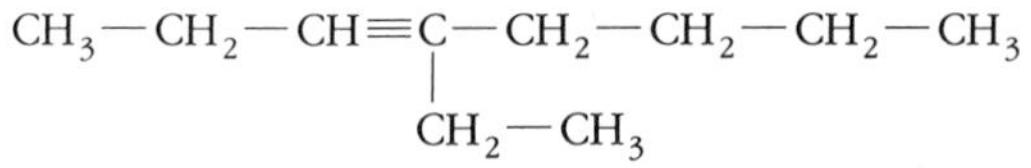

31. a) 1-pentyne   d) 5,7-dimethyl-3-octyne
b) 4-methyl-2-pentyne   e) 7-methyl-2-octyne
c) 4,4-dimethyl-2-hexyne

33. a) $HC{\equiv}C{-}CH_2{-}CH_2{-}CH_2{-}CH_2{-}CH_3$
b) $CH_3{-}CH_2{-}C{\equiv}C{-}CH_2{-}CH_3$
c)

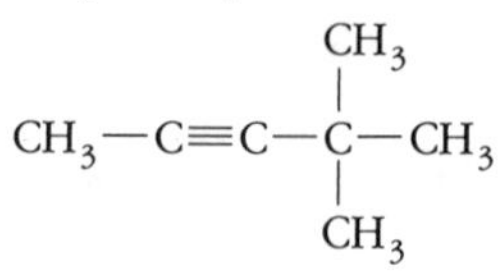

d) $CH_3-\overset{\underset{\displaystyle |}{CH_3}}{CH}-\overset{\underset{\displaystyle |}{CH_3}}{CH}-C\equiv C-CH_2-CH_2-CH_3$

e)

$CH_3-\overset{\overset{\displaystyle CH_3}{|}}{\underset{\underset{\displaystyle CH_3}{|}}{C}}-C\equiv C-\overset{\overset{\displaystyle CH_3}{|}}{\underset{\underset{\displaystyle CH_3}{|}}{C}}-CH_3$

35. a) $HC\equiv C-CH_2-CH_3$
$CH_3-C\equiv C-CH_3$

b) $CH_2=CH-CH=CH_2$
$CH_2=C=CH-CH_3$

$\begin{array}{cc} CH=CH & \overset{\overset{\displaystyle CH_3}{|}}{CH} \\ | \quad\quad | & \diagup \diagdown \\ CH_2-CH_2 & CH=CH \end{array}$

37. a) alkene   c) akyne   e) alkyne
b) alkane   d) alkene   f) aromatic

39. a) The second carbon has an excess hydrogen.
b) The second carbon from the right has an excess hydrogen.
c) The third carbon is missing a hydrogen.
d) The fourth carbon has an excess hydrogen.
e) The third carbon is missing a hydrogen.

41. a) $CH_3-CH=CH-CH_2-CH_3 + Br_2 \longrightarrow$
$\quad\quad\quad CH_3-CHBr-CHBr-CH_2-CH_3$

b) $2\,CH_2=CH-CH_3 + 9\,O_2 \longrightarrow 6\,CO_2 + 6\,H_2O$

c) $CH_3-CH_2-\overset{\overset{\displaystyle CH_3}{|}}{C}=\overset{\overset{\displaystyle CH_3}{|}}{C}-CH_2-CH_3 + H_2 \overset{Pt}{\longrightarrow}$

$\quad\quad\quad CH_3-CH_2-\overset{\overset{\displaystyle CH_3}{|}}{CH}-\overset{\overset{\displaystyle CH_3}{|}}{CH}-CH_2-CH_3$

d) $HC\equiv C-CH_2-CH_3 + 2\,Br_2 \longrightarrow$
$\quad\quad\quad CHBr_2-CBr_2-CH_2-CH_3$

43. a)

$\begin{array}{c} \quad\quad CH_2 \\ H_2C\diagup\quad\diagdown CH_2 \\ HC=CH \end{array}$

b)

$CH_3-\overset{\overset{\displaystyle CH_3}{|}}{CH}-CH_3$

c) $CH_3-CH_2-CH_2-CH_2-CH_2-CH_2-CH_2-CH_3$

45. a) $2\,C_8H_{18\,(\ell)} + 25\,O_{2\,(g)} \longrightarrow 16\,CO_{2\,(g)} + 18\,H_2O_{(\ell)}$

b) 1.2×10^3 L (or 1.2 kL)

Chapter 15

13. a) methanal (formaldehyde), $H-\overset{\overset{\displaystyle O}{\diagup}}{C}_{\diagdown H}$

b) methanoic acid (formic acid), $H-\overset{\overset{\displaystyle O}{\diagup}}{C}_{\diagdown OH}$

c) ethanoic acid (acetic acid), $CH_3-\overset{\overset{\displaystyle O}{\diagup}}{C}_{\diagdown OH}$

d) glycine, $\underset{\underset{\displaystyle NH_2}{|}}{CH_2}-\overset{\overset{\displaystyle O}{\diagup}}{C}_{\diagdown OH}$

15. a) starting material for the manufacture of dyes
b) paint solvent, windshield-wiper fluid, starting material for the synthesis of formaldehyde
c) component of cosmetics, sweetening agent, solvent for medicines

17. a) amine, phenyl
b) carboxylic acid, ester, phenyl
c) alkyne (2), alkene, alcohol, phenyl
d) ether, carboxylic acid, halogen (chloro), phenyl
e) alcohol, amine, carboxylic acid

19. a) 3   b) 4   c) 2   d) 3

21. $CH_3-CH_2-O-CH_2-CH_3$ diethyl ether, ethoxyethane

$CH_3-O-CH_2-CH_2-CH_3$ methyl propyl ether, 1-methyoxypropane

$CH_3-O-\underset{\underset{\displaystyle CH_3}{|}}{CH}-CH_3$ methyl isopropyl ether, 2-methoxypropane

23. $CH_3-CH_2-\overset{\overset{\displaystyle O}{\diagup}}{C}_{\diagdown H}$ $CH_3-\overset{\overset{\displaystyle O}{\|}}{C}-CH_3$

propanal   propanone

25. a) propanal (propionaldehyde)
b) 2-aminobutane
c) butanoic acid (butyric acid)
d) 2-pentanol
e) 2-chloropropanoic acid
f) methlpropanoate (methyl propionate)
g) 2-bromopentane
h) 2-iodo-3-chlorohexane
i) 1-methoxypentane (methyl pentyl ether)
j) 2-pentanone (methyl propyl ketone)

27. a)

$$CH_3-\overset{\overset{\displaystyle O}{\|}}{C}-CH_2-CH_2-CH_3$$

b) $CH_3-CH_2-\overset{\overset{\displaystyle O}{\|}}{C}{\diagdown}{O-CH_3}$

c) $\begin{array}{c}CH_3-CH_2\\CH_3-CH_2\end{array}\!\!\diagup\!\!N-CH_2-CH_3$

d) $CH_3-CH_2-CH_2-CH_2-CH_2-\overset{\overset{\displaystyle O}{\|}}{C}{\diagdown}{OH}$

e) $CH_3-CCl_2-CH_2-CH_3$

29. $CH_3-CH_2-CH_2-\overset{\overset{\displaystyle O}{\|}}{C}{\diagdown}{OH}$

$$CH_3-\overset{\overset{\displaystyle CH_3}{|}}{CH}-\overset{\overset{\displaystyle O}{}}{C}{\diagdown}{OH}$$

$$CH_3-CH_2-\overset{\overset{\displaystyle O}{}}{C}{\diagdown}{O-CH_3}$$

$$CH_3-\overset{\overset{\displaystyle O}{}}{C}{\diagdown}{O-CH_2-CH_3}$$

$$H-\overset{\overset{\displaystyle O}{}}{C}{\diagdown}{O-CH_2-CH_2-CH_3}$$

$$H-\overset{\overset{\displaystyle O}{}}{C}{\diagdown}{O-\overset{\overset{\displaystyle |}{}}{CH}-CH_3}$$ with CH_3

31. a) $2\ CH_3OH_{(g)} + O_2\ _{(g)} \xrightarrow[\text{catalyst}]{\Delta} 2\ HCHO_{(g)} + 2\ H_2O_{(g)}$

b) $HCO_2H_{(aq)} + KOH_{(aq)} \longrightarrow HCO^-_2K^+_{(aq)} + H_2O_{(g)}$

33. a) $HCO_2H + CH_3CH_2OH \longrightarrow HCO_2CH_2CH_3 + H_2O$

b) $CH_3CO_2H + CH_3OH \longrightarrow CH_3CO_2CH_3 + H_2O$

35. $3.97\ g \cdot L^{-1}$

37. a) $CH_3CH_2OH_{(\ell)} + 3\ O_2\ _{(g)} \longrightarrow 2\ CO_2\ _{(g)} + 2\ H_2O_{(g)}$

b) 1.24×10^3 L (or 1.24 kL)

39. a) C_3H_7Br b) $123.0\ g \cdot mol^{-1}$

Chapter 16

17. a) $2\ NaOH_{(aq)} + Al_2O_3\ _{(s)} \longrightarrow 2\ NaAlO_2\ _{(aq)} + H_2O_{(\ell)}$

$2\ NaAlO_2\ _{(aq)} + H_2O_{(\ell)} \longrightarrow Al_2O_3\ _{(s)} + 2\ NaOH_{(aq)}$

$Al_2O_3 \cdot 3H_2O_{(s)} \longrightarrow Al_2O_3\ _{(s)} + 3\ H_2O_{(g)}$

$2\ O^{2-} + C_{(s)} \longrightarrow CO_2\ _{(g)} + 4\ e^-$

$Al^{3+} + 3\ e^- \longrightarrow Al_{(\ell)}$

b) $2\ C_{(s)} + O_2\ _{(g)} \longrightarrow 2\ Co_{(s)}$

$3\ Co_{(g)} + Fe_2O_3\ _{(s)} \longrightarrow 2\ Fe_{(\ell)} + 3\ CO_2\ _{(g)}$

$CaCO_3\ _{(s)} \longrightarrow CaO_{(s)} + CO_2\ _{(g)}$

$CaO_{(s)} + SiO_2\ _{(s)} \longrightarrow CaSiO_3\ _{(\ell)}$

19. a) carbon improves hardness

b) chromium reduces rusting

c) silicon improves chemical resistance

21. White phophorus catches fire in air — it must be stored under water. Uranium compounds emit low levels of radioactivity — they must be stored in sealed, thick-walled containers.

23. a) $Ca_3(PO_4)_{(s)} + 3\ H_2SO_4\ _{(aq)} \longrightarrow 3\ CaSO_4\ _{(s)} + 2\ H_3PO_4\ _{(aq)}$

$3\ NH_3\ _{(aq)} + H_3PO_4\ _{(aq)} \longrightarrow (NH_4)_3PO_4\ _{(s)}$

b) $UO_2\ _{(s)} + 4\ HF_{(aq)} \longrightarrow UF_4\ _{(s)} + 2\ H_2O_{(\ell)}$

$UF_4\ _{(s)} + F_2\ _{(g)} \longrightarrow UF_6\ _{(s)}$

25. carbon monoxide, used as a fuel in the drying furnaces; iron (III) phosphate, used for making specialty steels; calcium silicate, used as road fill

27. 3.06×10^2 t, 3.12×10^6 t

29. 1.12×10^{11} L O_2, 1.12×10^{11} L SO_2

Chapter 17

19. a) natural decay, beta particles

b) artificial transmutation, fusion

c) natural decay, positron

d) artificial transmutation, fusion

e) artificial transmutation, fusion

21. a) $^{18}_{9}F$ c) $^{0}_{-1}e$ e) $^{0}_{+1}e$

b) $^{4}_{2}He$ d) $^{210}_{81}Tl$

23. a) $^{1}_{1}n$ b) $^{1}_{1}H$ (or $^{1}_{1}p$)   c) $^{7}_{4}Be$

25. 0.50 mg

27. 5.0×10^{11} J

29. 2.86×10^{-8} g

31. $^{99}_{43}\text{Te} \longrightarrow \,^{0}_{-1}\text{e} + \,^{99}_{44}\text{Ru}$

33. $^{238}_{92}\text{U} \longrightarrow \,^{234}_{90}\text{Th} + \,^{4}_{2}\text{He}$

$^{234}_{90}\text{Th} \longrightarrow \,^{234}_{91}\text{Pa} + \,^{0}_{-1}\text{e}$

$^{234}_{91}\text{Pa} \longrightarrow \,^{234}_{92}\text{U} + \,^{0}_{-1}\text{e}$

$^{234}_{92}\text{U} \longrightarrow \,^{230}_{90}\text{Th} + \,^{4}_{2}\text{He}$

$^{230}_{90}\text{Th} \longrightarrow \,^{226}_{88}\text{Ra} + \,^{4}_{2}\text{He}$

$^{226}_{88}\text{Ra} \longrightarrow \,^{222}_{86}\text{Rn} + \,^{4}_{2}\text{He}$

$^{222}_{86}\text{Rn} \longrightarrow \,^{218}_{84}\text{Po} + \,^{4}_{2}\text{He}$

$^{218}_{84}\text{Po} \longrightarrow \,^{214}_{82}\text{Pb} + \,^{4}_{2}\text{He}$

35. Some of the decay products will always remain in the sample.

Index

Key words are indicated by **boldface** references; tables and figures are indicated by (t) and (f) respectively; colour plates are indicated by the letter P.

Photo Credits

$$22.4^\circ C \times \frac{1K}{1C^\circ} + 273K$$

Chemistry

Soh Cah Toa

			Group III A	Group IV A	Group V A	Group VI A	Group VII A	Group (VIII A) NOBLE GASES
								2 **He** 4.0
			5 **B** 10.8	6 **C** 12.0	7 **N** 14.0	8 **O** 16.0	9 **F** 19.0	10 **Ne** 20.2
Group I B	Group II B		13 **Al** 27.0	14 **Si** 28.1	15 **P** 31.0	16 **S** 32.1	17 **Cl** 35.5	18 **Ar** 40.0
28 **Ni** 58.7	29 **Cu** 63.5	30 **Zn** 65.4	31 **Ga** 69.7	32 **Ge** 72.6	33 **As** 74.9	34 **Se** 79.0	35 **Br** 79.9	36 **Kr** 83.8
46 **Pd** 106.4	47 **Ag** 107.9	48 **Cd** 112.4	49 **In** 114.8	50 **Sn** 118.7	51 **Sb** 121.8	52 **Te** 127.6	53 **I** 126.9	54 **Xe** 131.3
78 **Pt** 195.1	79 **Au** 197.0	80 **Hg** 200.6	81 **Tl** 204.4	82 **Pb** 207.2	83 **Bi** 209.0	84 **Po** (210)	85 **At** (210)	86 **Rn** (222)

non-metals
Halogens diatomic
semi sudo metals

1.01(10)

63.5
32.1
16(4)

63.5
32.1
64.0
10.1
80.0

64 **Gd** 157.2	65 **Tb** 158.9	66 **Dy** 162.5	67 **Ho** 164.9	68 **Er** 167.3	69 **Tm** 168.9	70 **Yb** 173.0	71 **Lu** 175.0
96 **Cm** (247)	97 **Bk** (247)	98 **Cf** (249)	99 **Es** (254)	100 **Fm** (253)	101 **Md** (256)	102 **No** (254)	103 **Lr** (257)

Sandy